ANNUAL REVIEW OF BIOPHYSICS AND BIOMOLECULAR STRUCTURE

ANNUAL REVIEW OF
BIOPHYSICS AND
BIOMOLECULAR
STRUCTURE

VOLUME 31, 2002

ROBERT M. STROUD, *Editor*
University of California, San Francisco

WILMA K. OLSON, *Associate Editor*
Rutgers University

MICHAEL P. SHEETZ, *Associate Editor*
Columbia University

www.annualreviews.org   science@annualreviews.org   650-493-4400

ANNUAL REVIEWS
4139 El Camino Way • P.O. Box 10139 • Palo Alto, California 94303-0139

ANNUAL REVIEWS
Palo Alto, California, USA

International Standard Serial Number: 1056-8700
International Standard Book Number: 0-8243-1831-5
Library of Congress Catalog Card Number: 79-188446

TYPESET BY TECHBOOKS, FAIRFAX, VA
PRINTED AND BOUND IN THE UNITED STATES OF AMERICA

PREFACE

As lives in science are enriched with the joys of new insights, sadly they are punctuated by the loss of those among us who have pioneered their ways and revealed new horizons. This comes as a particular loss when those who are contributing at the peak of their productivity are prematurely plucked from our midst. Such events this year cause reflection on two colleagues who, in very different and unique ways, shaped the foundations of science within their fields of biomolecular structure and interactions. They are not the only ones tragically lost. They are individuals especially close to those in the fields that this *Annual Review* represents. Their loss is tragic. Their contributions are eternal and of enduring significance.

Peter A. Kollman (1944–2001), a dearly loved and a very close colleague to most in the fields covered within the fields of biophysics and biomolecular structure and far beyond, died on May 25, 2001, after a brief month's warning, of cancer. Peter is a pioneer in the development and application of theoretical methods to understand the underpinnings of chemistry, molecular interactions, pharmaceutical chemistry, biochemistry, enzyme mechanisms, nucleic acids, and biology.

Last year Peter and members of his group contributed an invited review published in Volume 30 (2001), entitled "Biomolecular Simulations: Recent Developments in Force Fields, Simulations of Enzyme Catalysis, Protein-Ligand, Protein-Protein, and Protein-Nucleic Acid Noncovalent Interactions." This will remain a visionary reminder of how far this field has come and the huge impact that it now has attained in molecular biology. It is also an eternal reminder of Peter's own search.

This was not the only review Peter contributed last year. Peter and Thomas E. Cheatham III also focused on "Molecular Dynamics Simulation of Nucleic Acids" in the *Annual Review of Physical Chemistry*, Volume 51 (2000). The underlying thinking behind molecular mechanics has increasingly established itself as the ultimate basis for understanding the structures and trajectories that determine folded structure and molecular interactions.

Peter was born in Iowa City and attended Grinnell College, where he obtained a B.A. in Chemistry in 1966. He went on to Princeton where he obtained an M.A. in 1967, and a Ph.D. in 1970. After a fellowship in Cambridge for one year, Peter joined the faculty of the Department of Pharmaceutical Chemistry at the University of California in San Francisco in 1971, where he remained throughout his career. His engaging enthusiasm and eagerness to contribute powerfully to any scientific discussion into which he was drawn became a key factor in the breadth of field and the great impact that his work engendered. Peter's own works are reported in over 400 publications. His insights are represented for the entire scientific community in the molecular mechanics suite of programs AMBER. The development of force fields is a cornerstone of computer simulations and one that Peter and his group contributed greatly to. His force fields were based on experimental observations and on fundamental quantum mechanical axioms. Peter showed the importance of linking thermodynamics and relative free energies to molecular structure and molecular interactions. He continued to work on these elements and to assist his students and postdoctoral scholars to his own final moments. Peter's brilliant and inspirational impact will surely resonate with scientific endeavor far and wide into the future.

Don C. Wiley (1944–2001), a dearly loved and a brilliant experimentalist proponent of molecular structure and interactions, particularly in virology and immunology, and an inspirational colleague of most in these fields and far beyond, died on the early morning of Friday, November 16, 2001. Don sought to understand the mechanisms by which viruses infect cells and to discover how cells respond to external challenge by presenting antigens and mobilizing defensive cells at the level of molecular structure.

Don was born on October 21, 1944, in Akron, Ohio, and grew up in Pennsylvania and New Jersey. He obtained a B.S. in Physics in 1966 and obtained his Ph.D. in Biophysics at Harvard in 1971. He joined the faculty of Harvard's Department of Biochemistry and Molecular Biology in 1971, where he continued a brilliant and insightful career.

Don contributed an invited review for the *Annual Review of Biochemistry*, Volume 69 (2000), entitled "Receptor Binding and Membrane Fusion in Virus Entry: The Influenza Hemagglutinin." This review, coauthored by John J. Skehel, summarized one field of Don's many foci they had both defined since their first coauthored publication on the influenza hemagglutinin in 1977. Hemagglutinin, the receptor-binding and membrane fusion glycoprotein of influenza virus, is also the target for antibodies that neutralize infectivity of flu virus. By defining three conformations of the ectodomain of the 1968 Hong Kong influenza virus determined by X-ray crystallography, they describe the single-chain form of the protein, a metastable neutral-pH conformation found in flu virus, and the fusion form of the protein as induced by pH change. These structures provide an understanding of the way that emerging and reemerging epidemics are formed and how membrane fusion occurs during viral entry. Characteristically the review extends the insight out toward another entire field, that of the fusion of presynaptic vesicles as mediated by SNARE proteins, leading to synaptic transmission. Don also coauthored another review in 2001 on one of his other passionately pursued interests: "T Cell Receptor-MHC Interactions Up Close" (*Cell* Jan 12; 104(1):1–4.). The heritage of Don's insights and discoveries in most challenging areas is vast and leave us with pillars of foundations in the fields he sought to understand.

In science, reviews serve as landmarks and signposts. They can become a defining summary that serves to attract the next generation, the agent for regrouping or map reading, and the nexus for forming the plan to approach the next hilltop on the road. Sometimes they gather the added significance of a map left at the final frontier by a pioneer that those who follow will gratefully treasure.

This year's *Annual Review of Biophysics and Biomolecular Structure* begins with a brilliantly humored retrospective of a colorful life in science by George

Feher. It reminds one that there are often situations that determine circumstance and that a little humor can often serve to bounce upward to new horizons from what otherwise might seem like almost random fluctuations in life. Here, George's tuned mind and his sense of mischief often lead to profound changes in conception that changed biophysics.

This year has seen the atomic description of the ribosome with contributions by several research groups. These discoveries will stretch forward for many years as its impact is incorporated into biology and pharmaceutical chemistry. We are fortunate to have the perspectives of Ada Yonath who, with her group, grew the first crystals of the 50S subunit of the ribosomes from *E. coli* and *Bacillus stearothermophilus* ribosome, as reported in 1981 (*J. Biol. Chem.* 256(22):11787–90). Joachim Frank describes the revolution in electron microscopy that is rapidly closing the gap between locations of assemblies of molecules within the cell and molecular structure at the atomic level, especially so at this time for structural biology and interactions of the ribosome.

Ernesto Friere, Irene Luque, and Stephanie A. Leavitt pioneer the way forward in relating thermodynamics to an understanding of molecular interactions. Here he and his colleagues turn to address "The Linkage Between Protein Folding and Functional Cooperativity: Two Sides of the Same Coin?" Ian A. Wilson, Markus G. Rudolph, and John G. Luz also take a thermodynamic perspective of T cell signaling viewed in the light of structure.

In membrane biology, the impact of the first crystal structures of proteins of each functional group has been extremely invigorating and rewarding with new insights and paradigms. Douglas C. Rees and his group reported several new membrane protein structures that have had tremendous impact. Here Rees and Robert H. Spencer summarize some of the insights into transmembrane channels and the gating of channels, which is an essential key to all ion-conducting channels found in the surfaces of cells. Thomas P. Sakmar, Santosh T. Menon, Ethan P. Marin, and Elias S. Awad lead us onward into the understanding of rhodopsin, based on the first structure of a G protein–coupled receptor. Using mutational analysis coupled to functional assays, Judith Herzfeld and Jonathan C. Lansing lead us from the extremely well-defined structures of bacteriorhodopsin derived both from electron microscopy pioneered by Henderson and his colleagues over many years, and from the crystallography of Luecke and his colleagues toward an understanding of the rates of transition from one step to the next in the photo-reaction cycle. Motomu Shimaoka, Junichi Takagi, and Timothy A. Springer review the regulation of integrins, membrane molecules that hold cells together in appropriate linkages. Alongside this, Larry A. Sklar, Bruce S. Edwards, Steven W. Graves, John P. Nolan, and Eric R. Prossnitz remind us of one important way that receptor interaction affinities and dynamics can be measured.

Understanding the forces that determine protein folding is an exciting field that must presume an uncountable manifold of ways through an impossibly complex maze of trial-and-error stochasticism, to reach the near-Nirvanic state of a unified, uniquely folded quietude. Chris P. Ponting and Robert R. Russell introduce the origins of the structural domains of proteins that are often saved through evolution as functional entities. Stuart McLaughlin, Jiyao Wang, Alok Gambhir, and Diana Murray take apart an important case where a large multi-domain protein participates in an awesome cellular network of information transfer.

DNA-protein interactions cover a multitude of increasingly dynamic views of gene regulation. Rashmi S. Hegde reviews the fascinating biology of papillomavirus E2 proteins that regulate the transcription of all papillomavirus genes, a protein where mutations are commonly associated with cervical carcinoma, indicating a role in tumorogenesis. These proteins seem to detect DNA flexibility in finding their target DNA sequences. On the DNA theme, Jeffrey C. Hansen considers the recent advances in mechanisms by which the supramolecular structures of chromatin regulate transcription of DNA, the mechanism of action of the core histone amino termini, the structure and function of histone variants, and the function of linker histones in the chromatin fiber.

Modeling cellular physiology is an emerging frontier in which Boris M. Slepchenko, James C. Schaff, John H. Carson, and Leslie M. Loew review the issues and the revolutionary impact these models are having on understanding cell biology. "The virtual cell," and new computational modeling algorithms couple experimental observations made at the forefront of new imaging methods to intra- and intercellular networks. Remarkable forces are harnessed by many pathogenic fungi in penetrating the host cells. Specialized infection structures called appressoria send a penetration peg into underlying cells and generate enormous turgor pressure. Microscopic methods have been developed that visualize and measure forces locally exerted by single appressoria, as reviewed by key proponents Martin Bastmeyer, Holger B. Deising, and Clemens Bechinger.

In spectroscopic terms, Paul R. Selvin brings the field of lanthanide chelates as fluorescent labels to the fore and shows how knowledge of their detailed chemistry can provide efficient long-lived emitters, making them novel sensitive detection reagents and excellent donors in resonance energy transfer. M. Ubbink, J. A. R. Worrall, G. W. Canters, E. J. J. Groenen, and M. Huber consider the spectroscopic ways that biological metal centers can reveal aspects of the mechanisms of proteins and enzymes at close quarters to the metal sites—often precisely the zone of greatest interest from mechanistic points of view. Robert J. Cushley and Mark Okon review lipoprotein structures as determined by the ever more popular and capable new methods in NMR spectroscopy.

As departing Editor, after two most rewarding five-year terms, I am awed by the scholarship and insight that contributing authors and the care and attention that the Editorial Committee, especially Associate Editors, give to these reviews. Especially noteworthy are Amanda Suver and Cleo X. Ray for their diligence as Production Editors. Our intent remains to try to coordinate reviews of mature fields at lasting landmark stages, written by primary contributors to these areas, foundations that are stepping-stones to the future.

Robert M. Stroud
Editor

Ⓡ *Annual Review of Biophysics and Biomolecular Structure*
Volume 31, 2002

CONTENTS

ERRATA
An online log of corrections to *Annual Review of Biophysics and Biomolecular Structure* chapters may be found at http://biophys.annualreviews.org/errata.shtml

RELATED ARTICLES

From the *Annual Review of Biochemistry*, Volume 71, 2002

Active Site Tightness and Substrate Fit in DNA Replication, Eric T. Kool

Biochemistry of Na,K-ATPase, Jack H. Kaplan

Catalytic Proficiency: The Unusual Case of OMP Decarboxylase, Brian G. Miller and Richard Wolfenden

Great Metalloclusters in Enzymology, Douglas C. Rees

Neuronal Ca^{2+}/Calmodulin-Dependent Protein Kinase II: The Role of Structure and Autoregulation in Cellular Function, Andy Hudmon and Howard Schulman

Order Out of Chaos: Assembly of Ligand Binding Sites in Heparan Sulfate, Jeffrey D. Esko and Scott B. Selleck

V(D)J Recombination: RAG Proteins, Repair Factors, and Regulation, Martin Gellert

Nuclear Actin and Actin-Related Proteins in Chromatin Remodeling, Ivan A. Olave, Samara L. Reck-Peterson, and Gerald R. Crabtree

Mammalian ABC Transporters in Health and Disease, P. Borst and R. Oude Elferink

Homogeneous Glycopeptides and Glycoproteins for Biological Investigation, Michael J. Grogan, Matthew R. Pratt, Lisa A. Marcaurelle, and Carolyn R. Bertozzi

Long Distance Electron Transfer Through DNA, Bernd Giese

Eukaryotic Ribonuclease P: A Plurality of Ribonucleoprotein Enzymes, Shaohua Xiao, Felicia Scott, Carol A. Fierke, and David R. Engelke

Catalytic Strategies of the Hepatitis Delta Virus Ribozymes, I-hung Shih and Michael D. Been

Mechanisms of Fast Protein Folding, Jeffrey K. Myers and Terrence G. Oas

Biological Roles of Proteases in Parasitic Protozoa, Michael Klemba and Daniel E. Goldberg

From the *Annual Review of Cell and Developmental Biology*, Volume 17, 2001

Patterning Mechanisms Controlling Vertebrate Limb Development, Javier Capdevila and Juan Carlos Izpisúa Belmonte

The Changing Face of the Na+/H+ Exchanger, NHE1: Structure, Regulation, and Cellular Actions, L. K. Putney, S. P. Denker, and D. L. Barber

From the ***Annual Review of Physical Chemistry***, Volume 52, 2001

A Free Radical, Alan Carrington

Surface Biology of DNA by Atomic Force Microscopy, Helen G. Hansma

On the Characteristics of Migration of Oligomeric DNA in Polyacrylamide Gels and in Free Solution, Udayan Mohanty and Larry McLaughlin

Coincidence Spectroscopy, Robert E. Continetti

Ratiometric Single-Molecule Studies of Freely Diffusing Biomolecules, Ashok A. Deniz, Ted A. Laurence, Maxime Dahan, Daniel S. Chemla, Peter G. Schultz, and Shimon Weiss

Time-Resolved Photoelectron Spectroscopy of Molecules and Clusters, Daniel M. Neumark

Pulsed EPR Spectroscopy: Biological Applications, Thomas Prisner, Martin Rohrer, and Fraser MacMillan

Fast Protein Dynamics Probed with Infrared Vibrational Echo Experiments, Michael D. Fayer

Structure and Bonding of Molecules at Aqueous Surfaces, G. L. Richmond

Biomolecular Solid State NMR: Advances in Structural Methodology and Applications to Peptide and Protein Fibrils, Robert Tycko

Electron Transmission through Molecules and Molecular Interfaces, Abraham Nitzan

Early Events in RNA Folding, D. Thirumalai, Namkyung Lee, Sarah A. Woodson, and D. K. Klimov

From the ***Annual Review of Physiology***, Volume 64, 2002

A Hundred Years of Sodium Pumping, Ian M. Glynn

G Proteins and Pheromone Signaling, Henrik G. Dohlman

Prolactin: The New Biology of an Old Hormone, Vincent Goffin, Nadine Binart, Philippe Touraine, and Paul A. Kelly

G Proteins and Olfactory Signal Transduction, Gabriele V. Ronnett and Cheil Moon

G Proteins and Phototransduction, Vadim Y. Arshavsky, Trevor D. Lamb, and Edward N. Pugh, Jr.

Aromatase—A Brief Overview, Evan R. Simpson, Colin Clyne, Gary Rubin, Wah Chin Boon, Kirsten Robertson, Kara Britt, Caroline Speed, and Margaret Jones

Annu. Rev. Biophys. Biomol. Struct. 2002. 31:1–44
DOI: 10.1146/annurev.biophys.31.082901.134147

MY ROAD TO BIOPHYSICS: Picking Flowers on the Way to Photosynthesis

George Feher

*Department of Physics, University of California, San Diego, La Jolla, California 92037;
e-mail: gfeher@physics.ucsd.edu*

Key Words   EPR, ENDOR, fluctuation spectroscopy, nuclear polarization,
bacterial photosynthesis, protein crystallization

CONTENTS

1056-8700/02/0609-0001$14.00

1

PROLOGUE

When I was approached by the Editor to write the Prefatory chapter, I felt, of course, honored but was hesitant to accept the task because I had recently finished a personal account of three decades of research in photosynthesis, the first part of which included reminiscences and stories of my past (55). After some thought, however, I decided to accept the challenge. There was life before photosynthesis, after all. During my ~50 years of research activity, I worked on different topics in "straight" physics, some of which have close connections to the methodologies and approaches used in biophysics. I had also worked on several biophysics problems that were not covered in the previous review. I decided, therefore, to take this opportunity to give an account of this part of my research. To fill out the relatively short shrift that I give here to photosynthesis, the reader is referred to the previous review (55). The Editor asked me to write a personal account, including reminiscences and stories. In trying to follow his advice, some overlap with previously published accounts was unavoidable.

CZECHOSLOVAKIA 1924–1941

I was born in 1924 in Bratislava, a border town close to Austria and Hungary. My father had two passions: business (textiles) and sports (he held for many years the Czechoslovak record in the hammer throw). My mother was more intellectually inclined. She taught in a lyceum for teachers before my sister and I arrived on the scene. From my early childhood I was a tinkerer. I took apart all the clocks and watches in the household and, most of the time, put them back together in working condition. Interspersed with the mechanical activities were chemical experiments. I remember putting a chunk of sodium on a piece of blotting paper and watching it catch fire as it floated on the water surface in the bathtub. Alas, disaster struck when it hit the wall; the bathtub cracked and the entire apartment was flooded. At age 14, I became a radio ham and pursued vigorously what now would be called electronics. In parallel I developed another hobby: growing crystals. My fascination with growing crystals has not abated to this day.

In the meantime, the situation in Slovakia had become grim and perilous. Being a Jew, I was expelled from school in 1938 at age 14. Slovakia, although nominally independent, had become a puppet state of Nazi Germany. Interestingly, we youngsters, who joined a Zionist organization, saw the writing on the wall more clearly than our parents and their generation, and we were constantly exploring possibilities for an escape.

PALESTINE 1941–1946

In 1941, in the middle of the war, at age 17, I and eight other youngsters from the Zionist movement succeeded in escaping through Hungary, Romania, Turkey, and Lebanon to Palestine (what is now Israel), at the time a British mandate. At the border, we were promptly arrested and interned by the British.[1] A shocking welcome after having barely succeeded in escaping from hell. After a brief internment we were released and joined a kibbutz (communal settlement). Although we had prepared ourselves ideologically for the last three years to live a communal life, some of us found the conformity, drabness, and lack of opportunity for intellectual and professional growth difficult to take. After a year and a half I left for Haifa, where my sister lived and where a technical university, the Technion, was located. I started to work as a radio repairman in the evenings while taking some technical courses during the day in the trade school adjacent to the Technion. One of my teachers was Franz Ollendorff, an internationally recognized authority in electrical engineering, who was also a professor at the Technion. In the fall of 1943, he offered me a position as his laboratory assistant, which I enthusiastically accepted. One of the first challenges that Ollendorff confronted me with was to build an oscilloscope. It is difficult to imagine nowadays that in 1943 there was not a single oscilloscope in the Technion or probably in all of Palestine. From captured German and Italian equipment, I salvaged a cathode-ray tube plus other components and designed and constructed an oscilloscope. Being a patriot, I had the time axis running from right to left in accord with Hebrew writing. Ollendorff was delighted, and when Haim Weizmann (a scientist and one of the great Zionists, who later became the first president of Israel) visited the Technion, he was shown the "Hebrew oscilloscope." He enthusiastically shook my hand and I felt as though I was in Heaven (which in Israel is closer to earth than here).

In addition to repairing radios and being Ollendorff's lab assistant, I also worked for the Haganah (an underground organization whose ultimate goal was the establishment of an independent Jewish state) as an electronics expert. Let me describe a couple of projects as examples of my involvement in "applied research" to give you a feeling of the prevailing times. One dealt with tapping into the direct telephone line between the British High Commissioner in Jerusalem and 10 Downing Street in London and building an unscrambling device to make the conversations intelligible. This work was kept under wraps for over 50 years, and I was not privy to whether it actually worked in the field. An article describing this action appeared

---

[1] As I write this, I receive a phone call from Eli Bar-On, a fellow escapee, to remind me that this week (April, 2001) it is 60 years that we left Slovakia. He is arranging a get together in Israel of the surviving eight members of the group.

for the first time in an Israeli newspaper in 1992 (1), but a definitive acknowledgment of its working I received only in February 2000 from the Ministry of Defense of the state of Israel (9).

The second project dealt with the invention, in collaboration with a friend, Hanan Myer, of a secret optical signaling device. It worked on the following principle: A neon lamp connected to a 50 Hz power line extinguishes and lights up 100 (i.e. 2 × 50) times per second. The eye cannot follow such a high frequency and instead sees a steady light. However, when viewed through a telescope whose view is alternately obscured and cleared by a reed vibrating 100 times per second, the lamp is seen either lit or dark, depending on the relative phase of the vibration of the reed with respect to the voltage on the neon lamp. By changing the phase of the voltage feeding it, the neon lamp appears to the viewer either as dark or lit. Thus, Morse code signaling is accomplished by changing the phase. Viewers equipped with a vibrating reed telescope would receive the signal. The unaided eye, being insensitive to the changes in the phase, sees a steady light. The neon lamps were installed on the roofs of hospitals in the form of Stars of David (the Israeli equivalent of the Red Cross), forming a connecting network throughout Israel.

I experienced a flashback of these episodes, combined with strange feelings, when I met John Kendrew at the Board of Governors meeting at the Weizmann Institute a few years ago and he told me that he was stationed as a British officer in Palestine at about the same time I performed these jobs.

Unfortunately, none of the above activities made up for the lack of a high school education, and I could not get accepted into the Technion, which I very much wanted to attend. In 1944, Ollendorff arranged for me to take a special entrance examination. I passed all subjects except the Bible (Old Testament). All of Ollendorff's pleading with the administration did no good. As rector Kaplanski and his admission committee declared, "A Jewish engineer has to know the Bible." I was devastated at that time, although some amusing incidents played out decades later in connection with my failing the exam. One of them occurred in 1975. I was invited to give a set of lectures in connection with the opening of the Solid State Institute at the Technion. After my last talk, an old man with a cane hobbled to the podium, congratulated me on my research and delivery, and remarked that part of the credit for my career should be given to him. "We have never met," he said, "but I was a member of the admission committee in 1944 that refused your entrance to the Technion." And when I received an honorary doctorate from the Hebrew University of Jerusalem in 1994, I could not resist pointing out how much easier it was to obtain that degree than to be accepted to the Technion. Concerning the lack of a high school education, I wonder whether it actually did not have a beneficial effect. The rigidity of the high school system might easily have suppressed any creativity and imagination.

So in 1944, there was nothing left for me but to try to get accepted into a university abroad where the Bible would not be a required subject for admission. I applied to about 50 universities in the United States; only 2 were willing to accept me as a special student: Harvard and the University of California at Berkeley. Harvard was out for financial reasons and so I opted for Berkeley. There was still the financial problem of the passage to the United States, which was by no means trivial, considering the poor economic situation in Palestine at that time. My previous hobby helped me out.

I remembered the beautiful Rochelle salt crystals I grew in Slovakia. These crystals are piezoelectric. They can therefore be used to construct microphones and phonograph pickups. During the war, none of these items could be imported to Palestine, and there was a dire need to have them for public address systems to entertain Allied troops stationed there. I set up a small production line to manufacture piezoelectric devices, mostly microphones that I sold to the entertainment establishments. By 1946, I had accumulated enough money to embark on the trip to the United States.

UNIVERSITY OF CALIFORNIA, BERKELEY 1947–1954

Undergraduate Studies 1947–1950

I arrived in Berkeley in December 1946, in time for the start of the semester in January 1947. I was excited to get started after an ~eight-year hiatus in my formal education. I really wanted to study biophysics, having been influenced by Schrödinger's *What Is Life* (142), which I had read while still in Israel. But U.C. Berkeley did not have an undergraduate program in biophysics. Furthermore, the Jewish authorities in Palestine did not look favorably on studying such "useless" fields. Not even physics was condoned. It had to be something more practical like engineering, so I chose the closest field, engineering physics. Like a sponge, I soaked up courses in math, physics, chemistry, astronomy, engineering drawing, and physiology. This was above the allowed limit, but I received permission to do it.

There was a little problem. I had some money to cover tuition and rent for one semester, but there wasn't much left for food. I roomed with an equally poor Israeli, Aaron Gibor, who majored in biology. We took Physiology 1A together, a huge class with laboratory sessions where we dissected frogs. After class, we collected them and boiled the legs for dinner. Fortunately, toward the end of the semester we worked on rabbits, so our diet improved. Somehow, we managed to get through the semester. When summer arrived, I got a job picking fruit in the San Joaquin Valley. I thought my kibbutz experience would come in handy, but I was in for a surprise. The pace of the Mexican fruit pickers was breathtaking (literally). In the kibbutz we discussed ideological issues, like the plight of the suffering proletariat, while picking fruit at a relatively leisurely pace, whereas here I encountered the suffering proletariat that had no time to discuss anything, trying to pick as much fruit as possible because we were paid by the box. It was hard work. The money I made in the summer, together with working for room and board (washing dishes and cleaning rooms), carried me through the fall semester of 1947. Thereafter I became a reader, which meant correcting homework papers and exams at $1.00/h in all courses in which I had received a good grade. In my senior year, I worked part time as an electronic technician in the Electrical Engineering department. In 1950, I graduated with a B.S. in Engineering Physics.

Graduate Studies in Electrical Engineering 1950–1951

In 1949, I married a fellow student and we were expecting a baby. To support the family, I started to work full time as an engineer in the electrical engineering department under the supervision of David Sloan, the inventor of the Resnatron, a high-power microwave tube that was used in England during the war to jam German radar. He continued to build bigger and bigger Resnatrons, and I was given the task of designing the cathode to supply the high currents required by these giant tubes. In parallel, I was able to take some graduate courses in electrical engineering, and fortunately, my work (on thermionic emission of a new dispenser-type cathode) was accepted as a thesis topic. I received a M.S. in electrical engineering in 1951.

Graduate Studies in Physics 1951–1954

Now married to an American citizen, I had the equivalent of a green card and therefore felt less constrained by the desires of the Israeli authorities. Consequently, I switched to physics and joined the solid-state group of A. Kip and C. Kittel. They had a program in electron paramagnetic resonance (EPR), which was a relatively new field, and they needed somebody with an engineering background to design and build EPR spectrometers. My thesis project was electron spin resonance of conduction electrons in metals. But I still had biophysics on my mind, and so on Sundays I came to the lab and put miscellaneous biological materials such as leaves and blood into the microwave cavity. Lo and behold, when the leaves were illuminated a signal appeared. This, incidentally was before the publication of the pioneering paper by Commoner et al. (26) on EPR in biological systems. I also found a signal in blood at $g = 6$, but all hell broke loose when one Sunday Kittel came in and found me doing these frivolous experiments instead of focusing on my thesis project. He threatened to throw me out if he caught me at it again. (Another confrontation with Kittel is discussed in the section on acceptors in silicon.) In addition, he pooh-poohed the signal at $g = 6$, which he was convinced must be an artifact, "Every fool knows that angular momentum is quenched and the g-values cannot deviate far from $g = 2$." It was later that Ingram's group published their work on hemoglobin (14) and that Griffith (77) explained the origin of the $g = 6$ signal. This experience reinforced my belief not to be awed by authority. I wonder now whether these frustrating early experiments had anything to do with my working on heme proteins and photosynthesis decades later. I received a Ph.D. in physics in 1954.

BELL TELEPHONE LABS (BTL) 1954–1960

As I was finishing my Ph.D. thesis, I decided to apply for a job in industry rather than academia. There were essentially two reasons for that decision. One was the academic rat race I witnessed in Berkeley. The stress on assistant professors seemed awesome. I reasoned that by going to a high-caliber industrial research lab and doing good work, I had a chance to later step into a tenured academic position. The second reason was my intention to return to Israel, in which case the industrial experience would be important because there were no academic research jobs available in Israel at that time.

After receiving my Ph.D. in physics, I joined the research group at Bell Telephone Labs in Murray Hill, New Jersey. I had been interviewed by Bill Shockley of transistor fame, but by the time I arrived, Shockley had left. The reason for his leaving is rather interesting. Shockley argued that the prevalent system for remunerating scientists made no sense. He pointed out that the contributions of scientists differed by orders of magnitude, whereas their salaries differed by only factors of $\sim$2. He advocated a linear rather than logarithmic relation between contributions and salaries. He circulated a memo in which he proposed this idea and outlined how to measure contributions (e.g., number of patents, papers, talks, and acknowledgments) As an example, he used himself and came up with a yearly salary of one million dollars, which he requested be paid to him. The management balked and Shockley walked.

Systematic Investigation of EPR Spectrometers

Arriving at Bell Labs, I was given complete freedom to pick a project of my own choosing. Arnie Honig, a postdoc at Berkeley during my last year at UCB, had published an exciting, but to me not quite believable, result on EPR in silicon (82). I decided to look into that problem. However, first I wanted to build a good EPR spectrometer. At that time, no commercial EPR spectrometers were available, and everybody was building them haphazardly, making unsubstantiated claims of sensitivities and superiority. I delayed the silicon experiments and instead undertook a detailed, systematic investigation of the sensitivity problems of EPR spectrometers, a topic that I had discussed at length with a fellow graduate student, Alan Portis, when I was still at Berkeley. The outcome of this work was published in an in-house journal (44) after it was rejected by the *Review of Scientific Instruments* for being too long. I must admit to mixed feelings that this, essentially an engineering article, is the most quoted of all my papers. Perhaps it should be a consolation that Jim Hyde, who contributed greatly to the design of the commercial Varian EPR spectrometer, told me that he had used the results of this paper extensively.

Development of the Electron Nuclear Double Resonance (ENDOR) Technique

Honig had found that EPR signals of shallow donors in phosphorous-doped silicon have long relaxation times at helium temperatures (82). Such long spin-lattice relaxation times had never been observed for electrons. Honig therefore interpreted these results in terms of nuclear relaxation times with a concomitant high ($\sim$100%) nuclear polarization (82). This interpretation, which created great excitement in the field, did not feel right to me, and I soon showed that his finding was the result of unexpectedly long electronic (and not nuclear) spin-lattice relaxation times (42).

These long relaxation times made it easy to apply to the system various "spin calisthenics" techniques, among them the inversion of energy levels (15). In P-doped Si, the hyperfine interaction of the P^{31} nucleus with the electron creates a four-level system ($I = {}^1/_2$, $S = {}^1/_2$). By judiciously flipping the populations of the electronic and nuclear levels, a sizable nuclear polarization (equivalent to the electron spin polarization) could be obtained (42). Because we flipped nuclei and monitored their population via the EPR signal, this represented the first electron nuclear double resonance (ENDOR) experiment.

Investigation of Nuclear Structures by ENDOR

DETERMINATION OF NUCLEAR MAGNETIC MOMENTS   In ENDOR experiments, one observes nuclear transitions via the electron spin resonance. Because the magnetic moment of the electrons is $\sim 10^3$ larger than that of nuclei, one has an NMR technique many orders of magnitude more sensitive than standard NMR. The method is, therefore, well-suited to determine magnetic moments of radioactive (or rare) nuclei, whose low abundance requires the high sensitivity. We determined the spin and magnetic moment of P^{32} (57). Several other nuclei were subsequently investigated by ENDOR (reviewed in 53).

DETERMINATION OF THE HYPERFINE STRUCTURE ANOMALY   The isotropic hyperfine coupling is proportional to the probability of the electron being at the nucleus, i.e., to the square of the electronic wavefunction $|\Psi(0)|^2$ and to the nuclear g-factor (71). One usually assumes the nucleus to be infinitely small and its moment a point dipole. However, the nucleus has a finite extent that has to be taken into account by integrating the wavefunction over the nucleus (90a). Thus, the ratio of the hyperfine couplings of two isotopes will differ from the ratio of their nuclear g-factors. This is a small (fraction of a percent) effect, and consequently, the hyperfine couplings have to be measured with high precision. ENDOR provides a method to do this, and together with J. Eisinger, we determined the hyperfine structure anomaly of the S^{121}, Sb^{123} nuclei in antimony-doped silicon (39). From the results of these experiments, we obtained the distribution of the magnetic moment inside the nucleus.

Determination of the Electronic Wavefunction of Paramagnetic Impurities in Solids by ENDOR

Probably the most important application of ENDOR is the determination of hf interactions when they are not resolved in the EPR spectrum. When an unpaired electron in a solid interacts with many nuclei, the individual hf lines are not resolved, and one obtains a single, so-called inhomogeneously broadened line (129). Using ENDOR, one can resolve these lines, thereby providing a method of mapping the electronic wavefunction of the unpaired electron.

The success of the ENDOR technique is based on the fact that the individual hyperfine lines that make up the inhomogeneously broadened line do not communicate with each other, i.e., they can be saturated in what is now called hole burning. Phil Anderson, whose office was around the corner from my lab, closely followed the ENDOR experiments. He was puzzled by the lack of diffusion of the spin packets, which led him to develop the now well-known Anderson localization theory (8).

Shortly after ENDOR was used to polarize nuclei (42), it was applied to investigate F-centers in KCl and shallow donors in silicon (43). The silicon work kept me occupied for the next two to three years and culminated in a long publication (45), in which I gave reference to the witch of ENDOR (also spelled Ein Dor) in the Old Testament[2] (137). The editor of the *Physical Review*, S. A. Goudsmit, was upset. He called and bawled me out not only for making frivolous references in a serious journal, but also for neglecting to reference to Mark Twain, who also wrote about the witch of ENDOR. It did not help to point out that one needs to refer only to the first publication; Goudsmit was adamant to delete it. When I finally gave in and pointed out that they would have to renumber the references, he gasped because this was the first reference followed by another 82. But he did it, and the reference to the bible appeared only later in a book by Low (97). In 1957, Wolfgang Pauli visited Bell Labs, and I had the daunting experience of explaining ENDOR to him. It was an interesting visit, which is described elsewhere (53).

The Construction of the Solid-State Maser

The first MASER (microwave amplification of stimulated emission by radiation), the precursor of the LASER, was constructed by Townes and collaborators in 1954 (74). It used a gas, ammonia, as the active element, had a miniscule power output, and filled up an entire room. It was, therefore, not yet a practical device. The search for a more powerful, user-friendly, solid-state maser was on. Bloembergen suggested a scheme in which at least three electron spin resonance levels were used (16). By saturating the outer levels with a strong microwave field, a population inversion (negative temperature) of two levels could, in principle, be obtained.

In collaboration with Scovil and Seidel, we constructed such a system using a single crystal of diluted gadolinium ethyl sulfate with cerium as an impurity. Cerium with its short relaxation time can interact at a given orientation of the magnetic field with two of three gadolinium levels, facilitating the population inversion (68). Although growing the crystal was not a great feat, my previous experience in crystallization came in handy once again. The maser worked (143) and created quite a splash. It was put on the first U.S. satellite, to the great satisfaction of Bell Labs and the U.S. scientific community, which had felt frustrated by Russia's leadership in the space program, as demonstrated by the launching of the first satellite Sputnik. Incidentally, when I visited Israel the following year, there was

---

[2]Briefly, the story relates how worried Saul went to consult the witch of ENDOR about his fate. When she told it to him, he fainted. The following analogy of this story to ENDOR can be made: Theoreticians calculate wavefunctions that were difficult to determine experimentally prior to the development of ENDOR, so they seldom could be proven wrong. Now, when they compare the experimental ENDOR results with their predictions, some of them faint.

great interest in the maser. The increased sensitivity of the radar, due to the use of the maser, made it possible for the Israeli army to see Cairo.

After the successful operation of the maser, the management of Bell Labs put on some pressure to publish the results as soon as possible, lest we be scooped by Bloembergen. I had no such fears and made a bet with Phil Anderson that nobody but us would have a working maser by the end of the year. Anderson conveyed this later to Bloembergen with the not-too-unexpected result of cooling the relation between us. (I guess the expression "horse-sense" originated from the fact that horses do not bet on the outcome of human affairs.) Nico, if by chance you should read these lines, I hope you will forgive me for the arrogance of my youth.

A different kind of solid-state maser was constructed in collaboration with Jim Gordon in 1957 (58). It was based on the adiabatic fast passage scheme (15) for inversion of two electron spin levels first proposed in connection with a maser by Combrisson et al. (24). We used the EPR transition in phosphorus-doped silicon. To satisfy the maser conditions, we had to reduce the EPR line width. This required removing the isotope Si^{29} ($\sim$5% abundant), whose magnetic moment interacts with the electron spins. To accomplish this, I had to convince the authorities of the isotope separation unit at Oak Ridge of the importance of the project. I convinced them and when we finally received the silicon sample and purified it, the two-level maser worked as predicted (58).

I should add that it was an awe-inspiring experience for me to stand in front of the several-stories-high mass spectrometer (the Calutron) that was used during the Manhattan Project to separate U^{235} from U^{238}. It seemed to me disproportionate that this huge machine would have to work several days exclusively for us to produce the tiny silicon sample, and I almost faltered in my resolve to request the sample.

A Bad Choice of Priorities: Parity Nonconservation

In the fall of 1956, I gave a colloquium at Columbia University on the nuclear polarization scheme. After the colloquium, C. S. Wu and T. D. Lee excitedly tried to persuade me to measure the asymmetry of ß-decay in a polarized sample of donor nuclei in silicon. T. D. Lee and C. N. Yang had circulated a preprint of an article in which they suggested that one of the conservation laws of physics, parity, did not hold in the case of weak interactions (92). This could be critically tested by measuring the asymmetry of ß-decay. I listened politely with limited interest and promised them I would get to it as soon as I finished the ENDOR experiments and the work on the maser. After finishing these at the end of 1956, I took an extended skiing vacation in the West. On the way back I stopped off at the University of Pittsburgh where I gave a colloquium describing the maser and the nuclear polarization scheme. At the conclusion, I mentioned that I would like to test Lee & Yang's hypothesis of parity nonconservation. I saw some blank faces among the faculty sitting in the front row, and it felt as if the temperature of the room had dropped by 10 degrees. Finally, G. C. Wick said, "But don't you know that parity nonconservation has already been proven by several groups?" (reviewed in 53). Of course, I did not know; I had been skiing for a month. So much for a bad choice of priorities and poor judgment: By not having jumped at the opportunity, I missed participating in one of the major upheavals in modern physics. I do not regret the skiing, but the maser? Who remembers that now? I am glad to see that ENDOR at least is still being used. Upon my return to Bell Labs, as promised, I did the parity nonconservation experiment in ^{32}P-doped silicon. But by that time, this was "old hat," and the results were never submitted for publication.

Speaking of bad judgment, in connection with parity nonconservation, the great W. Pauli also made one. T. D. Lee had sent a preprint of his article to Pauli who replied that he was convinced that parity is conserved and was willing to bet his reputation on it. While his letter was en route, the nonconservation of parity was proven. Everybody anxiously waited to see how Pauli would react to this. A letter finally arrived with Pauli acknowledging that he had been wrong but adding that we must admit how clever he was in betting his reputation of which he had plenty to spare and not betting money of which he had little.

A Brief, Unsuccessful Attempt at a Biophysics Experiment

In 1956, K. S. Cole, a well-known neurophysiologist from the National Institutes of Health (NIH), gave a lecture at Bell Labs describing nerve conduction. He described the unresolved problem of whether the sodium ion flux passing across the membrane is made up of individual ions or clusters of ions. At the time I was concerned with noise problems and suggested to Cole that one could, in principle, resolve this question by measuring the quantal nature of the fluctuations in the current, i.e., the noise amplitude should be proportional to the square root of the number of charged entities crossing the membrane. Cole invited me to spend a week in his laboratory at NIH, which I accepted. There I reacquainted myself with an old friend, the frog sartorius muscle, which had contributed to my diet a decade earlier. The experiments were inconclusive; they floundered because we did not have a sufficiently noise-free amplifier. I was in the middle of developing ENDOR and the solid-state maser and therefore did not pursue this problem further. Later I learned about the elegant experiments of Katz and others involving essentially the same idea of applying quantal analyses to neurotransmission [reviewed in (86)]. The topic of fluctuations and noise always held a special fascination for me, and I later took it up again at the University of California at San Diego.

The Puzzle of Shallow Acceptors in p-type Silicon

In contrast to the extensive work on shallow donors in silicon, several attempts to observe the paramagnetic resonance absorption from shallow acceptors in Si were unsuccessful. This remained a puzzle for several years. I remember in this connection an interaction (if it can be called that) with John Bardeen, the modest, quiet, two-time Nobel Prize winner. We were driving together from a semiconductor conference in Rochester, New York, to Murray Hill, New Jersey. At the start of the trip, Bardeen asked me whether I was still unsuccessful in observing an EPR resonance from acceptors. After hearing my answer, he puzzled over it and said, "That's strange, let me think about it." The next five hours were spent in complete silence. When he stepped out of the car in Murray Hill, all he said was, "I am sorry, I don't understand it."

The resolution to the puzzle came during a discussion with Walter Kohn. The valence band of silicon (at the wave vector $k = 0$) is degenerate. Local random strains lift the degeneracy by varying amounts, giving rise to a multitude of possible spin transitions with different g-values. The consequent broadening of the resonance line makes its observation difficult. By applying uniaxial stress to the silicon crystal, the degeneracy is lifted in a well-defined way and the resonance should be observable.

We performed the experiment on a single crystal of boron-doped silicon and applied uniaxial stress with a calibrated spring. Upon applying stress, the resonance appeared as if by magic (59). The puzzle of the acceptor was solved.

Acceptors in Si had a special meaning for me; they had almost cost me my Ph.D. years earlier. During the last year of my thesis work, I received a cable from Kittel asking me to stop working on EPR in metals and switch to p-type silicon. Kittel had visited Harvard, where Bloembergen showed him his EPR results on p-type silicon. Bloembergen interpreted these results as arising from acceptors. I considered the use of this information as unethical on Kittel's part and ignored his cable. When Kittel returned and heard my objections, he became furious and asked me to leave the group. It was only through the intervention of my cosupervisor A. F. Kip that I was allowed to return and finish my thesis. The story has an ironic ending. Bloembergen published his EPR results on p-type silicon (156). However, his interpretation was wrong. As I showed later, the resonance did not arise from acceptors but from surface states (45). It is probably the only published mistake that Bloembergen has ever made.

Industry Versus Academia: A Difficult Decision

After a few years at Bell Labs, the time had come to reevaluate my earlier decision to join an industrial lab. The research conditions at Bell Labs were superb. The management was enlightened and farsighted. There was complete freedom in the choice of problems with all the technical and financial support at one's disposal. There were no distractions from research like the ones in academia, e.g., committees, grant writing, and teaching. Yet there were some negative aspects. To start with, the lack of graduate students and postdocs that keep you on your toes and give the satisfaction of seeing them develop (although I did have, as an exception, one graduate student, Don Wilson, who was registered at Rutgers University). Then there were the inherent corporate annoyances. For example, a letter that I wrote to Communist Czechoslovakia in 1959 was opened and returned, stating that there should be no communication with communist countries on Bell Labs stationary. Another example was the company's celebration of the successful operation of the solid-state maser in a restaurant "For Whites Only." My refusal to participate brought unpleasant repercussions. There were also some rules that I did not like and fought. For instance, technicians were not supposed to be coauthors on papers because "they were paid to do the job." I did, nevertheless, put my excellent technician, Ed Gere, on several papers (e.g., 57–59) in spite of stiff resistance from the management. Finally, Bell Labs did not seem to be the right place to pursue biophysical research, which I ultimately planned to do. Although the management would have supported such efforts (and indeed it subsequently did), the infrastructure (e.g., activities in biology and biochemistry) was missing.

A recurring topic of discussion among us was whether "Bell Labs is a place to age gracefully." The answer to this was provided for me by the following incident. I frequently passed an office in which I saw an elderly gentleman slumped over a desk, reading. I was curious: Who was he? Nobody knew. I finally found out from the director of research: He was the famous J. B. Johnson, whose beautiful and seminal papers on the "Johnson Noise" in the 1920s I had read and admired. How sad, I thought, to see a person of this stature glide into obscurity instead of motivating generations of students at a university.

In 1958, Felix Bloch, the co-inventor of nuclear magnetic resonance (NMR), offered me a tenured position at Stanford. It was a tempting offer, but after much thought I refused in view of my still-existing plan to return to Israel. Bloch understood; he had similar feelings in the 1940s and went to see Einstein to discuss this problem. The great man's reply was that he is first a scientist and second a Jew. This satisfied Bloch, but unfortunately, not me. I never really made peace with not living in Israel.

In 1959 another opportunity arose. The physics department at Columbia University was thinking of starting a program in solid state physics. Furthermore, Charlie Townes, the co-inventor of the maser and laser was leaving and somebody had to take over his students. Having worked both on masers and in solid-state physics, I was approached to apply for the position. Its advantage over Stanford was that I could keep my lab at Bell and not burn my bridges in case the position did not work out.

A JOINT APPOINTMENT BETWEEN BELL LABS AND COLUMBIA UNIVERSITY 1959–1960

Despite the objections of I. I. Rabi, the strongman at Columbia, to a program in solid state physics (for details, see 55), the department decided to go ahead with it, and I was offered a joint appointment between Columbia University and Bell Labs. I inherited about 10 graduate students from Townes, among them Arno Penzias, the future Nobel Laureate and director of Bell Labs, whom at the time no one suspected would reach such heights (for details, see 55). Townes asked me to pay special attention to a promising young student from Argentina, Elsa Rosenvasser. I not only followed his advise, I went overboard. I essentially neglected the rest of the students and paid exclusive attention to Elsa, who in 1961 became my wife.

A Brief Excursion into High Energy Physics: Muonium Formation in Solids

At Columbia I collaborated with A. Sachs and R. Prepost on an experiment at the Nevis synchrocyclotron combining high-energy physics with solid-state physics. This gave me the opportunity to see how the high-energy half of the physics community lives.

When a spin-polarized μ-meson (muon) beam enters a solid, it may transiently attach itself to an electron, forming a (μ^+e^-) hydrogen-like atom, called muonium. This process can be studied by measuring the depolarization of the muon spin during the formation of muonium. Because the electronic structure of semiconductors was well understood, this system seemed well suited to study muonium formation with the goal of extending its use as a structural probe in less-well-understood materials. The results in silicon and germanium showed that muonium formed a transient shallow donor with a lifetime that depended on the number of free holes and electrons (i.e., impurity concentration) (66). Although the results were interesting, working at an accelerator with a large supporting group and a grueling schedule did not appeal to me. Twenty-five years later I had the same feeling doing extended X-ray absorption fine structure (EXAFS) experiments on reaction centers at the Stanford Linear Accelerator (37).

My association with Columbia was an interesting experience. However, it was not a long-term solution. The joint appointment with Bell Labs made it a neither here nor there situation. In addition, commuting was a pain, I did not like living in New York, and for that matter, I was not enamored of Murray Hill, New Jersey, either. At that point another opportunity presented itself.

UNIVERSITY OF CALIFORNIA, SAN DIEGO 1960–PRESENT

In 1960, Roger Revelle, Director of the Scripps Institute of Oceanography at La Jolla—a fascinating man, a combination of charismatic visionary and con man—convinced the Regents of the University of California to establish a new campus in San Diego (La Jolla). He came to Bell Labs to recruit solid-state physicists and invited three of us for a visit to La Jolla. He promised us that UCSD would remain a graduate school with a light teaching load and an emphasis on research. He also showed me a beautiful lot with an ocean view that I could get if I came. (We later found out that he showed the same lot to all of us). It sounded exciting to be in on the ground floor in building a new campus, where one's ideas can still make a difference. My colleagues at Columbia thought I was crazy to forego a professorship at Columbia and move to La Jolla. They and others thought that it would be impossible to build a first-rate university in an idyllic playground such as

La Jolla. They were wrong, of course. Scientists carry their compulsions, neuroses and talents with them and are, to first order, unaffected by the environment.

I accepted Revelle's offer with the proviso that after establishing an experimental solid-state research program, I would be free to pursue my interest in biophysics. My first experiments at UCSD were essentially continuations of my work at Bell Labs, which I briefly describe. It took the proverbial seven years to switch full-time to biophysics.

Resonance Experiments under Uniaxial Stress

The EPR spectrometer, including the capability of applying uniaxial stress that was developed at Bell Labs, was duplicated at UCSD by my wife Elsa and Roger Isaacson. Roger is an exceptionally capable coworker, part of my group for the past 40 years. During the first couple of years, I also continued to collaborate with my colleagues at Bell Labs.

EXCITED STATES OF SHALLOW DONORS   According to band theory, the energy levels of the conduction band in silicon are composed of a ground-state singlet and a doubly and triply degenerate set of excited states. Because the optical transitions from the ground state to these excited states are forbidden, it is difficult to obtain their position directly from optical spectra. However, application of uniaxial stress admixes the excited states into the ground state. We measured the effect of this admixture with Don Wilson, a graduate student at Rutgers who had worked with me at Bell Labs, by determining the shifts in electronic g-values and hyperfine couplings of shallow donors in a silicon crystal subjected to uniaxial stress (160). This allowed us to determine the positions of the excited states.

VALENCE BAND PARAMETERS FROM CYCLOTRON RESONANCE   At low temperature, free holes and electrons in a semiconductor crystal in an external magnetic field execute orbital or cyclotron motion at an angular frequency determined by their effective mass. Application of an external microwave field at the angular frequency gives rise to an absorption called cyclotron resonance (30). This technique has been used extensively to study the band structure of silicon and germanium. However, because of the degeneracy of the valence band in silicon (at $k = 0$), the sign of two of the three band parameters could not be determined, giving rise to a theoretical controversy among several groups. This controversy was settled in collaboration with J. Hensel at Bell Labs by measuring the cyclotron resonance in silicon at low temperature (1.2 K) subjected to uniaxial stress (80, 81). This enabled us to determine all band parameters.

COUPLING BETWEEN THE ELECTRON SPIN AND THE LATTICE   The EPR signal of a paramagnetic ion or atom embedded in a solid is determined by the strength and details of the interaction of the spin with the surrounding lattice. This interaction is difficult to calculate theoretically but can be determined by applying an external pressure, which displaces the atoms and ions from their equilibrium values. From the concomitant change (shifts) in the EPR spectra, one can deduce the spin-lattice couplings. These are of particular importance in trying to understand the spin-lattice relaxation time T_1 with which the electron spin system comes to thermal equilibrium with the lattice. The mechanism of this process is a time-varying strain associated with the lattice vibrations (phonons) that, at the right frequency, produces transitions between the electronic levels. The uniaxial stress can be viewed as a zero-frequency phonon.

A detailed analysis of the effect of uniaxial stress on the EPR spectra of Mn^{2+} and Fe^{3+} In MgO was the topic of Elsa's Ph.D. thesis (41): She obtained the spin-lattice coefficients and correlated them with the spin-lattice relaxation time as well as with the line widths, which were caused by random internal strains.

Nuclear Polarization via Hot Electrons

The attainment of nuclear polarization is important in the study of nuclear physics (e.g., see Parity Nonconservation above). Nuclear polarization schemes rely on high-magnetic fields and low temperatures (milli K) or on microwave fields inducing electronic transition. While still at Bell Labs, I thought of an alternate, simple scheme (46) that my first postdoc at UCSD, Gil Clark, set out to verify.

The method is based on the Overhauser effect, the extension of which is the well known nuclear Overhauser effect (NOE) that is used in the structure determination of biomolecules by NMR. Originally, Overhauser showed that an enhanced nuclear polarization in metals may be obtained by saturating the electron spin resonance absorption of the conduction electrons in an external radio frequency field (120). The degree of saturation of the electrons, i.e., the deviation of the ratio of spin-up to spin-down states from the Boltzmann thermal equilibrium can be characterized by the spin temperature T_S. I showed that the relevant parameter for nuclear polarization is not T_S but the difference between T_S and the temperature T_R that characterizes the kinetic energy of the electrons (46). In conductors, the electrons are in equilibrium with the lattice temperature T_L, i.e., $T_R = T_L$. However, in semiconductors at low temperatures, the mean free path of the electrons is large so that in an electric field, the acquired kinetic energy between collisions cannot be entirely gotten rid of during collisions with the lattice. This results in the creation of "hot electrons" (reviewed in 89), i.e., $T_R > T_L$. Analogously, the relaxation mechanisms of the electron spins and their kinetic energy are different, $T_S \neq T_R$, resulting in a nuclear polarization. Thus, by simply passing a direct current through a semiconductor at low temperature, a nuclear polarization is achieved. At the time this idea was floating around, Anatole Abragam, a leader in magnetic resonance, was visiting Bell Labs. Although he could not find a flaw in the argument, the simplicity of the scheme made him skeptical.

Gil Clark embarked on the project to prove the validity of the hot electron polarization scheme (22). We used the semiconductor InSb and measured the nuclear polarizations at 4.2 K of In^{115}, Sb^{121}, and Sb^{123} in the presence of an electric field. The nuclear relaxation times were several hours, and we ran the experiments uninterrupted for $\sim$24 h. Nuclear polarization enhancements of up to 100 were obtained in agreement with theoretical predictions.

Going over these old experiments, I am struck by two points. One is the leisurely pace at which research was pursued. The original idea was put forth in 1959; it took four years for the experiments to be completed. The other point is more general in nature. It deals with the disparity between one's own evaluation of the scientific and intellectual content of one's work and the reaction by the scientific community. The work described in this section did not make an impact when it was published and was mostly ignored. On the other hand, I value this work considerably more than other publications that received more attention from the scientific community. However, I was recently pleased and surprised when, after nearly 40 years, I came across a reference to this work in connection with the new field of spintronics and quantum computing (138). I should also mention an unexpected benefit derived from this work. In a footnote of our publication (22), we suggested the possibility of using these ideas to construct a d.c.-driven maser. General Dynamics was interested in pursuing this idea and filed for a patent. Their remuneration enabled us to build a nice house in La Jolla.

An Interesting Encounter with Albert Szent-Györgyi

While I was involved in establishing a solid-state program at UCSD, I tried to acquaint myself with biology and biochemistry by reading and attending lectures. One of the books that I came across in 1962 was by Albert Szent-Györgyi (149), the discoverer of vitamin C and for over half a century a colorful personality in science. The main theme of the book was the nature of ordered water around biological structures. He claimed that water is ordered over distances of several microns ($>10^4$ Å). As a solid-state physicist, I had a hard time believing the H_2O would be ordered over $\sim>10^4$ layers. I did a quick, "Friday afternoon" experiment to disprove Szent-Györgyi's contention. By measuring the frequency response of the dielectric constant of a water-soaked millipore filter with 100 Å pore sizes, I showed that H_2O is not ordered even at a distance of 100 Å. Just as I had finished reading the book, I received a letter from Szent-Györgyi inviting me and Elsa to spend a weekend at his home in Woods Hole to discuss EPR as free radicals had become his newest interest. I thought that this would be a good opportunity to raise the question of the ordered H_2O. Besides, I also wanted to meet my childhood hero about whom my mother used to tell bedtime stories. One of them described how Szent-Györgyi, after the establishment of Czechoslovakia in 1918, fearing for his life, built a raft, took his microscope, and floated down the Danube from Bratislava (where he held a professorship) to Budapest. We happily accepted the invitation. Szent-Györgyi was a charming host, a marvelous raconteur, but totally unreceptive when I tried to broach the subject on my mind. Finally, after two days of unreceptiveness, I dropped all diplomacy on the way to the airport and told him that the proposition in his book was wrong; H_2O is not ordered over several microns. He looked at me quizzically and nonchalantly replied, "Oh, did I say several microns? I am so bad with numbers, don't pay any attention to them." What an anticlimax and blow to the image of my childhood hero! This little vignette of Szent-Györgyi is in perfect accord with Max Perutz's recent description of him (125).

Paraelectrics

PARAELECTRIC RESONANCE OF ELECTRIC DIPOLES   The theories of magnetic and electric susceptibility have many features in common, and in fact, in Van Vleck's classic exposition on the subject, both are treated on an equal footing (153). However, in contrast to the large body of work on paramagnetic resonances, no paraelectrical resonance was ever observed despite a great deal of work on paraelectrics (reviewed in 17). The reason for this disparity is that the energy levels of the magnetic moment in an external magnetic field are quantized (i.e., the spins point along specific directions), whereas electric dipoles lacking an angular momentum are not quantized in an electric field. One needs therefore to impose the spatial quantization by embedding the dipole in a crystal that forces the dipole to orient along specific crystallographic axes. The possibility of observing paraelectric resonance in such a system was first mentioned by Kuhn & Lüty (91).

The system that we (Herb Shore, a colleague theorist at UCSD, and Ian Shepherd, a graduate student) picked was a KCl crystal into which OH^- ions were introduced as an impurity. The dipole moments of the OH^- ions orient themselves along the six $\langle 100 \rangle$ crystallographic directions (91). The application of an external electric field changes the energies of the different dipolar orientations, and transitions between the energy levels can be induced. The OH^--KCl crystal was introduced into the electric field of a microwave cavity of a conventional EPR spectrometer. Transitions were observed by varying the external electric field. From the spectra the dipole moment of OH^- and the zero-field splitting of the levels were deduced (69). A noteworthy difference between the electric dipole and magnetic dipole transitions is that the coupling of the former to the electromagnetic field is many orders of magnitude stronger, giving rise to large signals.

It was satisfying to finally observe paraelectric resonance. However, because of the special conditions required to observe these transitions, the interest of the scientific community in paraelectric resonance never came close to the interest in paramagnetic resonance.

COOLING BY ADIABATIC DEPOLARIZATION OF OH^- MOLECULES IN KCl   The method that had been universally employed for obtaining temperatures below a few tenths of a degree K makes use of the magnetocaloric effect first demonstrated in 1933 (73). The method is based on the change in entropy of an assembly of magnetic dipoles during the adiabatic removal of an externally applied magnetic field.

In analogy with the magnetic system, the removal of an electric field in a paraelectric system should also increase the entropy and cool the system (85).

Such cooling below 1 K was first observed by Ian Shepherd, a graduate student in our lab. Shepherd used the system of OH^- impurities in KCl. Upon removal of an electric field of 75 kV/cm, he reduced the temperature of the KCl crystal from 1.3 K to 0.36 K (144). The advantage of this system is that it does not use an external magnetic field. Therefore, in principle, it can be used in a two-stage tandem depolarization scheme in which the second stage uses adiabatic demagnetization to further reduce the temperature of the system.

The Electronic Structure of Porphyrins

Martin Kamen, who joined the chemistry department at UCSD in 1963, tried hard to get me interested in photosynthesis. He brought the physical chemist David Mauzerall as a visitor from the Rockefeller University to breach the gap between our disciplines. Mauzerall produced, photochemically, porphyrin-free radials whose EPR and optical spectra we investigated in detail (103, 104). The idea was that porphyrins may serve as model compounds for bacteriochlorophyl. But at that time, the connection to photosynthesis remained remote. However, this work stimulated us to do further spectroscopy on porphyrins.

J. R. Platt gave a seminar at UCSD around 1965, claiming that the excited state of porphyrins has the rather remarkably high magnetic quantum number $|M_z|$ of 9 units (128). With Mike Malley, a graduate student, we set out to investigate Platt's theory by measuring the optical absorption in a magnetic field of 10^5 Gauss. Circular polarized light of opposite senses induces transitions to the $+M_z$ and $-M_z$ states, respectively. From the optical splitting between the two polarizations, a value of $|\Delta M_z| = 9 \pm 1$ was indeed found, to our surprise (63), as predicted by Platt (128).

The change in the optical spectra of porphyrins in an applied electric field, i.e., the Stark effect, which determines the difference in polarizability of the excited and ground state, was also investigated (100). These experiments provided a useful experience for later work on the Stark effect in photosynthetic reaction centers (RCs) (95, 96).

A Sabbatical at MIT; Courses at Woods Hole and Cold Spring Harbor 1967–1968

After seven years at UCSD, I still hadn't switched to biophysics as originally planned. It became clear to me that if I seriously wanted to make the switch, I needed to leave the known and cozy environment of the physics department and immerse myself in a more biologically oriented surrounding. The opportunity came with an invitation from Cyrus Levinthal at MIT to spend a year there as a visiting professor in the biology department. Before going to MIT I spent the summer at Woods Hole taking the intense and highly instructive physiology course. One of the sections I took was on bacterial photosynthesis given by Rod Clayton. It greatly appealed to me, but I did not want to commit myself to this topic before exploring other areas during my sabbatical year at MIT.

MIT was quite an experience: the mad hustle and bustle compared to UCSD; the people, in obvious quest for fame and glory, had little time left for a visiting greenhorn. There was one exception, Lisa Steiner, an immunologist whose course I took. We became, and still are, good friends and colleagues. She taught me a lot of biology and protein chemistry, and we started a fruitful collaboration.

I soon came to realize the differences in research approaches pursued by physicists and biologists. This is perhaps best illustrated by an encounter with Salvador Luria at MIT.

"Hi, George, how nice to see you here. What are you doing?" he asked.

"I am sitting in on several biology and biochemistry courses," I answered.

"Yes, but what are you doing?"

"Well, I am going to seminars and talking to people about their work."

"Yes, but what are you doing?" he insisted.

"I am also getting some experience in the laboratory of Lisa Steiner."

"Yes, but what are you doing?"

So it finally dawned on me: Biology is a doer's field. You have to run centrifuges and gels and not spend time in deep thoughts as physicists are prone to do. The challenge for biophysicists is to effectively synthetize the approaches from both disciplines.

The difference between physics and biology may perhaps be best summarized as follows: Physics is difficult but simple (i.e., when you have mastered, often with great difficulty, the basic principles of quantum mechanics, Newton and Maxwell's equations, everything follows logically). Biology, on the other hand, is easy but complex (i.e., no difficult concepts but a great number of facts). This difference is exemplified by Leo Szilard's remark when he turned his interest from physics to biology: "I get my best ideas while taking a bath. But with biology I have problems; I always have to jump out and look up a fact."

After a year at MIT, I spent the summer of 1968 at Cold Spring Harbor taking a course with Max Delbruck. I had previously taken a course in 1964 at Cold Spring Harbor on phage and bacterial genetics, which had been started by Delbruck close to two decades earlier. Although it was a great experience, I did not follow it up as I spent the following sabbatical in Buenos Aires with my wife setting up an EPR program in solid state physics. I did, however, have the good fortune in 1964 to meet Delbruck, with whom I kept close contact until his death in 1981. Delbruck's course in 1968 dealt with phycomyces, a system that Delbruck championed over photosynthetic bacteria. He believed that photosynthesis is too complex a system to make significant progress in. A few years later he changed his mind, and in the late 1970s, he invited me to visit CalTech for a few days and to give two seminars (on photosynthesis and fluctuation spectroscopy). Delbruck was reputed to tell every seminar speaker that his was the worst presentation that Delbruck had ever heard. So I was a little apprehensive and started the first seminar by expressing my delight in being invited to give two seminars as both could not be the worst. Debruck immediately pointed out the fallacy of the argument as the second seminar could be worse than the first. Actually, he was kind to me and offered me a position at CalTech. I felt honored but saw no reason to leave La Jolla, where I was content at UCSD and where my wife had a position at San Diego State University.

By the end of the summer of 1968, I had made the decision to work on the primary processes in bacterial photosynthesis. The decision was based on several factors. I liked the seeming simplicity of the bacterial system in which, in principle, one can obtain from one bacterium in a few days "an ensemble of $\sim 10^9$/ml identical particles," a concept dear to a physicist's heart. It also had the advantage of the relative ease of genetic manipulation. Additional appealing aspects were the multidisciplinary nature of the field, the small number of people working in it, and the possibility of solving the basic question of the identity of the primary reactants using a technique with which we were familiar (EPR/ENDOR). Thus, photosynthesis has been the main theme of our work since 1968. I recently published a review on it (55) and, therefore, present here only some of the highlights. But before doing so, I want to discuss some other biophysics work performed in parallel with the photosynthesis work.

The Electronic Structure of Hemes

Hemes serve as prosthetic groups in an important class of biomolecules (e.g., myoglobin, hemoglobin, cytochrome). They have been extensively studied, and Mb and Hb were the first proteins whose three-dimensional structures were determined by J. Kendrew and M. F. Perutz (reviewed in 29). The business end of these molecules is the iron in the prosthetic heme group, which ligates to the protein and to which oxygen binds.

The electronic structure of the iron in the heme can be studied by a variety of physical methods, including magnetic resonance. The energy levels of high-spin Fe^{3+}, for example in metmyoglobin, are split in zero magnetic field. The zero-field splitting, D, reflects the strength and symmetry of the ligand field and therefore serves as a sensitive probe of the structure of the environment of the Fe^{3+}. Several methods have been used to determine D (reviewed in 47). The most direct is by the magnetic resonance absorption in the far infrared (submillimeter) region. This approach was taken in collaboration with Paul Richards at Bell Labs on myoglobin (67) and several hemin compounds (134). An alternative method that we used to obtain D in metmyoglobin utilized the temperature dependence of the spin-lattice relaxation time of Fe^{3+} (139). This method is based on the absorption and emission of phonons to and from the excited state (118).

More detailed information of the electronic structure of Fe^{3+} and its environment can be obtained from EPR (reviewed in 47) and ENDOR. The first ENDOR experiment that we performed with Charles Scholes, a postdoc, was on metmyoglobin in frozen solutions (140). Hyperfine couplings of the Fe^{3+} spin with the nuclei ^{14}N, ^{57}Fe and ^{1}H were observed (61). These experiments were subsequently extended to high-spin methemoglobin.

We also studied by ENDOR some of the abnormal (mutant) hemoglobins. For example in Hb-Hyde Park (79), the histidine on the fifth ligand of the β-subunits is replaced by tyrosine (i.e., α_2-oxy·$\beta_2$92His → Tyr). It had been postulated that the distal histidine takes over the role of the proximal histidine and binds to the iron. We showed by ENDOR that this is not the case (61).

The most intriguing problem is the cooperative oxygenation effect in hemoglobin (reviewed in 127) To study this effect by EPR or ENDOR, the hemes need to be converted into the high-spin met form. Fortunately, there exists a mutant Hb-Milwaukee ($\alpha_2 \cdot \beta_2$67Val → Gln) in which the normal α-subunits can be reversibly oxygenated while monitoring the ENDOR signal of the β-chain met hemes. Hb-Milwaukee undergoes a deoxy to oxy-quaternary structural change that is isomorphous with that of normal Hb (126). We focused on the ENDOR of the ^{14}N peak associated with the histidine of the β-subunit and found that it shifted by 100 kHz when the α-subunits were oxygenated (61). This shows that a primary event at the α-subunit produces a structural change at the β-subunit. To correlate the spectral shift with specific structural changes, more work needs to be done. An alternative approach to studying the cooperative oxygenation effect by EPR/ENDOR uses a nitrosyl (NO$^\bullet$) radical as a ligand to Fe^{2+} (reviewed in 83).

All the work described above was performed on frozen solution in which the molecules are randomly oriented. Consequently, information on the anisotropic contributions to the hyperfine couplings is lost. Several attempts to observe ENDOR in single crystals were unsuccessful (e.g., 38). This failure was due to the close distance between hemes (~25 Å), which shortens the spin-relaxation processes with detrimental results on the ENDOR signal. To avoid this problem, we prepared mixed crystals of myoglobin in which the majority of the molecules (90%) were in the diamagnetic CO-ligated form. In these crystals, we observed and analyzed in detail the ENDOR signals at different orientations of the crystal with respect to the magnetic field (141).

Fluctuation Spectroscopy

When I took the phage course at Cold Spring Harbor in 1964, Delbruck asked me whether I could think of a direct physical method to demonstrate the dynamics of unzipping and replication of DNA. Because in replicating *E. coli* the rate of breaking base pairs is ~100 per sec, the first thought that came to mind was that the frequency spectrum of some parameter, e.g., conductivity, should reflect this rate. I kept mulling this over and around 1970 finally decided to try the idea on a simple model system: the dissociation of an electrolyte.

DETERMINATION OF KINETIC PARAMETERS FROM THE NOISE SPECTRUM OF A CHEMICAL REACTION   Consider the simple chemical reaction $A \underset{k_2}{\overset{k_1}{\rightleftharpoons}} B$. To obtain the rate constants k_1 and k_2, one traditionally monitors the time dependence of the concentration of the reactants after the system has been perturbed. This is the well-known relaxation technique pioneered by Eigen & DeMaeyer (36). There is, however, in principle, an alternative way of obtaining the kinetic parameters without the application of an external perturbation. The method is based on the basic principle that the concentration of a reactant fluctuates around its equilibrium value. From a spectral analysis of the fluctuations, one should obtain the same kinetic information as from relaxation methods [This follows from the general "fluctuation-dissipation theorem" (132)].

To demonstrate the feasibility and validity of the fluctuation approach, we investigated the association-dissociation of a divalent electrolyte, a system that had been characterized in detail by the relaxation technique (90). An excellent graduate student, Mike Weissman, joined the effort. We measured the conductivity fluctuations of the divalent electrolyte ($Be^{2+} + SO_4^{--} \underset{k_2}{\overset{k_1}{\rightleftharpoons}} BeSO_4$) caused by the concentration fluctuations. The conductivity fluctuations were converted to voltage fluctuations by passing a constant current through the electrolyte (70). The frequency spectrum of the fluctuations is a Lorentzian given by $[1 + (\omega/\Delta\omega)^2]^{-1}$, where $\Delta\omega$ is related to the kinetic parameters by $\Delta\omega = k_1 + k_2$. The values that we obtained agreed with those obtained previously by the relaxation technique (90). For $BeSO_4$, the value of $\Delta\omega$ is in the audio range, and we recorded it on tape. With increasing temperature, $\Delta\omega$ increased. It made a nice lecture demonstration to listen to a chemical reaction and hear the pitch increase as the temperature was raised.

The stage was set to measure the fluctuations in a solution of DNA during the melting process. But, as so often happens, we got sidetracked by other experiments (described below) and never reached our original goal. In retrospect, it is a pity. Wouldn't it be exciting to listen to the replication of *E. coli*? A new form of voyeurism, I suppose.

DETERMINATION OF THE MOLECULAR WEIGHT OF DNA   In a seminar given in 1973, Bruno Zimm pointed out the difficulties of obtaining the molecular weight (M) of large macromolecules such as DNA by using classical methods (e.g., light scattering and sedimentation). Since I was tuned to the concept of fluctuations, an obvious solution presented itself to me. The idea is based again on the inherent fluctuations of the concentration of solute molecules in a given volume. If on the average there are N molecules in a volume, there is an inherent uncertainty of $\sqrt{N}$ in their number. Thus, from the fluctuations in concentration, obtained by sampling different equal volumes, the number of molecules N can be determined. By measuring independently the weight per volume of solute molecules W, M is obtained from the relation $M = W/N$.

The two problems that needed to be addressed were the determination of the concentration of DNA and the production of a large number of precisely equal volumes. The work was done in collaboration with Mike Weissman and a postdoc, Hansgeorg Schindler (155). A rotating cylindrical cell was filled with the DNA solution, and a precise volume within it was defined by a beam of laser light. The concentration of DNA was determined from the fluorescence of bound ethidium bromide. As the cell rotates, the beam of light exposes a continuous set of volumes that are precisely equal and statistically independent.

The molecular-weight values obtained for T2 phage DNA (1.14×10^8) and *E. coli* DNA (3.0×10^9) were in agreement with results obtained by classical methods (reviewed in 135). The advantage of the fluctuation method is that it is absolute and that it gives rapid and precise results. (For T_2 phage, $\pm 5\%$ in one minute of data collection).

Fluctuation spectroscopy (FLUSY) has been and is being used on a large variety of different systems (reviewed in 49). It now represents an important part of the tool kit for investigating kinetic processes. In concluding this section, I have to admit that these fluctuation experiments gave me a special thrill. Perhaps it is the satisfaction of obtaining useful information from noise after battling it for so many years.

Systematic Investigation of Protein Crystallization

To determine the structures of macromolecules by X-ray or neutron diffraction, one requires well-ordered single crystals. It seemed rather scandalous that in the 1970s, more than 100 years after the crystallization of the first protein by Hartvig (119), the process of crystallization remained more of an art than a science. Our optimistic goal was to change this state of affairs by embarking on a systematic investigation of the crystallization process.

Zvi Kam, a graduate from the Technion in Israel joined our group in 1971 and undertook the challenge. We were ultimately interested in crystallizing the RC from photosynthetic bacteria, but we decided to start with a simpler, easily crystallizable protein, egg white lysozyme (5), as a model compound. We divided the crystallization process into three temporally distinct phases: (*a*) nucleation, (*b*) postnucleation growth, and (*c*) cessation of growth. (62, 84).

The nucleation of crystals has many similarities with the condensation of droplets from supersaturated vapor, first described by Gibbs in 1875 and later elaborated by Volmer (e.g., 154). Protein molecules attach to each other to form aggregates whose total free energy depends on their size. Above a critical size, the aggregate starts to grow spontaneously. The main question is whether the aggregate is an ordered crystallized entity or a disordered amorphous precipitate. From the size distribution of the aggregate during the prenucleation phase, one can distinguish between the two alternatives. To determine the distribution, we introduced the use of quasi-elastic light scattering (13), which is now used by many protein crystallographers. The advantage of monitoring the prenucleation phase is that one does not need to wait long periods of time to determine whether a change in a parameter favors crystallization over precipitation.

The postnucleation growth involves the attachment of molecules to the aggregate. The kinetics and mechanism of this process were studied by a variety of techniques. In one, the formation of a protein-depletion layer around a growing crystal was measured optically to determine the kinetics of attachment (84). In another technique, crystal growth was measured in a flow system that eliminated the protein-depletion layer. This work was carried out by Steve Durbin (31), a postdoc who succeeded Kam in our lab. The most direct method of studying the mechanism of growth is to visualize the surface of the crystal using electron microscopy. With this technique, we visualized lattice defects (e.g., dislocations) and showed that they play an important role in postnucleation growth (32). We reproduced the main features of the observed crystal growth of lysozyme by a Monte Carlo simulation (33). The cessation of growth of crystals in the presence of an adequate supply of protein in solution has been attributed to an accumulation of defects at the surface, which makes the attachment of molecules unfavorable (reviewed in 34).

In conclusion, it may be worth pointing out that crystallization can be viewed as an example of a large class of biological problems dealing with recognition on a molecular level. Thus, a better understanding of crystallization may open up vistas in other areas. Finally, how far have we come in understanding crystallization of proteins, i.e., have we reached our original goal? I would say not quite yet, but we and a large number of other groups (including those reviewed in 34, 108) have made significant progress to that end.

Bacterial Photosynthesis

One of the attractions of this field was that so few people worked on bacterial photosynthesis as compared with green plant photosynthesis. It seemed puzzling to me why people did not try to understand the simpler system first, before proceeding to a more complicated one. I mentioned this to Martin Kamen who, being a wise man and having worked in the field a long time, had an answer, "Alas, that's because everybody is an m.c.p." (mammalian chauvinistic pig). People (mammals) work on plants because they feed on plants or on animals that feed on plants. There was another equally poor reason. Many workers in green plant photosynthesis considered bacterial photosynthesis an oddity that has nothing to do with real photosynthesis. I had faith in the parsimony of nature. It seemed to me unlikely that nature would develop two unrelated systems to accomplish the same goal. Indeed, it turned out that green plant photosynthesis has a great deal in common with bacterial photosynthesis, and it is now generally accepted that work on the bacterial system contributed greatly to the understanding of the more complex oxygen-evolving system of green plants.

Bacterial photosynthesis has occupied us for the past three decades. As mentioned in the introduction, this work was covered in detail in a recent review (55). Consequently, only the highlights are covered here.

ISOLATION AND PURIFICATION OF THE REACTION CENTER   In photosynthesis, light is converted into chemical energy. The primary event of this process is a photon-induced charge separation that occurs in an integral membrane protein called the reaction center (RC). Its existence was first postulated in 1932 (40), and direct spectral evidence for its presence in bacteria was obtained in 1952 (35). When I returned to UCSD in the fall of 1968, my first goal was to isolate and purify the RC and identify the primary reactant of the charge separation process.

The pioneering work on the isolation of a photosynthetic unit was done by Reed & Clayton in 1968 (130). They obtained a complex having a molecular weight of $\sim 10^6$. Our goal was to reduce the size of the complex and obtain the smallest structural unit capable of performing the charge separation. The critical step in the isolation procedure was the detergent solubilization. After trying a large number of different detergents, we found that LDAO (lauryl dimethyl amine oxide) gave the best results; the purified photosynthetic unit had a molecular weight of $\sim 10^5$, i.e., an order of magnitude smaller than the previously isolated unit. It represents the birth of the RC as we know it today.

The results on the isolation and characterization of the RC were presented at the International Conference on Photosynthesis in Gatlinburg, Tennessee, in May 1970 (48). I was excited about our accomplishment and expected a similar reaction from the audience. But to my surprise and disappointment, a large fraction of the people in the audience were not only unenthusiastic but downright skeptical. They thought that something must be wrong: "How can such a small unit with a molecular weight of $\sim 10^5$ be responsible for that marvelous process of photosynthesis? Those physicists, you must have lost something essential during your purification." Was it mistrust of physicists doing biochemistry, or was it the conservatism of some biochemists, reminiscent of their long opposition to Mitchell's chemiosmotic theory? At any rate, soon thereafter, the results were duplicated (23) and are now universally accepted.

IDENTIFICATION AND CHARACTERIZATION OF THE PRIMARY DONOR AND ACCEPTORS
When we started to work in this field, the chemical identities of the primary reactants were not known. What a scientific incongruity! After ~ 200 years of research in photosynthesis, the main actors participating in the light-induced charge separation had not been identified. So together with Jim McElroy, a physics graduate student, and David Mauzerall, who spent a sabbatical and several summers at UCSD, we embarked on identifying first the primary donor, D, and later the acceptors, A_1 and A_2.

The technique of choice to investigate the primary reactant was EPR/ENDOR, with which we were very familiar. In the charge-separation process, $DA \underset{k_{AD}}{\overset{h\nu}{\rightleftharpoons}} D^+A^-$, each species has an unpaired electron (or hole) that makes both of them amenable to EPR spectroscopy. The first photo-induced free radicals (the same signals I had observed earlier as a graduate student at UCB) were reported by Commoner et al. (25) and found in bacteria by Sogo et al. (145). These authors, however, did not identify the origin of the signal. The reason is the nature of EPR, which makes it difficult to identify the radical species from an inspection of the spectra. We resorted, therefore, to the model compound approach in which one compares the signal from different radicals, used as model compounds, with the unknown species. As the model compound, we picked the cation of bacteriochlorophyll. A comparison of the EPR signals from $BChl^+$ and D^+ showed their g-values to be identical (2.0026 ± 0.0001) (106). However, the line width of D^+ was $\sim 40\%$ narrower than that of $BChl^+$. This prevented us from claiming that $D \equiv BChl$, although it was clear that the primary donor had something to do with bacteriochlorophyll. This conclusion was further strengthened by showing that the kinetics of the optical absorbance changes that Duysens associated with a specialized bacteriochlorphyll (35) and of the light-induced EPR signal were the same (107).

The puzzle of the line width was solved by Norris et al. (112) who postulated that the electron on D^+ is shared between two bacteriochlorophylls that form a dimer. This should reduce the EPR line width by $\sqrt{2}$, i.e., $\sim$40%, as was observed. But to base the dimer hypothesis on a single number, i.e., the ratio of line widths, seemed a little shaky. A more definitive proof would be to show that the electron spends only half of the time on one BChl of the dimer, i.e., the square of its wavefunction, $|\Psi(r)|^2$, in the dimer should be half of that in the monomer of the model compound. So with Arnold Hoff, a postdoc in our lab, and Roger Isaacson, we used the ENDOR technique to measure the hyperfine couplings (which are proportional to $|\Psi(r)|^2$) in both the $BChl^+$ monomer and in the donor (60). The results showed that, on the average, the hyperfine couplings are smaller in the donor by a factor of 2. Similar results were obtained by Norris et al. (111). This showed unequivocally that the primary donor is a bacteriochlorophyll dimer.

Having identified the primary donor as a BChl dimer, the next task was to investigate its detailed electronic structure. Using ENDOR, we determined the spin-density distribution of the electron in the bacteriochlorophyll macrocycle. The work was performed on RCs in frozen solution as well as in single crystals. In single crystals, both the isotropic and anisotropic components of the hyperfine couplings could be determined (51, 93).

The identification of the primary acceptor proved to be more difficult. At the 1970 Gatlinburg Conference, we reported the observation of an unusually broad ($\sim$500 Gauss) EPR signal (in contrast to the $\sim$10 Gauss line for D^+), which we attributed to the primary acceptor (48). Such a broad line cannot be due to a free radical but is more likely associated with electrons in the unfilled d-shell of transition metals. Indeed, we found by atomic absorption that there is $\sim$1 Fe/RC (48). While we were investigating the broad EPR signal, we heard from Paul Loach that he observed a shift in the g-value of the narrow signal due to D^+, which he attributed to an overlapping unresolved signal from the acceptor (94). We exchanged samples and found that his RCs, which were prepared under rather harsh conditions (6 M urea, pH 12), had lost the Fe. We proceeded to develop milder conditions for the removal of the Fe and performed EPR experiments at higher frequencies (35 GHz rather than 9 GHz) to resolve the second line. To determine its chemical identity, we again used the model compound approach as we had done for the primary donor. We showed that the EPR spectrum of ubiquinone (Q) was identical to that of the acceptor A^- (64).

Supporting evidence for the role of quinones came from reconstitution experiments performed by Mel Okamura, a biochemist who joined us as a postdoc in 1970. Mel removed and re-added quinones to the RC and correlated the quinone content with photochemical activity (115). He showed that two quinones bind to the RC, one more tightly (the primary quinone, Q_A) and one less tightly (the secondary quinone, Q_B). Q_A was shown to have an obligatory role in the photochemical activity; Q_B was assigned the role of the secondary acceptor (115).

The broad EPR line was attributed to the electron on the quinone interacting with the large magnetic moment of the Fe, forming an Fe-quinone magnetic complex. Several techniques were used to elucidate the electronic structure of the complex. These included Mossbauer spectroscopy, static magnetic susceptibility measurements, EPR spectroscopy, and EXAFS (reviewed in 65). The main conclusion was that iron is in the high-spin Fe^{2+} state, irrespective of the reduction state of the quinone: We determined that Fe^{2+} is located approximately equidistantly between Q_A and Q_B but does not form ligands to them.

The electronic structure of the quinones was investigated by ENDOR in RCs in which the Fe was replaced by diamagnetic Zn (27) to reduce the EPR line width. This work (98) was started in 1983 in collaboration with a postdoc, Wolfgang Lubitz, with whom we are continuing to collaborate to this day. A detailed account of the quinone work, including the history of their identification, can be found in (54, 65, 99).

In addition to the single-electron radicals D^+ and Q^-, we also investigated the biradicals $BPhe^{-\cdot}Q_A^{-\cdot}$ (114) and $Q_A^{-\cdot}Q_B^{-\cdot}$ (19), which form intermediate states in the electron transfer path (BPhe is an intermediate acceptor). In these biradicals, one observes a splitting of the EPR spectrum related to the exchange interaction J between the unpaired spins. The value of J is an important parameter in calculating electron transfer rates.

FURTHER CHARACTERIZATION OF THE RC   A preliminary characterization of the RC was done in 1970 in conjunction with its initial isolation and purification (48). We determined by SDS-PAGE that the RC has three subunits, which we labeled according to their electrophoretic mobility L, M, H (for light, medium, and heavy). We did not want to assign molecular weight to the subunits because we knew that SDS-PAGE gave reliable, quantitative, molecular-weight values only for water-soluble proteins. Unfortunately, as it turned out later, molecular-weight determinations were even qualitatively off, and H had the lowest molecular weight. But by that time, the nomenclature had already been accepted and it remains to this day. We also sent samples of RCs to Lisa Steiner at MIT who determined the amino acid composition and found the RC to be the most hydrophobic protein thus far reported. We subsequently isolated the three subunits, determined their stoichiometry to be 1:1:1 (117), and Lisa Steiner determined the amino acid composition of each subunit (146).

The determination of the amino acid sequence proved to be more difficult as the isolated subunits were insoluble in aqueous solutions, which at the time were used in sequencing proteins. I remember a few frustrating but interesting weeks spent in John Walker's lab at the MRC in Cambridge, United Kingdom, trying to work out the proper conditions for the liquid-phase sequencer. Lisa finally succeeded with a postdoc, M. R. Sutton, in sequencing the amino-terminal 25–28 residues of the three subunits (148). These sequences were later used by JoAnn Williams, a talented graduate student with a green thumb for recombinant DNA techniques. JoAnn isolated the genes that encode the L- and M-subunits and determined the sequence of these subunits (158, 159). Each subunit showed five hydrophobic regions that were postulated to form transmembrane helices. The sequence of the H-subunit showed only one transmembrane helix (157). An exciting result of the sequence work was the homology that was found between the L- and M-subunits and the D_1 and D_2 polypeptides found in green plants (159).

The subunit harboring the Q_A-binding site was determined by Tim Marinetti, a postdoc in our lab in 1978–1979. He introduced the photoaffinity label [^{3}H] 2-azidoanthraquinone in the Q_A site. When illuminated with UV light, it photolyzed and became attached to the protein. Analysis of the photolyzed protein by SDS-PAGE revealed that the M-subunit was selectively labeled. This showed that the primary quinone site is located at or close ($\sim$5 Å) to the M-subunit (102). The Q_B site could not be determined by photoaffinity labeling because of the more stringent structural requirement for the binding of the secondary quinone.

The topography of the RC in the bacterial membrane was investigated by Gunars Valkirs, a graduate student, by using indirect immunoferritin labeling (152). Ferritin is an electron-dense molecule, which permits the localization of the binding site by direct electron-microscopic visualization. Anti-M antibodies to which ferritin was attached labeled both sides of the membrane, showing that the M-subunit spans the membrane. Because of the similarity of the amino acid compositions of L and M, the L-subunit was assumed to also span the membrane. Most anti-H preparations labeled the cytoplasmic side, and only one out of six labeled the periplasmic side. From this we concluded that H is asymmetrically oriented with respect to the membrane, most of it being on the cytoplasmic side (152).

CRYSTALLIZATION OF THE RC AND DETERMINATION OF ITS STRUCTURE BY X-RAY DIFFRACTION   While pursuing a systematic approach to try to understand the crystallization of proteins, we did occasionally try the nonscientific trial-and-error approach to crystallize RCs. The prevailing dogma at the time was that integral membrane proteins cannot be crystallized because of the presence of randomly oriented detergent molecules. This was brought home to us in the review of our 1978 grant in which we were severely criticized for suggesting the crystallization of a membrane protein [For a verbatim excerpt of the review see (52)]. We did not agree with the criticism, and to keep up hope we posted one of Escher's pictures in our lab showing an ordered array (crystal) of ducks [see Figure 12 in (55)].

By 1980, two membrane proteins, bacteriorhodopsin (109) and porin (72), had been crystallized; in 1982, H. Michel successfully crystallized the RC from the photosynthetic bacterium *Rhodopseudomonas viridis* (110). Shortly thereafter with Jim Allen, a postdoc, we crystallized the RC from *Rhodobacter sphaeroides* as I described in the National Lecture of the Biophysical Society in February 1983 (50).

Following the crystallization, the X-ray structure of the cofactors and proteins were published by Deisenhofer et al. (28). In 1985, we started a collaboration with the crystallography group of Doug Rees at UCLA to determine the structure of the RC from *R. sphaeroides*.

Preliminary phases and structures of the RC from *R. sphaeroides* were obtained by the molecular replacement method using the coordinates of the RC from *R. viridis* (7, 20). By 1987, the structure of the RC from *R. sphaeroides* reached a resolution of 2.8 Å (6) and is now 2.1–2.2 Å (105, 147). It is probably fair to say that the photosynthetic RC had for a long time been the best-characterized membrane-bound protein and served as a good model for this class of proteins (131).

The structure of the cofactors is shown in Figure 1*a* (see color insert), and of the RC protein with its modeled location in the membrane is shown in Figure 1*b*. Both the cofactors and the L- and M-subunits exhibit an approximate twofold symmetry about a line joining the donor and the Fe. It was gratifying to us that the main features of the structure corroborated our previous findings, i.e., the L- and M-subunits have each five transmembrane helices, and the H-subunit has one (157) with most of it exposed on the cytoplasmic side (152). The cofactors are all associated with the L- and M-subunits (117), the primary donor is a bacteriochlorophyll dimer (51), Q_A is associated with the M-subunit (102), and the Fe is approximately equidistant from Q_A and Q_B (18) [for additional details, see (55)]. In a review article that appeared before the results of the X-ray diffraction were obtained, we proposed a structure that bears a remarkable resemblance to the structure shown in Figure 1 [see Figure 35 in (113)]. What nobody had predicted was the beautiful twofold symmetry. In retrospect, in view of the sequence homology of the L- and M-subunits, a far-sighted person could have predicted the symmetry. But it was not predicted and the result falls, therefore, into the category of "I thought of it, the minute I saw it."

The structure shown in Figure 1 represents the native RC in its ground state. Considerable experimental evidence had accumulated to show that a conformational change occurs during charge separation [reviewed in (75)]. To determine the molecular nature of this change, we trapped the charge-separated state $D^+Q_B^-$ at cryogenic temperatures and determined the structure by X-ray diffraction. We found that Q_B^- had moved 5 Å toward the cytoplasmic side with an accompanying 180 degree propeller twist about the isoprene chain (147). This structural change has important implications on electron transfer. Another important point we addressed is whether there are structural changes accompanying the site-directed mutations introduced to investigate the mechanisms of electron and proton transfers in the RC (21).

Thoughts of Switching Fields Again

With the X-ray determination of the three-dimensional structure of the RC, which corroborated most of the preceding work, the field of bacterial photosynthesis seemed to have reached its apogee. Although knowledge of the structure opened

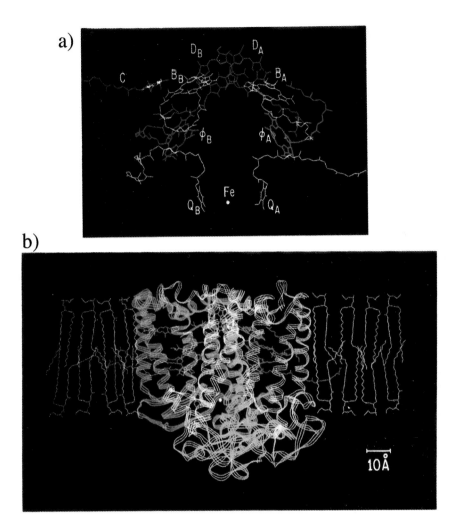

Figure 1 The structure of the reaction center from *Rb. sphaeroides*. (*a*) Cofactor structure. D-Bacteriochlorophyll dimer, B-Bacteriochlorophyll, φ-Bacteriopheophytin, Q-Ubiquinone 10, subscripts A and B refer to the two pseudosymmetrical branches. (Electron transfer proceeds preferentially along the A-branch.) (*b*) The structure of the reaction center and its position modeled into a sketch of the lipid bilayer. L-subunit, *yellow*; M-subunit, *blue*; H-subunit, *green*. Cofactors in *red*. The twofold symmetry axis is in the plane of the paper joining the Fe (*dot*) near the cytoplasmic side (*bottom*) with the bacteriochlorophyll dimer near the periplasmic side (*top*) (56).

up new approaches and many questions remained unanswered, the field seemed to me less challenging than when we had started 15 years ago. Perhaps that feeling was engendered by the fact that I had never worked such a long period in one specific field. I felt that at age 60 I was still good for one last switch in my career. Neurobiology seemed to me an exciting field, and in the summer of 1984 I took once more a course in Woods Hole. It was a demanding but exciting experience to work for two months in a new field. The project that I had in mind was to grow nerve cells on a silicon chip and follow electrically their development and connections. Bell Labs, known for its chip technology, offered me a position, and in the Spring of 1985 I visited them to discuss the details of the sabbatical arrangement. Unfortunately, on my return from Newark to Boston I suffered a heart attack on the plane. After listening to the prognosis of the cardiologists (which turned out to be too pessimistic), I did not feel up to investing a few years to get started in a new field, and all previous plans were scrapped. Bacterial photosynthesis was a familiar and comfortable field, in which it was easy for me to direct students and postdocs. Therefore, I opted to stay with it. But the style of my research changed. I had always been involved in the actual lab work, and in addition, I always had my own pet project on the side that was not necessarily connected with photosynthesis. To be honest, I miss these activities. In supervising research rather than doing it oneself, something vital is lost. The best analogy that I can come up with is "kissing through a veil." It is, of course, still fun and I am enthusiastic about our research as I hope comes through in the next sections.

Back to Bacterial Photosynthesis

THE STRUCTURE OF THE RC: CYT C_2 COMPLEX   The secondary donor in $R. sphaeroides$ is cyt c_2^{2+}, which forms a transient docked structure with the RC in which electron transfer occurs between reduced cyt c_2^{2+} and the oxidized donor, D^+. Several models for the structure of the transient RC-cyt c_2 complex have been proposed (reviewed in 151). They were all based on indirect experimental evidence and theoretical considerations. Our goal was to determine the structure by X-ray diffraction. Although it was generally believed that because of the transient nature of the complex, cocrystals would not form. Noam Adir, who joined us in 1990, succeeded after many trials in obtaining cocrystals that diffracted to 3.5 Å. Unfortunately, the cyt c_2 occupancy in the crystals was low ($\sim$25%), and only a preliminary structure was obtained (4). Herb Axelrod, who had previously determined the structure of cyt c_2 (12) in our lab, continued Adir's work and obtained cocrystals that had an $\sim$80% occupancy of cyt c_2 (10). In collaboration with Doug Rees's group, Herb collected a complete data set at the Berkeley Synchrotron source to a resolution of 2.4 Å. The data are now being processed, and a reliable structure should soon be forthcoming. An important point in this study was to show that the structure of the complex in the crystal is the same as in vivo. This was accomplished by comparing the electron transfer kinetics (which depend critically on the detailed structure) in the crystal and in solutions. They were the same (4).

An alternative approach to study the structure of the complex is to probe the area of contact between the RC and cyt c_2 by selectively mutating residues on the periplasmic side of the RC and measuring the effect of the mutation on the binding affinity and electron transfer. This work was performed by two graduate students, Scott Rongey, who started it (136), and Michelle Tetrault, who completed it (151). The results are in good agreement with the crystal structure.

ELECTRON TRANSFERS: KINETICS AND MECHANISMS   The RC catalyzes the reduction of the secondary quinone, Q_B, to quinol, Q_BH_2, by a series of light-induced electron and proton transfers (see Figure 2). The initial electron transfer reaction, which occurs on a picosecond timescale, has been omitted for simplicity (reviewed in 87). We focused on the slower electron transfer reactions, $k_{AB}^{(1)}$, and $k_{AB}^{(2)}$ (steps 2 and 4 in Figure 2).

The transfer of the first electron from $Q_A^{-\cdot}$ to Q_B ($k_{AB}^{(1)}$) has been investigated by several groups, starting with the pioneering work of Parson (124) (reviewed in 116). In 1984, David Kleinfeld, a graduate student in our lab, provided convincing evidence that $k_{AB}^{(1)}$ is associated with a conformational change (88). He observed that electron transfer from Q_A^- to Q_B proceeds at cryogenic temperatures when the RCs were cooled under illumination but did not occur in RCs cooled in the dark. It is clear that different conformations were frozen in depending on whether the RCs

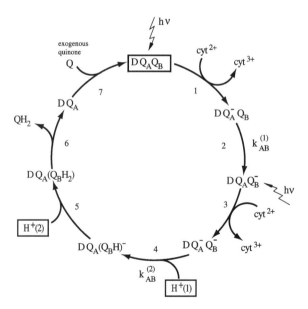

Figure 2   The quinone reduction cycle in bacterial RCs. Q_B is reduced in two one-electron reactions, $k_{AB}^{(1)}$, and $k_{AB}^{(2)}$, and binds two protons, H+(1) and H+(2), The reduced QH_2 leaves the RC and is replaced by an exogenous quinone, thereby resetting the cycle. Time to complete the cycles is $\sim$1 ms (116).

were in the charge-separated state or not. The molecular basis of the conformational change has been determined by X-ray diffraction (147), as discussed in a previous section. Mike Graige, a graduate student, has shown that $k_{AB}^{(1)}$ is a conformationally gated process in which the rate-limiting step is the conformational change and not the intrinsic electron transfer (75). To prove this, Graige used the driving force assay, which he had developed earlier (76). In this assay, quinones with different redox potentials are substituted into the Q_A^- site, thereby changing the driving force for electron transfer. If electron transfer were rate limiting, $k_{AB}^{(1)}$ should increase, according to the Marcus theory, with increasing driving force (101). No dependence of $k_{AB}^{(1)}$ on driving force was found, proving that another step, e.g., a conformational change, is rate limiting. But what parameters determine the kinetics of the rate-limiting step is at present not understood.

The transfer of the second electron, $k_{AB}^{(2)}$, which proceeds on a millisecond timescale, (see step 4 in Figure 2) is coupled to proton transfer as represented by the net reaction [reviewed in (116)]

$$Q_A^- \cdot Q_B^- \cdot + H^+ \overset{k_{AB}^{(2)}}{\rightleftarrows} Q_A(Q_BH)^- \cdot \tag{1}$$

Graige, using the driving force assay, showed that this is a two-step process: one involving proton uptake, the other electron transfer. The process involves an intermediate state $Q_A^- \cdot (Q_BH)$. By a detailed analysis, Graige showed that proton transfer precedes rate-limiting electron transfer (76).

PROTON TRANSFERS: MECHANISMS AND PATHWAYS   The protonation of Q_B and its release as Q_BH_2 (steps 4–6 in Figure 2) is, from a physiological point of view, the important process in the RC, with electron transfer serving as a prerequisite for protonation. Q_B is located in the interior of the RC protein, which presents a problem for the transport of protons from the aqueous exterior through the protein with a low dielectric constant. The two main problems of protonation are, therefore, the mechanism of proton transfer and the identification of the protein pathway(s).

It is now commonly accepted that proton transfer to $Q_B^- \cdot$ occurs via a donor-acceptor chain of protonatable amino acid residues and/or water molecules (reviewed in 116). To identify the residues involved in the pathway, protonatable residues were replaced with nonprotonatable residues by site-directed mutagenesis, the X-ray structure providing guidance for picking prospective candidates. The first mutant that affected proton transfer was constructed in 1989 by Paddock (123), then a graduate student and now a research associate in our group. This was followed by a large number of mutations performed by several groups (e.g., 150, 116). From the results of these experiments and with the aid of the X-ray crystal structure, we identified at least three possible proton transfer pathways (2). A chance observation by Paddock helped us to identify the predominant pathway. Paddock found that divalent metals (e.g., Zn^{2+}, Cd^{2+}) reduced $k_{AB}^{(2)}$ by an order of magnitude, presumably by blocking proton transfer (122). X-ray structure analysis revealed that these metals bind to His-H126, His-H128, and Asp-H124 (11),

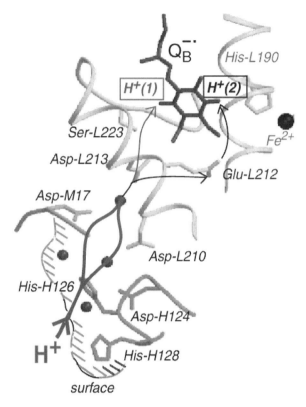

Figure 3   Part of the RC structure showing the region between the protein entry point and $Q_B^{-\cdot}$. The pathways of the two protons are shared up to the bifurcation near Asp L213 (3). The surface of the protein (*stippled*) and a few water molecules (*dots*) are indicated. Modified from (121).

which were therefore identified as being at or near the entry points of both protons (3). From the results of the mutagenesis work and the metal-binding studies, the proton transfer pathway shown in Figure 3 was deduced. The detailed kinetics of each protonation step are not understood and are being investigated at present.

CONCLUDING REMARKS

As I look over five decades of research, wandering from topic to topic, picking a flower here and there, I feel that it has been a wondrous and joyful journey. I really should add a decade or two to include my childhood and adolescent tinkering, which seems to have been as enjoyable, intense, and meaningful as doing research in later years. As time has gone by, the feelings have remained the same; only the budget and the type of questions asked have changed.

A recent prefatory chapter entitled, "Whatever happened to the fun?" (133), disturbed me and made me ponder the question. Part of the loss of fun can, no doubt, be attributed to the unavoidable added responsibilities that accrue during one's career and that detract from one's research activities. But another likely contributor, that one may be loath to admit, is the striving for recognition. I believe it is important to keep this enemy—our ego—in check lest we get lost in the clouds climbing the endless ladder to fame and glory.

Occasionally, I was asked which of my experiments I found most exciting and rewarding. My standard glib answer used to be, "The next one to be performed." I shall now try to answer the question in a more serious and general way. Rather than focus on a specific experiment, I want to explore the features that make a project exciting and satisfying. Aesthetics plays an important role, e.g., the beauty of crystals that made me originally grow them without regard to their usefulness, the beauty of symmetries (e.g., paraelectric resonance/paramagnetic resonance), and the simplicity of concepts (nuclear polarization by hot electrons, molecular weight of DNA by fluctuation spectroscopy). Another feature that attracts me is the combination of techniques and fields. On the technique side, for example, is the development of ENDOR, which resulted from a combination of two well-developed techniques, NMR and EPR. The combination of fields resulted in applying solid-state techniques to nuclear physics (determination of nuclear moments, hyperfine structures anomaly) to high-energy physics (muonium) and electronics (maser). This attraction of combining fields was surely an important component in my choosing research in biophysics, which is truly interdisciplinary. Nature does not care which tools from what discipline are used. The approach in our lab is to pick a relevant problem and use whatever technique is required to solve it.

The choice of bacterial photosynthesis was motivated by a desire to have a theme, to develop a field from its infancy to maturity, in contrast to the series of unconnected experiments that comprised most of my other research. Thus, the photosynthesis work resulted in a change in style. It was not a single experiment that brought the field to maturity but a large number of successive ones, each addressing different problems as they appeared, and in the process using a variety of techniques that we either knew or had to learn.

Speaking of styles and attitudes, there is one point that I want to get off my chest. I dislike the paranoia that leads some researchers to be excessively secretive in communicating with colleagues. Open discussions of one's work, in my opinion, are well worth the risk of being scooped.

Over the past years, I have come to realize the importance of not having been swayed by authority, dogmas, or fads, i.e., of not conforming. I consider conformity the nemesis of research as well as of private and public life. In research, it can destroy originality and creativity. In politics, it can destroy democracy and lead to aberrations like the Holocaust, an event that has haunted me and shaped a significant part of my life.

I wish I could finish with some noble thought, such as saying that my work was motivated by a desire to improve the condition of mankind. After all, understanding photosynthesis could help solve the energy crisis and the global food problem. But such altruistic motivation has not driven me. I simply enjoy tinkering and doing research; it fulfills an inner need. If it also contributes to something useful, so much the better. It is the icing on the cake.

ACKNOWLEDGMENTS

I remember with pleasure and gratitude the many students, postdocs, collaborators, and colleagues who helped, guided, and accompanied me on parts of my long (50 years) journey in scientific research. There are clearly too many to name them all, but I would like to highlight a few. I wish to express my indebtness to Martin Kamen and Rod Clayton for introducing me to bacterial photosynthesis; Dave Mauzerall for our early collaboration in photosynthesis; Lisa Steiner for teaching me biochemistry and for remaining a valuable colleague, sounding board, and friend; Doug Rees for collaborating and teaching us X-ray crystallography; and foremost Mel Okamura for collaborating on all aspects of photosynthesis and for the pleasure of working with him all these years. I wish to thank Ed Gere for his expert technical help at Bell Labs, Roger Isaacson for his superb and dedicated technical assistance for the past 40 years, and Ed Abresch for his assistance with the biochemical work and for supplying our group with reaction centers for the past ~25 years. I am grateful to the NSF and NIH for supporting our research all these years. Finally and most importantly, I wish to thank my wife, Elsa, for her support and active interest in my work and my daughters for putting up with my long working hours and frequent absences.

Visit the Annual Reviews home page at www.annualreviews.org

LITERATURE CITED

1. Abranovich S. 1992. The Best Kept Secret. *Yediot Ahronot.* 23 April:13–20

2. Abresch EC, Paddock ML, Stowell MHB, McPhillips TM, Axelrod HL, et al. 1998. Identification of proton transfer pathways in the X-ray crystal structure of the bacterial reaction center from *Rhodobacter sphaeroides. Photosynth. Res.* 55:119–25

3. Ädelroth P, Paddock ML, Sagle LB, Feher G, Okamura MY. 2000. Identification of the proton pathway in bacterial reaction centers: both protons associated with reduction of Q_B to Q_BH_2 share a common entry point. *Proc. Natl. Acad. Sci. USA* 97:13086–91

4. Adir N, Axelrod HL, Beroza P, Isaacson RA, Rongey SH, et al. 1996. Co-crystallization and characterization of the photosynthetic reaction center-cytochrome c_2 complex from *Rhodobacter sphaeroides. Biochemistry* 35:2535–47

5. Alderton G, Fevold HL. 1946. Direct crystallization of lysozyme from egg white and some crystalline salts of lysozyme. *J. Biol. Chem.* 164:1–5

6. Allen JP, Feher G, Yeates TO, Komiya H, Rees DC. 1987. Structure of the reaction center from *Rhodobacter sphaeroides* R-26: II. The protein subunits. *Proc. Natl. Acad. Sci. USA* 84:6162–66

7. Allen JP, Feher G, Yeates TO, Rees DC,

Deisenhofer J, et al. 1986. Structural homology of reaction centers from *R. sphaeroides* and *R. viridis* as determined by X-ray diffraction. *Proc. Natl. Acad. Sci. USA* 83:8589–93

8. Anderson PW. 1978. Local moments and localized states. *Science* 201(4353):307–16

9. Archive of "Haganah" History, Ref. 1193

10. Axelrod HL, Abresch EC, Okamura MY, Feher G, Yeh AP, Rees DC. 1999. X-ray structure determination of the RC-cyt c_2 complex from *Rhodobacter sphaeroides*. *Biophys. J.* 76:A20 (Abstr.)

11. Axelrod HL, Abresch EC, Paddock ML, Okamura MY, Feher G. 2000. Determination of the binding sites of the proton transfer inhibitors Cd^{2+} and Zn^{2+} in bacterial reaction centers. *Proc. Natl. Acad. Sci. USA* 97:1542–47

12. Axelrod HL, Feher G, Allen JP, Chirino AJ, Day MW, et al. 1994. Crystallization and X-ray structure determination of cytochrome c_2 from *Rhodobacter sphaeroides* in three crystal forms. *Acta Crystallogr. D* 50:596–602

13. Benedek GB. 1969. Optical mixing spectroscopy, with applications to problems in physics, chemistry, biology and engineering. In *Polarisation, Matière et Rayonnement, Livre de Jubilé en l'honneur d'Alfred Kastler*, pp. 49–84. Paris: Presses Univ. France

14. Bennet JE, Ingram DJE, George P, Griffith JS. 1955. Paramagnetic resonance absorption of ferrihaemoglobin and ferrimyoglobin derivatives. *Nature* 176:394

15. Bloch F. 1946. Nuclear induction. *Phys. Rev.* 70(7–8):460–74

16. Bloembergen N. 1956. Proposal for a new type solid state maser. *Phys. Rev.* 104(2):324–27

17. Bridges F. 1975. Paraelectric phenomena in CRC. *Crit. Rev. Solid State Phys.* 5:1–88

18. Butler WF, Calvo R, Fredkin DR, Isaacson RA, Okamura MY, Feher G. 1984. The electronic structure of Fe^{2+} in reaction centers from *Rhodopseudomonas sphaeroides* III. EPR measurements of the reduced acceptor complex. *Biophys. J.* 45:947–73

19. Calvo R, Isaacson RA, Paddock ML, Abresch EC, Okamura MY, et al. 2001. EPR study of the semiquinone biradical $Q_A^- Q_B^-$ in photosynthetic reaction centers from *Rb. sphaeroides* at 326 GHz: determination of the exchange interaction J_0. *J. Phys. Chem. B* 105(19):4053–57

20. Chang CH, Tiede D, Tang J, Smith U, Norris J, Schiffer M. 1986. Structure of *Rodopseudomonas sphaeroides* R-26 reaction center. *FEBS Lett.* 205:82–86

21. Chirino AJ, Lous EJ, Huber M, Allen JP, Schenck CC, et al. 1994. Crystallographic analyses of site-directed mutants of the photosynthetic reaction center from *Rhodobacter sphaeroides*. *Biochemistry* 33:4584–93

22. Clark WG, Feher G. 1963. Nuclear polarization in InSb by a d.c. current. *Phys. Rev. Lett.* 10(4):134–38

23. Clayton RK, Wang RT. 1971. Photochemical reaction centers from *Rhodopseudomonas sphaeroides*. *Methods Enzymol.* 23:696–704

24. Combrisson J, Honig A, Townes CH. 1956. *Compt. Rend.* 242:2451–53

25. Commoner B, Heise JJ, Townsend J. 1956. Light-induced paramagnetism in chloroplasts. *Proc. Natl. Acad. Sci. USA* 42(10):710–18

26. Commoner B, Townsend J, Pake GE. 1954. Free radicals in biological materials. *Nature* 174:689–91

27. Debus RJ, Feher G, Okamura MY. 1986. Iron-depleted reaction centers from *Rhodopseudomonas sphaeroides* R-26.1: characterization and reconstitution with Fe^{2+}, Mn^{2+}, Co^{2+}, Ni^{2+}, Cu^{2+}, Zn^{2+}. *Biochemistry* 25(8):2276–87

28. Deisenhofer J, Epp O, Miki K, Huber R, Michel H. 1984. X-ray structure analysis of a membrane protein complex. Electron density map at 3 Å resolution and a model of the chromophores of the photosynthetic

reaction center from *Rhodopseudomonas viridis. J. Mol. Biol.* 180(2):385–98

29. Dickerson RE, Geis I. 1969. *The Structure and Action of Proteins.* New York: Harper & Row. 120 pp.

30. Dresselhaus G, Kip AF, Kittel C. 1955. Cyclotron resonance of electrons and holes in silicon and germanium crystals. *Phys. Rev.* 98(2):368–84

31. Durbin SD, Feher G. 1986. Crystal growth studies of lysozyme as a model for protein crystallization. *J. Cryst. Growth* 76:583–92

32. Durbin SD, Feher G. 1990. Studies of crystal growth mechanisms of proteins by electron microscopy. *J. Mol. Biol.* 212(4):763–74

33. Durbin SD, Feher G. 1991. Simulation of lysozyme crystal growth by the Monte Carlo method. *J. Cryst. Growth* 110:41–51

34. Durbin SD, Feher G. 1996. Protein crystallization. *Annu. Rev. Phys. Chem.* 47:171–204

35. Duysens LNM. 1952. *Transfer of excitation energy in photosynthesis.* PhD thesis. Univ. Utrecht, The Netherlands

35a. Ehrenberg A, Malmstrom BG, Vanngard T, eds. 1967. *Magnetic Resonance in Biological Systems,* Vol. 9. New York: Pergamon

36. Eigen M, DeMaeyer L. 1963. Relaxation methods. In *Techniques of Organic Chemistry,* ed. A Weissberger, 8:895–1054. New York: Intersci. Publ.

37. Eisenberger P, Okamura MY, Feher G. 1982. The electronic structure of Fe^{2+} in reaction centers from *Rhodopseudomonas sphaeroides* II. Extended X-ray fine structure studies. *Biophys. J.* 37:523–38

38. Eisenberger P, Pershan PS. 1967. Magnetic resonance studies of met-myoglobin and myoglobin azide. *J. Chem. Phys.* 47(9):3327–33

39. Eisinger J, Feher G. 1958. Hfs anomaly of Sb^{121} and Sb^{123} determined by the electron nuclear double-resonance technique. *Phys. Rev.* 109(4):1172–83

40. Emerson R, Arnold W. 1932. The photochemical reaction in photosynthesis. *J. Gen. Physiol.* 16:191–205

41. Feher ER. 1964. Effect of uniaxial stresses on the paramagnetic spectra of Mn^{3+} and Fe^{3+} in MgO. *Phys. Rev.* 136(1):A145–57

42. Feher G. 1956. Method of polarizing nuclei in paramagnetic substances. *Phys. Rev.* 103(2):500–1

43. Feher G. 1956. Observation of nuclear magnetic resonances via the electron spin resonance line. *Phys. Rev.* 103(3):834–35

44. Feher G. 1957. Sensitivity considerations in microwave paramagnetic resonance absorption techniques. *Bell. Syst. Technol. J.* 36(2):449–84

45. Feher G. 1959. Electron spin resonance experiments on donors in silicon. I. Electronic structure of donors by the electron nuclear double resonance technique. *Phys. Rev.* 114(5):1219–44

46. Feher G. 1959. Nuclear polarization via "hot" conduction electrons. *Phys. Rev. Lett.* 3(3):135–37

47. Feher G. 1970. Determination of the zero field splitting parameter "D". In *Electron Paramagnetic Resonance with Application to Selected Problems in Biology,* ed. C deWitt, J Matricon, pp. 61–64. New York: Gordon & Breach

48. Feher G. 1971. Some chemical and physical properties of a bacterial reaction center particle and its primary photochemical reactants. *Photochem. Photobiol.* 14(3):373–87

49. Feher G. 1978. Fluctuation spectroscopy. *Trends Biochem. Sci.* 3(5):N111–13

50. Feher G. 1983. Primary process in bacterial photosynthesis. Biophys. Soc., Natl. Lect. *Biophys. J.* 41:3

51. Feher G. 1992. Identification and characterization of the primary donor in bacterial photosynthesis: a chronological account of an EPR/ENDOR investigation. *J. Chem. Soc. Perkin Trans.* 2, pp. 1861–74

52. Feher G. 1998. Light reflections III. *Photosynth. Res.* 55(2–3):375–78

53. Feher G. 1998. The development of EN-DOR and other reminiscences of the 1950's. In *Foundations of Modern EPR*, ed. GR Eaton, SS Eaton, KM Salikov, 1:548–56. Singapore: World Sci. Publ.

54. Feher G. 1998. The primary and secondary electron acceptors in bacterial photosynthesis: I. A chronological account of their identification by EPR. *Appl. Magn. Reson.* 15:23–38

55. Feher G. 1998. Three decades of research in bacterial photosynthesis and the road leading to it: a personal account. *Photosynth. Res.* 55:1–40

56. Feher G, Allen JP, Okamura MY, Rees DC. 1989. Structure and function of photosynthetic reaction centers. *Nature* 339:111–16

57. Feher G, Fuller CS, Gere EA. 1957. Spin and magnetic moment of P^{22} by the electron nuclear double-resonance technique. *Phys. Rev.* 107(5):1462–64

58. Feher G, Gordon JP, Buehler E, Gere EA, Thurmond CD. 1958. Spontaneous emission of radiation from an electron spin system. *Phys. Rev.* 109(1):221–22

59. Feher G, Hensel JC, Gere EA. 1960. Paramagnetic resonance absorption from acceptors in silicon. *Phys. Rev. Lett.* 5(7):309–11

60. Feher G, Hoff AJ, Isaacson RA, Ackerson LC. 1975. ENDOR experiments on chlorophyll and bacteriochlorophyll in vitro and in the photosynthetic unit. *Ann. NY Acad. Sci.* 244:239–59

61. Feher G, Isaacson RA, Scholes GP, Nagel R. 1973. Electron nuclear double resonance (ENDOR) investigation on myoglobin and hemoglobin. *Ann. NY Acad. Sci.* 222:86–101

62. Feher G, Kam Z. 1985. Nucleation and growth of protein crystals; general principles and assays. *Methods Enzymol.* 114:77–112

63. Feher G, Malley M, Mauzerall D. 1967. Direct observation of the Zeeman splitting of the excited state of porphyrins. See Ref. 35a, pp. 145–57

64. Feher G, Okamura MY, McElroy JD. 1972. Identification of an electron acceptor in reaction centers of *Rhodopseudomonas spheroides* by EPR spectroscopy. *Biochim. Biophys. Acta* 267:222–26

65. Feher G, Okamura MY. 1999. The primary and secondary acceptors in bacterial photosynthesis: II. The structure of the Fe^{2+}-Q^- complex. *Appl. Magn. Reson.* 16:63–100

66. Feher G, Prepost R, Sachs AM. 1960. Muonium formation in semiconductors. *Phys. Rev. Lett.* 5(11):515–17

67. Feher G, Richards PL. 1967. Determination of the zero-field splitting "D" in heme chloride by far-infrared spectroscopy. See Ref. 35a, pp. 141–44

68. Feher G, Scovil HED. 1957. Electron spin relaxation times in gadolinium ethyl sulfate. *Phys. Rev.* 105(2):760–62

69. Feher G, Shepherd IW, Shore HB. 1966. Paraelectric resonance of OH^- dipoles in KC1. *Phys. Rev. Lett.* 16(12):500–3

70. Feher G, Weissman M. 1973. Fluctuation spectroscopy: determination of chemical reaction kinetics from the frequency spectrum of fluctuations. *Proc. Natl. Acad. Sci. USA* 70(3):870–75

71. Fermi E. 1930. Über die magnetischen Momente der Atomkerne. *Z. Phys.* 60:320–33

72. Garavito RM, Rosenbusch JP. 1980. Three-dimensional crystals of an integral membrane protein: an initial X-ray analysis. *J. Cell Biol.* 86(1):327–29

73. Giauque WF, Macdougall DP. 1933. Attainment of temperatures below 1° absolute by demagnetization of $Gd_2(SO_4)_3 \cdot 8H_2O$. *Phys. Rev.* 43(9):768–68

74. Gordon JP, Zeiger HJ, Townes CH. 1954. Molecular microwave oscillator and new hyperfine structure in the microwave spectrum of NH_3. *Phys. Rev.* 95(1):282–84

75. Graige MS, Feher G, Okamura MY. 1998. Conformational gating of the electron transfer reaction $Q_A^- Q_B \rightarrow Q_A Q_B^-$, in bacterial reaction centers of *Rb.*

sphaeroides determined by a driving force assay. *Proc. Natl. Acad. Sci. USA* 95:11679–84

76. Graige MS, Paddock ML, Bruce JM, Feher G, Okamura MY. 1996. Mechanism of proton-coupled electron transfer for quinone (Q_B) reduction in reaction centers of *Rb. sphaeroides*. *J. Am. Chem. Soc.* 118(38):9005–16

77. Griffith JS. 1956. On the magnetic properties of some haemoglobin complexes. *Proc. R. Soc. London Ser. A* 235:23–36

78. Deleted in proof

79. Heller P. 1966. Hemoglobinopathic dysfunction of the red cell. *Am. J. Med.* 41(5): 799–814

80. Hensel JC, Feher G. 1960. Valence band parameters in silicon from cyclotron resonances in crystals subjected to uniaxial stress. *Phys. Rev. Lett.* 5(7):307–9

81. Hensel JC, Feher G. 1963. Cyclotron resonance experiments in uniaxially stressed silicon: valence band inverse mass parameters and deformation potentials. *Phys. Rev.* 129(3):1041–62

82. Honig A. 1954. Polarization of arsenic nuclei in a silicon semiconductor. *Phys. Rev.* 96(1):234–35

83. Hutterman J. 1993. ENDOR of randomly oriented mononuclear metalloproteins. In *Biological Magnetic Resonance*, ed. LJ Berliner, J Reuben, 13:219–52. New York: Plenum

84. Kam Z, Shore HB, Feher G. 1978. On the crystallization of proteins. *J. Mol. Biol.* 123(4):539–55

85. Känzig W, Hart RH Jr, Roberts S. 1964. Paraelectricity and ferroelectricity due to hydroxyl ions in alkali halides; paraelectric cooling. *Phys. Rev. Lett.* 13(18):543–45

86. Katz B. 1966. Quantal nature of chemical transmission. In *Nerve, Muscle and Synapse*, pp. 129–41. New York: McGraw-Hill

87. Kirmaier C, Holten D. 1993. Electron transfer and charge recombination reactions in wild-type and mutant bacterial reaction centers. In *The Photosynthetic Reaction Center*, ed. J Deisenhofer, JR Norris, 2:49–70. San Diego, CA: Academic

88. Kleinfeld D, Okamura MY, Feher G. 1984. Electron-transfer kinetics in photosynthetic reaction centers cooled to cryogenic temperatures in the charge-separated state: evidence for light-induced structural changes. *Biochemistry* 23: 5780–86

89. Koenig SH. 1959. Hot and warm electrons—a review. *J. Phys. Chem. Solids* 8:227–34

90. Köhler G, Wendt H. 1966. Di Bestimmung von Gleichgewichtskonstanten aus kinetischen messungen. *Ber. Bunsenges. Phys. Chem.* 70:674–81

90a. Kopfermann H. 1956. *Kernmomente.* Frankfurt: Akad. Verlag.

91. Kuhn U, Lüty F. 1965. Paraelectric heating and cooling with OH^--dipoles in alkali halides. *Solid State Commun.* 4:31–33

92. Lee TD, Yang CN. 1956. Question of parity conservation in weak interactions. *Phys. Rev.* 104(1):254–58

93. Lendzian F, Huber M, Isaacson RA, Endeward B, Plato M, et al. 1993. The electronic structure of the primary donor cation radical in *Rhodobacter sphaeroides* R-26: ENDOR and TRIPLE resonance studies in single crystals of reaction centers. *Biochim. Biophys. Acta* 1183:139–60

94. Loach PA, Hall RL. 1972. The question of the primary electron acceptor in bacterial photosynthesis. *Proc. Natl. Acad. Sci. USA* 69(4):786–90

95. Lockhart DJ, Boxer SG. 1987. Magnitude and direction of the change in dipole moment associated with excitation of the primary electron donor in *Rhodopseudomonas sphaeroides* reaction centers. *Biochemistry* 26:664–68

96. Lösche M, Feher G, Okamura MY. 1987. The Stark effect in reaction centers from *Rhodobacter sphaeroides* R-26 and *Rhodopseudomonas viridis*. *Proc. Natl. Acad. Sci. USA* 84:7537–41

97. Low W. 1960. In *Paramagnetic Resonance in Solids*, ed. F Seitz, D Turnbull, p. 67. New York: Academic

98. Lubitz W, Abresch EC, Debus RJ, Isaacson RA, Okamura MY, Feher G. 1985. Electron nuclear double resonance of semiquinones in reaction centers of *Rhodopseudomonas sphaeroides*. *Biochim. Biophys. Acta* 808(3):464–69

99. Lubitz W, Feher G. 1999. The primary and secondary acceptors in bacterial photosynthesis: III characterization of the quinone radicals Q_A^- and Q_B^- by EPR and ENDOR. *Appl. Magn. Reson.* 17:1–48

100. Malley M, Feher G, Mauzerall D. 1968. The Stark effect in porphyrins. *J. Mol. Spectrosc.* 25(4):544–48

101. Marcus RA. 1993. Electron-transfer reactions in chemistry: theory and experiment (Nobel Lecture). *Angew. Chem.* 32:1111–21

102. Marinetti TD, Okamura MY, Feher G. 1979. Localization of the primary quinone binding site in reaction centers from *Rhodopseudomonas sphaeroides* R-26 by photoaffinity labeling. *Biochemistry* 18: 3126–33

103. Mauzerall D, Feher G. 1964. A study of the photoinduced porphyrin free radical by electron spin resonance. *Biochim. Biophys. Acta* 79:430–32

104. Mauzerall D, Feher G. 1964. Optical absorption of the porphyrin free radical formed in a reversible photochemical reaction. *Biochim. Biophys. Acta* 88:658–60

105. McAuley KE, Fyfe PK, Ridge JP, Isaacs NW, Cogdell RJ, Jones MR. 1999. Structural details of an interaction between cardiolipin and an integral membrane protein. *Proc. Natl. Acad. Sci. USA* 96(26): 14706–11

106. McElroy JD, Feher G, David C, Mauzerall DC. 1972. Characterization of primary reactants in bacterial photosynthesis. I. Comparison of the light-induced EPR signal (g = 2.0026) with that of a bacteriochlorophyll radical. *Biochim. Biophys. Acta* 267:363–74

107. McElroy JD, Mauzerall DC, Feher G. 1974. Characterization of primary reactants in bacterial photosynthesis II. Kinetic studies of the light-induced signal (g = 2.0026) and the optical absorbance changes at cryogenic temperatures. *Biochim. Biophys. Acta* 333:261–78

108. McPherson A. 1999. *Crystallization of Biological Macromolecules*. New York: Cold Spring Harbor Lab. Press. 586 pp.

109. Michel H, Oesterhelt D. 1980. Three-dimensional crystals of membrane proteins: bacteriorhodopsin. *Proc. Natl. Acad. Sci. USA* 77(3):1283–85

110. Michel H. 1982. Three-dimensional crystals of a membrane protein complex: the photosynthetic reaction center from *Rhodopseudomonas viridis*. *J. Mol. Biol.* 158(3):567–72

111. Norris JR, Scheer H, Katz JJ. 1975. Models for antenna and reaction center chlorophylls. *Ann. NY Acad. Sci.* 244:260–80

112. Norris JR, Uphaus RA, Crespi HL, Katz JJ. 1971. Electron spin resonance of chlorophyll and the origin of signal I in photosynthesis. *Proc. Natl. Acad. Sci. USA* 68(3):625–28

113. Okamura MY, Feher G, Nelson N. 1982. Reaction centers. In *Photosynthesis: Energy Conversion by Plants and Bacteria*, ed. Govindjee, 1:195–272. New York: Academic

114. Okamura MY, Fredkin DR, Isaacson RA, Feher G. 1979. Magnetic interactions and electron transfer kinetics of the reduced intermediate acceptor in reaction centers (RCs) of *Rhodopseudomonas sphaeroides* R-26. Evidence for thermally induced tunneling. In *Tunneling in Biological Systems*, ed. B Chance, D DeVault, H Frauenfelder, RA Marcus, JR Schrieffer, N Sutin, pp. 729–43. New York: Academic

115. Okamura MY, Isaacson RA, Feher G. 1975. Primary acceptor in bacterial photosynthesis: the obligatory role of ubiquinone in photoactive reaction centers of *Rhodopseudomonas sphaeroides*.

Proc. Natl. Acad. Sci. USA 72(9):3491–95

116. Okamura MY, Paddock ML, Graige MS, Feher G. 2000. Proton and electron transfer in bacterial reaction centers. *Biochim. Biophys. Acta* 1458:148–63

117. Okamura MY, Steiner LA, Feher G. 1974. Characterization of reaction centers from photosynthetic bacteria. I. Subunit structure of the protein mediating the primary photochemistry in *Rhodopseudomonas sphaeroides* R-26. *Biochemistry* 13(7):1394–403

118. Orbach R. 1961. Spin-lattice relaxation in rare-earth salts. *Proc. R. Soc. London Ser. A* 264:458–84

119. Osborne TB. 1892. Crystallized vegetable proteins. *Am. Chem. J.* 14:662–89

120. Overhauser AW. 1953. Polarization of nuclei in metals. *Phys. Rev.* 92(2):411–15

121. Paddock ML, Ädelroth P, Chang C, Abresch EC, Feher G, Okamura MY. 2001. Identification of the proton pathway in bacterial reaction centers: cooperation between Asp-M17 and Asp-L210 facilitates proton transfer to the secondary quinone (Q_B). *Biochemistry* 40:6893–902

122. Paddock ML, Graige MS, Feher G, Okamura MY. 1999. Identification of the proton pathway in bacterial reaction centers: inhibition of proton transfer by binding of Zn^{2+} or Cd^{2+}. *Proc. Natl. Acad. Sci. USA* 96:6183–88

123. Paddock ML, Rongey SH, Feher G, Okamura MY. 1989. Pathway of proton transfer in bacterial reaction centers: replacement of glutamic acid 212 in the L subunit by glutamine inhibits quinone (secondary acceptor) turnover. *Proc. Natl. Acad. Sci. USA* 86:6602–6

124. Parson WW. 1969. The reaction between primary and secondary electron acceptors in bacterial photosynthesis. *Biochim. Biophys. Acta* 1098:151–58

125. Perutz MF. 1998. *I Wish I Had Made You Angry Earlier*. New York: Cold Spring Harbor Lab. Press

126. Perutz MF, Pulsinelli PD, Ranney HM. 1972. Structure and subunit interaction of haemoglobin M Milwaukee. *Nat. New Biol.* 237(78):259–63

127. Perutz MF, Wilkinson AJ, Paoli M, Dodson GG. 1998. The stereochemical mechanism of the cooperative effects in hemoglobin revisited. *Annu. Rev. Biophys. Biomol. Struct.* 27:1–34

128. Platt JR. 1965. Electronic structure and excitation of polyenes and porphyrins. In *Radiation Biology III*, ed. A Hollaender, 2:71–123. New York: McGraw-Hill

129. Portis AM. 1953. Electronic structure of F centers: saturation of the electron spin resonance. *Phys. Rev.* 91(5):1071–78

130. Reed DW, Clayton RK. 1968. Isolation of a reaction center fraction from *Rhodopseudomonas spheroids. Biochem. Biophys. Res. Commun.* 30(5):471–75

131. Rees DC, Komiya H, Yeates TO, Allen JP, Feher G. 1989. The bacterial photosynthetic reaction center as a model for membrane proteins. *Annu. Rev. Biochem.* 58:607–33

132. Reif F. 1965. *Fundamentals of Statistical and Thermal Physics*, ed. EU Condon, Sect. 15:572–73. New York: McGraw-Hill

133. Richards FM. 1997. Whatever happened to the fun? An autobiographical investigation. *Annu. Rev. Biophys. Biomol. Struct.* 26:1–25

134. Richards PL, Caughey WS, Eberspaecher H, Feher G, Malley M. 1967. Determination of the zero-field splitting of Fe^{3+} in several hemin compounds. *J. Chem. Phys.* 47(3):1187–88

135. Roberts TM, Lauer GD, Klotz LC. 1975. Physical studies on DNA from "primitive" eucaryotes. *CRC Crit. Rev. Biochem.* 3(4):349–449

136. Rongey SH, Feher G, Okamura MY. 1995. Investigation of the binding domain in the *Rhodobacter sphaeroides* cyt c_2: reaction center complex by site-directed mutagenesis of Asp-M184 and Asp-L155 to Lys. *Int. Photosynth. Congr., 10th,*

Montpellier, Fr., ed. P Mathis, pp. 635–38. Dordrecht: Kluwer

137. Samuel I. The Old Testament. Chapter 28:7

138. Das Sarma S, Fabian J, Hu XD, Zutic I. 2000. Theoretical perspectives on spintronics and spin-polarized transport. *IEEE Trans. Magn.* 36(5):2821–26

139. Scholes CP, Isaacson RA, Feher G. 1971. Determination of the zero-field splitting of Fe^{3+} in heme proteins from the temperature dependence of the spin-lattice relaxation rate. *Biochim. Biophys. Acta* 244(1):206–10

140. Scholes CP, Isaacson RA, Feher G. 1972. Electron nuclear double resonance studies on heme proteins: determination of the interaction of Fe^{3+} with its ligand nitrogens in metmyoglobin. *Biochim. Biophys. Acta* 263(2):448–52

141. Scholes CP, Lapidot A, Mascarenhas R, Inubushi T, Isaacson RA, Feher G. 1982. Electron nuclear double resonance (ENDOR) from heme and histidine nitrogens in single crystals of aquometmyoglobin. *J. Am. Chem. Soc.* 104(10):2724–35

142. Schrödinger E. 1944. *What is Life*. Cambridge, UK: Cambridge Univ. Press. 92 pp.

143. Scovil HED, Feher G, Seidel H. 1957. Operation of a solid state maser. *Phys. Rev.* 105(2):762–63

144. Shepherd I, Feher G. 1965. Cooling by adiabatic depolarization of OH^- molecules in KCl. *Phys. Rev. Lett.* 15(5):194–98

145. Sogo P, Jost M, Calvin M. 1959. Evidence for free-radical production in photosynthesizing systems. *Radiat. Res. Suppl.* I:511–18

146. Steiner LA, Okamura MY, Lopes AD, Moskowitz E, Feher G. 1974. Characterization of reaction centers from photosynthetic bacteria. II. Amino acid composition of the reaction center protein and its subunits in *Rhodopseudomonas sphaeroides* R-26. *Biochemistry* 13(7):1403–10

147. Stowell MHB, McPhillips TM, Rees DC, Soltis SM, Abresch E, Feher G. 1997. Light induced structural changes in photosynthetic reaction centers. *Science* 276:812–16

148. Sutton MR, Rosen D, Feher G, Steiner LA. 1982. Amino-terminal sequences of L, M, and H subunits of reaction centers from photosynthetic bacterium, *Rhodopseudomonas sphaeroides* R-26. *Biochemistry* 21(16):3842–49

149. Szent-Györgyi A. 1957. Excitations and the biological matrix. In *Bioenergetics*, pp. 32–40. New York: Academic

150. Takahashi E, Wraight CA. 1990. A crucial role for AspL213 in the proton transfer pathway to the secondary quinone of reaction centers from *Rhodobacter sphaeroides*. *Biochim. Biophys. Acta* 1020:107–11

151. Tetreault M, Rongey SH, Feher G, Okamura MY. 2001. Interaction between cytochrome c_2 and the photosynthetic reaction center from *Rhodobacter sphaeroides*: effects of charge modifying mutations on binding and electron transfer. *Biochemistry* 40(29):8452–62

152. Valkirs GE, Feher G. 1982. Topography of reaction center subunits in the membrane of the photosynthetic bacterium *Rhodopseudomonas sphaeroides*. *J. Cell Biol.* 95(1):179–88

153. Van Vleck JH. 1932. *The Theory of Electric and Magnetic Susceptibilities*. New York: Oxford Univ. Press. 384 pp.

154. Volmer M. 1939. *Kinetik der Phasenbildung*, ed. KF Bonhoeffer. Dresden: Steinkopff

155. Weissman M, Schindler H, Feher G. 1976. Determination of molecular weights by fluctuation spectroscopy; application to DNA. *Proc. Natl. Acad. Sci. USA* 73(8):2776–80

156. Willenbrock FK, Blombergen N. 1953. Paramagnetic resonance in n- and p-type silicon. *Phys. Rev.* 91(5):1281–81

157. Williams JC, Steiner LA, Feher G. 1986.

Primary structure of the reaction center from *Rhodopseudomonas sphaeroides*. *Proteins* 1(4):312–25

158. Williams JC, Steiner LA, Feher G, Simon MI. 1984. Primary structure of the L subunit of the reaction center from *Rhodopseudomonas sphaeroides*. *Proc. Natl. Acad. Sci. USA* 81(23):7303–7

159. Williams JC, Steiner LA, Ogden RC, Simon MI, Feher G. 1983. Primary structure of the M subunit of the reaction center from *Rhodopseudomonas sphaeroides*. *Proc. Natl. Acad. Sci. USA* 80:6505–9

160. Wilson DK, Feher G. 1961. Electron spin resonance experiments on donors in silicon. III. Investigation of excited states by the application of uniaxial stress and their importance in relaxation processes. *Phys. Rev.* 124(4):1068–83

Annu. Rev. Biophys. Biomol. Struct. 2002. 31:45–71
DOI: 10.1146/annurev.biophys.31.082901.134314

THE NATURAL HISTORY OF PROTEIN DOMAINS

Chris P. Ponting[1] and Robert R. Russell[2]

[1]Department of Human Anatomy and Genetics, University of Oxford, MRC Functional
Genetics Unit, South Parks Road, Oxford OX1 3QX, United Kingdom;
e-mail: Chris.Ponting@Human-Anatomy.oxford.ac.uk
[2]EMBL, Meyerhofstrasse 1, Postfach 10 22 09, D69012 Heidelberg, Germany;
e-mail: Russell@embl-heidelberg.de

Key Words   protein evolution, protein structure, sequence analysis, domain
classification, function prediction

■ **Abstract**   Genome sequencing and structural genomics projects are providing
new insights into the evolutionary history of protein domains. As methods for sequence and structure comparison improve, more distantly related domains are shown
to be homologous. Thus there is a need for domain families to be classified within
a hierarchy similar to Linnaeus' *Systema Naturae*, the classification of species. With
such a hierarchy in mind, we discuss the evolution of domains, their combination into
proteins, and evidence as to the likely origin of protein domains. We also discuss when
and how analysis of domains can be used to understand details of protein function. Un-
conventional features of domain evolution such as intragenomic competition, domain
insertion, horizontal gene transfer, and convergent evolution are seen as analogs of
organismal evolutionary events. These parallels illustrate how the concept of domains
can be applied to provide insights into evolutionary biology.

CONTENTS

DOMAIN IDENTIFICATION

In recent decades the concepts of domains and domain families have risen to greater prominence within science. This has been due to an increasing realization that division of a protein's structure or sequence into domains often precedes reliable and accurate predictions of molecular function. A view of a multidomain protein's function as the sum of its constituent parts is obviously simplistic, as it ignores possible interdomain interactions and cooperative effects. Nevertheless this view does provide a first-approximation prediction that is amenable to investigation and subsequent refinement using experimental approaches.

Although domains now permeate descriptions of biology, definitions vary. In protein structure, a domain is often viewed as a compact, spatially distinct unit. In biochemistry, domains are frequently described as protein regions with assigned experimental functions, irrespective of their three-dimensional (3D) structures. In sequence comparison, domains are viewed from an evolutionary perspective and described as significantly sequence-similar homologs that are often present in different molecular contexts. These three views are compatible for the many cases where sequence-similar homologs adopt similar folds and possess comparable functions.

In this review, we consider how domains are identified and classified into sequence- or structure-based families related by common ancestry (homology). Function will not be used to define domains because most domain families contain representatives with different functions. Additionally, providing a standard definition of function is fraught with problems greater even than those that arise in defining domains (49). The classification of domains by homology raises many interesting questions concerning their evolution. In particular, how do the rates of change of gene structure, protein structure, sequence, and function vary? Can distinct domain families be related by common ancestry, even when their sequences, and even structures, differ radically? Finally, how did domains first arise and has "domain genesis" been occurring in relatively recent times?

Domains in Three-Dimensional Structures

The concept of a domain was first used to describe distinct regions of protein 3D structures. In the 1960s, the earliest enzyme structures of lysozyme (13) and ribonuclease (51) contained spatially distinct structural units, which were termed domains. Subsequent structures, such as pyruvate kinase (109), also showed a similar division into these units. Gradually, it emerged that such domains could recur either in different structural contexts [such as Rossmann folds in lactate and alcohol dehydrogenases (90)] or in multiple copies in the same polypeptide chain (such as for trypsin, pepsin, and rhodanese). The more recent availability of large numbers of protein sequences and structures has resolved many initial domain-assignment ambiguities. In addition, many early domain assignments have been corrected. Ironically, one such case is the protein lysozyme, which was thought originally to contain two domains. Lysozyme is now assigned as a member of a single-domain family whose representatives can contain elaborations to the original single-domain ancestral fold (43).

Today, domains within protein structures are usually defined as spatially distinct structures that could conceivably fold and function in isolation (Figure 1). Many methods that exist assign protein domains based on 3D structure, most of which are based on geometric measures of compactness (e.g., 48, 101, 104, 110). However, the advent of structure comparison has enabled the important principle of recurrence to play a central role in domain definition. The observation of a similar structure within a different context is a powerful indicator of a protein domain, and this can be irrespective of whether a unit is spatially distinct. This important principle of recurrence has been implemented in at least one method (47), and of course it is central to methods of domain assignment based on sequence similarity, which are discussed in the sections that follow.

Domains in Protein Sequences

The arrangement of different domain types in protein sequences causes considerable difficulties in sequence analysis. This can be seen from consideration of the proteins represented in Figure 2. These each contain a pleckstrin homology (PH) domain and a src homology 3 (SH3) domain, but in both orientations (PH then SH3, and SH3 then PH). Src homology 2 (SH2) and SH3 domains co-occur in Vav and Rgs1, but in two combinations: SH3-SH2-SH3 and SH2-SH3-SH2. Comparison of any one of these sequences with databases generates a plethora of significant alignments, a few with proteins that possess the same arrangement of domains, many more with proteins with different domain arrangements, and some with multiple hits within the same sequence. Teasing out the evolutionary relationships among the different regions of multidomain protein sequences therefore requires careful analysis of each set of regions that possesses a distinct evolutionary history.

Such a set of regions represents a family of homologous domains. Although the detection of homologous domain sequences in databases requires sophisticated analysis tools such as BLAST (2, 96), these are freely available on the Internet and, more importantly, are easy to use. Detecting homologous sequences may employ pairwise methods or, more effectively, generalized profile (GP) or hidden Markov model (HMM) methods (41, 78). GPs and HMMs are "domain descriptors," meaning they can easily retrieve from databases all domain sequences that make up their corresponding multiple alignments, as well as other homologs that might not have been previously thought to be members of the domain family.

Not all sequence families represent domains. Some sequence- and structure-similar entities are too small, or are lacking in secondary structures, to represent

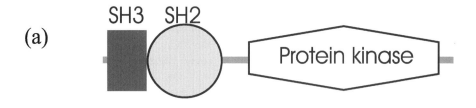

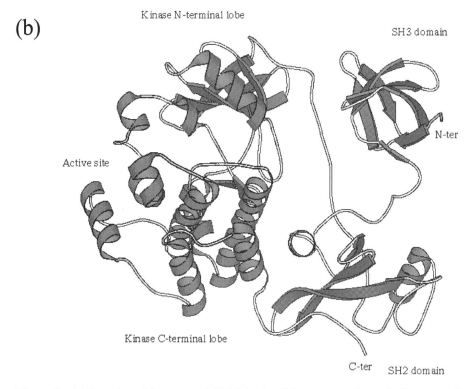

Figure 1   (*a*) Domain architecture and (*b*) Molscript (54) representations of a fragment of the structure of hematopoetic cell kinase (hck; PDB code 1qcf), containing protein kinase and src homology 2 and 3 (SH2 and SH3) domains.

domains. Examples of such motifs are DNA-binding AT-hooks (5) and short sequences that specifically target proteins to subcellular localizations (71). Some structural domains are entirely composed of repetitive structures of varying numbers (3). These repeat families can be classified into those that form linear rods (e.g., in spectrin) or superhelices (e.g., HEAT repeats) or closed structures (e.g., β-propellers or β-trefoils).

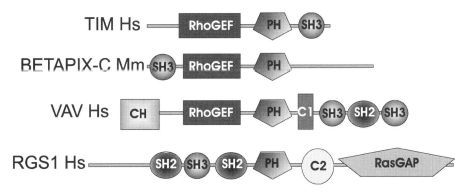

Figure 2 Representations of the domain architectures of human p60 tim (transforming immortalized mammary oncogene), mouse βPix-c, human Vav oncogene, and human RGS1 (regulator of G-protein signalling 1). Domain abbreviations: C1, protein kinase C conserved region 1; C2, protein kinase C conserved region 2; CH, calponin homology; PH, pleckstrin homology; RasGAP, GTPase activator protein specific for Ras-like small GTPases; RhoGEF, guanine nucleotide exchange factor specific for Rho-type small GTPases; SH2, src homology 2; SH3, src homology 3. Species abbreviations: Hs, *Homo sapiens*; Mm, *Mus musculus*.

Libraries of Domain Sequences

Libraries of domain, repeat, and motif alignments, and their associated GPs or HMMs, are available to automatically assign domains in protein sequences. These have become invaluable tools in sequence analysis, particularly in domain-based analyses of completely sequenced eukaryotic genomes (e.g., 20, 56, 115). They represent the current knowledge of domain families (thus avoiding much tedious repetition of previous analyses), and they allow results to be provided quickly and automatically.

These domain libraries have their own specialities. Of the HMM libraries, SMART [http://smart.embl-heidelberg.de/ (97)] and TIGRFAMs [http://www.tigr. org/TIGRFAMs/]; (39) focus on in-depth eukaryotic and prokaryotic families, respectively, and Pfam [http://www.sanger.ac.uk/Pfam/ (8)] is intent on providing comprehensive domain annotation of all proteins. Prosite provides a search of GPs, centered mostly on eukaryotic domains [http://www.isrec.isb-sib.ch/software/ PFSCAN_form.html (42)]. To obtain all possible predictions, a user should visit each of these sites in turn. However, the ready availability of these libraries has spawned several meta-sites, such as InterPro [http://www.ebi.ac.uk/interpro/ (4)], CDD (http://web.ncbi.nlm.nih.gov/Structure/cdd/cdd.shtml), and Panal [http:// mgd.ahc.umn.edu/panal/ (102)], that enable searches of several libraries to be performed simultaneously.

By assigning domains to homologous groups, these libraries provide a measure of objectivity. Where there is subjectivity is in the definition of what constitutes a domain family. In a model of evolution where domains evolve from antecedent domains rather than de novo, decisions need to be taken regarding whether a sequence belongs to one subfamily rather than a second related subfamily, and regarding when a sequence is best considered to be within a larger family encompassing both such subfamilies. For example, SMART primarily predicts mouse Rho-A to be a member of the Rho-type subfamily of small GTPases (Figure 3). However, as Rho-type small GTPases represent a subfamily within the larger family of Ras-like GTPases, Rho-A is also viewed by SMART as being more distantly related (i.e., with less significant statistics) to Rab, Ras, Arf, and Ran small GTPases. On the other hand, Pfam assigns Rho-A to the large Ras family defined to encompass all of the Ras, Rab, Rac, Ral, Ran, Rap, and Ypt1 subfamilies of small GTPases.

Thus a hierarchy is required to represent each of these evolutionary relationships: that Rho-A is a Rho-type small GTPase of the Ras family, which, in addition, is a member of a larger superfamily of GTPases and ATPases including dynein, myosin, and elongation factor Tu. The establishment of such hierarchies within domain libraries would provide significant added value to these resources. However, at present this development remains in its infancy.

Structure and Sequence Conservation

Domain recurrences among 3D structures consistently reveal that protein structure is more conserved than sequence. There are many examples of domains adopting highly similar 3D structures despite no apparent similarity in sequence. For many of these examples, proteins have diverged beyond the limits of sequence similarity detection methods but have nevertheless retained a common structure and similar function. For example, adenylate cyclase and DNA polymerase contain a similar domain that was recognized by 3D structure comparison (7). Despite a lack of obvious sequence similarity, both domains contain the active sites of these enzymes, and conserved residues are involved in catalyzing a similar reaction.

It is now usually accepted that proteins sharing a common fold and showing signs of a common ancestor reside in the same superfamily. Murzin and coworkers have been instrumental in making use of unusual features to classify proteins as being remote homologs. The most obvious indicators of common ancestry are features relating to function, such as catalytic or binding sites (e.g., 7, 15, 46, 68). However, other unusual features can also be used, such as left-handed β-α-β motifs (67) or other unusual topological connections unlikely to arise multiple times in the same structural position.

Figure 4 shows an example of such a feature. We argue that four superfamilies within the "swiveling" $\beta\beta\alpha$ domain (60) are homologous owing to the presence of an unusual loop connecting two β-strands at the edge of the core secondary structure elements that make up this fold. For two other superfamilies this feature is absent. Consequently, this unusual feature unites some, but not all, proteins adopting this fold.

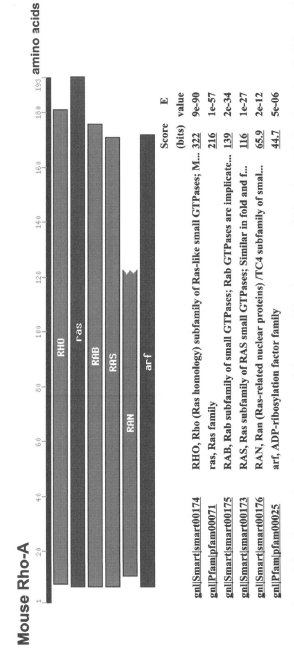

Figure 3 Web-based output from the comparison of the mouse Rho-A sequence (193 amino acids long) against the Pfam and SMART libraries of domains using the CDD (http://web.ncbi.nlm.nih.gov/Structure/cdd/cdd.shtml) system. Rho-A is seen to be most similar to the Rho (Ras homology) subfamily of Ras-like small GTPases as comparison with this domain alignment yields the lowest Expect (E-) value of 9×10^{-90}. If an alignment results in a score x, then its associated E-value represents the number of sequences expected to be aligned against the query with scores x or greater in this search simply by chance.

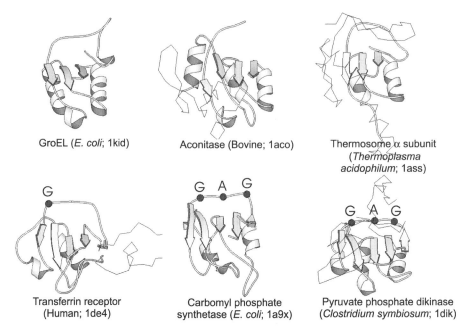

Figure 4   Molscript (54) figures showing the relationship between proteins from six superfamilies that adopt the "swiveling" $\beta\beta\alpha$ domain. The unusual loop connecting two edge β-strands in carbomyl phosphate synthetase, pyruvate phosphate dikinase, transferrin receptor, and GroEL suggests that they may be homologous. The core structure common to most proteins is shown as arrows (β-strands), ribbons (α-helices), or coil, with additional regions shown in C_α trace. Spheres show the location of conserved glycine (G) or alanine (A) residues found in some members containing an unusual loop as discussed in the text.

Attempts to automate superfamily assignment have failed to detect all such relationships but have nevertheless gone some way toward faster recognition of homology. Approaches have used sequence similarity (see below), the definition of a homologous core structure (64), or a combination of approaches, including sequence bridges or functional annotations from sequence databases (45, 62).

In recent years methods have been developed that use structure and sequence together to assess whether pairs of sequence-dissimilar domains that adopt the same fold are homologs. Russell et al. (94) found that when comparing only the structurally equivalent positions of such domain pairs, sequence identities of 12% or higher were likely to indicate homology. Murzin (66) devised a probability measure for assessing the significance of structurally equivalent and identical residues and used this to argue for a common evolutionary origin of cystatins and monelins. More recently, this measure was employed for determining a common ancestor for β-trefoil proteins, such as interleukin-1 (IL-1), fibroblast growth factors, and actin-binding proteins (87).

Classification of Three-Dimensional Structures

Over the past eight years, several schemes for protein structure classification have developed and matured and are now widely used for studies of protein structure, function, and evolution. It is beyond the scope of this review to discuss them all in detail, but salient points of three main schemes are discussed here. All classifications attempt to build a hierarchy of protein structural domains and highlight instances when protein structures show evidence of a common ancestry despite low sequence similarity.

Murzin et al. maintain and manually curate the structural classification of proteins (SCOP) database [http://scop.mrc-lmb.cam.ac.uk/scop/index.html (60, 69)]. The authors often point out that SCOP is an evolutionary classification, the main focus being to place proteins in the correct evolutionary framework, based on conserved features discussed in the previous section. Manual curation of SCOP means that sometimes it is not as up-to-date as the Protein Data Bank (PDB) and that some protein folds have been the subject of more attention than others. Nevertheless, the limits of its construction should not be overstated because it remains a key resource applicable to many purposes.

Orengo et al. maintain the CATH database [http://www.biochem.ucl.ac.uk/bsm/cath_new/index.html (76)]. This is constructed using a mixture of manual and automated methods and contains excellent supplementary information and cross-referencing for all structures. Information concerning active sites and homologous sequences is also readily available.

Holm & Sander offer the fully automated fold classification based on structure-structure alignment of proteins (FSSP) database [http://www.ebi.ac.uk/dali/fssp (44)], which is as up-to-date as the PDB. Automated procedures for domain assignment and protein structure comparison group proteins into clusters sharing similar folds. The authors have also provided a means for assigning homology despite low sequence similarity (45).

Despite differences in philosophy and design, the three classifications often agree (38). However, as is the case for domain assignment from sequence, the methods and details are sufficiently different to warrant inspection of their results in cases when one is attempting to place a structure in the correct structural, functional, or evolutionary context. This is particularly true in instances when either domain assignment or structural similarity is ambiguous.

EVOLUTION OF DOMAINS

Sequence-based analyses have demonstrated that some domains have ancient origins because they are widespread in each of the three forms of cellular life, archaea, bacteria, and eukarya, whose common ancestor existed over three billion years ago. The persistence of such domains implies that they are either hyperadaptable, suited to many beneficial functional niches, or that they are essential to fundamental cellular processes. Many enzymatic domains of central metabolism [e.g., $(\beta/\alpha)_8$ TIM barrels, flavoproteins, and Rossmann-like fold proteins] (32, 119) appear to owe their heritage to ancestors that preceded the last common ancestor of archaea, bacteria, and eukarya (30).

Ancient domains are not all enzymatic. PSD-95, Dlg, Zo1 (PDZ) domains, for example, occur in bacterial periplasmic proteins and archaeal tricorn-like proteases, as well as in numerous eukaryotic signaling proteins (82, 85). The binding of nonpolar protein C termini to PDZ domains is conserved among prokaryotic and eukaryotic proteins (10). Thus the molecular function of this domain family has been retained over several billion years. Other nonenzymatic domains are also likely to have been present in the last common ancestor of cellular life, including cystathionine β-synthase, plant pathogenesis-related-1, and von Willebrand factor A domains (84). Whether these ancient domains also retain conserved functions remains unknown.

Other domain families appear to be eukaryotic inventions because homologs cannot be detected in known prokaryotic sequences. Enzymatic and nonenzymatic domains of ubiquitin-mediated proteolysis, actin-binding cytoskeletal domains, and chromatin-associated domains, among many others, are represented only in eukaryotic proteomes (88). Other domain families, such as DEATH, DED, CARD, and PYRIN, are specific to eukarya that exhibit apoptosis and consequently are thought to be metazoan inventions. All four domains possess similar dimerization roles and similar tertiary structures (118). Thus they have arisen from a common ancestor, early in metazoan history, and have since diverged in sequence. This demonstrates the limitation inherent in defining domain families using sequence information alone.

Many extracellular domain families (e.g., apple, CCP, C-lectin, furin, fibronectin type-1 and -2, Gla, and kringle) are represented in metazoan proteins when they are absent elsewhere. The evolution of multicellularity in animals occurred concurrently with the proliferation of extracellular domain types that would have been required for cell-cell communication roles. Many of these metazoan extracellular domains are absent from known plant sequences, which suggests that multicellularity in plants and animals evolved independently (6, 23).

Domain Origin and Antecedent Domain Segments

Cytokines, such as IL-1α, -2, -4, -7, -9, -10, and -13, and the immunoglobulins required for the acquired immune response appear to have arisen in more recent times, since the emergence of chordates (56). All such discussions of domain emergence beg a fundamental question: From what did these domains evolve? Were they products of preexisting domain families that became extinct or else considerably diverged in sequence? Did such domains originate from noncoding DNA predecessors? The fundamental difference between these alternatives is that the former assumes a continuous evolution and vertical descent of domains, whereas the latter describes a discontinuity of domain evolution, a "domain parthenogenesis," where novel domains are generated ab initio.

A study of IL-1α, a β-trefoil-fold domain (87), using the structure- and sequence-dependent similarity method of Murzin (66) described previously, recently showed that this cytokine arose from a protein precursor homologous to invertebrate fibroblast growth factors, and slime mold and fungal actin-binding proteins. This illustrates a conclusion common to many findings (e.g., 9, 98): The more the sensitivity of sequence and structure database searching algorithms improves, the more it is realized that previously isolated domain families are instead part of larger, evolutionarily related superfamilies.

Consequently, as fast as new domain families are being found, old family ties are being discovered. There might appear to be a fundamental limit to this merging procedure because domain families with different folds are not usually considered as potential homologs. However, there is evidence that not only domains, but also their folds, might have radically changed. If so, then this suggests that most modern folds might have arisen from, at most, a few ancestors.

Regardless of how many times domains with different folds have arisen, there is little explanation of what were the precursors of the earliest domains. Recently, Lupas et al. (61) considered a variety of phenomena and suggested that domains may be descended from conglomerates of short polypeptide segments that together were capable of folding and conveying a beneficial function. Evidence for the past importance of short polypeptides was twofold and was gathered from modern proteins that contain either homologous repeats or short sequence-similar motifs embedded in nonhomologous structures.

First, it was argued that proteins containing multiple copies of a homologous repeat, by definition, must be derived from a short polypeptide ancestor that possessed only a single repeat. In order to possess a biological function, it is argued, this ancestral repeat must have oligomerized in order to adopt a structure comparable to that of modern homologs. For example, a study of IL-1α homologs (87) revealed that the three pseudosymmetrical regions of the β-trefoil fold are homologous, having arisen from a common ancestor. The implication is that this common ancestor once adopted a β-trefoil fold by forming a trimer of identical subunits and that its descendants arose by intrachain subunit duplication. A similar argument may be made for all internally repetitive domains, such as β-propellers (65) and triple β-spirals (114).

Second, short highly sequence-similar motifs, such as Asp-box and helix-hairpin-helix (HhH) motifs (22, 28), have been identified in nonhomologous structures. One model for the evolution and spread of these unusual short sequence and structure motifs is that they represent ancient conserved domain cores that have persisted owing to their relatively high importance for function and structure while their surrounding structures have been subjected to greater alteration. Another model is that they represent short gene segments that have been successfully duplicated and incorporated into different nonhomologous contexts.

Whether such motifs are ancient or more modern, their existence indicates that domains might be divisible and have arisen by recombination of smaller sequences.

The past occurrence of short polypeptides, which are seen today as internal repeats and structure-integrated motifs, argues that complex single-domain structures might have arisen by the fusion of simpler substructures, much in the same manner as complex multidomain proteins are thought to have arisen by domain shuffling (61). The ancient predomain world would thus have contained much shorter proteins [antecedent domain segments (ADSs)] that would have acted in concert to produce single-domain homo- or hetero-multimers. This idea agrees with preconceptions as to the nature of the early protein world where, if proteins were as long as often they are today, higher error rates in transcription and translation would have been likely to produce misfolded variants.

A degree of support for this ADS hypothesis comes from recent improvements in protein tertiary structure prediction. Bystroff et al. and Simons et al. (16, 17, 103) have made use of a library, containing local regions of structure similarity (I-sites) common to different protein folds, to obtain outstanding prediction accuracies. These I-sites might correspond to ancient ADSs because their prediction success might have arisen from an identification of regions of genuine ancient homology among otherwise different 3D structures.

Correspondence Between Exons and Three-Dimensional Structure

Since exons were first identified it has been proposed that they might correspond to units of protein 3D structure or function (12, 29, 33). An underlying assumption to this proposition is that the combination of exons was once key to the construction of protein structures seen today (29). Many studies have been performed during the past two decades searching for a link between intron positions and units of 3D structure or function (e.g., 25, 107, 113).

The role of introns in evolution has been the subject of much controversy. In one camp are adherents of the introns-early theory (e.g., 25, 34). They argue that introns were present in the progenitor of all living organisms and were subsequently lost in bacteria and archaea. For this theory to be true, one expects, at least for ancient proteins, that intron positions will lie at key junctions in protein structures, suggesting their original assembly by exon-shuffling, the evidence for which is now missing in bacteria and archaea.

In the opposite camp are those who believe that the absence of introns from bacteria and archaea reflects the fact that introns are eukaryotic inventions (19, 77, 81, 99). A perceived failure to correlate exons with units of structure or function, the apparent recent origin of exons, and recent evidence highlighting key roles for exons during various stages of eukaryotic evolution (see below) have led many to argue that introns have arrived only recently in eukaryotic evolution (the introns-late hypothesis).

There have been many studies during the past two decades attempting to resolve this debate. In summary, much of the community agrees that the introns-early theory is untenable (e.g., 107), although de Souza and coworkers continue to argue that there is evidence that certain key exons likely represent ancient building blocks for many ubiquitous proteins (25). The sudden availability of thousands of genomic sequences for proteins is likely to resolve this debate soon.

Despite controversy as to the role of introns in the origin of ancient proteins, there is a growing body of convincing evidence for the role of exon-shuffling in the assembly of recently evolved proteins in eukaryotes. For example, Patthy (79–81) has provided convincing evidence for a role in exon-shuffling during the "big bang" of metazoan radiation. This period saw the emergence of the first multicellular animals, an event that is correlated with the first appearance of many new extracellular signaling proteins. These proteins, which are needed to mediate communication between cells in multicellular organisms, are often complex combinations of many different domains. Many show a good correlation in the location of domain boundaries and the location of introns, particularly those of phase 1. (The phase of an intron is defined as 0, 1, or 2, where the number refers to the location of the intron relative to the nucleotide triplet; e.g., 0 implies that the intron does not interrupt a codon.) For this reason, Patthy argues that exon-shuffling played a key role in the construction of multidomain extracellular signaling proteins. This is in contrast to proteins found inside the cell (such as kinases, SH2, SH3, and PH domains) where there is scant evidence for correlation. He thus argues in addition that such intracellular signaling molecules probably first arose prior to the emergence of exon-shuffling as a major evolutionary force.

Recently, Betts et al. (11) investigated the degree to which intron positions are conserved within protein domains rather than within multidomain proteins. They found a surprising number of families where intron positions were conserved despite little or no sequence similarity. Here similarity between proteins was only inferred following 3D structure comparison. Most intriguingly the proteins that showed conservation of intron positions were often in the same functional class (such as immune system proteins) or restricted to particular evolutionary lineages (such as nematodes). This suggests that such intron conservation is a relic of comparatively recent divergence, followed by rapid evolution owing to key events in evolutionary history, such as the developments of the immune system in vertebrates or the chemical response system in nematodes. It also raises the possibility that unequal crossing-over (essentially exon-shuffling) might have created domain hybrids, thus increasing the rate at which these domain families could diverge.

Fold Changes During Domain Evolution

It has long been clear that proteins adopting similar folds often differ from each other outside of a conserved core. Homologs can have additional segments at their N- or C-terminal ends, and loop regions often differ, particularly when sequence similarity is low and functions are different. Sometimes loop regions are the site of domain insertions, where domain duplications have led to one domain being copied into the middle of another (see below). Another simple but drastic evolutionary event is circular permutation, which presumably occurs by gene duplication, fusion, and partial deletion (93) and can lead to substantial changes to the topology of a protein fold. Conceptually it can be considered to involve a fusion of the N and C termini and a cleavage at a different location to create new termini. It is thus only strictly permitted in proteins where N and C termini are close to each other in space.

It is also possible for regions of proteins to change dramatically in structure with conventional mutation and insertion events. The landmark work of Grishin (37) has demonstrated that the current population of protein structures contains numerous instances where seemingly different protein structures can be argued to have descended from a common ancestor. It is possible, for example, for regions of α-helix to change over time to become short β-sheets. It has even been proposed that it is theoretically possible for an evolutionary transition to occur between all-α and all-β protein structures by a series of events already seen in the current set of protein structures.

Convergent Evolution

Although there is growing evidence that an increasing number of apparently different structures may share a common ancestor, it is also clear that nature has reinvented, by convergent evolution, similar local structures multiple times. Probably the best-known example is that of the Ser/His/Asp catalytic triad (27), which is found in at least five different protein folds that cannot easily be considered to be homologous by any of the evolutionary events discussed above. It is likely that nature has been limited by the 20–amino acid alphabet in the choice of residues that can perform similar functions.

Methods detecting recurrent 3D side chain patterns have found numerous instances of localized structure convergence (e.g., 92, 117). Convergence of function has also been observed within homologous protein families. In these cases nature has invented a substrate specificity more than once within the same homologous family (e.g., 24, 120). One of the more fascinating cases of structure convergence concerns thermolysin and mitochondrial processing peptidase (63). These proteins show striking similarities not only in their active site residues but also in their structures. The arrangement and packing of the core secondary structure elements is the same, yet the connectivity (i.e., the order of the elements along the polypeptide chains) is completely different, often in the reverse main chain orientation, thus making their descent from a common ancestor extremely unlikely.

It remains an open question as to whether whole-protein folds, rather than localized structures and functional sites, have arisen multiple times during evolution. Nature could have stumbled upon simple folds, such as four α-helical bundles, multiple times, but for more complicated structures this is not so easy to argue convincingly. By contrast, several folds [such as β/α-(TIM)-barrels and β-trefoils], which were previously thought to be examples of convergence, are increasingly being revealed as homologs (21, 87) due to enhanced sensitivity in sequence comparison techniques.

Domains and Protein Evolution

Duplication of genes within a genome has been a major evolutionary process in the acquisition of novel function (74). The initial functional redundancy after duplication reduces mutational constraints for one or both copies and gives rise to an increased likelihood of functional differentiation. Gene duplicates that have persisted to the present day are known as paralogs; this contrasts with orthologs, which are genes that arose by speciation rather than by intragenome duplication. Partial gene duplication has also been a prominent mechanism for function diversification. Frequently, this has generated multiple tandem repeats or else the occurrence of homologous domains in different domain architectures. A third prominent evolutionary mechanism is deletion, either deletion of genes or portions of genes.

Domain duplication and acquisition lead to variations in the tandem arrangement of domains along a sequence. However, duplicated domains are not always inserted into genes in a manner that results in tandem domains. In relatively rare instances, duplication can give rise to the insertion of a domain within another domain. For such cases whose tertiary structures are known, the fold and structural integrity of the two inserted and parent domains remain intact. The polypeptide backbone of the parent domain is interrupted by an excursion from an external loop to form the inserted domain before returning to complete the parent domain fold (91). This is made possible, it is thought, by the frequent spatial proximity of N- and C-terminal ends of protein domains. Detecting cases of domain insertion using sequence analysis is problematic (93). However, among documented cases, several involve PH domains. PH domains can have embedded C1 and PDZ domains (in Rho-associated kinase α and syntrophins, respectively) or else be inserted into a band 4.1 domain or another PH domain (in Mig2 and myosin X, respectively) (93).

The importance of duplication and deletion events in past evolution can be inferred from the repetitive and piece-meal nature of modern proteins. This is illustrated here by a family of proteins typified by mouse Ky (14) and leech hillarin (50) (Figure 5). The members of this protein family are closely related to each other in sequence, yet their domain architectures differ in key respects. Leech hillarin is duplicated with respect to mouse Ky, and *Caenorhabditis elegans* and *Saccharomyces cerevisiae* Ky homologs have independently acquired LIM and SH3 domains, respectively. The effect of these duplication and domain acquisition events on molecular function remains unknown. Although the C-terminal regions of these genes are likely to be orthologous, having arisen from a common ancestor by speciation events, the lineage-specific evolution of domain architectures implies that their molecular functions have diverged significantly. This matter is made more

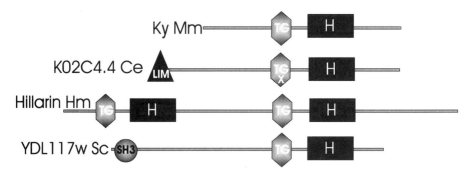

Figure 5   Representations of the domain architectures of *Mus musculus* (Mm) Ky homologues from *Caenorhabditis elegans* (Ce), *Hirudo medicinalis* (Hm), and *Saccharomyces cerevisiae* (Sc). Conserved transglutaminase (TG) homology domains and H domains (50) are shown, together with src homology 3 (SH3) and Lin-11, Isl-1, Mec-3 (LIM) domains.

complex by the realization (14) that the *C. elegans* Ky homolog alone among these proteins has substitutions within the putative active site of its transglutaminase homology domain, implying a further divergence of their functions.

Differences in domain architectures among genes that have clearly arisen, at least in part, from a common ancestor raise the question of whether these genes are orthologous. If, as is likely, the Ky ancestor contained only transglutaminase and H domains, then only the regions of leech, mouse, *C. elegans*, and yeast Ky homologs that contain transglutaminase and H domains are orthologous (Figure 5). The remaining regions that were absent from the common gene ancestor, a SH3 domain in yeast and a LIM domain in *C. elegans*, appear to be later additions and consequently are not orthologous or even homologous. Similar to the conventional use of the concept of homology, it is suggested that descriptions of orthology are most appropriately applied to domains, rather than proteins, except when proteins contain identical domain architectures. Although this may appear at first to be a question of semantics, the identification of orthologs is crucial for the comparison of function across species (52). Furthermore, the comparison of function across species is central to the issue of whether science is to take full advantage of the newly sequenced genomes.

THE ROLE OF DOMAINS IN PREDICTING FUNCTION

Domains and Organismal Function

Libraries of domain families, in particular Pfam and SMART, have recently been used to great effect to provide insights into eukaryotic evolution (56, 115). In one of these studies (56), 94 domain families were identified to have arisen in the chordate lineage and reflect the emergence of novel physiological systems. Of these, 23 function in the defense and immunity systems (e.g., ILs), 18 are plasma factors (e.g., uteroglobin), 17 are found in the peripheral nervous system (e.g., ependymin), and 14 are involved in bone and cartilage formation (e.g., calcitonin), lactation (e.g., caseins), or vascular (e.g., endothelin) or dietary (e.g., glucagon) homeostasis. Clearly these families are markers of the chordate lineage and reflect the participation of emergent domain types in the evolution of the immune, nervous, skeletal, mammary, vascular, and digestive systems in chordates in general, and vertebrates in particular.

These 94 domains, however, are a small minority of all families represented in vertebrates. The great majority of domain families (over 90%) originated prior to the appearance of the first chordates (56). Yet, although most vertebrate domains are ancient in origin, the proteins in which they appear often are not, having been constructed by combining domains into an abundance of different architectures: The number of such architectures in vertebrates exceeds that in invertebrates by about 80% (56). The recent availability of the complete genome sequences for *Homo sapiens*, *Drosophila*, *C. elegans*, *Arabidopsis*, and *S. cerevisiae*, therefore, has demonstrated the significant contribution made to the evolution of organismal function by the variation of domain combinations.

Thus far, the propagation of genes and domains has been described only as a process of transferral by vertical descent. However, considerable evidence has been amassed that among prokaryotes, and bacteria in particular, genes have been passed between genomes (31, 72). This horizontal gene transfer among genomes stymies our attempts to understand the relatedness of anciently diverged organisms but may provide insights into the evolutionary relationships between coexisting organisms, such as pathogen and host or symbiont pairs (55, 73). Clearly, a gain by horizontal gene transfer to the germ line of a domain that confers advantages to the acquisitive organism enhances the perpetuation of its genome.

At first, it appeared that the human genome might have acquired domains and genes via horizontal gene transfer from bacterial sources (56); this is now considered less likely (106). Horizontal gene transfer from vertebrates into bacteria, however, certainly has occurred (84). Bacteria are likely to have benefited from acquisition of domains that, in vertebrates, function in cell-cell signaling (integrin, cadherin, and fasciclin domains), intracellular signaling (Sec7 domain and WD40 and ankyrin repeats), and chromatin remodeling [Su(var)3-9, enhancer-of-zeste, trithorase (SET) domain]. Each of these acquired domains is likely to have been fixed in its recipient bacterial genome as a result of a direct benefit conferred to the organism. One approach to enhancing our understanding of pathogenicity in vertebrates therefore is to identify pathogen genes gained from host organisms by horizontal gene transfer. One such example is the apparent acquisition by the intracellular human pathogen *Chlamydia* of a perforin-homologous gene from a vertebrate source (83).

The principle of natural selection is applicable to many different biological objects (36), including clades, species, individuals within species, and single genes within individuals. Could one such biological object be a domain family? We believe that there is evidence for intragenomic competition among domain families for particular functional niches.

Consider the example of protein kinases. These may be divided into two major families: (*a*) histidine kinases (HisKs) that phosphorylate predominantly on histidine and (*b*) kinases that phosphorylate on serine or threonine or tyrosine (STYKs). Each of these families is involved in intracellular signaling, and each contains an ATPase active site that appears to have arisen from a common ancestor (53). However, HisKs are almost exclusively limited to bacteria and archaea, with a few present in fungi and plants, and STYKs are almost exclusively limited to eukarya, with the exception of antibiotic kinases and bacterial kinases acquired from eukarya via horizontal gene transfer (58). For example, *Escherichia coli* has 30 HisKs and no STYKs, whereas *H. sapiens* has over 550 STYKs and only 4 extremely distant HisK homologs (pyruvate dehydrogenase kinases). Phylogenetic analysis evidence suggests that eukaryotic STYKs are relatively recent inventions, arising since the last common ancestor with bacteria and archaea, and that HisKs are ancient, being present in the last common ancestor of the three forms of cellular life. This suggests that, in animals where STYKs are abundant, the success of this family of kinases in colonizing intracellular signaling niches has led to the virtual extinction of HisKs. This effect may be simply due to an enhanced stability of phospho-Ser/Thr/Tyr over phospho-His, which is required for larger cells, where signals need to be transduced over greater distances.

A more contemporaneous example of interfamily rivalry might involve the PH domain family, which is specific to eukarya. The archetypal PH domain family is known to be multifunctional, as it associates with membranes, inositolphosphates, and proteins (100). In eukaryotes, five major intracellular signaling modes exist that are mediated by the binding of phosphoserine or threonine, phosphotyrosine, polyproline, phospholipids, or small GTPases. Of these, the latter four modes are performed by domain families (PTB, WH1, PH, and RanBD domains, respectively) that adopt the PH domain fold. As these domain families occur only in eukaryotes and the PH domain fold has not yet been found outside of eukarya, there is reason to believe that each of the PTB, WH1, PH, and RanBD domain families arose from a PH domain fold common ancestor that arose early in eukaryotic history. The four signaling modes are also performed by other domain families (e.g., SH2, SH3, C2, and RA domains, respectively) that do not adopt the PH domain fold and also arose early in eukaryotic evolution. Thus it would appear that the PH domain fold has successfully colonized each of the four different signaling modes in direct competition with other domain folds. The basis for this hyperadaptability of the PH domain fold remains unclear.

Domain Families and Function

Knowledge that a protein adopts a particular protein fold is often insufficient to infer details of function (75). As discussed in previous sections, proteins with no apparent similarity in function can adopt similar 3D structures. Sometimes structure similarity does imply an ancient evolutionary relationship and often a similar function, but for other structure similarities the situation is not so clear. Even in the absence of clear indicators of common ancestry or function, it is still possible to predict details of function if the protein adopts one of the folds known to show a preference for binding ligands in a particular location. Russell et al. (95) identified nine folds that showed a statistically significant tendency to bind ligands in a common location. This they termed a supersite because it occurs by definition in a protein adopting a superfold (75). β/α-barrels, doubly wound Rossmann-like folds, β-propellers, four α-helical bundles, ferredoxin-like folds, and others have a preferred location for binding to ligands that could well be dictated by principles of protein structure rather than by a common ancestry.

Although less useful than identifying a clear case of homology, knowledge that a protein adopts a fold containing a supersite can assist experimental design. The bacterial periplasmic protein TolB provides an example. TolB was predicted to contain a β-propeller domain, and the knowledge that β-propellers predominantly bind ligands in a common location led to a prediction of the TolB-binding site (86). This prediction corresponds well with several amino acids involved in suppressor mutations of *pal* A88V (89).

The completion of genomic sequencing projects means that many proteins of known sequence are of unknown function. In addition, high-throughput structural biology projects ("structural genomics") are producing 3D structures of proteins, whose functions remain unknown. Because comparison of sequence and structure is key to predicting function for new proteins, understanding the degree to which functional information can be transferred from one protein to associated homologs remains a major issue. An important question that has been addressed recently is how functional information can be transferred from one domain to its homologs. Todd et al. (112) investigated functional similarity for 31 diverse superfamilies in the CATH database. They described instances spanning most conceivable scenarios, ranging from those where fine mechanistic details are preserved even when sequence similarity is low to examples where obviously homologous proteins have essentially no functional similarity. Devos & Valencia (26) investigated the similarity between enzyme class, functional descriptions from key words, cellular functional classes, and binding sites in proteins with similar structures showing significant (but low) sequence similarity. They found that these attributes can only be reliably transferred from one protein to another to a limited degree and furthermore established sequence identity limits for such transfers. These studies suggest that one must exercise caution when attempting to transfer functional information between proteins, particularly when sequence identities are low (i.e., <40%).

Approaches have also been developed to identify functionally important regions on protein surfaces (e.g., 1, 18, 57, 59) and to predict when functional sites on one protein can be used to predict a similar site on others (1). Although it is important to recognize similarities in functional sites, differences are also important because they are often related to specificity. Many protein families share details of molecular function (e.g., dehydrogenase) but vary in finer details such as their particular substrates (e.g., lactate/malate) or interacting partners. Methods have thus been developed that attempt to identify not just common functional residues but those that are important in discerning subclasses (e.g., 18, 40, 57, 59). For example, key catalytic residues are common to all protein kinases, but two regions of the sequence differ and are known to confer the specificity for either serine/threonine (which differ only slightly) or the chemically distinct tyrosine. Such methods will be vital for the future development of evolution-based hierarchies of domain subfamilies, families, and superfamilies.

Using Domains to Interpret the Pathoetiology of Disease

Understanding domain function can lead to a greater appreciation of organismal function, particularly for domains present in the products of genes mutated in human disease (disease genes). Sequence analysis in general, and domain detection in particular, has played a pivotal role in elucidating the pathoetiology of disease (105). The majority (91%) of human disease gene products contain a domain assigned by Pfam or SMART (35). Thus both resources should represent the first ports-of-call for investigators wishing to predict the functions of newly sequenced disease genes.

The identification of disease gene orthologs and paralogs, by sequence analysis and domain prediction, also plays a part in understanding the molecular bases of diseases. Ortholog prediction allows the investigation of gene function in model organisms such as mouse, fruit fly, and nematode worm. Identification of human paralogs of disease genes generates additional disease gene candidates; this is because paralogs are often mutated in similar diseases. Due care is required, however, to establish that orthologs contain identical domain compositions and orders and to conserve functionally important active and/or binding sites. Otherwise, as was described previously for Ky orthologs (Figure 5), the conservation of function becomes less certain.

Although the molecular and/or domain functions of most newly identified disease genes can be predicted by sequence analysis, this knowledge is often inadequate to establish the critical deficit in organismal function for individuals suffering from the disease. If this divide between genotype and phenotype is to be spanned, protein function must be deduced from its constituent domains' functions; cellular function must be established from determination of the set of molecular interactions and reactions involving the protein; and organismal function must be considered as the grand synthesis of tissue expression, gene expression, post-translational modification, cellular localization, and molecular interaction data. The central position of domains within this informational hierarchy argues that their future contribution to biology will be enduring.

CONCLUSIONS

Many analogies can be drawn between the evolution of organisms and of domains. Competition among species and among domain families drives the selection of advantageous mutations in the occupation of both novel ecological and physiological niches. Convergence of function is apparent for both species and domain family lineages. For example, the skull and body morphologies of the extinct marsupial wolf (Tasmanian tiger, *Thylacinus cynocephalus*) are similar to those of placental wolves (111), while trypsin-like and subtilisin-like serine proteases have independently evolved equivalent active sites. The embedding of domains within other domains parallels the presence of cellular endosymbionts within other cells: The insertion of SH2 and SH3 domains within a PH domain that is inserted within a TIM barrel domain (70) mirrors the presence of endosymbionts within endosymbionts within insect cells (116). Horizontal gene transfer between organisms is comparable to the transfer of genetic material between domain families which gives rise to sequence- and structure-similar motifs in unrelated molecules, as described previously for HhH and Asp box motifs. Indeed, the idea that domains once were composed mostly of multiple polypeptide segments (ADSs) is the molecular counterpart to the proposition that prokaryotes' genomes have a composite origin.

These analogies extend to the systems of classifying organisms and domains. In 1735 Carl Linnaeus published his *Systema Naturae*, a species classification system, which was codified one hundred years later (108). Modern domain classification systems are analogous to the Linnean system, not only because they are based on predicted evolutionary relationships but also because they are equivalent in structure. Just as a taxonomic family may contain several genera (a genus is a group of closely related species), a domain family also may contain several distinct sets of related domains (subfamilies). Progressing toward the base of the taxonomic tree from family to order to class to phylum is analogous to domain-based classification schema [e.g., SCOP (60)] that proceed from family to superfamily to fold to class.

For over a century zoologists have classified organisms using the Linnean system in order to provide insights into their natural history. Biologists are beginning to appreciate the benefits of hierarchical domain classification systems based on sequence, structure, and evolution. The numerous parallels between these systems suggest that domain classifications will prove to be key to our further understanding of the natural history of domain families.

ACKNOWLEDGMENT

We would like to thank Prof. A. N. Lupas for helpful discussions.

Visit the Annual Reviews home page at www.annualreviews.org

LITERATURE CITED

1. Aloy P, Querol E, Aviles FX, Sternberg MJE. 2001. Automated structure-based prediction of functional sites in proteins: applications to assessing the validity of inheriting protein function from homology in genome annotation and to protein docking. *J. Mol. Biol.* 311:395–408

2. Altschul SF, Boguski MS, Gish W,

Wootton JC. 1994. Issues in searching molecular sequence databases. *Nat. Genet.* 6:119–29

3. Andrade MA, Perez-Iratxeta C, Ponting CP. 2001. Protein repeats: structures, functions and evolution. *J. Struct. Biol.* 134:117–31

4. Apweiler R, Attwood TK, Bairoch A, Bateman A, Birney E, et al. 2000. Inter-Pro—an integrated documentation resource for protein families, domains and functional sites. *Bioinformatics* 16:1145–50

5. Aravind L, Landsman D. 1998. AT-hook motifs identified in a wide variety of DNA-binding proteins. *Nucleic Acids Res.* 26:4413–21

6. Aravind L, Subramanian G. 1999. Origin of multicellular eukaryotes—insights from proteome comparisons. *Curr. Opin. Genet. Dev.* 9:688–94

7. Artymiuk PJ, Poirette AR, Rice DW, Willet P. 1997. A polymerase palm domain in adenylyl cyclase? *Nature* 388:33–34

8. Bateman A, Birney E, Durbin R, Eddy SR, Howe KL, Sonnhammer EL. 2000. The Pfam protein families database. *Nucleic Acids Res.* 28:263–66

9. Beckmann G, Hanke J, Bork P, Reich JG. 1998. Merging extracellular domains: fold prediction for laminin G-like and amino-terminal thrombospondin-like modules based on homology to pentraxins. *J. Mol. Biol.* 275:725–30

10. Beebe KD, Shin J, Peng J, Chaudhury C, Khera J, Pei D. 2000. Substrate recognition through a PDZ domain in tail-specific protease. *Biochemistry* 39:3149–55

11. Betts MJ, Guigo R, Agarwal P, Russell RB. 2001. Exon/intron structure conservation in the absence of protein sequence similarity: a record of dramatic events in evolution? *EMBO J.* 20:5354–60

12. Blake CCF. 1978. Do genes-in-pieces imply proteins-in-pieces? *Nature* 273:267

13. Blake CCF, Koenig DF, Mair GA, North ACT, Phillips DC, Sarma VR. 1965. Structure of hen egg-white lysozyme. *Nature* 206:757–61

14. Blanco G, Coulton GR, Biggin A, Grainge C, Moss J, Barrett M, et al. 2001. The kyphoscoliosis (ky) mouse is deficient in hypertrophic responses and is caused by a mutation in a novel muscle-specific protein. *Hum. Mol. Genet.* 10:9–16

15. Brannigan JA, Dodson G, Duggleby HJ, Moody PC, Smith JL, et al. 1995. A protein catalytic framework with an N-terminal nucleophile is capable of self-activation. *Nature* 378:416–19

16. Bystroff C, Baker D. 1998. Prediction of local structure in proteins using a library of sequence-structure motifs. *J. Mol. Biol.* 281:565–77

17. Bystroff C, Thorsson V, Baker D. 2000. HMMSTR: a hidden Markov model for local sequence-structure correlations in proteins. *J. Mol. Biol.* 301:173–90

18. Casari G, Sander C, Valencia A. 1995. A method to predict functional residues in proteins. *Nat. Struct. Biol.* 2:171–78

19. Cavalier-Smith T. 1985. Selfish DNA and the origin of introns. *Nature* 315:283–84

20. Chervitz SA, Aravind L, Sherlock G, Ball CA, Koonin EV, et al. 1998. Comparison of the complete protein sets of worm and yeast: orthology and divergence. *Science* 282:2022–28

21. Copley RR, Bork P. 2000. Homology among $(\beta\alpha)_8$ barrels: implications for the evolution of metabolic pathways. *J. Mol. Biol.* 303:627–41

22. Copley RR, Russell RB, Ponting CP. 2001. Sialidase like Asp-boxes: sequence-similar structures within different protein folds. *Protein Sci.* 10:285–92

23. Copley RR, Schultz J, Ponting CP, Bork P. 1999. Protein families in multicellular organisms. *Curr. Opin. Struct. Biol.* 9:408–15

24. Deshimaru M, Ogawa T, Nakashima K, Nobuhisa I, Chijiwa T, et al. 1996. Accelerated evolution of *crotalinae* snake venom gland serine proteases. *FEBS Lett.* 397:83–88

25. de Souza SJ, Long M, Klein RJ, Roy S, Lin S, Gilbert W. 1998. Toward a resolution of the introns early/late debate: Only phase zero introns are correlated with the structure of ancient proteins. *Proc. Natl. Acad. Sci. USA* 95:5094–99

26. Devos D, Valencia A. 2000. Practical limits of function prediction. *Proteins* 41:98–107

27. Dodson G, Wlodawer A. 1998. Catalytic triads and their relatives. *Trends Biochem. Sci.* 23:347–52

28. Doherty AJ, Serpell LC, Ponting CP. 1996. The helix-hairpin-helix DNA-binding motif: a structural basis for non-sequence-specific recognition of DNA. *Nucleic Acids Res.* 24:2488–97

29. Doolittle WF. 1978. Genes in pieces: Were they ever together? *Nature* 272:581–82

30. Doolittle WF, Brown JR. 1994. Tempo, mode, the progenote, and the universal root. *Proc. Natl. Acad. Sci. USA* 91:6721–28

31. Garcia-Vallve S, Romeu A, Palau J. 2000. Horizontal gene transfer in bacterial and archaeal complete genomes. *Genome Res.* 10:1719–25

32. Gerstein M. 1997. A structural census of genomes: comparing bacterial, eukaryotic, and archaeal genomes in terms of protein structure. *J. Mol. Biol.* 274:562–76

33. Gilbert W. 1978. Why genes in pieces? *Nature* 271:501

34. Gilbert W. 1986. The RNA world. *Nature* 319:618

35. Goodstadt L, Ponting CP. 2001. Sequence variation and disease in the wake of the draft human genome. *Hum. Mol. Genet.* 10:2209–14

36. Gould SJ. 1994. Tempo and mode in the macroevolutionary reconstruction of Darwinism. *Proc. Natl. Acad. Sci. USA* 91:6764–71

37. Grishin NV. 2001. Fold change in the evolution of protein structure. *J. Struct. Biol.* 134:167–85

38. Hadley C, Jones DT. 1999. A systematic comparison of protein structure classifications: SCOP, CATH and FSSP. *Structure* 7:1099–112

39. Haft DH, Loftus BJ, Richardson DL, Yang F, Eisen JA, et al. 2001. TIGR-FAMs: a protein family resource for the functional identification of proteins. *Nucleic Acids Res.* 29:41–43

40. Hannenhalli SS, Russell RB. 2000. Analysis and prediction of protein functional sub-types from multiple sequence alignments. *J. Mol. Biol.* 303:61–76

41. Hofmann K. 2000. Sensitive protein comparisons with profiles and hidden Markov models. *Brief. Bioinform.* 1:167–78

42. Hofmann K, Bucher P, Falquet L, Bairoch A. 1999. The PROSITE database, its status in 1999. *Nucleic Acids Res.* 27:215–19

43. Holm L, Sander C. 1994. Structural similarity of plant chitinase and lysozymes from animals and phage: an evolutionary connection. *FEBS Lett.* 340:129–32

44. Holm L, Sander C. 1996. Mapping the protein universe. *Science* 273:595–603

45. Holm L, Sander C. 1997. Decision support system for the evolutionary classification of protein structures. *Proc. Int. Conf. Intell. Syst. Mol. Biol.* 5:140–46

46. Holm L, Sander C. 1997. Enzyme HIT. *Trends Biochem. Sci.* 22:116–17

47. Holm L, Sander C. 1998. Dictionary of recurrent domains in protein structures. *Proteins* 33:88–96

48. Islam SA, Luo J, Sternberg MJE. 1995. Identification and analysis of domains in proteins. *Protein Eng.* 8:513–25

49. Jacq B. 2001. Protein function from the perspective of molecular interactions and genetic networks. *Brief. Bioinform.* 2:38–50

50. Ji Y, Schroeder D, Byrne D, Zipser B, Jellies J, et al. 2001. Molecular identification and sequence analysis of Hillarin, a novel protein localized at the axon hillock. *Biochim. Biophys. Acta* 1519:246–49

51. Kartha G, Bello J, Harker D. 1967.

Tertiary structure of ribonuclease. *Nature* 213:862–65

52. Koonin EV. 2001. An apology for orthologs—or brave new memes. *Gen. Biol.* 2:COMMENT1005

53. Koretke KK, Lupas AN, Warren PV, Rosenberg M, Brown JR. 2000. Evolution of two-component signal transduction. *Mol. Biol. Evol.* 17:1956–70

54. Kraulis PJ. 1991. MOLSCRIPT: a program to produce both detailed and schematic plots of protein structures. *J. Appl. Crystallogr.* 24:946–50

55. Kurland CG. 2000. Something for everyone. Horizontal gene transfer in evolution. *EMBO Rep.* 1:92–95

56. Lander ES, Linton LM, Birren B, Nusbaum C, Zody MC, et al. 2001. Initial sequencing and analysis of the human genome. *Nature* 409:860–921. Errata. 2001. *Nature* 412:565–66

57. Landgraf R, Xenarios I, Eisenberg D. 2001. Three-dimensional cluster analysis identifies interfaces and functional residue clusters in proteins. *J. Mol. Biol.* 307:1487–502

58. Leonard CJ, Aravind L, Koonin EV. 1998. Novel families of putative protein kinases in bacteria and archaea: evolution of the "eukaryotic" protein kinase superfamily. *Genome Res.* 8:1038–47

59. Lichtarge O, Bourne HR, Cohen FA. 1996. An evolutionary trace method defines binding surfaces common to protein families. *J. Mol. Biol.* 257:342–58

60. Lo Conte L, Ailey B, Hubbard TJ, Brenner SE, Murzin AG, Chothia C. 2000. SCOP: a structural classification of proteins database. *Nucleic Acids Res.* 28:257–59

61. Lupas AN, Ponting CP, Russell RB. 2001. On the evolution of protein folds. Are similar motifs in different protein folds the result of convergence, insertion or relics of an ancient peptide world? *J. Struct. Biol.* 134:191–203

62. MacCallum RM, Kelley LA, Sternberg MJ. 2000. SAWTED: structure assignment with text description—enhanced detection of remote homologous with automated SWISS-PROT annotation comparison. *Bioinformatics* 16:125–29

63. Makarova KS, Grishin NV. 1999. Thermolysin and mitochondrial processing peptidase: how far structure-functional convergence goes. *Protein Sci.* 8:2537–40

64. Matsuo Y, Bryant SH. 1999. Identification of homologous core structures. *Proteins* 35:70–79

65. Murzin AG. 1992. Structural principles for the propeller assembly of β-sheets: the preference for seven-fold symmetry. *Proteins* 14:191–201

66. Murzin AG. 1993. Sweet-tasting protein monellin is related to the cystatin family of thiol proteinase inhibitors *J. Mol. Biol.* 230:689–94

67. Murzin AG. 1995. A ribosomal protein module in EF-G and DNA gyrase. *Nat. Struct. Biol.* 2:25–26

68. Murzin AG. 1998. Probable circular permutation in the flavin-binding domain. *Nat. Struct. Biol.* 5:101

69. Murzin AG, Brenner SE, Hubbard T, Chothia C. 1995. SCOP: a structural classification of proteins database for the investigation of sequences and structures. *J. Mol. Biol.* 247:536–40

70. Musacchio A, Gibson T, Rice P, Thompson J, Saraste M. 1993. The PH domain: a common piece in the structural patchwork of signalling proteins. *Trends Biochem. Sci.* 18:343–48

71. Nakai K. 2000. Protein sorting signals and prediction of subcellular localization. *Adv. Protein Chem.* 54:277–344

72. Ochman H, Lawrence JG, Groisman EA. 2000. Bacterial gene transfer and the nature of bacterial innovation. *Nature* 405:299–304

73. Ochman H, Moran NA. 2001. Genes lost and genes found: evolution of bacterial pathogenesis and symbiosis. *Science* 292:1096–98

74. Ohno S. 1999. Gene duplication and the

uniqueness of vertebrate genomes circa 1970–1999. *Semin. Cell Dev. Biol.* 10: 517–22

75. Orengo CA, Jones DT, Thornton JM. 1994. Protein superfamilies and domain superfolds. *Nature* 372:631–34

76. Orengo CA, Michie AD, Jones S, Jones DT, Swindells MB, Thornton JM. 1997. CATH—a hierarchic classification of protein domain structures. *Structure* 5:1093–108

77. Orgel LE, Crick FH. 1980. Selfish DNA: the ultimate parasite. *Nature* 284:604–7

78. Park J, Karplus K, Barrett C, Hughey R, Haussler D, et al. 1998. Sequence comparisons using multiple sequences detect three times as many remote homologues as pairwise methods. *J. Mol. Biol.* 284:1201–10

79. Patthy L. 1994. Exons and introns. *Curr. Opin. Struct. Biol.* 4:383–92

80. Patthy L. 1998. Genome evolution and the evolution of exon-shuffling—a review. *Gene* 238:103–14

81. Patthy L. 1999. *Protein Evolution.* Oxford: Blackwell Sci.

82. Ponting CP. 1997. Evidence for PDZ domains in bacteria, yeast, and plants. *Protein Sci.* 6:464–68

83. Ponting CP. 1999. Chlamydial homologues of the MACPF (MAC/perforin) domain. *Curr. Biol.* 9:R911–13

84. Ponting CP, Aravind L, Schultz J, Bork P, Koonin EV. 1999. Eukaryotic signalling domain homologues in archaea and bacteria. Ancient ancestry and horizontal gene transfer. *J. Mol. Biol.* 289:729–45

85. Ponting CP, Pallen MJ. 1999. β-propeller repeats and a PDZ domain in the tricorn protease: predicted self-compartmentalisation and C-terminal polypeptide-binding strategies of substrate selection. *FEMS Microbiol. Lett.* 179: 447–51

86. Ponting CP, Pallen MJ. 1999. A β-propeller within TolB. *Mol. Microbiol.* 31: 739–40

87. Ponting CP, Russell RB. 2000. Identifi-cation of distant homologues of fibroblast growth factors suggests a common ancestor for all β-trefoil proteins. *J. Mol. Biol.* 302:1041–47

88. Ponting CP, Schultz J, Copley RR, Andrade MA, Bork P. 2000. Evolution of domain families. *Adv. Protein Chem.* 54:185–244

89. Ray M-C, Germon P, Vianney A, Portalier R, Lazzaroni JC. 2000. Identification by genetic suppression of *Escherichia coli* TolB residues important for TolB-Pal interaction. *J. Bacteriol.* 182:821–24

90. Rossmann MG, Moras D, Olsen KW. 1974. Chemical and biological evolution of nucleotide-binding protein. *Nature* 250:194–99

91. Russell RB. 1994. Domain insertion. *Protein Eng.* 7:1407–10

92. Russell RB. 1998. Detection of protein three-dimensional side-chain patterns: new examples of convergent evolution. *J. Mol. Biol.* 279:1211–27

93. Russell RB, Ponting CP. 1998. Protein fold irregularities that hinder sequence analysis. *Curr. Opin. Struct. Biol.* 8:364–71

94. Russell RB, Saqi MA, Sayle RA, Bates PA, Sternberg MJ. 1997. Recognition of analogous and homologous protein folds: analysis of sequence and structure conservation *J. Mol. Biol.* 269:423–39

95. Russell RB, Saseini PD, Sternberg MJ. 1998. Supersites within superfolds: binding site similarity in the absence of homology. *J. Mol. Biol.* 282:903–18

96. Schäffer AA, Aravind L, Madden TL, Shavirin S, Spouge JL, et al. 2001. Improving the accuracy of PSI-BLAST protein database searches with composition-based statistics and other refinements. *Nucleic Acids Res.* 29:2994–3005

97. Schultz J, Milpetz F, Bork P, Ponting CP. 1998. SMART, a simple modular architecture research tool: identification of signaling domains. *Proc. Natl. Acad. Sci. USA* 95:5857–64

98. Shapiro L, Scherer PE. 1998. The crystal structure of a complement-1q family protein suggests an evolutionary link to tumor necrosis factor. *Curr. Biol.* 8:335–38

99. Sharp PA. 1985. On the origin of RNA splicing and introns. *Cell* 42:397–400

100. Shaw G. 1996. The pleckstrin homology domain: an intriguing multifunctional protein module. *Bioessays* 18:35–46

101. Siddiqui AS, Barton GJ. 1994. Continuous and discontinuous domains: an algorithm for the automatic generation of reliable protein domain definitions. *Protein Sci.* 4:872–84

102. Silverstein KA, Kilian A, Freeman JL, Johnson JE, Awad IA, Retzel EF. 2000. PANAL: an integrated resource for protein sequence ANALysis. *Bioinformatics* 16:1157–58

103. Simons KT, Ruczinski I, Kooperberg C, Fox BA, Bystroff C, Baker D. 1999. Improved recognition of native-like protein structures using a combination of sequence-dependent and sequence-independent features of proteins. *Proteins* 34:82–95

104. Sowdhamini R, Blundell TL. 1995. An automatic method involving cluster analysis of secondary structures for the identification of domains in proteins. *Protein Sci.* 4:506–20

105. Sreekumar KR, Aravind L, Koonin EV. 2001. Computational analysis of human disease-associated genes and their protein products. *Curr. Opin. Genet. Dev.* 11:247–57

106. Stanhope MJ, Lupas A, Italia MJ, Koretke KK, Volker C, Brown JR. 2001. Phylogenetic analyses do not support horizontal gene transfers from bacteria to vertebrates. *Nature* 411:940–44

107. Stoltzfus A, Spencer DF, Zuker M, Logsdon JM, Doolittle WF. 1994. Testing the exon theory of genes: the evidence from protein structure. *Science* 265:202–7

108. Strickland HE, Philipps J, Richardson J, Owen R, Jenyns L, et al. 1843. Report of a committee appointed "to consider the rules by which the Nomenclature of Zoology may be established on a uniform and permanent basis." *Br. Assoc. Adv. Sci. Rep. 12th Meet.* pp. 105–21

109. Stuart DI, Levine M, Muirhead H, Stammers DK. 1979. Crystal structure of cat muscle pyruvate kinase at a resolution of 2.6 Å. *J. Mol. Biol.* 134:109–42

110. Swindells MB. 1995. A procedure for detecting structural domains in proteins. *Protein Sci.* 4:103–12

111. Thomas RH, Schaffner W, Wilson AC, Paabo S. 1989. DNA phylogeny of the extinct marsupial wolf. *Nature* 340:465–67

112. Todd AE, Orengo CA, Thornton JM. 2001. Evolution of function in protein superfamilies, from a structural perspective. *J. Mol. Biol.* 307:1113–43

113. Traut TW. 1988. Do exons code for structural or functional units in proteins? *Proc. Natl. Acad. Sci. USA* 85:2944–48

114. van Raaij MJ, Mitraki A, Lavigne G, Cusack S. 1999. A triple β-spiral in the adenovirus fibre shaft reveals a new structural motif for a fibrous protein. *Nature* 401:935–38

115. Venter JC, Adams MD, Myers EW, Li PW, Mural RJ, et al. 2001. The sequence of the human genome. *Science* 291:1304–51

116. von Dohlen CD, Kohler S, Alsop ST, McManus WR. 2001. Mealybug beta-proteobacterial endosymbionts contain gamma-proteobacterial symbionts. *Nature* 412:433–36

117. Wallace AC, Borkakoti N, Thornton JM. 1997. TESS: a geometric hashing algorithm for deriving 3D coordinate templates for searching structural databases. Application to enzyme active sites. *Protein Sci.* 6:2308–23

118. Weber CH, Vincenz C. 2001. The death domain superfamily: a tale of two interfaces? *Trends Biochem. Sci.* 26:475–81

119. Wolf YI, Brenner SE, Bash PA, Koonin EV. 1999. Distribution of protein folds in the three superkingdoms of life. *Genome Res.* 9:17–26

120. Wu G, Fiser A, ter Kuile B, Sali A, Muller M. 1999. Convergent evolution of *Trichomonas vaginalis* lactate dehydrogenase from malate dehydrogenase. *Proc. Natl. Acad. Sci. USA* 96:6285–90

Annu. Rev. Biophys. Biomol. Struct. 2002. 31:73–95
DOI: 10.1146/annurev.biophys.31.082901.134233
Copyright © 2002 by Annual Reviews. All rights reserved

MAGNETIC RESONANCE STUDIES OF THE BACTERIORHODOPSIN PUMP CYCLE

Judith Herzfeld[1] and Jonathan C. Lansing[2]

[1]*Department of Chemistry and Keck Institute for Cellular Visualization, Brandeis University, Waltham, Massachusetts 02454-9110; e-mail: herzfeld@brandeis.edu*
[2]*Department of Chemistry and Center for Magnetic Resonance, Francis Bitter Magnet Laboratory, Massachusetts Institute of Technology, Cambridge, Massachusetts 02139; e-mail: lansing@ccnmr.mit.edu*

Key Words   photocycle, proton transport, anion pump, hydroxide pump, connectivity switch, torsion

■ **Abstract**   Active transport requires the alternation of substrate uptake and release with a switch in the access of the substrate binding site to the two sides of the membrane. Both the transfer and switch aspects of the photocycle have been subjects of magnetic resonance studies in bacteriorhodopsin. The results for ion transfer indicate that the Schiff base of the chromophore is hydrogen bonded before, during, and after its deprotonation. This suggests that the initial complex counterion of the Schiff base decomposes in such a way that the Schiff base carries its immediate hydrogen-bonding partner with it as it rotates during the first half of the photocycle. If so, bacteriorhodopsin acts as an inward-directed hydroxide pump rather than as an outward-directed proton pump. The studies of the access switch explore both protein-based and chromophore-based mechanisms. Combined with evidence from functional studies of mutants and other forms of spectroscopy, the results suggest that maintaining access to the extracellular side of the protein after photoisomerization involves twisting of the chromophore and that the decisive switch in access to the cytoplasmic side results from relaxation of the chromophore when the constraints on the Schiff base are released by decomposition of the complex counterion.

CONTENTS

1056-8700/02/0609-0073$14.00

73

RETINAL PIGMENTS

Owing largely to its relatively ready availability, bacteriorhodopsin (bR) is an exceptionally thoroughly studied molecule, often serving as a prototype for integral membrane proteins. More specifically, however, bR is a member of a large family of retinal pigments (i.e., rhodopsins) once thought to occur only in mammalian visual systems but now found in many microorganisms, including archae, eubacteria and eukaryotes (68). Most retinal pigments serve as signal transducers, including sensors for phototaxis in microorganisms and sensors for vision in higher organisms. These receptors are light-driven analogs of the chemical receptors more commonly found in cells. Other retinal pigments, such as bR, are energy transducers, with photocycles that result in ion transport. These ion pumps are light-driven analogs of the chemically driven ion pumps found more widely in biology.

Structurally, the rhodopsins have in common a relatively simple structure comprising a single polypeptide chain folded to form a bundle of seven transmembrane helices that encapsulates the retinylidene chromophore formed by a Schiff base (SB) between retinal and a buried lysine residue (Figure 1, see color insert). That this motif should serve for both sensors and pumps is intriguing given the differing requirements for the two functions. On the one hand, a sensor needs a change in protein conformation that transforms the cytoplasmic (CP) surface into an active site for interactions with elements of the intracellular signaling cascade. Furthermore, this change must last long enough for the interactions with intracellular proteins to be effective. However, the activation need not involve a change in ionization state of the protein. On the other hand, an ion pump requires a change in ion binding that is coordinated with a change in the connectivity of transport pathways directed to opposite sides of the membrane. In this case, the changes need to be short-lived to allow efficient cycling, but the changes need not alter the structure of the CP surface of the protein.

The rhodopsin structural motif has several compelling features that suit both sensors and pumps. First, the 7-helix bundle is both stable and versatile, with the functionalities of many different amino acid side chains converging in the central channel. Second, photoisomerization of the elongated retinylidene chromophore generates a substantial shape change (Figure 2), which is expected to cause significant steric conflict in the active site and alter interactions at the SB. At the same time, the wavelength of the highly conjugated chromophore is tunable over

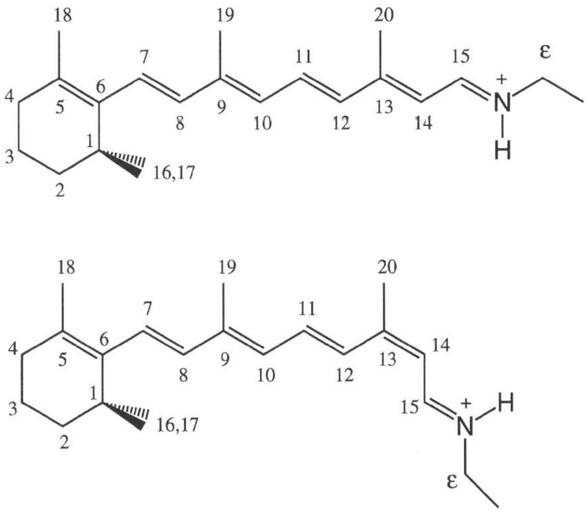

Figure 2 The all-*trans* (*top*) and 13-*cis* (*bottom*) forms of the retinylidene chromophore of bacteriorhodopsin. A photo-induced transition from the former to the latter initiates the pump cycle.

a wide range by interactions with the surroundings, especially when the SB is protonated. Not only does this allow for color vision in complex organisms, but in microorganisms it allows pumps to take advantage of suitable spectral niches and sensors to provide both photophobic and photophilic functions (for damaging short wavelengths and beneficial long wavelengths, respectively). The retinylidene chromophore even provides for the contrasting recovery dynamics of sensors and pumps, depending on the protonation state of the SB. Thermal reisomerization is slow when the SB is unprotonated (and bond alternation in the polyene is strong) and relatively fast when the SB is protonated (and bond alternation is weak, with the positive charge delocalized from the SB to odd-numbered carbons). Therefore, we expect (and find) the SB to be deprotonated only briefly, if at all, in the ion pumps, even though changes in ion binding are critical for pumping. Reciprocally, we expect (and find) the SB to be deprotonated for an extended period in the sensors, although the change in ionization state is otherwise unnecessary for interactions with the intracellular signaling machinery.

MAGNETIC RESONANCE APPROACHES

Several recent reviews have surveyed the application of nuclear magnetic resonance (NMR) spectroscopy to various aspects of bR (16, 30, 31, 65). Here we focus on studies of the proton-motive photocycle of bR by various forms of magnetic resonance (MR) spectroscopy. Because the most routine MR techniques are not applicable to membrane proteins or suitable for observing intermediate species, we need to consider the various ways in which the anisotropic and transient nature of the system have been addressed in MR experiments.

Anisotropy

In MR spectroscopy, the effective magnetic field experienced by an electronic or nuclear spin depends on the orientation of the molecule in the applied magnetic field. Most generally, this is due to the fact that the electron currents induced by the applied field depend on the orientations of the occupied and unoccupied orbitals relative to the applied field. The resulting variation of the directions and magnitudes of the current-induced magnetic fields with molecular orientation is expressed by the chemical-shielding tensor in NMR and the g-tensor in electron spin resonance (ESR). Additional contributions to the orientation dependence of the effective magnetic field come from any nearby spins in the sample. This is because the strength of the spin-spin interaction varies with the angle between the dipole-dipole vector and the direction of the applied field.

For molecules that tumble freely and rapidly on the timescale of spin transitions, the effective field is the isotropic average of the fields for different orientations, and the spectra show narrow resonance peaks. However, membrane proteins have little motional freedom, and molecules with different orientations contribute to spectra at different frequencies. This orientation dependence carries valuable information. However, unless the molecules in the sample are well aligned, they will produce broad signals that reduce both signal-to-noise and resolution.

Different MR strategies approach these considerations in different ways. The most straightforward is ESR. Here, signal-to-noise is less of an issue than it is in NMR because the relatively high energy of electron spin transitions involves a more favorable Boltzmann distribution. Resolution is also less of an issue because the number of spins is controlled by specific labeling. A powerful technique for site-specific placement of spin labels makes use of mutant proteins with just one or two cysteine residues to which spin labels can be covalently attached. Single spins are introduced to assess dynamics (according to the degree that it narrows the signal) and solvent exposure (according to the degree that magnetic agents in the solvent relax the protein label), whereas pairs of spins are introduced to measure distances (according to the strength of dipole-dipole interactions). (For recent reviews of ESR techniques suitable for studies of membrane proteins see 5, 40, 41.)

For NMR, both signal-to-noise and resolution are serious issues and three types of approaches have been taken. One is to facilitate the rotational diffusion of the protein by solubilization in micelles. This creates conditions suitable for solution NMR techniques. Due to the power of these techniques, considerable effort has been given to finding the best conditions for solubilizing membrane proteins. This approach has been used in several studies of bR (13, 57), yielding information from chemical shifts and nuclear Overhauser effects. Unfortunately, the functionality of these preparations is unclear and extension to photocycle intermediates has proven difficult.

The alternative to solution NMR is solid-state NMR (SSNMR), where only rare spins (e.g., ^{13}C, ^{15}N, ^{2}H) are monitored because the anisotropic interactions between the abundant ^{1}Hs are too strong in the absence of rapid rotational diffusion. SSNMR takes different forms depending on how the signal-to-noise and resolution problems are addressed. As suggested above, one approach is to align the molecules. This can be partially achieved by layering the membranes on glass or mica sheets. When the membrane normal is parallel to the applied field, the same local fields will occur in each molecule, and the spectrum will show narrow resonances at the corresponding frequencies. Because these frequencies are not the isotropic values, assignment can be relatively challenging. However, once assignment is complete, the frequencies provide direct information on the orientation of each functional group relative to the normal axis of the membrane (10, 56). Furthermore, supplementary orientational information can be obtained by tilting the membrane normal away from the field (54).

A more common method for improving signal-to-noise and resolution in SSNMR is magic angle spinning (MAS). It is a property of second-rank tensors (such as those that describe the orientation dependence of dipole-dipole interactions and chemical shielding) that rotation about an axis at an angle $\cos^{-1}(1/\sqrt{3})$ relative to the field averages them to their isotropic values (i.e., $1/3$ of their trace). Thus, at sufficiently high MAS frequencies, SSNMR spectra are similar to those obtained in solution. At lower MAS speeds, the resolution remains high, but the isotropic signal is flanked by extra signals spaced at multiples of the spinning frequency. The intensities of these "spinning sidebands" carry valuable information about the anisotropy of the environment. However, signal-to-noise is best if the MAS frequency is fast enough to collect the entire signal in the isotropic center band.

Whether samples are aligned or spun [or even both (22)], signal-to-noise in SSNMR is further enhanced by cross-polarization from protons, which have relatively strong polarization and rapid relaxation due to their high gyromagnetic ratio and high natural abundance. In both solution and SSNMR, signal-to-noise is also enhanced by isotopic labeling [with difference spectroscopy as needed to remove natural abundance signals (11)]. For bR, the protein is generally labeled biosynthetically, with specificity and incorporation rates varying from one amino acid to another. On the other hand, the retinal is generally labeled by bleaching and regenerating with a synthetic isotopomer (47).

In both solution and SSNMR, resolution of individual sites requires selective labeling and/or pulse sequences that edit spectra and distribute signals in multiple dimensions according to spin interactions [for a recent review see (15)]. Pulse sequences for solution and solid-state experiments differ because different motions (tumbling in solution versus MAS in the solid state) cause interactions to be averaged differently. In solution, only those interactions that survive rapid isotropic rotation can be used. In MAS, rotor-synchronized pulse sequences are designed to selectively undo the averaging effects of spinning. This reinstates dipolar interactions and allows them to be used to measure internuclear distances and dihedral angles.

Transience

To study functional intermediates, one can either observe them on the fly or trap them. The former requires synchronizing the molecules in coordination with time-resolved spectroscopic measurements. The necessary time resolution depends on the intermediate of interest, and some latitude in timescales can be obtained by adjusting the temperature to control the reaction rate. So far, time-resolved MR studies have only been carried out for the M state of bR using ESR. For the M state, 10^{-4} s time resolution suffices, and for ESR, relatively small sample requirements allow rapid activation of all the molecules at moderate laser strengths. Because NMR requires much larger, optically dense samples, time-resolved studies have not yet been an option, and all NMR studies of bR photocycle intermediates have required trapping.

Trapping photocycle intermediates depends on manipulating the rates of the steps in the photocycle by adjusting the temperature and other conditions. Specific considerations for different intermediates have recently been reviewed (1). As a sample is irradiated, molecules accumulate in the first state that has forward and backward activation barriers that are difficult to surmount at the ambient temperature. Thus, different states accumulate at different temperatures, and the relationships between the various states can be ascertained by examining the relaxation products that result from brief warming in the dark. Alkaline conditions are also useful for trapping photocycle intermediates. bR pumps over a wide range of pHs, and the rates of steps that involve proton binding are reduced at high pH. In addition, guanidinium (free or in arginine) is useful for manipulating photocycle dynamics because it inhibits proton uptake without denaturing the protein (probably by binding to surface acid groups). Some trapping procedures make use of mutants in which at least one of the steps in the photocycle has been inhibited. The problem is that mutations may have secondary effects that are poorly characterized. Regardless of the conditions used to accumulate intermediates, the species can then be preserved in the dark for the duration of the MR experiment by operating at a sufficiently low temperature.

ION-MOTIVE PHOTOCYCLES

Not all photocycle intermediates are of equal interest. To understand how a pump works, we want to focus on the features of its cycle that correspond to the requirements for active transport. At the most abstract level, all that a pump requires is substrate uptake on one side of the membrane and release on the other side. Thus, a change in connectivity between the two sides of the membrane must be coordinated with a change in substrate binding affinity, and these two changes are the essential elements of the pump that we want to understand. If the connectivity and affinity changes occur together, then the duty cycle can be reduced to four steps, as illustrated in Figure 3. The cycle can start in any of the four states and proceed clockwise for an inward pump or counter-clockwise for an outward pump.

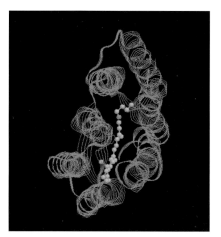 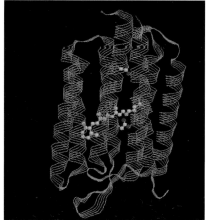

Figure 1 Overall view of bacteriorhodopsin from the extracellular end (*left*) and in the membrane plane with the cytoplasmic surface at the top (*right*) [based on Protein Data Bank entry 1c3w (46)]. Shown are the fold of the backbone, the retinylidene chromophore formed by a Schiff base between retinal and K216, and (in the side view only) D85 (on the extracellular side of the Schiff base), which becomes protonated with the Schiff base deprotonates, and D212 (on the cytoplasmic side of the Schiff base), which becomes deprotonated when the Schiff base reprotonates.

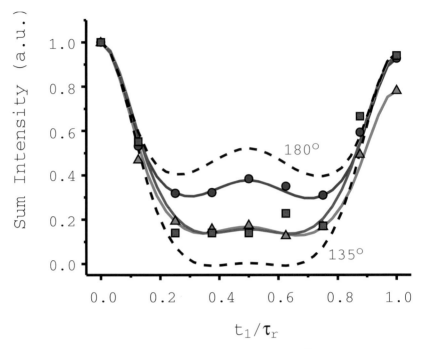

Figure 8 HCCH dihedral angle measurement in [14,15-^{13}C] retinal-labeled bR. Modulation of the double-quantum filtered intensity is plotted against the fraction of the rotor cycle with dipolar evolution and the data (*symbols*) are compared with simulations (*lines*) for bR$_{568}$ (*blue circles*), early M (*red squares*), and late M (*green triangles*). For details, see (44).

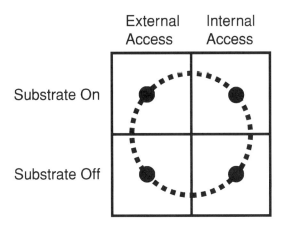

Figure 3   A generic pump cycle in which substrate is taken up on one side of the membrane and is released on the other side (see text).

Using the same framework as in Figure 3, Figure 4 shows the intermediates in the bR photocycle that have been distinguished by time-resolved UV-vis spectroscopy. The numerous changes in the optical spectrum show the sensitivity of the electronic structure of the chromophore to changes in the surrounding protein. Notice that, as required, a change in connectivity (horizontal arrows) occurs once when the SB is protonated and once when it is deprotonated. Thus, the SB deprotonates (in L $\rightarrow$ M) to the extracellular (EC) side of the membrane [as inferred from Fourier transform infrared (FTIR) observations of concomitant protonation of D85] and reprotonates (in M $\rightarrow$ N) from the CP side of the membrane (as indicated by FTIR observations of coincident deprotonation of D96). However, both the photoisomerization and the thermal reisomerization of the chromophore occur when the retinylidene is protonated, allowing the pump to use long wavelengths on the one hand and recover rapidly on the other. To achieve this, the connectivity of the SB does not change after photoisomerization until deprotonation has occurred. Elucidation of the pump mechanism therefore particularly demands an understanding of the fact that the SB remains connected to the EC side of the membrane during the first half of the photocycle (in spite of the photo-induced isomerization of the chromophore from all-*trans* to 13-*cis*) and yet switches its connectivity to the intracellular side promptly after the SB deprotonates (i.e., before it reprotonates).

ION TRANSFER

The vertical dimension in Figure 4 corresponds to ion transfer. Although extended hydrogen-bonded chains have long been postulated as proton wires for conducting protons across bR, NMR studies indicate specifically that water plays an important local role in the distribution and transfer of charge.

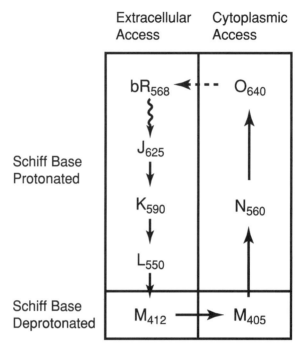

Figure 4 The bacteriorhodopsin pump cycle in which both photoisomerization (*wavy arrow*) and thermal reisomerization (*dotted arrow*) occur while the Schiff base is protonated and the change in Schiff base connectivity that follows photoisomerization is delayed until the Schiff base has deprotonated. For each state, the subscript indicates the wavelength of maximum visible absorbance in nm. The wavelengths for the successive M states are adopted from (59).

bR_{568}: The Initial, Protonated All-*trans* State

In the dark, a thermal equilibrium exists between two states of bR, bR_{555} and bR_{568} (where each subscript indicates the wavelength of maximum visible absorbance). Only the bR_{568} photocycle pumps protons. On the other hand, the bR_{555} photocycle branches into the bR_{568} cycle. Therefore, bR_{555} disappears on light exposure, and a pure sample of the active bR_{568} state can be prepared by light adaptation.

Early extraction studies showed that the retinal in dark-adapted bR was a mixture of 13-*cis* and all-*trans* but could provide no information about the $C_{15} = N$ SB linkage, which is broken during extraction, or single-bond conformations, which are labile upon extraction. Through γ-effects (due to steric interactions between protons on atoms three bonds apart) on the chemical shifts, ^{13}C SSNMR confirmed and extended the characterization of the retinylidene in dark-adapted bR, showing that in both cases the ionone ring is coplanar with the polyene chain (i.e., the 6-*s* bond is *trans*) and that bR_{555} is 13,15-di*cis*, whereas bR_{568}

is all-*trans* (28, 29). Thus thermal isomerization is a "bicycle pedal" process, involving both the $C_{13}=C_{14}$ and $C_{15}=N$ bonds, such that the chromophore maintains an essentially straight shape that is presumably compatible with the shape of the binding pocket. Subsequent SSNMR studies of methyl group dynamics on the ring and internuclear distance measurements along the polyene backbone have confirmed the above interpretations of the observed chemical shifts (8, 9).

An exceptionally useful probe of the active site is the ^{15}N signal of the SB observed in $[\zeta^{-15}N]$lys-labeled samples (see Figure 5). In various retinylidenes, the chemical shift of the SB nitrogen covers a range of almost 190 ppm. In bR_{568}, ^{15}N NMR reveals two remarkable things about the buried SB. One is that it exchanges protons with bulk water in less than 0.5 ms, which suggests that a hydrogen-bonding network extends from the SB to the surface of the membrane (27). The other is that the SB is more strongly shielded than in any model compound that has been studied. Since the degree of shielding was found to correlate with the degree of charge delocalization on the SB counterion, it was concluded that the SB counterion in bR is extraordinarily delocalized (12). In order to explain how such extreme delocalization can occur in a protein, it was proposed that the SB counterion comprised a hydrogen-bonded complex of polar residues with water (Figure 6, *left*). Here, the direct interaction of the SB is with a water molecule rather than with a carboxyl group, and a cluster of two acidic residues and one basic residue gives the complex counterion an overall negative charge. These predictions were subsequently borne out by diffraction results (Figure 6, *right*). The crystal structure also shows a hydrogen-bonding network that extends to the CP surface of the protein. This is presumably responsible for the rapid exchange of the SB proton with bulk water.

The complex counterion has been further studied by ^{13}C NMR in $[4-^{13}C]$asp-labeled samples (18, 25, 52, 53), and the signals of the critical aspartic acid residues were assigned by examination of mutants (19). The surface aspartic acid residues, which are presumably fully deprotonated, appear well downfield (177.0 ppm). On the other hand, the buried and protonated D115 appears well upfield (170.3 ppm). The other buried aspartic acids have intermediate shifts (D212 at 176.0 ppm, D85 at 174.0 ppm, and D96 at 171.3 ppm), which suggest that they are sharing proton density with neighbors in varying degrees. This is consistent with hydrogen-bonding possibilities found in diffraction studies. In particular, the relative chemical shifts of the two aspartic acids of the complex counterion suggest that D85 carries more proton density than D212 already in the resting state of the protein. This is consistent with high-resolution diffraction, which shows D85 more strongly hydrogen bonded to the interior water molecules than D212 (46).

Delocalization of negative charge in the counterion is essential for the stable protonation of the SB in the resting state of the pump. First, the delocalization of negative charge makes the hydrogen-bonded complex a stronger acid than a simple aliphatic acid. Second, by weakening the electrostatic interaction with the SB, the delocalization of negative charge in the counterion also promotes delocalization

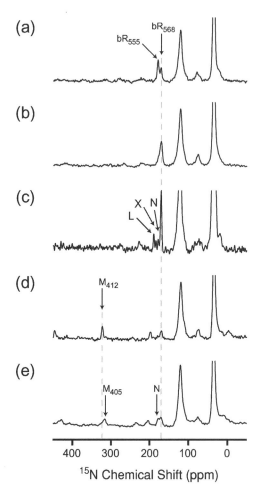

Figure 5   ^{15}N NMR spectra of [ζ-^{15}N]lysine-labeled bacteriorhodopsin in (*a*) the dark-adapted mixture (bR_{555} and bR_{568}); (*b*) the light-adapted state (bR_{568}); (*c*) a mixture containing the L_{550} state and a two-photon product X; (*d*) the early M (M_{412}) state; and (*e*) a mixture of the late M (M_{405}) and N_{560} states. In each case, the sharp upfield signal is from the six free lysine residues; the broad signal at ~120 ppm is from natural abundance and scrambled ^{15}N in the peptide backbone; and the other signals are isotropic (*labeled*) and sideband (*unlabeled*) signals of the Schiff base. [For details see (26, 36, 39).]

of positive charge along the retinylidene backbone, making the chromophore a stronger base than it otherwise would be. In the absence of halogenated or aromatic acid functionalities, delocalization of both positive and negative charge is achieved in bR through the use of a complex, hydrogen-bonded SB counterion in which geometry (6, 63) and water (3) play critical roles.

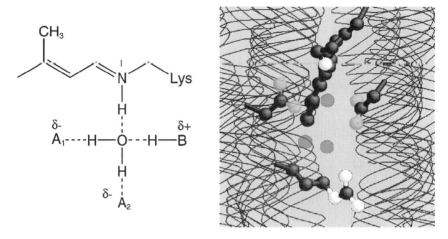

Figure 6 Counterion charge delocalization. *Left*: One configuration of a hydrogen-bonded counterion complex (including two acidic residues, A_1 and A_2, and one basic residue, B) proposed in 1990 to explain the chemical shift of Schiff base nitrogen in bacteriorhodopsin (12). *Right*: The counterion complex found subsequently by X-ray crystallography with waters in *dark gray*, the Schiff base at the *top*, R82 at the *bottom*, D85 to the *left*, and D212 to the *right* [based on Protein Data Bank entry 1c3w (46)].

L_{550}: The Predischarge State

The L state is the last photocycle intermediate before the SB is deprotonated. Accumulating the L intermediate is difficult in optically dense samples because its spectrum overlaps so much with the bR_{568} spectrum. However, signals of L can be distinguished from those of extraneous photoproducts according to the way the intensity of the signal varies with the wavelength of irradiation.

So far, the L state has only been studied in [ζ-^{15}N]lys-labeled bR (39). The surprise is that the ^{15}N signal of the SB is well downfield from that of bR_{568} (see Figure 5*c*) This reduced shielding indicates that, following the photo-induced bending of the chromophore (by *trans-cis* isomerization of the 13=14 bond), the SB has a much stronger interaction with its counterion. On the scale of the halide model compounds (34), the interaction has gone from a distant, iodide-like one in bR_{568} to a proximate, chloride-like one in L. Thus the negative charge on the counterion in L is apparently no longer as delocalized as in bR_{568} and is centered ~3.5 Å from the SB nitrogen instead of ~3.9 Å away. Only two possible scenarios seem consistent with this change. In one, the distance between the SB and the car-boxyl group of either D85 or D212 is reduced, presumably with displacement of the intervening water. The trouble with this scenario is that diffraction studies show that isomerization of the chromophore moves the SB a little farther from the car-boxylic acids rather than closer. The alternative is that water remains associated with the SB but that it has lost some proton density to hydrogen-bonding part-ners and gained some hydroxide character. In this scenario, decomposition of the original complex counterion involves the breakdown of the water molecule closest to the SB rather than its displacement.

M_{412}: The Early Deprotonated State

The ^{15}N NMR spectrum of $[\zeta\text{-}^{15}N]$lys-labeled bR trapped in the early M state is shown in Figure 5d. When the SB deprotonates, the ^{15}N signal moves far downfield. In addition, a large increase in the chemical-shielding anisotropy causes significant loss of centerband intensity at ordinary MAS frequencies. The notable feature of the early M spectrum is that the SB signal [at 323.3 ppm (36)] is not nearly as far downfield as that of retinylidene butylimine [at 342.2 ppm (26)]. This suggests the presence of a hydrogen bond donor at the SB. The most likely hydrogen-bonding partner is water because alternative hydrogen bond donors from the protein do not seem to be well-situated in the diffraction structures. On the other hand, given the water present in the original structure, it seems plausible that at least one molecule remains associated with the SB. Hydrogen bonding of the SB to water in the M state has previously been argued on the basis of the red shift of the UV-vis spectrum relative to model compounds (21). This view is consistent with the ^{15}N chemical shift, which probes the interactions of the SB more specifically. Association of water with the SB as it moves away from the counterion is also consistent with ^{13}C NMR spectra of $[4\text{-}^{13}C]$asp-labeled bR, which indicate that D212 is less well hydrogen bonded in the early M state than in bR$_{568}$ (25), and with FTIR analysis, which suggests that D85 loses an important hydrogen-bonding partner in the M state (14, 42).

M_{405}: The Late Deprotonated State

The ^{15}N NMR spectrum of a $[\zeta\text{-}^{15}N]$lys-labeled mixture of the late M state and the N state is shown in Figure 5e. In the late M state, the ^{15}N signal of the SB [at 315.7 ppm (36)] is still farther upfield from retinylidene butylimine than in early M. Thus the interaction of the SB with a hydrogen bond donor has become stronger, consistent with preparation for reprotonation. A plausible scenario is that water associated with the SB in early M stays with the SB during the lifetime of M and becomes more closely associated with the SB by late M. Perhaps the water becomes a stronger hydrogen bond donor for the SB in late M because it falls into position to acquire additional hydrogen bonds with other partners. Theoretical calculations have found thermodynamically favorable sites for water molecules on the CP side of the chromophore even in the resting state of the protein (55, 64).

N_{560}: The Protonated 13-*cis* State

In the N state, the SB is reprotonated and the nitrogen is once again well shielded, with a ^{15}N resonance between that for bR$_{568}$ and L (43) that corresponds to interaction with a bromide-like counterion (i.e., centered ~3.7 Å from the SB nitrogen). The candidates for this counterion are few. By this point in the photocycle the SB must be oriented toward the CP side of the membrane where the protein offers no nearby anionic groups. However, if water is associated with the SB in late M, it is likely to be the immediate source of the proton that transfers to the SB. Although a shift in proton density from a lone water molecule would leave a bare hydroxide ion, a shift in proton density from an otherwise hydrogen-bonded water molecule would produce a somewhat delocalized counterion consistent with the bromide-like ^{15}N signal of the SB. Such delocalization would also stabilize the proton transfer to the SB.

CONNECTIVITY SWITCH

The horizontal dimension in Figure 4 corresponds to the change in SB connectivity. The switch at the end of the bR photocycle can be easily explained by the thermal reisomerization of the chromophore from 13-*cis* to all-*trans*. This rotates the SB proton from an orientation toward the CP side to an orientation toward the EC side (see Figure 2). However, the change in SB connectivity in the middle of the bR photocycle is more mysterious, delayed as it is from the photoisomerization of the chromophore from all-*trans* to 13-*cis*. Proposals for the control of SB connectivity in the middle of the bR photocycle have distinguished between a chromophore-based mechanism and a protein-based mechanism. In the former, a conformational change in the chromophore (distinct from the earlier photoisomerization but a delayed consequence of it) causes the SB to move relative to functional groups in the protein (66). In the latter, a protein conformational change (also a delayed consequence of the photoisomerization of the chromophore) rearranges critical functional groups around the SB (49). Both of these possibilities have received attention in MR studies. In order to characterize the molecular details of the switch, we need to compare states before and after. Thus we could compare a sufficiently early M state (having just lost a proton to the EC side) with a sufficiently late M state (poised to accept a proton from the CP side). Alternatively, one step further removed, we could compare the L state (poised to release a proton to the EC side) with the N state (having just gained a proton from the CP side).

A Protein-Based Switch?

The earliest evidence for protein conformational change during the bR photocycle came from the amide bands in FTIR spectra, and the most prominent changes have been characterized by diffraction. These include ordering of the G helix, tilt of the CP part of the F helix, and minor changes close to the B and C helices. The major result is an opening of the CP end of the channel that is thought to be essential for efficient reprotonation of the SB (for recent reviews see 45, 71).

To these studies, time-resolved ESR has contributed spatial and temporal specificity. In one approach, single-spin labels were introduced at sites of interest and changes in their signals were monitored over time (61, 69). By this means, it was possible to distinguish between sites that change during the lifetime of the M state and those that change during the M → N transition. Spin labels have also been introduced pairwise into bR on different surface loops. This has allowed the monitoring of distance changes to show that the outward tilt of the F helix occurs during the late M intermediate (60) and a rotation of the F helix occurs in the M→N transition (75).

NMR has the ability to study changes in the peptide backbone of bR without perturbing sensitive regions by mutation or introduction of a spin label. Because the X-pro peptide bonds isomerize relatively readily, they were considered likely sites for conformational change. However, ^{13}C NMR studies indicated that all the X-pro bonds are *trans* in the resting state [whether in micelles (13) or in the native membrane (17)], and ^{15}N and ^{13}C NMR spectra have shown that the X-pro bonds are not much perturbed in the early and late M states (33; J. C. Lansing, J. G. Hu, B. Q. Sun, M Belenky, R. G. Griffin & J. Herzfeld, manuscript in preparation).

In contrast, ^{13}C NMR of [1-^{13}C]val-labeled samples (Figure 7) shows significant perturbations of several of the 21 X-val peptide bonds. By the early M state, two

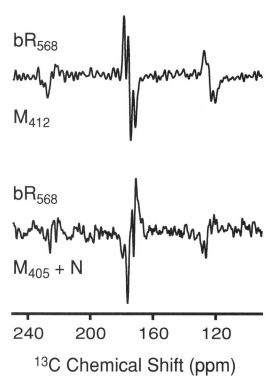

Figure 7 ^{13}C NMR difference spectra of [1-^{13}C]val-labeled bacteriorhodopsin in various states. *Top*: bR$_{568}$ − early M (M$_{412}$). *Bottom*: bR$_{568}$ − [mixture of late M (M$_{405}$) and N]. The strong isotropic signal is flanked on each side by a sidebands spaced at multiples of the MAS frequency. For details, see Reference 36.

valine signals have moved upfield, whereas in the late M state, these valines have relaxed and two other valines have moved downfield. This shows energy traveling around the peptide backbone during the photocycle. Specifically, it suggests that the hydrogen bonding of two valines is loosened in the early M state relative to bR_{568}, and while these hydrogen bonds recover by late M, the hydrogen bonding of two other valines has tightened (74). Because the valine residues are located disproportionately in the F and G helices, the changes in valine hydrogen bonding are likely to be related to the movements in these helices detected by diffraction and ESR. However, NMR shows that some backbone changes already occur before early M and that these relax while new perturbations develop in the transition to late M. In the transition from early to late M, all four changes correspond to tightening hydrogen bonds, although two are recovering from a previously loosened state.

For a protein conformational change to switch the connectivity of the SB, it needs to produce a rearrangement of residues in the vicinity of the SB. One suggestion for such a switch has been movement of the R82 side chain toward the EC surface following proton transfer from the SB to D85. Evidence for a dramatic change in one arginine side chain was found in ^{15}N NMR spectra of $[\eta^{15}N\text{-arg}]$-labeled bR in the M state versus bR_{568} (58). By the use of spin exchange, it was shown that the spectral change corresponds to movement of a single arginine residue to a highly asymmetric hydrogen-bonding environment. The change was tentatively assigned to R82 because it is also seen in the D85N mutant at rest whether the SB is protonated or not. In the meantime, diffraction studies have also shown that R82 moves to an asymmetric environment in the M state. The problem is that the NMR shows that movement of R82 has occurred already in early M and remains unchanged in late M. That the switch mechanism does not depend on R82 is also indicated by the pump activity of the R82Q and R82A mutants (24, 70).

NMR has also been used to look for distance changes in the chromophore binding pocket during the photocycle. So far there is no evidence of significant protein rearrangement. In a homonuclear recoupling experiment using radio-frequency-driven recoupling (RFDR), it was determined that the distance between $14\text{-}^{13}C$ on the retinal and $4\text{-}^{13}C$ on D212 is 4.4 ± 0.6 Å in bR_{568} and 4.8 ± 1.0 Å in the early M state (25). And in a heteronuclear recoupling experiment using rotational echo double resonance (REDOR), it was determined that the distance between $20\text{-}^{13}C$ on the retinal and indole-^{15}N of W182 on the CP side of the chromophore is 3.36 ± 0.2 Å in bR_{568} and 3.16 ± 0.4 Å in the early M state (57a). In the same study, it was shown that the hydrogen bonds of several indoles are significantly perturbed during the photocycle, with some perturbations found in the early M state relaxing in the transition to the late M state while new perturbations arise. However, the hydrogen bonding of W182 is hardly affected in either early or late M, although crystal structures show W182 moving in the CP direction, presumably under the steric influence of the bending chromophore. Thus W182 seems to keep its hydrogen-bonding partner with it, suggesting that the partner is a mobile moiety.

A Chromophore-Based Switch?

In wild-type bR, the timing of the opening of the CP uptake channel seems suitable for constituting a connectivity switch. However, this is not the case in the D96G/F171C/F219L triple mutant in which the photocycle of the all-*trans* form pumps normally (73), even though the CP channel is already open in the resting state and diffraction finds no discernible change in protein conformation during the photocycle (72). Because a more local connectivity switch must be at work in this mutant, it is probably also used by the wild-type system. Thus we are compelled to take a detailed look at the chromophore. Changes in the chromophore have been followed three ways: (*a*) from the orientation of specific groups relative to the membrane normal, (*b*) from the orientations of specific groups relative to each other, and (*c*) from comparison of experimental probes that monitor different features of the chromophore. We consider each in turn.

A sensitive measure of the orientation of retinal relative to the membrane normal is obtained from ^{2}H NMR spectra of specifically deuterated methyl groups in oriented samples. Owing to rapid threefold hopping of the methyl group around its axis of symmetry, the residual ^{2}H quadrupole interaction is axially symmetric, and the observed quadrupole splitting simply reflects the angle between the C-CD$_3$ axis and the magnetic field. When the magnetic field and the membrane normal are made to coincide, the spectrum gives the orientation of the methyl group relative to the membrane normal. The sensitivity of the experiment is relatively good because three ^{2}H contribute to the signal for a given methyl group. The key to interpretation of the spectra is in an accurate treatment of the effect of mosaic spread on the line shape. The results of this approach have recently been thoroughly reviewed and are consistent with linear dichroism and diffraction assessments of chromophore orientation (31). With respect to the photocycle, the changes in the orientations of the various methyl groups in the transition from bR$_{568}$ to M (probably early M in wild-type samples and late M in D96A samples) indicate that the C$_5$–C$_{13}$ portion of the chromophore tilts farther out of the membrane plane by about $11°$. This is consistent with minimal movement of the ionone ring and SB, while 13-*cis* isomerization is primarily accommodated by movement of the C$_{13}$=C$_{14}$ bond toward the CP side of the membrane.

In the CD$_3$ experiments it is not possible to distinguish unambiguously between methyl group tilt due to tilt of the polyene chain as a whole and methyl group tilt due to twist within the polyene chain. Twist within the polyene chain is also difficult to discern in diffraction studies. However, because twist is one way for the SB to maintain interactions with the EC side of the membrane after 13-*cis* isomerization, it is important to measure dihedral angles along the chromophore backbone. SSNMR methods for such measurements have been based on the dependence of correlations between two nearby dipoles on the angle between them. The first dihedral angle measurement in bR has been for the C$_{14}$–C$_{15}$ bond (44). This bond was the focus of the original proposal for twist in the early photocycle intermediates

(66). The correlations observed between the ^{13}C-^1H dipolar interactions on the adjacent carbons (Figure 8, see color insert) indicate that the $HC_{14}C_{15}H$ dihedral angle is distorted $16 \pm 4°$ away from *trans* in bR_{568} and further distorted to $33 \pm 10°$ from *trans* in early M. However, the distortion is still $30 \pm 4°$ from *trans* in late M, confirming the view that twist about this bond is not responsible for the change in SB connectivity between early and late M. Measurements of other dihedral angles of the chromophore are in progress.

Distortion of the polyene chain in retinylidenes shifts the UV-vis spectrum in characteristic ways. Because the excited state has greater charge delocalization and less bond alternation than the ground state, twist around the nominal single bonds increases the energy gap between the ground and excited states (resulting in a blue shift), whereas twist around nominal double bonds decreases the energy gap (resulting in a red shift). However, the visible spectrum of retinylidenes is also strongly influenced by the interaction of the SB with its neighbors. Because the ^{15}N chemical shift provides a measure of the SB interactions, these can be factored into interpretations of the UV-vis absorbances. The striking finding is that if we take into account the strengths of the SB interactions indicated by their ^{15}N chemical shifts, both the L and early M states absorb at wavelengths much longer than expected for planar 13-*cis* retinylidenes. This suggests that there is double-bond twist in L (39) that persists in early M (29a). However, there is no longer any evidence of this twist in the late M or N states, which absorb close to the wavelengths expected for planar 13-*cis* retinylidenes with the SB interactions indicated by their ^{15}N chemical shifts. This evidence for twist in the early photocycle that disappears in the late photocycle is consistent with earlier FTIR results (reviewed in 48). However, the NMR analysis locates the twist particularly in double bonds and finds that its disappearance occurs during the period that the SB is deprotonated.

SUMMARY AND PROSPECTS

MR studies of bR have been targeted primarily at the changes that seem most significant for the mechanism of active transport. The results to date suggest some new ways of looking at the pump.

The Case for a Hydroxide Pump

The notion that bR may be an inward-directed hydroxide pump rather than an outward-directed proton pump has been advanced by analogy with halide transport in halorhodopsin and bR variants (4) and by consideration of changes in the locations and/or ordering of internal water molecules during the bR photocycle (45). However, the interactions of the SB are most sensitively probed by spectroscopy. A critical distinction is that the SB in halide pumps never deprotonates, whereas in bR it does. However, both ^{15}N NMR and UV-vis spectroscopy suggest that the deprotonated SB in bR interacts with a hydrogen bond donor in both the early and late M states. Furthermore, NMR indicates that the counterion of the protonated SB in the L and N states is a relatively strong proton acceptor. This suggests that (*a*) from the L through the N state, the SB carries a hydrogen-bonded oxygen with it, and (*b*) the shifts in proton density off the SB in L → M and back on in M → N are related, respectively, to the rupture of the original extended hydrogen-bonding network on the EC side of the protein and the establishment of another extended hydrogen-bonding network on the intracellular side of the protein. This scenario is consistent with the known importance of charge delocalization for stabilizing protonation of retinylidene compounds. It is also consistent with calculations that indicate the possibility of a chain of water molecules on the CP side of the chromophore as well as on the EC side (64).

The Case for a Torsion-Based Switch

The idea that chromophore distortions could be at the heart of the bR pump mechanism was proposed long ago by Schulten & Tavan (66). However, they focused on the nominal single bond closest to the SB, and subsequent resonance Raman and ^{13}C SSNMR results found that twist around this particular bond cannot be responsible for the connectivity switch (44, 50, 51). In the meantime, it has become better appreciated that bond alternation is weak in protonated retinylidenes and the possibility of twist around nominal double bonds should be taken into consideration. Analysis of UV-vis data in the light of ^{15}N SSNMR data suggests that such twist occurs in the L and early M states and has dissipated by the late M and N states. Thus the chromophore seems to unwind during the lifetime of M, coincident with the switch in connectivity of the SB from the EC side of the membrane to the CP side.

The question then is what maintains the torsion through the first half of the photocycle and releases it when the SB is deprotonated. There would seem to be two ways to look at the interactions involved. Electrostatically, the protonated SB is attracted to its counterion, and this force may cause the chromophore to be twisted until the electrostatic charges are neutralized by proton transfer. We have previously called this an "electrostatic steering" mechanism (30). On the other hand, it is important that the mechanism not be construed in terms of simple point charges. The counterion is diffuse with a shifting center. Thus it may be more suitable to recognize the SB as part of a large web of hydrogen bonds from which it cannot break free until the protons in the network are suitably redistributed. Either way, the interactions of the SB result in torsion, and the release of torsion occurs at just the right time to prevent ion backflow.

Torsion provides a robust switch mechanism that is consistent with a wide variety of data. Over the years, studies of bR mutants and analogues have shown that proton pumping occurs even when (*a*) the chromophore is not covalently linked to the peptide backbone (20, 67), (*b*) the CP channel is open already at the start of the photocycle (72, 73), (c) proton release is delayed to the end of the photocycle (2, 7, 23, 76), and (d) reprotonation of the chromophore is severely delayed (32). These findings are readily understood in light of a torsion-based switch.

New Tools

The main constraint on the use of NMR to elucidate the pump mechanism of bR has been the unfavorable Boltzmann distribution between spin states. That this can be overcome at all for large immobilized molecules is partly due to cross polarization from protons that have larger gyromagnetic ratios than ^{13}C or ^{15}N. However, recently it has become possible to transfer polarization from unpaired electrons, a technique known as dynamic nuclear polarization. The resulting large improvement in signal-to-noise will make old experiments quicker and new experiments feasible (62). In particular, it will be possible to use pulse sequences that spread signals over more dimensions and sample conditions that spread signals over more coexisting photocycle intermediates. It will also be possible to use samples of lower density to facilitate the preparation of early photocycle intermediates. With these possibilities in hand, we can look forward to new distance and torsion angle measurements with a precision beyond that available by diffraction. bR remains an ideal protein for such experiments—as well studied as it is, there is no shortage of exciting hypotheses to test in this functionally significant protein.

Visit the Annual Reviews home page at www.annualreviews.org

LITERATURE CITED

1. Balashov SP, Ebrey TG. 2001. Trapping and spectroscopic identification of the photointermediates of bacteriorhodopsin at low temperatures. *Photochem. Photobiol.* 73:453–62
2. Balashov SP, Govindjee R, Kono M, Imasheva E, Lukashev E, et al. 1993. Effect of the arginine-82 to alanine mutation in bacteriorhodopsin on dark adaptation, proton release, and the photochemical cycle. *Biochemistry* 32:10331–43
3. Beppu Y, Kakitani T, Tokunaga F. 1992. Energetics of protonation deprotonation of the chromophore in retinal proteins. *Photochem. Photobiol.* 56:1113–17
4. Betancourt FMH, Glaeser RM. 2000. Chemical and physical evidence for multiple functional steps comprising the M state of the bacteriorhodopsin photocycle. *Biochim. Biophys. Acta* 1460:106–18

5. Borbat PP, Costa-Filho AJ, Earle KA, Moscicki JK, Freed JH. 2001. Electron spin resonance in studies of membranes and proteins. *Science* 291:266–69
6. Brown LS, Gat Y, Sheves M, Yamazaki Y, Maeda A, et al. 1994. The retinal Schiff base-counterion complex of bacteriorhodopsin: changed geometry during the photocycle is a cause of proton transfer to aspartate 85. *Biochemistry* 33:12001–11
7. Cao Y, Brown LS, Sasaki J, Maeda A, Needleman R, Lanyi JK. 1995. Relationship of proton release at the extracellular surface to deprotonation of the Schiff base in the bacteriorhodopsin photocycle. *Biophys. J.* 68:1518–30
8. Copie V, McDermott AE, Beshah K, Williams JC, Spijker-Assink M, et al. 1994. Deuterium solid-state nuclear magnetic resonance studies of methyl-group

dynamics in bacteriorhodopsin and retinal model compounds: evidence for a 6-s-*trans* chromophore in the protein. *Biochemistry* 33:3280–86

9. Creuzet F, McDermott AE, Gebhard R, van der Hoef K, Spijker-Assink MB, et al. 1991. Determination of membrane protein structure by rotational resonance NMR: bacteriorhodopsin. *Science* 251:783–86

10. Cross TA, Opella SJ. 1994. Solid-state NMR structural studies of peptides and proteins in membranes. *Curr. Opin. Struct. Biol.* 4:574–81

11. de Groot HJM, Copie VC, Smith SO, Allen PJ, Winkel C, et al. 1988. Magic-angle-sample-spinning NMR difference spectroscopy. *J. Magn. Reson.* 77:251–57

12. de Groot HJM, Smith SO, Courtin J, van den Berg E, Winkel C, et al. 1990. Solid-state ^{13}C and ^{15}N NMR study of the low pH forms of bacteriorhodopsin. *Biochemistry* 29:6873–83

13. Deber CM, Sorrell BJ, Xu GY. 1990. Conformation of proline residues in bacteriorhodopsin. *Biochem. Biophys. Res. Commun.* 172:862–69

14. Dioumaev AK, Braiman MS. 1995. Modeling vibrational spectra of amino acid side chains in proteins: the carbonyl stretch frequency of buried carboxylic residues. *J. Am. Chem. Soc.* 117:10572–74

15. Dusold S, Sebald A. 2000. Dipolar recoupling under magic-angle spinning conditions. *Ann. Rep. NMR Spectrosc.* 41:185–264

16. Engelhard M, Bechinger B. 1995. Application of NMR-spectroscopy to retinal proteins. *Isr. J. Chem.* 35:273–88

17. Engelhard M, Finkler S, Metz G, Siebert F. 1996. Solid-state C-13-NMR of [(3-C-13)Pro]bacteriorhodopsin and [(4-C-13)Pro]bacteriorhodopsin—evidence for a flexible segment of the C-terminal tail. *Eur. J. Biochem.* 235:526–33

18. Engelhard M, Hess B, Emeis D, Metz G, Kreutz W, Siebert F. 1989. Magic angle sample spinning ^{13}C nuclear magnetic resonance of isotopically labeled bacteriorhodopsin. *Biochemistry* 28:3967–75

19. Engelhard M, Hess B, Metz G, Kreutz W, Siebert F, et al. 1990. High resolution ^{13}C-solid state NMR of bacteriorhodopsin: assignment of specific aspartic acids and structural implications of single site mutations. *Eur. Biophys. J.* 18:17–24

20. Friedman N, Druckmann S, Lanyi J, Needleman R, Lewis A, et al. 1994. A covalent link between the chromophore and the protein backbone of bacteriorhodopsin is not required for forming a photochemically active pigment analogous to the wild type. *Biochemistry* 33:1971–76

21. Gat Y, Sheves M. 1994. The origin of the red-shifted absorption maximum of the M_{412} intermediate in the bacteriorhodopsin photocycle. *Photochem. Photobiol.* 59:371–78

22. Glaubitz C, Watts A. 1998. Magic angle-oriented sample spinning (MAOSS): a new approach toward biomembrane studies. *J. Magn. Reson.* 130:305–16

23. Govindjee R, Imasheva ES, Misra S, Balashov SP, Ebrey TG, et al. 1997. Mutation of a surface residue, lysine-129, reverses the order of proton release and uptake in bacteriorhodopsin; guanidine hydrochloride restores it. *Biophys. J.* 72:886–98

24. Govindjee R, Misra S, Balashov SP, Ebrey TG, Crouch RK, Menick DR. 1996. Arginine-82 regulates the pKa of the group responsible for the light-driven proton release in bacteriorhodopsin. *Biophys. J.* 71:1011–23

25. Griffiths JM, Bennett AE, Engelhard M, Siebert F, Raap J, et al. 2000. Structural investigation of the active site in bacteriorhodopsin: geometric constraints on the roles of Asp-85 and Asp-212 in the proton-pumping mechanism from solid state NMR. *Biochemistry* 39:362–71

26. Harbison GS, Herzfeld J, Griffin RG. 1983. Solid-state nitrogen-15 nuclear magnetic resonance study of the Schiff

base in bacteriorhodopsin. *Biochemistry* 22:1–5

27. Harbison GS, Roberts JE, Herzfeld J, Griffin RG. 1988. Solid-state NMR detection of proton-exchange between the bacteriorhodopsin Schiff-base and bulk water. *J. Am. Chem. Soc.* 110:7221–23

28. Harbison GS, Smith SO, Pardoen JA, Courtin JMJ, Lugtenburg J, et al. 1985. Solid state ^{13}C-NMR detection of a perturbed 6-s-*trans* chromophore in bacteriorhodopsin. *Biochemistry* 24:6955–62

29. Harbison GS, Smith SO, Pardoen JA, Winkel C, Lugtenburg J, et al. 1984. Dark-adapted bacteriorhodopsin contains 13-*cis*, 15-*syn* and all-*trans*, 15-anti retinal Schiff bases. *Proc. Natl. Acad. Sci. USA* 81:1706–9

29a. Hatcher ME, Hu JG, Belenky M, Verdegem P, Lugtenburg J, et al. 2002. Control of the pump cycle in bacteriorhodopsin: mechanisms elucidated by solid state NMR of the D85N mutant. *Biophys. J.* In press

30. Herzfeld J, Tounge B. 2000. NMR probes of vectoriality in the proton-motive photocycle of bacteriorhodopsin: evidence for an "electrostatic steering" mechanism. *Biochim. Biophys. Acta-Bioenerg.* 1460:95–105

31. Heyn MP, Borucki B, Otto H. 2000. Chromophore reorientation during the photocycle of bacteriorhodopsin: experimental methods and functional significance. *Biochim. Biophys. Acta-Bioenerg.* 1460:60–74

32. Holz M, Drachev LA, Mogi T, Otto H, Kaulen AD, et al. 1989. Replacement of aspartic acid-96 by asparagine in bacteriorhodopsin slows both the decay of the M intermediate and the associated proton movement. *Proc. Natl. Acad. Sci. USA* 86:2167–71

33. Hu JG. 1995. *Solid-state NMR studies of bacteriorhodopsin and model compounds: insight into the spectral tuning and the photocycle.* PhD thesis. Brandeis Univ. 235 pp.

34. Hu JG, Griffin RG, Herzfeld J. 1997. Interactions between the protonated Schiff base and its counterion in the photointermediates of bacteriorhodopsin. *J. Am. Chem. Soc.* 119:9495–98

35. Deleted in proof

36. Hu JG, Sun BQ, Bizounok M, Hatcher ME, Lansing JC, et al. 1998. Early and late M photointermediates in the bacteriorhodopsin photocycle: a solid state NMR study. *Biochemistry* 37:8088–96

37. Deleted in proof

38. Deleted in proof

39. Hu JG, Sun BQ, Petkova AT, Griffin RG, Herzfeld J. 1997. The predischarge chromophore in bacteriorhodopsin: a ^{15}N solid-state NMR study of the L photointermediate. *Biochemistry* 36:9316–22

40. Hubbell WL, Cafisio DS, Altenback C. 2000. Identifying conformational changes with site-directed spin labeling. *Nat. Struct. Biol.* 7:735–39

41. Hustedt EJ, Beth AH. 1999. Nitroxide spin-spin interactions: applications to protein structure and dynamics. *Annu. Rev. Biophys. Biomol. Struct.* 28:129–53

42. Kandori H, Yamazaki Y, Shichida Y, Raap J, Lugtenburg J, et al. 2001. Tight asp-85-Thr-89 association during the pump switch of bacteriorhodopsin. *Proc. Natl. Acad. Sci. USA* 98:1571–76

43. Lakshmi KV, Farrar MR, Raap J, Lugtenburg J, Griffin RG, Herzfeld J. 1994. Solid-state ^{13}C NMR and ^{15}N NMR investigations of the N intermediate of bacteriorhodopsin. *Biochemistry* 33:8853–57

44. Lansing JC, Hohwy M, Jaroniec CP, Creemers AFL, Lugtenburg J, et al. 2002. Chromophore distortions in the bacteriorhodopsin photocycle: evolution of the H-C14-C15-H dihedral angle measured by solid-state NMR. *Biochemistry* In press

45. Luecke H. 2000. Atomic resolution structures of bacteriorhodopsin photocycle intermediates: the role of discrete water

molecules in the function of this light-driven ion pump. *Biochim. Biophys. Acta* 1460:133–56

46. Luecke H, Schobert B, Richter H-T, Cartailler J-P, Lanyi JK. 1999. Structure of bacteriorhodopsin at 1.55 Å resolution. *J. Mol. Biol.* 291:899–911

47. Lugtenburg J, Creemers AFL, Verhoeven MA, van Wijk AAC, Verdegem PJE, et al. 1999. Synthesis of C-13-labeled carotenoids and retinoids. *Pure Appl. Chem.* 71:2245–51

48. Maeda A. 1995. Application of FTIR spectroscopy to the structural study on the function of bacteriorhodopsin. *Isr. J. Chem.* 35:387–400

49. Mathies RA. 1991. From femtoseconds to biology: mechanism of bacteriorhodopsin's light-driven proton pump. *Proc. Indian Acad. Sci.* 103:283–93

50. Mathies RA, Li X-Y. 1995. On modeling the vibrational spectra of 14-s-*cis* retinal conformers in bacteriorhodopsin. *Biophys. Chem.* 56:47–55

51. Mathies RA, Lin SW, Ames JB, Pollard WT. 1991. From femtoseconds to biology: mechanism of bacteriorhodopsin's light-driven proton pump. *Annu. Rev. Biophys. Biophys. Chem.* 20:491–518

52. Metz G, Siebert F, Engelhard M. 1992. Asp[85] is the only internal aspartic acid that gets protonated in the M intermediate and the purple-to-blue transition of bacteriorhodopsin. A solid-state ^{13}C CP-MAS NMR investigation. *FEBS Lett.* 303:237–41

53. Metz G, Siebert F, Engelhard M. 1992. High-resolution solid state 13C NMR of bacteriorhodopsin: characterization of [4-^{13}C]Asp resonances. *Biochemistry* 31:455–62

54. Nevzorov AA, Moltke S, Heyn MP, Brown MF. 1999. Solid-state NMR line shapes of uniaxially oriented immobile systems. *J. Am. Chem. Soc.* 121:7636–43

55. Nina M, Roux B, Smith JC. 1995. Functional interactions in bacteriorhodopsin: a theoretical analysis of retinal hydrogen bonding with water. *Biophys. J.* 68:25–39

56. Opella SJ. 1997. NMR and membrane proteins. *Nat. Struct. Biol.* 4:845–48

57. Patzelt H, Ulrich AS, Egbringhoff H, Dux P, Ashurst J, et al. 1997. Towards structural investigations on isotope labelled native bacteriorhodopsin in detergent micelles by solutions-state NMR spectroscopy. *J. Biomol. NMR* 10:95–106

57a. Petkova A, Hatanaka M, Jaroniec CP, Hu JG, Belenky M, et al. 2002. Tryptophan interactions in bacteriorhodopsin: a heteronuclear solid-state NMR study. *Biochemistry* In press

58. Petkova AT, Hu JG, Bizounok M, Simpson M, Griffin RG, Herzfeld J. 1999. Arginine activity in the proton-motive photocycle of bacteriorhodopsin: solid-state NMR studies of the wild-type and D85N proteins. *Biochemistry* 38:1562–72

59. Radionov AN, Klyachko VA, Kaulen AD. 1999. Formation of the M_N (M_{open}) intermediate in the wild-type bacteriorhodopsin photocycle is accompanied by an absorption spectrum shift to shorter wavelength, like that in the mutant D96N bacteriorhodopsin photocycle. *Biochemistry (Moscow)* 64:1210–14

60. Radzwill N, Gerwert K, Steinhoff HJ. 2001. Time-resolved detection of transient movement of helices F and G in doubly spin-labeled bacteriorhodopsin. *Biophys. J.* 80:2856–66

61. Rink T, Pfeiffer M, Oesterhelt D, Gerwert K, Steinhoff HJ. 2000. Unraveling photoexcited conformational changes of bacteriorhodopsin by time resolved electron paramagnetic resonance spectroscopy. *Biophys. J.* 78:1519–30

62. Rosay M, Zeri AC, Astrof NS, Opella SJ, Herzfeld J, Griffin RG. 2001. Sensitivity-enhanced NMR of biological solids: dynamic nuclear polarization of Y21M fd bacteriophage and purple membrane. *J. Am. Chem. Soc.* 123:1010–11

63. Rousso I, Friedman N, Sheves M, Ottolenghi M. 1995. pKa of the protonated

Schiff base and aspartic 85 in the bacteriorhodopsin binding site is controlled by a specific geometry between the two residues. *Biochemistry* 34:12059–65

64. Roux B, Nina M, Pomes R, Smith JC. 1996. Thermodynamic stability of water molecules in the bacteriorhodopsin proton channel: a molecular dynamics free energy perturbation study. *Biophys. J.* 71:670–81

65. Saito H, Tuzi S, Yamaguchi S, Tanio M, Naito A. 2000. Conformation and backbone dynamics of bacteriorhodopsin revealed by 13C-NMR. *Biochim. Biophys. Acta-Bioenerg.* 1460:39–48

66. Schulten K, Tavan P. 1978. A mechanism for the light-driven proton pump of Halobacterium halobium. *Nature* 2721: 85–86

67. Schweiger U, Tittor J, Oesterhelt D. 1994. Bacteriorhodopsin can function without a covalent linkage between retinal and protein. *Biochemistry* 33:535–41

68. Spudich JL, Yang CS, Jung KH, Spudich EN. 2000. Retinylidene proteins: structures and functions from archaea to humans. *Annu. Rev. Cell Dev. Biol.* 16:365–92

69. Steinhoff H-J, Mollaaghababa R, Altenbach C, Hideg K, Krebs M, et al. 1994. Time-resolved detection of structural changes during the photocycle of spin-labeled bacteriorhodopsin. *Science* 266: 105–7

70. Stern LJ, Khorana HG. 1989. Structure-function studies on bacteriorhodopsin. X. Individual substitutions of arginine residues by glutamine affect chromophore formation, photocycle, and proton translocation. *J. Biol. Chem.* 264:14202–8

71. Subramaniam S, Henderson R. 2000. Crystallographic analysis of protein conformational changes in the bacteriorhodopsin photocycle. *Biochim. Biophys. Acta-Bioenerg.* 1460:157–65

72. Subramaniam S, Lindahl I, Bullough P, Faruqi AR, Tittor J, et al. 1999. Protein conformational changes in the bacteriorhodopsin photocycle. *J. Mol. Biol.* 287:145–61

73. Tittor J, Paula S, Subramaniam S, Heberle J, Henderson R, Oesterhelt D. 2000. Bacteriorhodopsin can translocate protons without a significant conformational change. *Biophys. J.* 78:A478

74. Tjandra N, Bax A. 1997. Solution NMR measurement of amide proton chemical shift anisotropy in N-15-enriched proteins. Correlation with hydrogen bond length. *J. Am. Chem. Soc.* 119:8076–82

75. Xiao WZ, Brown LS, Needleman R, Lanyi JK, Shin YK. 2000. Light-induced rotation of a transmembrane alpha-helix in bacteriorhodopsin. *J. Mol. Biol.* 304:715–21

76. Zimanyi L, Varo G, Chang M, Ni B, Needleman R, Lanyi JK. 1992. Pathways of proton release in the bacteriorhodopsin photocycle. *Biochemistry* 31:8535–43

Annu. Rev. Biophys. Biomol. Struct. 2002. 31:97–119
DOI: 10.1146/annurev.biophys.31.082901.134406

FLOW CYTOMETRIC ANALYSIS OF LIGAND-RECEPTOR INTERACTIONS AND MOLECULAR ASSEMBLIES*

Larry A. Sklar,[1,2] Bruce S. Edwards,[1] Steven W. Graves,[2] John P. Nolan,[2] and Eric R. Prossnitz[1]

[1]*Cancer Center and Departments of Pathology and Cell Biology and Physiology, University of New Mexico, Albuquerque, New Mexico 87131; e-mail: lsklar@salud.unm.edu; bedwards@salud.unm.edu; eprossnitz@salud.unm.edu* [2]*National Flow Cytometry Resource and Bioscience Division, Los Alamos National Laboratory, Los Alamos, New Mexico 87545; e-mail: graves@telomere.lanl.gov; nolan@telomere.lanl.gov*

Key Words   drug discovery, genomics, immunoassay, proteomics, fluorescence resonance energy transfer

■ **Abstract**   Flow cytometers make homogeneous real-time measurements of ligand-receptor interactions and, simultaneously, the physiological responses of cells. Their multiparameter capabilities are also useful in resolving multicomponent assemblies or in developing multiplexed assays. Recent advances suggest that these approaches can be extended in several important ways. Sample delivery in the millisecond time domain is applicable to the analysis of complex binding kinetics and reaction mechanisms. The homogeneous discrimination of free components and particle-based assemblies can be extended into the micromolar concentration range. Measurements can be made of molecular assemblies among proteins, DNA, RNA, lipids, and carbohydrates on beads. The topography and assembly of components within cells can be evaluated with resonance energy transfer. Temperature dependence can be evaluated with Peltier temperature control. Many assembly endpoints can be assessed through new tools for high-throughput flow cytometry using plate-based assay formats and small volume samples.

CONTENTS

INTRODUCTION

Interactions among molecules that control cell, organ, or animal physiology are targets in human disease. These macromolecular assemblies often function in signal transduction and adhesion (protein complexes) or DNA replication (nucleic acid/protein complexes). Flow cytometry represents a general approach that could make sensitive and quantitative measurements of molecular interactions with kinetic resolution and high throughput. Flow cytometry measures the fluorescence or light scatter of particles and resolves the fluorescence of particle-associated and free-fluorescent complexes (84). This article describes developments that allow flow cytometry to meet the needs for molecular analysis in diverse fields such as ligand binding, assembly topography, enzyme kinetics, drug development, biosensing, and DNA sequence detection. The developments include (*a*) computer-controlled sample handling to enable subsecond sample mixing for kinetic analysis, high-throughput screening, and temperature control; (*b*) molecular incorporation of affinity tags or fluorescent probes into proteins; and (*c*) particle-based surface chemistries and calibration approaches that allow the molecular advances to be used quantitatively for flow cytometry. Recent reviews regarding kinetics, molecular assembly, calibration, and sample handling in flow cytometry have appeared (66, 67, 71, 72, 82, 90).

Molecular interactions can be measured by heterogeneous or homogeneous assays. The former involve a physical separation of ligand from receptor or product from substrate. The latter measure continuously without a separation step. The classic heterogeneous assays use radioisotopes, where filtration, centrifugation, or electrophoresis is used to separate free from bound ligand or product from substrate. Radioisotopes are typically nonperturbing, sensitive and specific, and represent the standard for characterizing receptor site number and affinity. Radioisotopes are not especially well-suited for kinetic studies because each time point is handled as a separate sample. Although rapid-quench methods provide subsecond resolution for studies of enzyme mechanism, they have reduced sensitivity owing to the dissociation of low-affinity molecular assemblies during the requisite separation step.

Homogeneous suspension assays typically measure a signal specific to the assembled complex. For example, intrinsic protein fluorescence, which is often sensitive to binding and associated with conformational changes of proteins, allows measurements at μM concentrations (26). Exogenous fluorescent labels for polarization or resonance energy transfer improves the sensitivity to nM concentrations (44), often allowing measurements in cells or unpurified mixtures (90). Stoichiometric ratios of components are required to detect assembly by fluorescent polarization or energy transfer. When the number of complexes formed represent a significant fraction of one of the components, that component is depleted and the binding analysis could be skewed. With stopped-flow mixing, these detection methods offer millisecond kinetic resolution.

In contrast, when the complex is assembled on a surface, the signal is associated with the surface. Several surface-based assays are now commercially available. Scintillation proximity assay typically measures the binding of a tritium-labeled molecule to an immobilized partner on an yttrium bead, resulting in a luminescence signal. This approach provides μM sensitivity with resolution on the time scale of a minute. Optical methods including surface plasmon resonance, and evanescent waves offer continuous kinetic analysis of binding reactions on surfaces without labels. Detection is based on mass. Sample handling capabilities and flow characteristics of these systems suggest they could provide dead times of seconds for kinetics.

Since its inception, the potential of flow cytometry to study ligand binding to cells and for measuring cell responses has been recognized, and time was accommodated as a parameter in the 1980s (53). Although appreciated, the ability of a flow cytometer to discriminate free and bound ligand without a wash step was not widely applied. Nonetheless, early applications of flow cytometry to time-dependent receptor processes on living cells drove the development of instrumental capabilities for improved time resolution. The realization that flow cytometry was not limited to cell analysis, but could be applied more generally, led to the development of particle-based molecular assemblies.

INSTRUMENTATION

In a flow cytometer (Figure 1), particles (or recently, single molecules) are carried in a sample stream in single file through a focused laser beam. The laser light excites one or more fluorescent probes associated with the particle. The fluorescence as well as scattered light are collected, spectrally separated by mirrors and filters, and detected with a photo-multiplier tube. The probe volume defined by the intersection of the laser beam with the sample stream is typically several pL. Thus the background contribution of light scatter, fluorescent impurities, or free probe

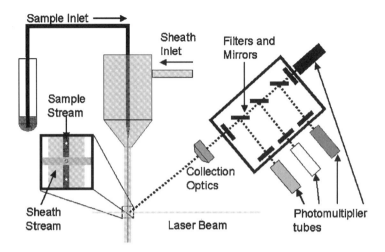

Figure 1   Flow cytometer schematic.

can be minimized compared with specific signals. A commercial flow cytometer can detect several hundred fluorescent molecules per particle at measurement rates of tens of thousands per second with digital signal processing. Using slower rates to increase the time the particle is in the illumination volume from micro- to milliseconds, special flow cytometers can detect a single molecule (2). With multiple lasers and light paths, as many as 10 probes can be detected simultaneously on each particle (20).

Calibration particles are commercially available, and systematic approaches to analyze the number of molecules present on a particle or cell have been described (47, 81). Some products report the numbers of fluorophores per particle or site densities for ligands such as monoclonal antibodies (mAbs). Calibration requires consideration of the labeling efficiency of a labeled fluorescent molecule and its relative fluorescence yield compared with free fluorophore in solution. Fluorescein and phycoerythrin are the most extensively used standards because they represent the two predominant probes for immunofluorescence, a primary research and clinical application for flow cytometry. However, the calibration strategies are applicable to any fluorophore.

Kinetic Flow Cytometry

Given the capability of measuring thousands of particles per second with a homogeneous assay, flow cytometry is in principle well-suited for kinetic analysis. Commercial software provides each particle with a "time stamp" from the time the data file was opened. As meaningful particle statistics require hundreds of particles per time interval, time resolution to 100 msec can readily be achieved. Kinetic studies in flow cytometry typically require removing the sample tube from the cytometer and manual reagent mixing, resulting in a dead time of 10 sec

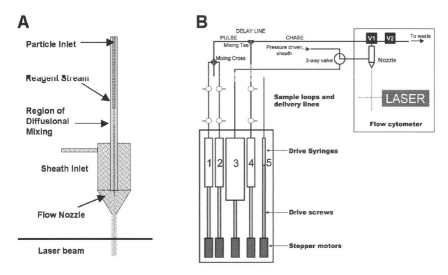

Figure 2   Coaxial (*A*) and stopped-flow (*B*) mixing for flow cytometry.

or more. Several online mixing schemes have reduced this dead time to seconds (82). More recently, subsecond mixing (Figure 2) has allowed access to the time scales on which macromolecular complexes assemble and cells respond.

A coaxial mixing approach is based on flow injection analysis instrumentation (80). It employs separate streams of reagents brought into coaxial flow via a specially designed flow nozzle and allowed to mix via diffusion (Figure 2*A*). The mixing time is determined by the time required to transit the distance from the flow nozzle to the point of measurement and is varied by changing that distance, allowing measurements within 100 msec after mixing. The coaxial configuration is well-suited to a single-step mixing experiment and individual, fast time points.

Another mixing approach integrates a computer-controlled, syringe-based mixing device with a commercial cytometer (Figure 2*B*). We reported a stepper-motor-driven mixing device that provides mixing and delivery with a 300-msec dead time (69) and a lower cost system that provides nearly as good performance [500-msec dead time, (83)]. We have just implemented a sample mixer with two fast valves and five syringes with dead time below 100 msecs (33). Three syringes are used for sample mixing: Two syringes are used to mix reagents to start a reaction and the third to mix additional reagents after the sample has passed through a delay line. A fourth syringe is used to deliver the mixed sample to the cytometer in two phases, one which boosts sample into the cytometer and a second phase in which sample is delivered. The fifth syringe is used to control the sheath flow to the cytometer. We learned that both nozzle geometry and pressure affect performance, but in general flow cytometers operating at lower pressures (5–20 PSI) are better suited to kinetic analysis (33). This approach is flexible, allowing continuous kinetic measurements after single-step or multiple-step mixing protocols.

Discrimination of Free and Bound Probes

In 1980, one of us performed a simple experiment in which a fluorescent formyl peptide, an analog of a bacterial product, was bound to neutrophils, cells that participate in the acute phase of host response to bacterial infection (e.g., 90). These experiments showed that the binding signal of the peptide was similar when free peptide was washed away after binding or not. Moreover, they showed the signal from the cells alone or in the presence of a low concentration of fluorescent peptide, and high concentration of nonfluorescent peptide were similar. Sensitivity in flow cytometric analysis requires that the number of sites on the cell or particle of interest yield a signal at least comparable to the background fluorescence. In practice, for a blood cell, the cell autofluorescence is comparable to 1000–10,000 fluorescein molecules and for a cultured cell between 10,000–100,000 fluorescein molecules.

The discrimination of free versus bound probes in flow cytometry depends on maximizing the signal of the particle-associated probe relative to the signal of the unbound probe. The quantitative aspects of this effect have been considered, and the sensitivity of a flow cytometer depends on the number of binding sites on the particle, the affinity of the probe for those sites, and the interrogation volume (63). In general, reducing the illumination volume and the sample stream diameter reduces the signal of the unbound probe. As the light scatter signal generated by the particle typically serves as a trigger for data acquisition, the fluorescence reported depends on the concentration of fluorophore present in the interrogation volume where the laser and the sample stream intersect (Figure 1). Thus, with low concentrations ($\sim$1 nM) of free probe and high-affinity binding, discrimination of tens of thousands of bound probes is accomplished because the ratio of free to bound probe is small. However, when low-affinity interactions are studied, higher concentrations of free probe are required for binding. Here, the background probe present in the interrogation volume causes a direct current signal that obscures specific probe binding and limits the range of probe concentrations at which flow cytometry can discriminate free versus bound (Figure 3). The direct current signal caused by the free fluorophore is sensitive to particle size, resulting in the fluorescence exclusion phenomena (34). Negative signals are generated when a particle excludes

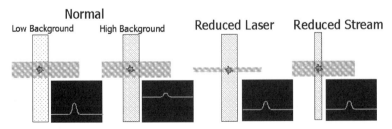

Figure 3   Effect of interrogation volume on subsequent direct current signal output.

fluorescent molecules from the interrogation point that could conceivably be used to discriminate low levels of bound probe in a high background of fluorophore.

Thus, optical, fluidic, and electronic principles could be coordinated for optimal discrimination of free and bound probe. We have, in addition, described an approach in which rapid mixing could also be used (92). In this case, a low-affinity ligand could be detected in an online dilution experiment. Thus, particles and probe are preincubated at high probe concentration. Then, the particles and probe are diluted rapidly by mixing with buffer (containing unlabeled probe). The dissociation kinetics can be examined under conditions where the direct current contribution (and potentially nonspecific binding) are reduced by the dilution. K_ds as high as 1 μM and dissociation rates constants to 10/sec should be accessible.

Dynamic Temperature Control for Flow Cytometry

Two of us introduced dynamic temperature control capabilities for flow cytometry (32). Temperature is used routinely in nucleic acid–based assays to control the specificity of oligonucleotide hybridization reactions. Thermal (or chemical) denaturation is often used in enzymology to discern nucleic acid substrates from products. The in-line, thermal-control device consists of a Peltier-based heating/cooling element that can be dynamically controlled to heat or cool the contents of the sample line between 20 and 94°C in less than one minute (Figure 4). We have tested

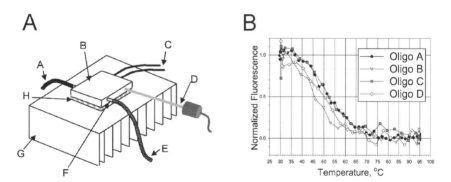

Figure 4   Peltier-based heating of the sample line. (*A*) Schematic of the Peltier-based device. A, silicone rubber portion of delay line ($\sim$63 mm in length by 1.5875 mm OD by 0.254 mm ID); B, heat transfer block (40 mm $\times$ 40 mm $\times$ 3.5 mm); C, power lines for the Peltier module; D, thermocouple (1.5875 mm OD); E, sample inlet line; F, titanium sample line (50 mm in length by 1.5875 mm OD by 0.254 mm ID); G, heat sink. (*B*) Melting curves for oligos A, B, C, and D. The measured Tms were 53.2, 46.3, 52.7, and 49.7°C, respectively; these values compared well to the predicted Tms of 52, 50, 54, and 46°C, respectively. The Tms measured differed from predictions based on nucleotide base composition (32), by an average of 2.7°C, and compared favorably to Tms determined by traditional spectrophotometric methods, which differ from predictions by an average of 2 to 6°C.

and verified the instrument by measuring the melting temperatures of a family of oligonucleotides (32).

BINDING ANALYSIS ON CELLS IN FLOW CYTOMETRY

There have been many applications of flow cytometry to study ligand-receptor interactions on the cell surface and the relationship of ligand-receptor interactions to cell response [(39, 90) PerkinElmer Life Sciences catalog]. Fluorescent ligands have been used to study many binding interactions on cell surface receptors. These include lectins, lipoproteins (43), peptides for the urokinase/plasminogen activation receptor (11), peptides that bind to adhesion molecules (27, 37), as well as nucleotide aptamers that bind to the adhesion molecule L-selectin (78). They have also been useful in describing complex steps in receptor activation, clustering, desensitization, and internalization during signaling. Because it is possible to simultaneously measure the consequences of ligand binding such as changes in second messenger levels, pH, cell morphology, or secretion, flow cytometry is proving especially important in unraveling mechanisms of cell response.

Binding of several fluorescent G protein–coupled receptors (GPCRs) ligands has been reported (reviewed in 39, 41, 99, 101). Our own work on the formyl peptide receptor, a member of the GPCR family, motivated us to develop tools for the analysis of kinetics and molecular assembly. Our earliest measurements showed that equilibrium-binding measurements by flow cytometry, with calibration, allowed the determination of the site number and equilibrium constant for the ligand. Kinetic measurements allowed the quantification of the rates of ligand binding and dissociation, receptor internalization over time, and time-dependent changes in the state of the receptor reflected in the dissociation kinetics (90). Experiments could be performed with sufficient precision to define rate constants for unlabeled peptides (91) and to determine whether binding was diffusion limited (61). Efforts at modeling cell data have tried to incorporate G protein coupling and receptor-elicited cycles of actin polymerization and depolymerization (1, 46, 66).

Resolution of the molecular details of receptor pathways requires a combination of several approaches. For example, while the activation steps involve G protein, the desensitization and internalization steps involve receptor phosphorylation and arrestin. Thus mutational studies of the phosphorylation sites on the receptor alters internalization [measured by receptor numbers left on the cell surface as a function of time following stimulus (76)], receptor desensitization [measured through analysis of calcium elevation following repetitive stimulation (75)], and receptor associations with arrestin and G proteins. These latter assemblies have been measured both by colocalization using confocal microscopy (5) and a soluble receptor assay that measures the ability of receptors to reconstitute with G proteins and arrestin (4, 49).

Simple binding equilibrium measurements have also turned out to be useful for studies of the ligand-binding regions of this and related receptors (99). In studies where the receptor has been mutated, flow cytometry has played a significant role in the binding analysis of fluorescent ligands for variations in the receptor and the ligand as well (58). Spectroscopic analysis located a hydrophobic interaction in the galanin binding pocket (101).

Multivalent Interactions

In cells, valency contributes to binding interactions for signaling and adhesive mechanisms. Although several groups have taken advantage of multivalent ligands, the analysis of major histocompatability tetramers is proving critical for studying immune self-recognition (7). Receptor crosslinking for immunologic and cytokine receptors often gives rise to bell-shaped dose response curves. To quantify antigen-induced aggregation of IgE-FcεRI complexes, Posner et al. have monitored both occupancy of surface IgE-combining sites and association of antigen with the cell surface. The theory of multivalent ligand binding to cell surface receptors predicts that at equilibrium the fraction of receptor sites crosslinked will be a bell-shaped function of the logarithm of the ligand concentration. Flow cytometric measurements and modeling show that the bell-shaped form of the dose response curve occurs because these cells are responding to receptor clustering rather than simply receptor occupancy (45).

Cell Adhesion

Multivalent ligand-receptor interactions are also important in cell adhesion, such as leukocyte emigration into lymphoid tissues and sites of inflammation that is mediated by the sequential engagement of several distinct classes of adhesion molecules. Flow cytometry is represented in the adhesion field in several ways. A common approach uses mAbs to identify adhesion molecules, to estimate their number, and to block adhesive function (between cells or with particles displaying adhesion molecules). In addition, it has been used to identify receptors that express an activation-specific epitope or topographical feature recognized by unusual antibodies sensitive to molecular conformation. Molecules that mimic natural ligands for adhesion molecules are particularly interesting. For example, RGD-like peptides for β_3-integrin (3, 100) and an LDV peptide for α_4-integrins (17) are sensitive to the affinity of the interaction. Thus, flow cytometric analysis of binding equilibrium and kinetics contains information about the affinity of the resting and activated receptors as well as the transition between active and inactive receptors.

The avidity of cell adhesion reflects ligand affinity as well as the valency. Avidity varies with changes in adhesion receptor distribution (e.g., clustered versus diffuse), membrane location (e.g., microvillus tips or troughs), or number (shedding, recycling) and dynamic interactions between adhesion receptors and the cytoskeleton under the control of intracellular signaling cascades. To measure cell adhesion, one may exploit innate differences between cells (e.g., cell size or "granularity" as measured by light scatter) or label cell populations with distinct fluorescent dyes. For example, two adhering cell populations labeled, respectively, with red and green fluorescent dyes will exhibit aggregate clusters of red and green cells referred to as conjugates. These types of measurements have been exploited along with blocking antibodies to show that neutrophil aggregation involves two sets of counter-structures (38). When conjugate particles are mostly doublets with one cell from each population, the adhesion calculations are straightforward. When the conjugates are heterogeneous aggregates containing more than one cell from each population, they are not. With a fluorescent dye that labels cells uniformly, it may be possible to resolve the number of labeled cells in individual conjugate particles (87). A singlet depletion methodology has been used to show more efficient recognition between eosinophils than neutrophils for P-selectin-transfected cells that could contribute to the preferential accumulation of eosinophils in asthmatic lungs (22, 24).

Viscometers have been used to subject cells to a uniform and quantifiable fluid shear environment. Cells have been removed from the viscometer into a formalin fixative solution for subsequent offline flow cytometric analysis (98), and plug flow cytometry sample handling technology allows online analysis in which the cell mixtures are transported within seconds directly from the viscometer to the flow cytometer under computer control (22, 24). Smoluchowski's flocculation theory has been applied to obtain estimates of adhesion efficiency related to the rate of aggregate formation. Experiments showed a remarkable potentiation of adhesion efficiency through the combined action of two sets of adhesion molecules and a progression of adhesion molecule utilization from one class to another over time (42, 65, 88).

Cellular Topography

Fluorescence resonance energy transfer (FRET) is turning out to be a powerful direct measurement of assemblies in cells (54). FRET has recently been applied to molecular topography (36), assembly (18), conformation (89), and enzymology (16). Fluorescent detection systems have also been used for gene expression initiated as a consequence of the activation of cellular signaling pathways (105). The most widely available reagents for FRET in flow cytometry have been pairs of mAbs labeled heterogeneously with donor and acceptor fluorophores. Measurements based on antibodies are imprecise because their size is similar to the molecular distances measured, and the transfer between the antibodies is usually small.

New probes are changing the face of FRET for flow cytometry. FRET has been observed by microscopy and cytometry in cells between the cyan fluorescent protein and yellow fluorescent protein variants (60; L. He, X. Zhang, X. Wu, R. Fischer, A. C. Grammer, P. E. Lipsky, personal communication). Other genetically encoded probes include fluorescent proteins with different spectral properties and small organic fluorophores that can be made to label specifically encoded polypeptide sequences. This latter approach, exemplified by the labeling of engineered cysteine-containing sequences (*CCXXCC*, where *X* is any amino acid other than cysteine) with fluorescein arsenoxide, is especially attractive because the fusion element that is linked to a target protein is generally less than 2 kDa compared with 27 kDa for the green fluorescent protein (GFP) variants (35).

FRET has already begun to have a significant impact in protein engineering with flow cytometry. This has allowed the sorting of members of expressed combinatorial libraries based on function, such as using a FRET pair enzyme substrate (8, 9, 19, 73). One can imagine analogies with the yeast two-hybrid screen, such as chromophores that can only assemble when the pair is brought together as assemblies of two-fusion proteins to which the halves were attached. Thus libraries could be expressed with each protein in the library configured as a fusion with FRET donor and FRET acceptor. Upon cotransfection and expression, interaction of one member of the donor library with a member of the acceptor library, FRET will result.

PARTICLE-BASED MOLECULAR ASSEMBLIES

Flow cytometry has been extensively used to analyze the formation of macromolecular assemblies on particulate surfaces (see 68, 70–72). The introduction of lipid bilayers onto beads has allowed the study of mobile components associated with the membrane. In its simplest configuration, flow cytometric analysis of molecular assemblies requires that one of the interacting components be physically associated in a covalent or high-affinity state with the beads to be analyzed, while the other component be visible to the cytometer. This approach can be especially powerful to resolve the assembled complex in the presence of free components with low concentration of the particle-bound species. Fifty thousand target molecules and appropriate fluorescent-binding partners provide a bright particle with an excellent signal-to-noise ratio. With 10^5 to 10^6 particles/ml, the concentration of target molecule in solution is $\sim$10–100 pM, below the K_d of most biological interactions. The low concentration enables high-affinity interactions to be measured accurately, without complications introduced by ligand depletion. For enzymatic measurements, an immobilized substrate present at low concentrations makes it practical to provide enzyme in excess and to work in the presteady-state kinetic regime where steady-state assumptions are not required.

Attachment

The immobilized molecule on a surface needs to retain its biological activity and be oriented with appropriate uniformity for recognition by its binding partner. If the protein of interest is already pure, the adsorption of purified proteins to polystyrene microspheres occurs much as proteins are adsorbed to polystyrene microtiter plates for enzyme-linked immunosorbant assays (ELISAs). Covalent attachment utilizes microspheres that possess reactive groups such as carboxylates that conjugate protein (55). This approach gives rise to a number of commercial products in which antibodies create a platform specific for the antigen or goat anti-mouse IgG; coupled to particles, this creates a general platform for other antibodies to attach. Immunoprecipitations are mimicked by coating beads with Protein A or Protein G to capture antibodies or anti-epitope mAbs.

Genetic manipulation of the protein to be immobilized adds amino acids to an end of the protein. These tags may be as short as a few amino acids, representing commonplace antibody epitopes such as HA, myc, and FLAG^{TM}, or they may be in the form of entire protein or domain sequences. Glutathione S-transferase, often used in affinity purification of proteins by virtue of its binding to glutathione, can be exploited to immobilize glutathione S-transferase-fusion proteins to glutathione-derivatized microspheres. A short hexahistidine (6His) tag, usually added to one terminus of a protein or internally at a surface-exposed region through genetic manipulations, can also be used to immobilize a protein directly onto an appropriate microsphere or to antibody-coated beads. Recently, mAbs recognizing polyhistidine epitopes have become available, allowing for antibody-based immobilization as well. Due to the cationic character of chelated Ni^{++} resins and beads, this approach is at best an enrichment of the tagged protein. Not all cited microsphere chemistries have been routinely commercially available for flow cytometry.

Our groups have prepared and characterized polystyrene, dextran, and silica microspheres bearing Ni^{2+}-NTA. We used His-tagged EGFP to determine the specificity, capacity, and stability of these microspheres by flow cytometry. In general the surfaces showed binding of His-EGFP in the low nanomolar range and binding capacities $>1 \times 10^6$ binding sites/microsphere, although nonspecific binding observed with polystyrene was reduced with Tween. Whereas microspheres with covalently attached Ni^{2+}-NTA are stable for at least six months, the stability of His-binding to Ni^{2+}-NTA-based microspheres varies.

Microspheres derivatized with streptavidin are commercially available. As the derivatization of oligonucleotides and peptides can be accomplished during the synthetic process, the site of biotinylation can be unambiguously defined. Proteins and other biological molecules such as lipids and carbohydrates can be easily derivatized with biotin. Mobile components can be generated though the incorporation of biotinylated lipids into lipid bilayer–encased microspheres. Many epitope-specific antibodies are commercially available in a biotinylated form, making derivatization of streptavidin beads straightforward.

A less-specific attachment method employs lectin-coated beads to capture glycosylated proteins. Lectin-coated beads have been used to immobilize crude membrane fractions in the same way as for surface plasmon resonance experiments with rhodopsin (6). We have observed that the formyl peptide receptor can also be examined in this approach (S. Lauer, J. P. Nolan, E. R. Prossnitz & L. A. Sklar, unpublished data). Crude membrane fractions from various cell types overexpressing an array of G protein–coupled receptors are now commercially available and would be suitable for analysis by this method.

Fluorescent Labels

In immunological assays in flow cytometry, the antibody is usually fluorescent by direct conjugation or by biotinylation and capture of fluorescent streptavidin. In some cases, small molecule ligands have been attached to fluorescent albumin or detected by His-tags (102). For particle-based approaches, fluorescent reporters are usually conjugated with commercial reagents selected from a vast number of fluorophores (39). The amine-reactive fluorescein conjugate is still the most common reagent for labeling proteins. It offers relatively high absorbance, high fluorescence quantum yield, and good water solubility. Fluorescein has an excitation maximum that closely matches the 488 nm spectral line of the argon-ion laser for confocal laser scanning microscopy and flow cytometry applications. Fluorescein conjugates have several drawbacks, including photobleaching, pH-sensitive fluorescence ($pK_a \sim 6.4$), a broad emission spectrum that hinders some multicolor experiments, and self-quenching when compounds are labeled at high levels. The cyanine dyes (77) and rhodamine and its derivatives absorb and emit at longer wavelengths than fluorescein and can be used in combination. Two newer series of fluorophores, the BODIPY and Alexa dyes from Molecular Probes, have derivatives that span the visible spectrum. Recently, BODIPY ligands have become commercially available, providing the researcher access to receptor visualization reagents.

Labeling of proteins with derivatized fluorophores requires that the protein be available in a highly purified state. Alternatively, fluorescent chimeric proteins can be created through molecular biology by fusing the protein of interest and the GFP of *Aequoria victoria* (520-nm emission) (14, 74) or one of its variants (enhanced GFP 30-fold brighter; enhanced cyan, -475-nm emission; yellow, -540-nm emission; and UV excitable blue, -430-nm emission). A red fluorescent protein (580-nm emission) derived from *Discosoma* sp. can be used in conjunction with GFP or other nonspectrally overlapping fluorescent proteins. Although GFPs are ~ 27 kDa in size, their addition to either end of a protein often has little effect on protein function and makes them candidates for both in vivo and in vitro applications for molecular assemblies.

Applications

Interactions between proteins and small binding partners (ligands) have been studied in several schemes. A detergent-solubilized, carboxy-terminus 6 His-tagged N-formyl peptide receptor was bound to Ni^{2+}-NTA silica beads. Binding of fluoresceinated formyl peptide ligand to the immobilized receptor was demonstrated by flow cytometry (93). The efficiency of receptor uptake by the particles was greater than 80% with an apparent affinity for the bead in the nM range. The receptors displayed largely homogeneous dissociation characteristics, a native K_d for the ligand in the low nM range and a high occupancy number, with several million receptor molecules per particle. We have not achieved our goal to reconstitute soluble receptors with G proteins or arrestin because of high nonspecific binding of other proteins to the beads. Amino terminus His-tagged receptors have also been attached to Ni^{2+}-NTA beads. Formyl peptide receptors have also been captured by goat anti-mouse beads with anti-His mAb.

Biotinylated, fluoresceinated β-endorphin and FLAG peptides have been immobilized on streptavidin beads. Binding of rhodamine-labeled, anti-peptide antibody was assessed by FRET between the two fluorophores (10). Detection of antibodies in solution and on beads, either by FRET or capture of fluorescent ligands by non-fluorescent antibodies, allowed the determination of K_d values. There was good agreement between solution measurements and flow cytometric determinations.

PROTEIN-PROTEIN   Flow cytometric immunoassays are well known (55), and flow immunoprecipitation has recently been described as an alternative to Western blot-ting (52). This method utilizes mAbs bound to latex particles to immobilize pro-tein kinase substrates. The phosphorylation status of the immobilized protein is assessed by binding to phosphoepitope-specific antibodies. The total amount of immobilized protein on the particles is analyzed by immunofluorescence with anti-bodies to nonphosphorylated epitopes. Such a system is currently commercialized, using multiplexing technology that allows the simultaneous analysis of up to 100 different proteins.

Protein-protein interactions between heterotrimeric G protein subunits have been assessed (79). A detergent solubilized, biotinylated G protein $\beta\gamma$ subunit was attached to streptavidin beads, and the association of a fluorescently labeled $G\alpha$ subunit was measured. The K_d was 3 nM, and k_{on} and k_{off} rates were determined. Because prior radiolabel analysis required μM concentrations of reagents, the true nM K_d values were not detected previously. G protein $\beta\gamma$ subunits were reconstituted into biotinylated phospholipid vesicles and immobilized on beads, allowing a comparison of membrane-associated protein versus solubilized protein and demonstrating G protein subunit dissociation upon activation.

DNA-PROTEIN   Nolan and coworkers (70) have performed kinetic analyses of the enzymatic activity of FEN-1, an endonuclease with an important role in DNA replication and repair. They studied a fluorescently labeled DNA substrate immo-bilized on a microsphere with the fluorescent moiety attached to the distal end of the DNA. Following cleavage of the DNA by FEN-1 in the presence of Mg^{++}, fluorescence was lost from the bead. Kinetic analyses allowed the measurement of rates of formation and dissociation of the FEN-1-DNA complex as well as the catalytic rate constant. A series of kinetic measurements, including Mg^{++}-jump experiments with the rapid mix flow cytometer, allowed the rates of formation and dissociation of the enzyme-substrate complex as well as the cleavage rate constant to be measured. This method has been extended to analyze the structural features of FEN-1 through site-directed mutagenesis (28, 85). The approach has also been applied to measurements of DNA polymerases and DNA ligases (12, 13). Analo-gous enzymatic assays have also been developed for protein-protein interactions [e.g., gelatinase B activity (96)].

DNA-DNA   Determination of the complementarity of two strands of DNA has be-come an important task in genomic analysis. Whereas DNA from any two individu-als is more than 99.9% identical, variations in the remaining 0.1% of the DNA arises from single nucleotide polymorphisms (SNPs). Conventional DNA sequencing is not a practical approach in the analysis of dozens or hundreds of SNPs from an individual. Microarray-based approaches are attractive because of their ability to assess multiple genetic features simultaneously, and arrays of microspheres analyzed by flow cytometry are attractive owing to their greater flexibility and analysis throughput. By coupling robust enzyme-based sequence analysis methods, such as DNA polymerase-mediated single-base extension, with microsphere arrays, it is possible to efficiently genotype large numbers of samples. For example, this approach has been used to analyze the SNPs that define HLA alleles associated with chronic berylium disease (13). Several pharmaceutical and biotechnology companies have adopted this approach to SNP-scoring (16, 47, 72, 103), and other types of genomic analysis can be envisioned using the microsphere-based platform.

LIPIDS ON BEADS   The cellular environment of membranes and membrane-bound proteins has been mimicked by lipid bilayers enclosing beads. These beads have been used to study the binding of factor VIII, the anti-hemophiliac factor, a component of an enzyme complex required for the development of platelet pro-coagulant activity. Gilbert & Arena analyzed the binding interaction and determined the type and number of phospholipids involved in protein binding (31). Beads have been used clinically to diagnose anti-phospholipid antibodies, important in patients with clinical symptoms of the anti-phospholipid syndrome (21). Phospholipids such as cardiolipin, phosphatidylserine, and phosphatidylinositol were coated onto polystyrene beads of different sizes, allowing for simultaneous detection and quantitation of phospholipid antibody isotypes with greater sensitivity than ELISA-based techniques. Annexin V belongs to the family of calcium-dependent phospholipid-binding proteins. Its selectivity for phosphatidylserine leads to its use to detect loss of membrane asymmetry in cells due to apoptosis. The binding characteristics and specificities of annexin V, with respect to phospholipid bilayer composition, were measured on beads (97).

The mobility of lipids has made possible the detection of multivalent binding of pentavalent cholera toxin and the clustering of its receptor, the ganglioside GM1. Addition of the toxin leads to FRET (95) between green and red versions of GM1 incorporated into the bilayers. Sensitivity, as low as 1 pM, can be achieved with a two-tiered FRET system (94). Reconstitution of both GPCR (59) and adhesion molecules (T. Buranda, L. A. Sklar & R. Larson, unpublished data) into lipobeads has been accomplished.

HIGH-THROUGHPUT FLOW CYTOMETRY

Flow cytometry is usually associated with limited sample throughput, although automated sample loaders allow analysis of two to three samples per minute from multiwell plates. Several developments are improving the sample throughput for molecular assembly. Multiparameter detection allows multiplexing, in which dozens (30), and potentially hundreds (15), of assemblies are measured in a single sample using sets of colored microspheres. Individual microspheres are identified by staining levels of different dyes, for example, orange and red fluorophores, while a third color, green, is used for the molecular assembly assay. Several companies are now marketing particles, hardware, and software for multiplex analysis. High-speed analysis and sorting also allow screening of members of combinatorial expression libraries on the basis of function, often an assay based on a molecular assembly (16, 64, 73, 86). A one-bead one-peptide approach has also been used for screening (62). By contrast, flow cytometry has been slow to develop as an efficient means for large-scale operations involving multiple discrete suspensions of particles or reagents. Such a capability promises to benefit a number of areas of biological investigation. For example, modern drug discovery involves testing of cellular targets against millions of potentially valuable compounds that may bind cellular receptors to affect clinically therapeutic cellular responses.

Computer-controlled sample mixing and delivery systems have been adapted to provide flow cytometers with improved sample handling capabilities. The adaptation of flow injection analysis involving high-precision valves and stepper motor–driven syringes (51) has enabled unattended online bioprocess monitoring (104) and execution of subsecond resolution kinetics experiments. More recently, plug flow cytometry permitted analysis of as many as 9–10 samples per minute (23–25). Here, individual sample suspensions are sequentially inserted as a bolus or "plug" of precisely defined volume into a continuously flowing stream of fluid. The stream delivers the sample plugs, separated by buffer. Because sample plugs are of a precisely defined volume (5 μl at present), particle concentrations are directly determined from the total particle counts in each sample plug. This feature enabled the implementation of accurate singlet cell–depletion adhesion assays described above. As it is not necessary that the vessel containing the sample be pressurized, it has been possible to interface the flow cytometer with devices such as the cone-plate viscometer for cell-cell adhesion analysis in a uniform shear environment as well as a high-throughput pharmacology system for rapid evaluation of cell responses to pharmacological receptor-ligand interaction (25). Edwards et al. were able to relate the number of receptor sites occupied by a fluorescent ligand to the calcium response in cells transfected with the formyl peptide receptor. The cell responses were all-or-none, and the fraction of sites required for the response was small.

Recently, we reported an approach in which samples were aspirated from microplate wells and delivered to the flow cytometer for analysis at rates approaching 100 samples per minute (50). This approach uses air bubbles to separate samples with low carryover. The samples were introduced by an autosampler and peristaltic pump into a tubing line that directly connects to the flow cytometer. This autosampling method is compatible with the molecular assembly analyses as well as online mixing (48) for kinetic analysis at high throughput. Sampling from 10 μl volumes enables reagent cost savings, uses limited reagents at otherwise prohibitive concentrations, and maintains uniform suspensions of cells and particles for prolonged periods of time. Microfluidics has been formally introduced into flow cytometry systems (29).

FUTURE DIRECTIONS

Flow cytometry is proving to be well-suited to the biophysical research laboratory. The advent of benchtop cytometers and off-the-shelf kinetic hardware and software should increase cytometry applications to analysis of molecular assembly in genomics, proteomics, and combinatorial chemistry for drug discovery. Reagents for labeling biomolecules, generating fusion proteins, and suitable particle chemistries are increasingly available. The broad range of flow cytometric capabilities for measuring molecular assemblies in vitro as well as in live cells, combined with multiplex analysis and automated sample handling, promises to make flow cytometry an important assembly tool.

Instrumentation

The LANL team is working to improve the resolution of free and bound molecules by creating a flow cytometer with a smaller interrogation volume. The reduction in volume will be accomplished by using smaller laser spot sizes and reduced sample stream diameters. Electronics that allow for the collection of negative signals may enable the discrimination of negative signals in a high direct current background. These improvements could allow homogeneous analysis of reactions with much lower affinities than previously possible.

Fluorescent Ligands

An important opportunity is likely to be found with GFP-fusion proteins for soluble proteins (56). The UNM team has set its sights on expressing fluorescent fusions of soluble cell adhesion molecules. These reagents should enable a systematic characterization of the monovalent affinities and kinetics of interaction of cell adhesion molecules and should add considerably to understanding the relationship between affinity and avidity.

New Opportunities for the Use of Flow Cytometry in Molecular Assembly

Signaling complexes in cells often consist of multiprotein assemblies. The "arrestin scaffold" in cells (57), for example, consists of an activated and phosphorylated GPCR, arrestin, and potentially several intracellular kinases from a kinase cascade. The scaffold could be assessed in cells through energy transfer among fluorescent fusion proteins or on particles, one protein at a time, detecting the stepwise assembly through the use of antibodies or fluorescent fusion proteins.

Single Molecule Detection

Single molecule detection is possible in flowing systems by extending the transit time through the laser beam from microseconds to milliseconds. In a millisecond, a fluor can produce 100,000 photons. The addition of multicolor capabilities to single molecule detection could enable the direct detection of molecular assemblies, one at a time, in suspension. These highly sensitive systems have now been constructed with microfluidic principles that will be automated for high throughput (29).

ACKNOWLEDGMENTS

This work was supported by NIH GM60799, NIH RR14175, NIH RR01315, NIH AI36357, and the State of New Mexico Cigarette Tax at the University of New Mexico Cancer Research and Treatment Center.

NOTE ADDED IN PROOF

While this manuscript was in preparation, two publications appeared describing a detailed validation of competitive binding protocols in flow cytometry (Waller A, Pipkorn D, Sutton KL, Linderman JJ, Omann GM. 2001. Validation of flow cytometric competitive binding protocols and characterization of fluorescently labeled ligands. *Cytometry* 45:102–14) and an analysis of binding to EGF receptors (Stein RA, Wilkinson JC, Guyer GA, Staros JV. 2001. An analytical approach to the measurement of equilibrium binding constants: application to EGF binding to EGR receptors on intact cells measured by flow cytometry. *Biochemistry* 40:6142–54).

Visit the Annual Reviews home page at www.annualreviews.org

LITERATURE CITED

1. Adams JA, Omann GM, Linderman JJ. 1998. A mathematical model for ligand/receptor/G-protein dynamics and actin polymerization in human neutrophils. *J. Theor. Biol.* 193:543–60
2. Ambrose WP, Goodwin PM, Jett JH, VanOrden A, Werner JH, Keller RA. 1999. Single molecule fluorescence spectroscopy at ambient temperature. *Chem. Rev.* 99:2929–56
3. Bednar B, Cunningham ME, McQueney PA, Egbertson MS, Askew BC, et al. 1997. Flow cytometric measurement of kinetic and equilibrium binding parameters of arginine-glycine-aspartic acid ligands in binding to glycoprotein IIb/IIIa on platelets. *Cytometry* 28:58–65
4. Bennett TA, Key TA, Gurevich VV, Neubig R, Prossnitz ER, Sklar LA. 2001. Real-time analysis of G protein-coupled receptor reconstitution in a solu-bilized system. *J. Biol. Chem.* 276:22453–60
5. Bennett TA, Maestas DC, Prossnitz ER. 2000. Arrestin binding to the G protein-coupled N-formyl peptide receptor is regulated by the conserved 'DRY' sequence. *J. Biol. Chem.* 275:24590–94
6. Bieri C, Ernst OP, Heyse S, Hofmann KP, Vogel H. 1999. Micropatterned immobilization of a G protein-coupled receptor and direct detection of G protein activation. *Nat. Biotechnol.* 17:1105–8
7. Bleesing JJ, Fleisher TA. 2001. Cell function-based flow cytometry. *Semin. Hematol.* 38:169–78
8. Boder ET, Wittrup KD. 1998. Optimal screening of surface-displayed polypeptide libraries. *Biotechnol. Prog.* 14:55–62
9. Boder ET, Wittrup KD. 2000. Yeast surface display for directed evolution of

protein expression, affinity, and stability. *Methods Enzymol.* 328:430–44

10. Buranda T, Huang J, Lopez GP, Sklar LA. 2001. Detection of epitope-tagged proteins in flow cytometry: FRET-based assays on beads with femtomole resolution. *Anal. Biochem.* 298:151–62

11. Burgle M, Koppitz M, Riemer C, Kessler H, Konig B, et al. 1997. Inhibition of the interaction of urokinase-type plasminogen activator (uPA) with its receptor (uPAR) by synthetic peptides. *Biol. Chem.* 378:231–37

12. Cai H, Kommander K, White PS, Nolan JP. 1997. Flow cytometry-based hybridization and polymorphism detection and analysis. *Proc. SPIE* 3256:171–77

13. Cai H, White PS, Torney D, Deshpande A, Wang Z, et al. 2000. Flow cytometry-based minisequencing: a new platform for high-throughput single-nucleotide polymorphism scoring. *Genomics* 66:135–43

14. Chalfie M, Tu Y, Euskirchen G, Ward WW, Prasher DC. 1994. Green fluorescent protein as a marker for gene expression. *Science* 263:802–5

15. Chandler VS, Denton D, Pempsell P. 1998. Biomolecular multiplexing of up to 512 assays on a new solid-state 4 color flow analyzer. *Cytometry* 9(Suppl.):40

16. Chen G, Hayhurst A, Thomas JG, Harvey BR, Iverson BL, Georgiou G. 2001. Isolation of high-affinity ligand-binding proteins by periplasmic expression with cytometric screening (PECS). *Nat. Biotechnol.* 19:537–42

17. Chigaev A, Blenc A, Braaten JV, Kumaraswamy N, Kepley C, et al. 2001. Real-time analysis of the affinity regulation of VLA-4: the physiologically activated receptor is intermediate in affinity between resting and Mn or antibody activation. *J. Biol. Chem.* 276:48670–78

18. Damjanovich S, Matko J, Matyus L, Szabo G Jr, Szollosi J, et al. 1998. Supramolecular receptor structures in the plasma membrane of lymphocytes re-

vealed by flow cytometric energy transfer, scanning force- and transmission electron-microscopic analyses. *Cytometry* 33:225–33

19. Daugherty PS, Iverson BL, Georgiou G. 2000. Flow cytometric screening of cell-based libraries. *J. Immunol. Methods* 243:211–27

20. De Rosa SC, Herzenberg LA, Roederer M. 2001. 11-color, 13-parameter flow cytometry: identification of human naive T cells by phenotype, function, and T-cell receptor diversity. *Nat. Med.* 7:245–48

21. Drouvalakis KA, Neeson PJ, Buchanan RR. 1999. Detection of anti-phosphatidylethanolamine antibodies using flow cytometry. *Cytometry* 36:46–51

22. Edwards BS, Curry MS, Tsuji H, Brown D, Larson RS, Sklar LA. 2000. Expression of P-selectin at low site density promotes selective attachment of eosinophils over neutrophils. *J. Immunol. Methods* 165:404–10

23. Edwards BS, Kuckuck F, Sklar LA. 1999. Plug flow cytometry: an automated coupling device for rapid sequential flow cytometric sample analysis. *Cytometry* 37:156–59

24. Edwards BS, Kuckuck FW, Prossnitz ER, Okun A, Ransom JT, Sklar LA. 2001. Plug flow cytometry extends analytical capabilities in cell adhesion and receptor pharmacology. *Cytometry* 43:211–16

25. Edwards BS, Kuckuck FW, Prossnitz ER, Ransom JT, Sklar LA. 2001. HTPS flow cytometry: a novel platform for automated high throughput drug discovery and characterization. *J. Biomol. Screen.* 6:83–90

26. Eftink MR. 1997. Fluorescence methods for studying equilibrium macromolecule-ligand interactions. *Methods Enzymol.* 278:221–57

27. Faraday N, Goldschmidt-Clermont P, Dise K, Bray PF. 1994. Quantitation of soluble fibrinogen binding to platelets by fluorescence-activated flow cytometry. *J. Lab Clin. Med.* 123:728–40

28. Frank G, Qiu J, Somsouk M, Weng Y, Somsouk L, et al. 1998. Partial functional deficiency of E160D flap endonuclease-1 mutant in vitro and in vivo is due to defective cleavage of DNA substrates. *J. Biol. Chem.* 273:33064–72

29. Fu AY, Spence C, Scherer A, Arnold FH, Quake SR. 1999. A microfabricated fluorescence-activated cell sorter. *Nat. Biotechnol.* 17:1109–11

30. Fulton RJ, McDade RL, Smith PL, Kienker LJ, Kettman JR Jr. 1997. Advanced multiplexed analysis with the FlowMetrix system. *Clin. Chem.* 43:1749–56

31. Gilbert GE, Arena AA. 1995. Phosphatidylethanolamine induces high affinity binding sites for factor VIII on membranes containing phosphatidyl-L-serine. *J. Biol. Chem.* 270:18500–5

32. Graves SW, Habbersett RC, Nolan JP. 2001. A dynamic inline sample thermoregulation unit for flow cytometry. *Cytometry* 43:23–30

33. Graves SW, Nolan JP, Jett JH, Martin JC, Sklar LA. 2002. Nozzle design parameters and their effects on rapid sample delivery in flow cytometry. *Cytometry* In press

34. Gray ML, Hoffman RA, Hansen WP. 1983. A new method for cell volume measurement based on volume exclusion of a fluorescent dye. *Cytometry* 3:428–34

35. Griffin BA, Adams SR, Jones J, Tsien RY. 2000. Fluorescent labeling of recombinant proteins in living cells with FlAsH. *Methods Enzymol.* 327:565–78

36. Guo C, Dower SK, Holowka D, Baird B. 1995. Fluorescence resonance energy transfer reveals interleukin (IL)-1-dependent aggregation of IL-1 type I receptors that correlates with receptor activation. *J. Biol. Chem.* 270:27562–68

37. Gursoy RN, Jois DS, Siahaan TJ. 1999. Structural recognition of an ICAM-1 peptide by its receptor on the surface of T cells: conformational studies of cyclo (1, 12)-Pen-Pro-Arg-Gly-Gly-Ser-Val-Leu-Val-Thr-Gly-Cys-OH. *J. Pept. Res.* 53: 422–31

38. Guyer DA, Moore KL, Lynam EB, Schammel CM, Rogelj S, et al. 1996. P-selectin glycoprotein ligand-1 (PSGL-1) is a ligand for L-selectin in neutrophil aggregation. *Blood* 88:2415–21

39. Haughland RP. 2001. *Handbook of Fluorescent Probes and Research Products.* Eugene, OR: Molecular Probes

40. Deleted in proof

41. Heithier H, Hallmann D, Boege F, Reilander H, Dees C, et al. 1994. Synthesis and properties of fluorescent beta-adrenoceptor ligands. *Biochemistry* 33:9126–34

42. Hentzen ER, Neelamegham S, Kansas GS, Benanti JA, McIntire LV, et al. 2000. Sequential binding of CD11a/CD18 and CD11b/CD18 defines neutrophil capture and stable adhesion to intercellular adhesion molecule-1. *Blood* 95:911–20

43. Hidaka H, Hidaka E, Tozuka M, Nakayama J, Katsuyama T, Fidge N. 1999. The identification of specific high density lipoprotein 3 binding sites on human blood monocytes using fluorescence-labeled ligand. *J. Lipid Res.* 40:1131–39

44. Hill JJ, Royer CA. 1997. Fluorescence approaches to study of protein-nucleic acid complexation. *Methods Enzymol.* 278:390–416

45. Hlavacek WS, Perelson AS, Sulzer B, Bold J, Paar J, et al. 1999. Quantifying aggregation of IgE-FcepsilonRI by multivalent antigen. *Biophys. J.* 76:2421–31

46. Hoffman JF, Linderman JJ, Omann GM. 1996. Receptor up-regulation, internalization, and interconverting receptor states. Critical components of a quantitative description of N-formyl peptide-receptor dynamics in the neutrophil. *J. Biol. Chem.* 271:18394–404

47. Hoffman RA. 2001. Standardization and quantitation in flow cytometry. *Methods Cell Biol.* 63:299–340

48. Jackson WC, Kuckuck F, Edwards BS, Mammoli A, Gallegos CM, et al. 2002. Mixing small volumes for continuous

high throughput flow cytometry: performance of a mixing Y and peristaltic sample delivery. *Cytometry* In press

49. Key TA, Bennett TA, Gurevich VV, Sklar LA, Prossnitz ER. 2001. Regulation of solubilied N-formyl peptide receptor agonist affinity by reconstitution with β-arrestins and heterotrimeric G proteins. *J. Biol. Chem.* 276:49195–203

50. Kuckuck FW, Edwards BS, Sklar LA. 2001. High throughput flow cytometry. *Cytometry* 44:83–90

51. Lindberg W, Ruzicka J, Christian GD. 1993. Flow injection cytometry: a new approach for sample and solution handling in flow cytometry. *Cytometry* 14:230–36

52. Lund-Johansen F, Davis K, Bishop J, de Waal Malefyt R. 2000. Flow cytometric analysis of immunoprecipitates: high-throughput analysis of protein phosphorylation and protein-protein interactions. *Cytometry* 39:250–59

53. Martin JC, Schwartzenruber DE. 1980. Time: a new parameter for flow cytometry. *Science* 207:199–201

54. Matko J, Edidin M. 1997. Energy transfer methods for detecting molecular clusters on cell surfaces. *Methods Enzymol.* 278:444–62

55. McHugh TM. 1995. Flow microsphere immunoassay for the quantitative and simultaneous detection of multiple soluble analytes. In *Methods in Cell Biology*, ed. Z Darzynkiewicz, P Robinson, HA Crissman, pp. 575–95. San Diego: Academic

56. Medina-Kauwe LK, Leung V, Wu L, Kedes L. 2000. Assessing the binding and endocytosis activity of cellular receptors using GFP-ligand fusions. *Biotechniques* 29:602–9

57. Miller WE, Lefkowitz RJ. 2001. Expanding roles for beta-arrestins as scaffolds and adapters in GPCR signaling and trafficking. *Curr. Opin. Cell Biol.* 13:139–45

58. Mills JS, Miettinen HM, Cummings D, Jesaitis AJ. 2000. Characterization of the binding site on the formyl peptide receptor using three receptor mutants and analogs of Met-Leu-Phe and Met-Met-Trp-Leu-Leu. *J. Biol. Chem.* 275:39012–17

59. Mirzabekov T, Kontos H, Farzan M, Marasco W, Sodroski J. 2000. Paramagnetic proteoliposomes containing a pure, native, and oriented seven-transmembrane segment protein, CCR5. *Nat. Biotechnol.* 18:649–54

60. Miyawaki A, Tsien RY. 2000. Monitoring protein conformations and interactions by fluorescence resonance energy transfer between mutants of green fluorescent protein. *Methods Enzymol.* 327:472–500

61. Model MA, Omann GM. 1995. Ligand-receptor interaction rates in the presence of convective mass transport. *Biophys. J.* 69:1712–20

62. Muller K, Gombert FO, Manning U, Grossmuller F, Graff P, et al. 1996. Rapid identification of phosphopeptide ligands for SH2 domains. Screening of peptide libraries by fluorescence-activated bead sorting. *J. Biol. Chem.* 271:16500–5

63. Murphy RF. 1990. Ligand binding, endocytosis, and processing. In *Flow Cytometry and Sorting*, ed. M Melamed, T Lindmo, M Mendelsohn, pp. 355-66. New York: Wiley

64. Needels MC, Jones DG, Tate EH, Heinkel GL, Kochersperger LM, et al. 1993. Generation and screening of an oligonucleotide-encoded synthetic peptide library. *Proc. Natl. Acad. Sci. USA* 90:10700–4

65. Neelamegham S, Taylor AD, Shankaran H, Smith CW, Simon SI. 2000. Shear and time-dependent changes in Mac-1, LFA-1, and ICAM-3 binding regulate neutrophil homotypic adhesion. *J. Immunol. Methods* 164:3798–805

66. Nolan JP, Chambers JD, Sklar LA. 1998. Cytometric approaches to the study of receptors. In *Phagocytic Functions: A Guide for Research and Clinical Evaluation*, ed. JP Robinson, GF Babcock, pp. 1946. New York:Wiley

67. Nolan JP, Lauer S, Prossnitz ER, Sklar LA. 1999. Flow cytometry: a versatile tool

for all phases of drug discovery. *Drug Discov. Today* 4:173–80

68. Nolan JP, Mandy FF. 2002. Suspension array technology: new tools for gene and protein analysis. *Cell Mol. Biol.* In press

69. Nolan JP, Posner RG, Martin JC, Habbersett R, Sklar LA. 1995. A rapid mix flow cytometer with subsecond kinetic resolution. *Cytometry* 21:223–29

70. Nolan JP, Shen B, Park MS, Sklar LA. 1996. Kinetic analysis of human flap endonuclease-1 by flow cytometry. *Biochemistry* 35:11668–76

71. Nolan JP, Sklar LA. 1998. The emergence of flow cytometry for sensitive, real-time measurements of molecular interactions. *Nat. Biotechnol.* 16:633–38

72. Nolan JP, Sklar LA. 2002. Suspension array technology: evolution of the flat array paradigm. *Trends Biotechnol.* 20:9–12

73. Olsen MJ, Stephens D, Griffiths D, Daugherty P, Georgiou G, Iverson BL. 2000. Function-based isolation of novel enzymes from a large library. *Nat. Biotechnol.* 18:1071–74

74. Prasher DC, Eckenrode VK, Ward WW, Prendergast FG, Cormier MJ. 1992. Primary structure of the *Aequorea victoria* green-fluorescent protein. *Gene* 111:229–33

75. Prossnitz ER. 1997. Desensitization of N-formylpeptide receptor-mediated activation is dependent upon receptor phosphorylation. *J. Biol. Chem.* 272:15213–19

76. Prossnitz ER, Gilbert TL, Chiang S, Campbell JJ, Qin S, et al. 1999. Multiple activation steps of the N-formyl peptide receptor. *Biochemistry* 38:2240–47

77. Randolph JB, Waggoner AS. 1997. Stability, specificity and fluorescence brightness of multiply-labeled fluorescent DNA probes. *Nucleic Acids Res.* 25:2923–29

78. Ringquist S, Parma D. 1998. Anti-L-selectin oligonucleotide ligands recognize CD62L-positive leukocytes: binding affinity and specificity of univalent and bivalent ligands. *Cytometry* 33:394–405

79. Sarvazyan NA, Remmers AE, Neubig RR. 1998. Determinants of gi1alpha and beta gamma binding. Measuring high affinity interactions in a lipid environment using flow cytometry. *J. Biol. Chem.* 273:7934–40

80. Scampavia LD, Blankenstein G, Ruzicka J, Christian GD. 1995. A coaxial jet mixer for rapid kinetic analysis in flow injection and flow injection cytometry. *Anal. Chem.* 67:2743–49

81. Schwartz A, Fernandez-Repollet E, Vogt R, Gratama JW. 1996. Standardizing flow cytometry: construction of a standardized fluorescence calibration plot using matching spectral calibrators. *Cytometry* 26:22–31

82. Seamer L, Sklar LA. 2001. Time as a flow cytometric parameter. *Methods Cell Biol.* 63:169–83

83. Seamer LC, Kuckuck F, Sklar LA. 1999. Sheath fluid control to permit stable flow in rapid mix flow cytometry. *Cytometry* 35:75–79

84. Shapiro HM. 1995. *Practical Flow Cytometry*. New York: Wiley. 295 pp. 3rd ed.

85. Shen B, Nolan JP, Sklar LA, Park MS. 1996. Essential amino acids for substrate binding and catalysis of human flap endonuclease 1. *J. Biol. Chem.* 271:9173–76

86. Shusta EV, Holler PD, Kieke MC, Kranz DM, Wittrup KD. 2000. Directed evolution of a stable scaffold for T-cell receptor engineering. *Nat. Biotechnol.* 18:754–59

87. Simon SI, Chambers JD, Sklar LA. 1990. Flow cytometric analysis and modeling of cell-cell adhesive interactions: the neutrophil as a model. *J. Cell Biol.* 111:2747–56

88. Simon SI, Neelamegham S, Taylor A, Smith CW. 1998. The multistep process of homotypic neutrophil aggregation: a review of the molecules and effects of hydrodynamics. *Cell Adhes. Commun.* 6:263–76

89. Sims PJ, Ginsberg MH, Plow EF, Shattil SJ. 1991. Effect of platelet activation on the conformation of the plasma membrane

glycoprotein IIb-IIIa complex. *J. Biol. Chem.* 266:7345–52

90. Sklar LA. 1987. Real-time spectroscopic analysis of ligand-receptor dynamics. *Annu. Rev. Biophys. Biophys. Chem.* 16:479–506

91. Sklar LA, Sayre J, McNeil VM, Finney DA. 1985. Competitive binding kinetics in ligand-receptor-competitor systems. Rate parameters for unlabeled ligands for the formyl peptide receptor. *Mol. Pharmacol.* 28:323–30

92. Sklar LA, Seamer L, Kuckuck F, Posner RG, Nolan JP. 1998. Sample handling for molecular assembly in flow cytometry. *Proc. SPIE* 3256:144–53

93. Sklar LA, Vilven J, Lynam E, Neldon D, Bennett TA, Prossnitz E. 2000. Solubilization and display of G protein-coupled receptors on beads for real-time fluorescence and flow cytometric analysis. *Biotechniques* 28:976–85

94. Song X, Shi J, Nolan J, Swanson B. 2001. Detection of multivalent interactions through two-tiered energy transfer. *Anal. Biochem.* 291:133–41

95. Song X, Shi J, Swanson B. 2000. Flow cytometry-based biosensor for detection of multivalent proteins. *Anal. Biochem.* 284:35–41

96. St-Pierre Y, Desrosiers M, Tremblay P, Esteve PO, Opdenakker G. 1996. Flow cytometric analysis of gelatinase B (MMP-9) activity using immobilized fluorescent substrate on microspheres. *Cytometry* 25:374–80

97. Stuart MC, Reutelingsperger CP, Frederik PM. 1998. Binding of annexin V to bilayers with various phospholipid compositions using glass beads in a flow cytometer. *Cytometry* 33:414–19

98. Taylor AD, Neelamegham S, Hellums JD, Smith CW, Simon SI. 1996. Molecular dynamics of the transition from L-selectin- to beta 2-integrin-dependent neutrophil adhesion under defined hydrodynamic shear. *Biophys. J.* 71:3488–500

99. Tota MR, Xu L, Sirotina A, Strader CD, Graziano MP. 1995. Interaction of [fluorescein-Trp25]glucagon with the human glucagon receptor expressed in *Drosophila* Schneider 2 cells. *J. Biol. Chem.* 270:26466–72

100. Tsao PW, Bozarth JM, Jackson SA, Forsythe MS, Flint SK, Mousa SA. 1995. Platelet GPIIb/IIIa receptor occupancy studies using a novel fluoresceinated cyclic Arg-Gly-Asp peptide. *Thromb. Res.* 77:543–56

101. Wang S, Clemmons A, Strader C, Bayne M. 1998. Evidence for hydrophobic interaction between galanin and the GalR1 galanin receptor and GalR1-mediated ligand internalization: fluorescent probing with a fluorescein-galanin. *Biochemistry* 37:9528–35

102. Wilken HC, Rogge S, Gotze O, Werfel T, Zwirner J. 1999. Specific detection by flow cytometry of histidine-tagged ligands bound to their receptors using a tag-specific monoclonal antibody. *J. Immunol. Methods* 226:139–45

103. Ye F, Li MS, Taylor D, Nguyen Q, Coulton H, et al. 2001. Fluorescent microsphere-based readout technology for multiplexed single nucleotide polymorphism analysis and bacterial identification. *Hum. Mutat.* 17:305–16

104. Zhao R, Natarajan A, Srienc F. 1999. A flow injection flow cytometry system for on-line monitoring of bioreactors. *Biotechnol. Bioeng.* 62:609–17

105. Zlokarnik G, Negulescu PA, Knapp TE, Mere L, Burres N, et al. 1998. Quantitation of transcription and clonal selection of single living cells with beta-lactamase as reporter. *Science* 279:84–88

Annu. Rev. Biophys. Biomol. Struct. 2002. 31:121–49
DOI: 10.1146/annurev.biophys.31.082901.134423
Copyright © 2002 by Annual Reviews. All rights reserved

STRUCTURAL AND THERMODYNAMIC CORRELATES OF T CELL SIGNALING

Markus G. Rudolph, John G. Luz, and Ian A. Wilson

The Scripps Research Institute, Department of Molecular Biology and The Skaggs Institute for Chemical Biology, 10550 North Torrey Pines Road, La Jolla, California 92037; e-mail: mardolph@scripps.edu; jglma@scripps.edu; wilson@scripps.edu

Key Words T cell receptor, major histocompatibility complex, protein-protein interaction, coreceptors, crystal structure, immunological synapse, thermodynamic and kinetic properties

■ **Abstract** The first crystal structures of intact T cell receptors (TCRs) bound to class I peptide-MHC (pMHCs) antigens were determined in 1996. Since then, further structures of class I TCR/pMHC complexes have explored the degree of structural variability in the TCR-pMHC system and the structural basis for positive and negative selection. The recent determination of class II and allogeneic class I TCR/pMHC structures, as well as those of accessory molecules (e.g., CD3), has pushed our knowledge of TCR/pMHC interactions into new realms, shedding light on clinical pathologies, such as graft rejection and graft-versus-host disease. Furthermore, the determination of coreceptor structures lays the foundation for a more comprehensive structural description of the supramolecular TCR signaling events and those assemblies that arise in the immunological synapse. While these telling photodocumentaries of the TCR/pMHC interaction are composed mainly from static crystal structures, a full description of the biological snapshots in T cell signaling requires additional analytical methods that record the dynamics of the process. To this end, surface plasmon resonance (SPR), isothermal titration calorimetry (ITC), and ultracentrifugation (UC) have furnished both affinities and kinetics of the TCR/pMHC association. In the past year, structural, biochemical, and molecular biological data describing TCR/pMHC interactions have sublimely coalesced into a burgeoning well of understanding that promises to deliver further insights into T cell recognition. The coming years will, through a more intimate union of structural and kinetic data, allow many pressing questions to be addressed, such as how TCR/pMHC ligation is affected by coreceptor binding and what is the mechanism of TCR signaling in both early and late stages of T cell engagement with antigen-presenting cells.

CONTENTS

INTRODUCTION

T cells guard against foreign invasion of microbial pathogens by mechanisms that effectively distinguish foreign from self peptides through coupling TCR/pMHC recognition to processes of positive and negative selection and peripheral tolerance. Whereas in humoral immunity, antibodies identify antigenic molecules as distinct entities, in the cellular response, T cell receptors (TCRs) recognize antigenic peptide fragments only when presented by an appropriate major histocompatibility complex (MHC) molecule. A fundamental difference between antibody/antigen and TCR/pMHC recognition is that the specificity of the former is dependent on high affinity (K_d is nM) for the free antigen, whereas in the latter low affinities predominate (K_d is $\sim$0.1–500 μM), and, thus, specificity must be ensured by a different mechanism. The T cell response, characterized by phosphorylation of $\alpha\beta$ TCR-associated CD3ζ-chains and recruitment and activation of ZAP70, culminates in lysis of the target cell. This series of events, however, requires the coordinated activities of several other TCR-associated molecules, including CD3 and CD8 or CD4, and costimulatory receptors.

Mature T cells bearing clonotypic TCRs are culled from a pool of naïve progenitor cells by a two-stage process. In the first stage, T cells undergo positive selection, i.e., the TCRs they express must recognize self-peptides bound to self-, or syngeneic, MHCs before they can differentiate from "double positives" into CD4 or CD8 expressing "single positives." T cells that fail to recognize syngeneic pMHCs are destined to die within the thymus. However, positively selected T cells activated within the thymus by self-pMHCs die in the second stage of the process, negative selection. That T cells can be both positively and negatively selected using the same repertoire of antigens is paradoxical and one of the persistent mysteries of cellular immunity.

TCRs are cell-surface heterodimers consisting of disulfide-linked α and β chains or, alternatively, γ and δ chains, and, based on genetic analysis, were predicted to have a domain organization and binding site similar to antibodies (20, 25).

Each chain is composed of two Ig-like domains (one variable and one constant), a transmembrane domain, and a short cytoplasmic tail. The TCR binds pMHC antigen through complementarity determining regions (CDRs) present in the variable domains, with the membrane-proximal constant domains distal to the binding interface. Generally, the TCR heterodimer is oriented approximately diagonally relative to the long axis of the MHC peptide-binding groove (38, 40). The V_α domain is poised above the N-terminal half of the peptide, whereas the V_β domain is located over the C-terminal portion of the peptide (Figure 1, see color insert). Peptide contacts are made primarily through the CDR3 loops, which exhibit the greatest degree of genetic variability. The preponderance of conserved contacts with the MHC α-helices are mediated through CDRs 1 and 2 (42), particularly for V_α, with the CDR3 loops contributing MHC contacts in a far less conserved manner.

It should be noted that engagement of a pMHC with its cognate TCR does not necessarily lead to T cell activation. In fact, in the case of antagonist peptides, T cell activation is inhibited. Engagement with a partial agonist elicits some, but not all, of the responses that characterize T cell activation by agonist ligands. It was expected that, by examining crystal structures of TCR/pMHC with altered peptide ligands (APL), this range of responses could be correlated with structural rearrangements. Thus far, the crystal structures do not explain the large biological differences or outcomes that can arise in T cell signaling from binding of APLs (27, 28). Kinetic data have loosely correlated slower dissociation rates with increased agonism (24), although even that is not absolute (5, 12, 41, 43).

Insights into TCR structure have come from crystallized extracellular TCR fragments and individual chains (31, 32, 72, 78, 90, 102a), intact TCRs (40, 121), and TCR/pMHC complexes (27–29, 38–40, 48, 96, 97) (Figure 1). The accumulation of structural and kinetic data has allowed many pressing questions in cellular immunity to be answered, yet has also made some other questions seem even more confusing, such as what is the structural basis of positive and negative selection and how do TCRs distinguish between agonist, partial agonist, and antagonist ligands in order to elicit different signaling outcomes (103a). In this review, we discuss the recent remarkable advances in the understanding of TCR/pMHC interactions and associated coreceptors and some of the important questions that, to date, are left unanswered. We do not intend to review all of the fascinating recent work on the immunological synapse in which lateral receptor motions and rearrangements upon T cell engagement have been followed with the use of fluorescent labels (16, 21, 44, 46, 63, 84, 119). Other notable TCR/pMHC reviews include (39a, 42, 48a, 101, 103a, 122a).

STRUCTURES OF $\alpha\beta$ TCR AND PEPTIDE-MHC COMPLEXES

Clonotypic $\alpha\beta$ TCRs recognize peptides presented by either class I or class II MHCs. Class II MHCs present peptides originating from breakdown of extracellular antigens in endosomal compartments, whereas class I MHCs present peptides derived from intracellular degradation of proteins in the cytosol. TCRs that recognize these MHCs are found on two distinct cytotoxic and T-helper cell lineages, depending on the class of the MHC to which they are restricted. Class I and class II MHCs both present peptides in an extended conformation in a vice-like groove, with two flanking α-helices and a floor composed of anti-parallel β-strands (Figure 2, see color insert). While the ends of the peptide-binding groove are occluded in class I MHC molecules, they are open in class II molecules; therefore, the grooves of class II MHCs can accommodate peptides significantly longer than can those of their class I brethren (Figure 2). The first two turns of the class I MHC α_1-helix are replaced in class II MHCs by a β-strand. Although both classes of MHCs are composed of two noncovalently linked polypeptide chains, in class I MHCs the peptide-binding site is formed by the heavy chain only, and in class II MHCs both α and β chains are coopted into the tertiary structure of the binding groove. Given the biological and structural divergence between these two MHC classes, it is of interest to compare and contrast their interactions with their cognate TCRs (Figures 1, 2, 3). A detailed analysis of the TCR/pMHC interface that includes buried surface areas, relative contributions of CDR loops, hydrogen bonds, salt bridges, and van der Waals contacts is given in Tables 1 and 2.

Canonical Structures of CDR Loops

A plethora of structural and sequence data has facilitated characterization of a limited set of well-defined loop conformations, termed canonical structures, that the CDR loops of antibodies adopt (125). It had been hypothesized, based on sequence data and before the crystal structure of any TCR had been determined, that the conformations of TCR CDR loops would, like those of antibodies, be restricted to sets of canonical structures (19). With the sequencing of the human TCR α (61) and β (100) loci and the gradual accrual of structural information describing the three-dimensional atomic organization of TCRs, it has become possible to make a preliminary classification of TCR CDR loops into canonical structures (3).

Using the available atomic coordinates of TCRs, TCR fragments, and TCR/pMHC complexes, with specific reference to conserved key CDR loop residues, the majority of CDR loops 1 and 2, for both the α and β chain, have been assigned canonical structures (3). Of the 37 sequenced human functional V_α segments, 28 $\alpha1$ and 26 $\alpha2$ CDR loops fall within defined conformational groups. Of the 47 sequenced human functional V_β segments, 41 $\beta1$ and 44 $\beta2$ CDR loops fall within canonical groups. Several other classes of canonical structures have been predicted based on sequences that diverge from those clearly assigned to defined groups (3). Lack of sequencing data from the murine α locus has so far precluded a comprehensive assessment of how CDRs encoded therein would partition into the various groups of canonical structures. The number of canonical structures assigned to TCR CDR loops will probably need to be revised once these sequences are accounted for. Accordingly, the crystal structure of the murine $V\alpha11$ domain

TABLE 1 Crystal structures and analysis of TCR/pMHC class I complexes

TCR	2C	2C	2C	scBM3.3	B7	A6	A6	A6	A6
MHC	H-2K^b	H-2K^b	H-2K^bm3	H-2K^b	HLA-A2	HLA-A2	HLA-A2	HLA-A2	HLA-A2
Peptide[a]	dEV8	SIYR	dEV8	pBM1	Tax	Tax	TaxP6A	TaxV7R	TaxY8A
Resolution (Å)/R$_{free}$ (%)	3.0/32.2	2.8/32.7	2.4/31.1	2.5/27.6	2.5/31.2	2.6/32.0	2.8/27.3	2.8/29.0	2.8/28.6
PDB ID/(Ref.)	2ckb/(39)	1g6r/(27)	1jtr/e	1fo0/(97)	1bd2/(29)	1ao7/(28)	1qrn/(28)	1qse/(28)	1qsf/(28)
Buried surface area[b]	1891	1795	1866	1239	1651	1801	1767	1753	1666
TCR/pMHC (Å²)	906/985	847/948	901/965	597/642	787/864	900/901	850/917	838/914	810/856
MHC/peptide (%)	76/24	76/24	76/24	79/21	68/32	66/34	67/33	66/34	73/27
V$_\alpha$ (Å²)/(%)	490/54	438/52	470/52	221/37	526/67	577/64	560/66	536/64	598/74
CDR1/CDR2/CDR3 (%)	23/13/16	18/16/16	20/14/17	14/17/6	28/13/23	25/10/25	23/13/25	23/10/26	29/12/27
V$_\beta$ (Å²)/(%)	417/46	409/48	431/48	376/63	261/33	321/36	290/34	302/36	211/26
CDR1/CDR2/CDR3/HV4 (%)	16/17/10/1	15/21/11/2	18/18/11/1	10/14/39/1	0/11/22/0	2/0/33/0	2/0/34/0	2/0/34/0	0/0/26/0
Sc[c]	0.41	0.49	0.63	0.61	0.64	0.64	0.61	0.66	0.61
HB/salt links/vdW contacts[d]	7/1/80	5/6/68	8/1/115	8/3/83	7/1/98	15/4/104	11/5/120	9/5/134	7/3/102
V$_\alpha$	5/1/63	4/0/36	4/1/49	1/1/27	6/1/65	11/4/59	8/4/86	6/4/81	7/3/78
CDR1 (24–31)	2/0/21	2/0/17	1/0/14	1/0/10	1/0/24	3/0/21	3/0/20	2/0/19	2/0/21
CDR2 (48–55)	0/0/17	0/0/1	1/0/13	0/1/15	1/0/16	0/0/3	0/0/4	0/0/8	1/0/8
CDR3 (93–104)	2/0/24	2/0/18	2/0/22	0/2/0	4/1/25	5/3/33	4/3/49	4/3/49	3/3/43
HV4 (68–74)	1/1/1	0/0/0	1/1/0	0/0/0	0/0/0	3/1/2	3/1/34	0/1/4	1/0/6
V$_\beta$	0/0/17	1/0/32	4/0/66	7/2/56	1/0/33	4/0/45	3/1/53	3/1/53	0/0/24
CDR1 (26–31)	0/0/7	1/0/15	4/0/39	0/0/1	0/0/0	1/0/2	1/0/3	1/0/3	1/0/3
CDR2 (48–55)	0/0/6	0/0/2	0/0/10	1/0/8	0/0/3	0/0/0	0/0/0	0/0/0	0/0/0
CDR3 (95–107)	0/0/4	0/0/15	0/0/13	6/2/47	1/0/30	3/0/43	2/1/50	2/1/50	0/0/24
HV4 (69–74)	0/0/0	0/0/0	0/0/2	0/0/0	0/0/0	0/0/0	0/0/0	0/0/0	0/0/0
MHC	3/1/59	2/0/37	4/1/75	3/3/54	4/1/41	8/4/64	4/5/67	3/5/82	4/3/75
Peptide	2/0/21	3/0/31	4/0/40	5/0/29	3/0/57	7/0/40	7/0/53	6/0/52	3/0/27

[a]dEV8, weak agonist; SIYR, superagonist; pBM1, naturally processed agonist ligand; Tax, strong agonist; TaxV7R, weak agonist; TaxP6A and TaxY8A, null ligands or weak antagonists.

[b]Calculated with MS (23) using 1.7 Å probe radius.

[c]Calculated with SC (17) using a 1.7 Å probe radius.

[d]Number of hydrogen bonds (HB), salt links and van der Waals (vdW) interactions calculated with HBPLUS (82) and CONTACSYM (108).

[e]J. G. Luz, M. Huang, K. C. Garcia, M. G. Rudolph, L. Teyton & I. A. Wilson, manuscript submitted.

TABLE 2   Crystal structures and analysis of TCR/pMHC class II complexes

TCR	scD10	HA1.7	HA1.7
MHC	I-A^k	HLA-DR1	HLA-DR4
Peptide[a]	CA	HA	HA
Resolution (Å)/R$_{free}$ (%)	3.2/29.3	2.6/25.5	2.4/24.6
PDB ID/(Ref.)	1d9k/(96)	1fyt/(48)	1j8h/(48b)
Buried surface area[b]	1733	1931	1915
TCR/pMHC (Å^2)	868/865	961/970	957/958
MHC/peptide (%)	77/23	67/33	68/32
V$_\alpha$ (Å^2)/(%)	530/61	442/46	453/47
CDR1/CDR2/CDR3 (%)	22/15/22	15/8/22	15/9/23
V$_\beta$ (Å^2)/(%)	338/39	519/54	504/53
CDR1/CDR2/CDR3/HV4 (%)	3/13/16/0	8/23/22/1	8/16/23/1
Sc[c]	0.71	0.56	0.56
HB/salt links/vdW contacts[d]	9/5/118	8/9/104	7/8/101
V$_\alpha$	3/4/63	1/4/41	2/4/45
CDR1	2/3/24	0/0/13	0/0/16
CDR2	0/0/16	0/0/2	1/0/4
CDR3	0/0/23	0/4/26	1/3/25
HV4	0/1/0	0/0/0	0/0/0
V$_\beta$	6/1/55	7/5/63	5/5/56
CDR1	0/0/0	2/3/10	2/3/8
CDR2	2/0/29	2/1/25	1/1/15
CDR3	3/0/21	2/0/20	1/0/24
HV4	0/0/0	0/0/0	0/0/1
MHC	8/4/86	3/2/79	3/2/77
Peptide	1/1/32	5/7/25	4/6/24

[a]dEV8, weak agonist; SIYR, superagonist; pBM1, naturally processed agonist ligand; Tax, strong agonist; TaxV7R, weak agonist; TaxP6A and TaxY8A, null ligands or weak antagonists.

[b]Calculated with MS (23) using 1.7 Å probe radius.

[c]Calculated with SC (17) using a 1.7 Å probe radius.

[d]Number of hydrogen bonds (HB), salt links and van der Waals (vdW) interactions calculated with HBPLUS (82) and CONTACSYM (108).

[e]J. G. Luz, M. Huang, K. C. Garcia, M. G. Rudolph, L. Teyton & I. A. Wilson, manuscript submitted.

has revealed CDR1 and 2 loop structures that deviate from those previously defined as canonical (78).

From Antagonism to Superagonism

Altered peptide ligands (APLs), which are synthetic variants of peptides presented to TCRs by MHCs, can elicit entirely different T cell responses from the parent sequences from which they were derived, even though they might differ by only a single amino acid. In most cases, APLs elicit weaker responses than do their parental peptides and may even act as antagonists to T cell activation (110). However, albeit less frequently, an APL may have greater potency than the original

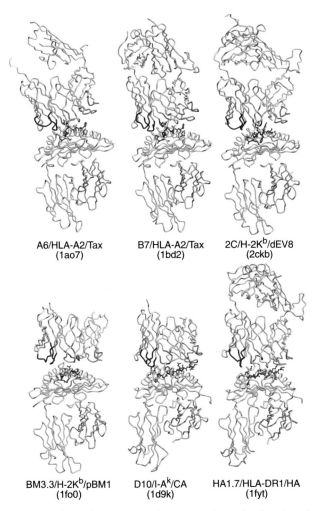

A6/HLA-A2/Tax
(1ao7)

B7/HLA-A2/Tax
(1bd2)

2C/H-2K^b/dEV8
(2ckb)

BM3.3/H-2K^b/pBM1
(1fo0)

D10/I-A^k/CA
(1d9k)

HA1.7/HLA-DR1/HA
(1fyt)

Figure 1 Overview of TCR/pMHC crystal structures determined to date. Only one representative structure is shown for TCRs where multiple structures are available. The Cα trace of the TCR is on *top*, with the CDR loops (*colored*) that contact the pMHC at the interface of each complex. The spatial relationship between the TCR and the pMHC is quite conserved, with the V_α and V_β domains positioned over the N-terminal and C-terminal halves of the peptide, respectively. The Cα domain is missing in the A6/HLA-A2/Tax complex due to lack of electron density but is present in the expression construct. BM3.3 and D10 TCRs are recombinantly constructed single chain (sc) variable constructs that do not contain the constant domains. The peptides are drawn as *red* ball-and-stick representations while the CDR loops are colored as follows: CDR1α (24–31), *dark blue*; CDR2α (48–55), *magenta*; CDR3α (93–104), *green*; CDR1β (26–31), *cyan*; CDR2β (48–55), *pink*; CDR3β (95–107), *yellow*; and HV4 (69–74), *orange*. This color scheme is continued through Figure 4. The D10 (96) and HA1.7 (48) complexes are with class II mouse and human pMHC, whereas the A6, B7 (29) and 2C (39), BM3.3 (97) complexes are with human (A6, B7) and mouse class I pMHC. PDB IDs are also given in Table 1.

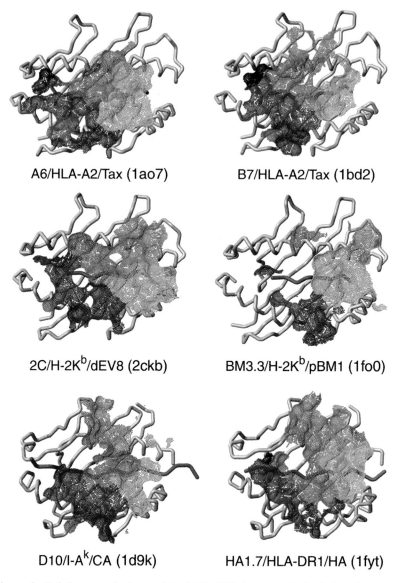

A6/HLA-A2/Tax (1ao7)   B7/HLA-A2/Tax (1bd2)

2C/H-2K^b/dEV8 (2ckb)   BM3.3/H-2K^b/pBM1 (1fo0)

D10/I-A^k/CA (1d9k)   HA1.7/HLA-DR1/HA (1fyt)

Figure 2 Relative contributions of the TCR CDR loops to the buried surface area of TCR/pMHC complexes. The view is from the TCR onto the peptide-binding site of the MHC with the peptide, and the MHC Cα backbones shown as *red* and *gray* tubes, respectively. The individual contributions of the CDR loops to the buried surface area are color-coded as in Figure 1. *Black* denotes contact area from non-CDR, i.e., framework residues. CDR3α and CDR3β bury surface areas that largely encompasses the exposed face of the peptide. CDR2α and CDR2β generally bury conserved helical elements of the MHC. Note the almost complete lack of CDR3α interactions (*dark green*) with the pMHC in the allogeneic BM3.3/H-2K^b/pBM1 complex.

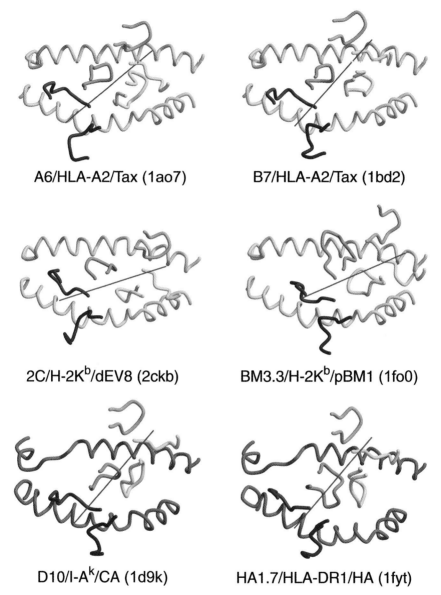

Figure 3 CDR loop conformation and TCR orientation in the TCR/pMHC complexes. Only the MHC α-helices (*light gray* for class I; *dark gray* for class II) that line the peptide-binding groove and the TCR CDR loops (colored as in Figures 1 and 2) are shown. The *red line* denotes the relative diagonal orientation of the TCR to the pMHC and is the linear fit to the centers of gravity of the CDR loops. 2C/H-2K^b/dEV8 (39) and D10/I-A^k/CA (96) structures represent the extremes in the relative angles of binding between the TCR and pMHC, being 30° and 80°, respectively. Note also the conserved locations of the V$_\alpha$ CDR loops compared to their V$_\beta$ counterparts.

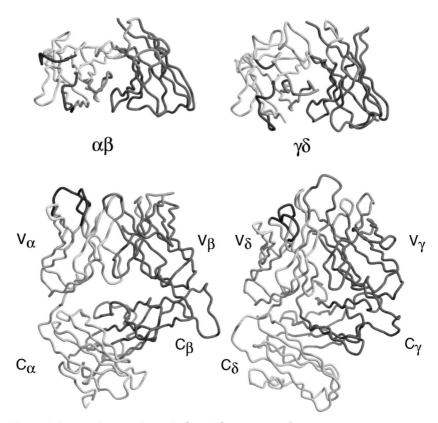

Figure 4 Structural comparison of αβ and γδ TCRs. The γδ TCR (4) (PDB ID 1hxm) is compared with the 2C TCR (39) (PDB ID 2ckb). The *top panel* is a view down into the binding site, highlighted by the CDR loops. The *bottom panel* is rotated 90° around the horizontal axis. The light and heavy chains are shaded in *light* and *dark gray*, respectively. Note the acute 42° angle between the V_γ and C_γ domains that leads to the unusually small elbow angle of 110° in the γδ TCR, whereas that in the 2C αβ TCR is 147°.

peptide and, therefore, behave as a strong or superagonist. Crystal structures of TCR/pMHC complexes containing APLs that range in activity from antagonism to superagonism have now been determined and compared with their parental agonist counterparts.

SIYR, an APL superagonist, is related to the self-dEV8 peptide but has significantly greater potency (8000×). Yet, when presented by H-2K^b, these two peptides do not manifest comparably large differences in binding affinities and kinetics with respect to the 2C TCR (27). Likewise, the 2C/H-2K^b/SIYR crystal structure revealed no large-scale movements of the TCR relative to the pMHC (27) nor any conformational changes that could be assigned to different signaling outcomes. However, small, but important, conformational changes were identified in the heart of the TCR/pMHC interface; a hinge movement of CDR3β created a better fit due to the only significant substitution of lysine to arginine at residue P4 of the peptide. The additional bulk and increased hydrogen-bonding potential of the arginine created more contacts and better complementarity, whereas the corresponding P6 tyrosine fit better in the superagonist complex due to the CDR3β movement. A corresponding prior analysis of A6 TCR bound to HLA-A2 complexes with weak agonist and antagonist APLs (28) showed that all the structures were highly similar to that of the parental strong agonist Tax peptide complex (38). Together, these results clearly demonstrate that these two TCRs do not require major conformational rearrangements in the $\alpha\beta$ TCR/pMHC components in order to carry out their different biological signaling events.

Allogeneic TCR/pMHC Complexes

Alloreactive T cells, comprising 1%–10% of all mature T cells (109), recognize and respond to nonself MHCs and are the primary impediment to the therapeutic success of organ transplantation and skin grafts. The effects of graft rejection and graft-versus-host disease, the clinical manifestations of alloreactivity can in principle be ameliorated by meticulous tissue-typing. Yet, inevitably, grafted tissue experiences an assault mounted by the host's cellular immune system or, in the case of patients whose immune systems have been compromised by radiation and chemotherapy, T cells in the grafted tissue, e.g., bone marrow, attack the host. Although immunosuppresive therapies moderate the pathological effects of incompatibility, the denouement is not symbiosis, and the course of transplantation proceeds inexorably toward rejection. Several models for alloreactivity have been proposed: TCRs may respond directly to allelic variations in MHCs, or, alternatively, allelic variants of MHCs may present novel constellations of peptides or have different affinities for the same TCR (109), thereby eliciting a T cell response. The first crystal structures of alloreactive TCR/pMHC complexes have been determined only recently, providing structural insights into this medically relevant immunological phenomenon.

BM3.3/H-2K^b/pBM1   The BM3.3/H-2K^b/pBM1 complex was the first TCR/pMHC allogeneic crystal structure determined (97) (Figure 1). Despite the radically different biological outcomes of syngeneic and allogeneic TCR/pMHC complex formation, BM3.3 binds H-2K^b in a diagonal orientation similar to that observed in previously determined TCR/pMHC structures (Figure 3, see color insert). Because the structure of the contrasting syngeneic complex is not available, it is not yet possible to delineate the specific features responsible for this complex's allogeneicity; however, the structure has several notable characteristics that bear on general principles of TCR/pMHC binding.

The absence of contacts between CDR3α and the peptide in the BM3.3/H-2K^b/pBM1 complex is anomalous when compared to the other complexes (Figure 2). In previous structures, peptide readout was primarily the province of both CDR3α and CDR3β. As sequence variation is greater in CDR3s relative to other CDRs, it was logical for CDR3s to bear the greater burden of peptide recognition and place the onus on the other germline-encoded CDRs at identifying the conserved helical elements in the MHC itself (42). It was surprising, therefore, that any CDR3α contact with peptide was completely expendable in this interaction and, furthermore, that CDR3α contributes only a single contact with the MHC. The unusual CDR3α loop conformation, flaring away from the peptide-binding groove (Figure 2), provides for formation of a large cavity that is filled by ~30 water molecules in the nexus of the interface. Also departing from convention, the TCR β-chain largely dominates the TCR/pMHC binding interface, contributing 63% of the total buried surface area (Table 1). Even though BM3.3 and 2C bury similar MHC residues, the nature of these interactions is not equivalent, the former being largely polar and the latter being mostly hydrophobic.

The BM3.3/H-2K^b/pBM1 complex thus exemplifies the essential paradox of TCR/pMHC interaction, that myriad variation must reside within a stringently conserved and narrow structural framework.

2C/H-2K^{BM3}/dEV8   The allogeneic 2C/H-2K^{bm3}/dEV8 complex structure (J. G. Luz, M. Huang, K. C. Garcia, M. G. Rudolph, L. Teyton & I. A. Wilson, manuscript submitted), when compared to its syngeneic counterpart 2C/H-2K^b/dEV8 (39), allows, for the first time, a comparative analysis of a single TCR bound to both self and nonself MHC. The extensive characterization of the H-2K^{bm} mutants and the 2C TCR provide an excellent biological context for the resultant observations. H-2K^b-bearing L cell clones elicit a cytolytic response from CTLs (cytotoxic T lymphocytes) expressing the clonotypic $\alpha\beta$TCR 2C, whereas H-2K^{bm3}-bearing L cell clones do not (91). In addition, transgenic 2C thymocytes are deleted by negative selection in an H-2K^{bm3} background (107). The dEV8 is also an endogenous allopeptide ligand for H-2K^{bm3} (115).

A single mutation, Asp77Ser, imparts H-2K^{bm3} with its alloreactivity. To preserve the hydrogen bond between the residue 77 side chain, which is shorter in the mutant but still contains a polar oxygen atom, and the amide nitrogen of the terminal peptide residue, the C terminus of the peptide main chain is displaced toward the α_1-helix of H-2K^{bm3}. An additional water molecule partially fills the cavity vacated by the Asp77Ser mutation, and the local hydrogen bond network is perturbed. As a result of these small changes, the TCR β-chain interacts more intimately with the pMHC; surface complementarity, number of contacts, and buried surface between the β-chain and the pMHC are increased in the mutant relative to the wild-type complex (Table 1). The β-chain/pMHC contacts are also an important feature of the BM3.3/H-2K^b/pBM1 interaction (97). Earlier modeling studies of H-2L^d/QL9, an alloligand for 2C, predicted that a large C-terminal bulge in the peptide, formed to accommodate a ridge in the floor of the H-2L^d peptide-binding groove, would substantially increase the extent of β-chain/pMHC association (111) such that it would dominate the TCR-peptide interaction. This prediction is consistent with both the BM3.3 and 2C allogeneic structures.

It is tempting to speculate that β-chain/pMHC interactions may become more predominant in allogeneic complexes; however, the available structural database is still too small to make such generalizations. Given the diametrically opposed biological outcomes of these two TCR/pMHC interactions, it is startling that the two representative structures are so similar, and it is a testimony to the exquisite subtlety of cellular immunity that, from the perspective of TCR recognition, such minute discrepancies are so eminently palpable.

TCR/pMHC Class II Complexes

The structure of D10 TCR bound to I-A^k/conalbumin (CA) peptide provided the first glimpse into the atomic details of TCR/class II MHC recognition (96). The most striking feature of this interaction was its similarity to the binding orientations previously observed in TCR/class I MHC complexes. The binding angle formed by D10 and I-A^k was 80° and was described by the authors as orthogonal. However, this angle is not significantly different from that of 70° for the B7/HLA-A2/Tax class I complex (29) (Figure 3). That the class II TCR orientation was at one end of the current, but limited, spectrum raised the possibility that class II MHCs might generally bind TCRs within a more confined range of orientations. In subsequent studies on the HA1.7/HLA-DR1/HA and HA1.7/HLA-DR4/HA TCR/class II MHC complexes, a relative binding orientation of 70° was observed (48, 48b), which mitigated against the existence of a distinct binding orientation for class I versus class II TCRs (Figure 3). The possibility still remains that TCRs might bind class II MHCs at angles that are on average greater than for the equivalent class I MHCs; however, any such generalities must also await a statistically significant number of observations.

The overall structure of the class II TCR D10, when bound to I-A^k/CA, was similar to those of TCRs binding class I MHCs; superposition of D10 onto the variable domains of B7 yielded r.m.s. deviations of only 0.98 Å and 0.72 Å for the V$_\alpha$ and V$_\beta$ domain C$_\alpha$ atoms, respectively. A total surface area of 1733 Å^2 was buried, 868 Å^2 from the pMHC and 865 Å^2 from the TCR, values similar to those reported for previous TCR/pMHC complexes (42) (Tables 1 and 2). The interface is dominated by pMHC-V$_\alpha$ domain contacts with 530 Å^2 of the V$_\alpha$ surface area buried. A surface complementarity coefficient of 0.71 for the D10/I-A^k/CA was high compared to the corresponding values (0.41–0.66) for other TCR/pMHC complexes. Although the binding grooves of class II MHCs can accommodate peptides significantly longer than can those of class I MHCs, only nine residues (P1–P9) in the core of the peptide participate in peptide-TCR interactions in the D10/I-A^k/CA complex. The N- and C-terminal peptide residues are not within the purview of the TCR/pMHC recognition in these complexes, although in some ways this is surprising given that their flexibility could allow them to come close to the interface with the TCR.

The 70° binding angle of the class II HA1.7/HLA-DR1/HA complex was exactly the same as that seen in the class I B7/HLA-A2/Tax complex, and, furthermore, 12 of the 15 HLA-DR1 residues contacted by HA1.7 were in positions equivalent to those contacted by $\alpha\beta$TCRs in class I complexes (48). In addition, CDR loop contacts were analogous to those found in class I complexes: CDRs 1 and 3 contacted both the peptide and MHC, whereas the CDR2s exclusively contacted the MHC. A TCR CDR2β contact with the MHC Lys39α was a feature common to the D10 class II complex.

Despite reaffirming commonality in TCR/pMHC binding, the HA1.7/HLA-DR1/HA complex has other interesting features that are not universal. In earlier complexes, V_α domain contacts had appeared to dominate the TCR/pMHC interface, but this has now proved not to be general. In the HA1.7/HLA-DR1/HA, V_β buries more pMHC surface area than does V_α, as was also the case in the BM3.3/H-2K^b/pBM1 class I complex. Because the peptide epitope in the HA1.7/HLA-DR1/HA complex was derived from influenza virus hemagglutinin—specifically the viral subtype that is the causative agent of the Hong Kong flu—and in vitro generates a strong HLA-DR T cell response (67, 68), it is interesting to note the biological implications of this structure. The HA peptide presents three positively charged lysine side chains, contacts to which are made by acidic CDR residues well conserved among TCRs that respond to HA in the context of the various HLA-DR alleles. As such, the HA1.7/HLA-DR1/HA complex illuminates a general solution that this group of TCRs has developed to a specific problem, recognition of a particular invading viral pathogen.

Structures of class II complexes have significantly expanded our understanding of T cell recognition, the sine qua non of cellular immunity. Ironically, they have also propagated an enigma, the inexplicable extent of biological diversity manifested by a system exhibiting such a remarkable degree of structural conformity. The remaining outstanding question is still what structural features dictate the relatively constant TCR orientation with pMHC molecules.

STRUCTURE OF A $\gamma\delta$ TCR

As opposed to $\alpha\beta$ T cells, where a variety of TCR structures have been determined over the past six years, much less is known about the structure of $\gamma\delta$ TCRs. The only structure available until recently was that of a V_δ domain (71). This lack of structural information is paralleled by the ill-defined biological functions of $\gamma\delta$ T cells. $\gamma\delta$ T cells respond to bacterial and parasitic infections (86) and can recognize, by an unknown mechanism, phosphate-containing antigens (phosphoantigen) from mycobacteria (9, 86). Known specific ligands for $\gamma\delta$ T cells are few, with the exception of the nonclassical MHC class I molecules T10 and T22, mouse MHC class II I-E^k, herpes simplex virus protein gIg (18), and CD1 (85). However, the mechanism of engagement of the $\gamma\delta$ TCR and these ligands has remained elusive.

The first crystal structure of the G115 V$_\gamma$9-V$_\delta$2 TCR has recently been determined and begins to address parts of this question (4). As expected, the overall structure of the $\gamma\delta$ TCR closely resembles that of $\alpha\beta$ TCRs and antibodies (Figure 4, see color insert). The most striking observation is an acute V$_\gamma$/C$_\gamma$ interdomain angle of $42°$, which defines an unusually small elbow angle (defined as the angle between the two pseudo-twofold axes that relate the two C and the two V domains to each other) of $110°$ and, hence, so far distinguishes the $\gamma\delta$ TCR from all known $\alpha\beta$ TCR and antibody domain organizations. Whether this will be a general feature in all $\gamma\delta$ TCRs or represents an extreme case must await determination of more $\gamma\delta$ TCR structures. The corresponding elbow angles of $\alpha\beta$ TCRs have only been restricted to a marginally narrower range so far ($140°-210°$) than for antibodies ($125°-225°$), presumably due to the smaller database of $\alpha\beta$ TCR structures, but any correlation with function and signaling events is questionable at present. The requirement of $\alpha\beta$ and $\gamma\delta$ TCRs to interact with the CD3 components could have been expected to result in some specific restriction of the in vitro V-C domain flexibility.

Another key question is how does the $\gamma\delta$ TCR recognize its phosphoantigen ligands? The $\gamma\delta$ structure shows that the central CDR3γ and CDR3δ loops point away from the combining site to create a cleft that may form the antigen-binding site. In support of this hypothesis, positively charged residues from CDR2γ and CDR3γ contributing to this cleft may provide the necessary electrostatic complementarity for phosphate binding, as seen in antibodies that bind similar phosphate antigens. However, cocrystallization experiments and soaking of $\gamma\delta$ TCR crystals using a synthetic phosphoantigen have been unsuccessful thus far (4). So the question remains as to whether phosphoantigens need to be presented by some other receptor, or in some other context, for recognition by the $\gamma\delta$ TCR. Additionally, a $\gamma\delta$ TCR/MHC complex structure will shed light on the question of whether $\gamma\delta$ TCRs are really more antibody-like in that they can bind intact proteins and small haptens rather than the restricted pMHC ligands of the $\alpha\beta$ TCR.

The $\gamma\delta$ TCR structure also raises an interesting issue for CD3 recognition in the TCR complex. Upon comparison of the C domain surfaces of both $\gamma\delta$ and $\alpha\beta$ TCRs, no apparent similarities were found (4) that could explain the dual-binding specificity of CD3 to these different classes of TCRs; only a few solvent-exposed residues are structurally conserved. The stark differences between the exposed surfaces of $\gamma\delta$ and $\alpha\beta$ TCRs are corroborated by the large differences of the respective CD3ϵ-binding FG loops of Cβ and Cγ and the different secondary-structure features of Cα and Cδ (Figure 4). Cα shows an unusual secondary structure from the normal Ig-fold in the outer β-sheet, as opposed to Cδ, which has a regular three-stranded β-sheet. Thus, the possibility of two different TCR/CD3 signaling complexes exists, the biological significance of which remains to be fully understood. With the recent determination of the CD3$\epsilon\gamma$ NMR structure (114) (see below), it is possible to gain some initial insight into the two different putative TCR/CD3 signaling complexes by modeling.

TOWARD THE STRUCTURAL ASSEMBLY OF THE IMMUNOLOGICAL SYNAPSE

Although penetrating insights into the workings of antigen recognition have been garnered from a host of TCR-pMHC crystal structures, one would be remiss in not considering these data within the structural context in which T cell activation and inhibition occur. In fact, the TCR and MHC are only two, albeit important, members of an extensive community of signaling molecules that must act in concert to orchestrate the exquisite and exceedingly subtle operations that govern cellular immunity. Therefore, the raison d'être of the various structural elements of the TCR can only be derived through knowledge of their interactions with associated molecules.

Coreceptors and Their MHC Complexes

CD8 and CD4 are coreceptors, along with their respective TCRs, for class I and class II MHCs, respectively. The crystal structures of human (36) and murine (54) CD8$\alpha\alpha$/MHC complexes revealed that the CD8$\alpha\alpha$ homodimer binds primarily to the α_3 domain of the MHC in an antibody-like manner with the α_3 CD3 loop, encompassed by residues 220–229, wedged between two loops from CD8, one from each subunit. The CD8$\alpha\alpha$/MHC crystal structures also defined the stoichiometry of binding as 1:1 and depicted an approximately orthogonal orientation between the CD8$\alpha\alpha$ homodimer and the face of the MHC α_3 domain. Because the C-terminal stalk region of CD8 was missing in the construct used for crystallization, no predictions for CD8/TCR interactions (if any) could be made, and the disposition of the TCR relative to the CD8$\alpha\alpha$/MHC scaffold is still in question.

The recently determined crystal structure of CD4 (domains 1 and 2) bound to I-A^k unveils how coreceptor binding is adapted in the analogous class II system (122) (Figure 5). Although the CD4/I-A^k crystal structure has been determined to be only 4.3 Å, the discrepancies between how CD4 and CD8 bind their respective MHCs are so large that they are easily discernable, even at low resolution. Whereas the two domains of CD8 cooperate to bind class I MHCs, only one domain, the N-terminal variable-like region, of CD4 makes contact with I-A^k; the second CD4 domain in the crystal structure is distal to the interface. A model of the complete TCR/pMHC trivalent complex was constructed by superimposing the independent crystal structures of the four-domain extracellular region of CD4 (127) and the TCR/pMHC complex D10/I-A^k/CA (96) onto their respective partners in the two-domain CD4/I-A^k complex. The results depict a V-shaped organization of the

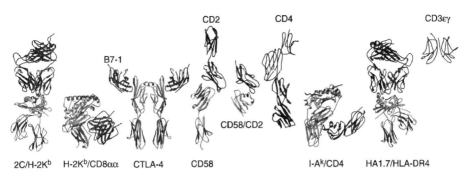

Figure 5 Known crystal structures of receptors in the immunological synapse. Shown are ribbon diagrams according to secondary structure of the class I 2C/H-2K^b/dEV8 complex (39) (PDB ID 2ckb), the H-2K^b/CD8$\alpha\alpha$ complex (54) (PDB ID 1bqh), the B7-1/CTLA-4 complex (113) (PDB ID 1i8l), the CD2-binding domain of CD58 (51) (PDB ID 1ccz), CD2 (10) (PDB ID 1hnf), the interacting domains of the CD58/CD2 complex (123) (PDB ID 1qa9), CD4 (127) (PDB ID 1wio), the I-Ak/CD4 complex (122) (PDB ID 1j14), the class II HA1.7/HLA-DR4 complex (48b) (PDB ID 1j8h), and an averaged C$_\alpha$ trace of the NMR structure of the CD3$\varepsilon\gamma$ complex (114) (PDB ID 1jbj). Receptor molecules from the T cell (*top*) and the APC (*bottom*) are in dark and light gray, and peptides are in black. The 26–amino acid linker between the CD3ε and CD3γ subunits is not shown for clarity. CD58 is the human ortholog of mouse CD48, the structure of which is not known yet. Also missing in this picture are the structures of CD22, CD40, CD45.ABC, CD54, CD80 (T cell) and CD3$\varepsilon\delta$, CD11a/CD18, CD28, CD43, CD45.R0, and CD154 (APC) (102). The molecules are drawn to scale. Note the domination of the Ig-fold in all structures.

TCR/pMHC/CD4 complex with the TCR/pMHC forming one length of the "V" and the four domains of CD4 approaching the membrane proximal domains of the MHC at an acute angle forming the second length of the "V." The functional implications for this arrangement are that CD4 likely does not oligomerize upon binding, that there are no direct contacts between the TCR and CD4, and that TCRs and MHCs, when bound, are tilted relative to the membrane. Accompanying mutational data also argue against previous models of CD4 oligomerization (60, 104). There is remarkable concordance between how HIV gp120 (64) and MHCs bind CD4, with Phe 43 of CD4 inserting into a junction between two gp120 domains and into a hydrophobic gap created by conserved α2 and β2 residues in MHC, respectively (122).

Comparing the CD4/I-A^k/CA and CD8/pMHC structures (Figure 5), a surprising structural flexibility of class I and class II architectures is evident, which implies profoundly different modes of organization in their respective immunological synapses. If this is true, one wonders why, on the other hand, the overall structure of class I and class II TCR/pMHC complexes is so conserved.

Furthermore, the constructed model of the CD4/TCR/pMHC V-shaped trimer would mean that the approximately equal distances spanned by the CTLA4/B7 and TCR/pMHC complexes might be in disagreement, as the membrane-to-membrane distance defined by the TCR/pMHC complex would be reduced by its angular (rather than perpendicular) orientation relative to the membrane.

Costimulatory Complexes

The recently reported CTLA-4/B7-1 (113) (Figure 5) and CTLA-4/B7-2 (106) structures provided specific information about inhibitory signaling and established general principles for the possible formation of intermolecular lattices within the immunological synapse. CTLA-4 and CD28 are cell-surface molecules that, when bound to B7 on APCs, modulate T cell activity. CTLA-4/B7 interactions attenuate, whereas CD28/B7 interactions enhance, T cell activation. CTLA-4 binds B7 in an orthogonal orientation with the outer-surface loops of CTLA-4 packing against the concavity formed by the front sheets of the B7 membrane-distal Ig domain. This peculiar Ig domain interaction had been observed previously in crystals of CD2 (10), CD2/CD58 (123), and coxsackie virus and adenovirus receptors (120). Because the binding of both CTLA-4 and B7 is bivalent, their ligation can form extended lateral networks of alternating CTLA-4 and B7 molecules, as observed within the crystal lattice. Accounting for membrane proximal stalks, the dimensions of this periodic unit correlate with the intrinsic internal geometry of the immunological synapse, extending vertically $\sim$140 Å, a distance similar to that spanned by CD2/CD58 and TCR/pMHC complexes. The potential for CTLA-4/B7 complexes to form bivalently linked periodic networks on the cell surface raises the intriguing possibility such higher-order protein networks may be an integral feature of cell membrane organization (106, 113). Perhaps even higher-order levels of organization exist, consisting of groups of distinct interacting bivalently coupled complexes or complexes composed of protein units exhibiting higher valency. No conformational change was noted in either molecule upon binding of CTLA-4 to B7.

The FG loop of CTLA-4 corresponds to CDR3 and contains three consecutive prolines that, when bound to B7, adopt a *cis-trans-cis* configuration. This unusual loop conformation is a salient feature of CTLA-4/B7 binding, providing for the establishment of numerous van der Waals contacts between the two molecules. Likewise, the FG loop of CD8α1 is an important component in CD8$\alpha\alpha$/MHC association (54). CDR3 loops of the 2C TCR form a functional hot spot that plays a pivotal role in antigen recognition (27). Furthermore, TCR CDR3 loops are genetically more variable than their counterparts (24), a trend also observed in antibodies. The versatility of Ig-like domains is evinced by the diverse and multitudinous set of proteins into which they have been incorporated (26). One might speculate as to the inherent properties that underlie their utility and why, in such a diverse set of interactions, FG loop contacts are a recurrent theme.

CD3 Signaling Module

One structurally elusive integral TCR component, the CD3 signaling module, has recently begun to be elucidated. CD3 consists of the subunits δ, ϵ, γ, and ξ, which noncovalently associate to form CD3$\xi\xi$ homodimers and CD3$\epsilon\delta$ and

CD3$\epsilon\gamma$ heterodimers (59, 80). From sequence comparisons, it was predicted that the extracellular domains of the CD3ϵ and CD3γ chains adopt an immunoglobulin fold (114). A cavity formed by the FG loop in the Cβ domain of $\alpha\beta$ TCRs was suggested to host a binding site for such an immunoglobulin domain (121).

The extracellular domains of the CD3ϵ and CD3γ subunits lacking the conserved RxCxxCxE stalk region motif were converted to a single-chain format by a 26–amino acid linker that ensured close proximity during folding from inclusion bodies (58). The solution structure of this construct indeed revealed an immunoglobulin fold of canonical type C2 (a Greek key motif) for the CD3ϵ and CD3γ subunits (114) (Figure 5). Despite the fact that the two domains share only 31% sequence identity (37% homology) over a 56-residue interval, their backbone rmsd value is only 1.4 Å (30 core Cα atoms). The two subunits form a 14-stranded intersubunit β-sheet, which appears to be responsible for the increased stability of the CD3$\epsilon\gamma$ heterodimer compared with the individual CD3ϵ (50, 58). A total of 1300 Å^2 are buried in the half-hydrophobic/half-hydrophilic CD3$\epsilon\gamma$ dimer interface, putting this interaction in the same range as antibody V_H/V_L and TCR Vα/Vβ interactions (42). The chemical nature of the CD3$\epsilon\gamma$ interface is, however, significantly different from that of antibody and TCR V domains, which are predominantly hydrophobic. The surface of the CD3$\epsilon\gamma$ dimer is nonflat, such that homodimeric CD3$\epsilon\epsilon$ and CD3$\gamma\gamma$ complexes would have poor surface complementarity and, therefore, most likely do not exist in this arrangement (114).

The parallel orientation of the CD3ϵ and CD3γ subunits would bring the conserved RxCxxCxE stalk region motifs, which are missing in this structure, into close proximity to each other. It has been speculated that the cysteine residues in this motif may chelate a cation such as Zn^{2+} (114) because they apparently are not involved in intersubunit disulfide bonds. However, using the Zn^{2+} chelator phenanthroline, dimerization of CD3ϵ and CD3γ subunits could not be inhibited (13). The possibility of intrasubunit disulfide bonds remains, as these are found close to the dimer interface in a number of homo- and heterodimeric extracellular receptors, such as NKG2D (126), CD94 (14), and Ly49A (117), although not as close in sequence as in the case of CD3$\epsilon\gamma$.

Interestingly, an acidic and highly solvent-exposed loop in CD3ϵ not involved in dimer formation would be electrostatically complementary to the positively charged cavity between the V$_\beta$ and C$_\beta$ domains of the $\alpha\beta$ TCR (4, 121). This negative potential on CD3ϵ is contrasted by an excess of positive potential on CD3γ, which suggests that the CD3$\epsilon\gamma$ heterodimer indeed binds to the TCR using the CD3ϵ subunit. Direct binding of the single-chain CD3$\epsilon\gamma$ construct to the N15 TCR could, however, not be demonstrated using heteronuclear NMR (58). Preliminary docking studies indicated that the 26–amino acid linker of the artificial single-chain construct might interfere with $\alpha\beta$ TCR binding but still suggested that the proposed binding mode via the acidic CD3ϵ loop might be feasible. Further structural studies are needed to unambiguously clarify the nature of the TCR/CD3 interaction, which is at the heart of immunological signal transduction.

THERMODYNAMICS OF T CELL RECOGNITION

Crystal structures provide a time- and space-averaged picture. By contrast, immunological recognition is a dynamic process, the nature of which can only incompletely be inferred from static structures. This fact has been impressively demonstrated by four nearly identical crystal structures of the A6 TCR/HLA-A2 complex, with both agonist and antagonist peptides derived from the HTLV-1 Tax protein (28). These structures show that different biological activities are not paralleled by profound conformational changes in the TCR/pMHC interface. A similar conclusion was reached in the 2C TCR system, where the 2C TCR/H-2K^b/peptide structures of a weak agonist (dEV8) and a superagonist (SIYR) were remarkably similar (27, 39). For a complete understanding of the various T cell activities, it is essential to complement the structural snapshots with biophysical studies in solution. The thermodynamic and kinetic properties of TCR/pMHC interactions have been studied extensively using a variety of biophysical methods, such as surface plasmon resonance (SPR), ultracentrifugation (UC), and microcalorimetry. Other methods such as cytotoxicity assays and ELISA are less quantitative and are, therefore, not discussed further.

Methods Used for Analyzing TCR/Ligand Interaction

Although SPR is extensively used to study receptor/ligand binding both qualitatively and quantitatively, the results are often ambiguous and conclusions may need to be independently verified by another biophysical method. The reasons for the popularity of SPR stem from the fact that both kinetic and equilibrium data can be collected with the same setup; data acquisition is fast, comparative studies are easily performed, and low affinities can be detected with relatively low amounts of protein. Also, the results are apparently straightforward to interpret after global analysis of whole data sets, which is implemented in standard SPR software, although misinterpretation is easy. An added bonus of the SPR system may be the immobilization of a normally membrane-bound ligand to a sensor chip, thereby to a certain extent mimicking the in vivo situation. However, significant drawbacks to the technique can somewhat limit the significance of the results. For instance, most studies use amine chemistry to immobilize the primary ligand, which results in nonuniform orientation, possibly giving rise to multiple phases during association and dissociation reactions (70, 74, 98, 105). This has been circumvented by the use of thiol chemistry at cysteine residues (7, 56) or by ligate immobilization via monoclonal antibodies (116) or by other affinity tags, such as oligo-histidine (79) or biotin (37, 79) using the appropriate matrices (98).

Many equilibrium dissociation constant (K_d) values are calculated as the ratio of the microscopic dissociation and association rate constants ($K_d = k_{off}/k_{on}$). This is only true if the system under study follows a simple one-step binding mechanism and no conformational changes occur at the sensor chip. But the occurrence of such changes in antibodies has been measured in competition experiments by the dependence of the observed k_{off} values on the association time (74). Additionally, the accuracy of the kinetic constants depends crucially on various other parameters such as mass transport, sensor chip capacity, and flow rate. Global fitting of the data cannot prove a kinetic mechanism unambiguously (47), and the goodness of fit will not distinguish between alternative kinetic models (74). Alternatively, the K_d value may be derived by fitting the solution of a quadratic equation describing a 1:1 binding model to the resonance amplitudes as a function of the ligand concentration. Because most TCR/pMHC affinities are low, with K_d in the micromolar range ($\sim$0.1–500 μM) (81), saturation of the sensor chip, which is required for this analysis, is seldom achieved and the incomplete data are often linearized for a Scatchard analysis. This introduces nonlinear errors into the data that preclude quantitative interpretation of derived K_d values (87). Indeed, recent reviews on SPR note that the kinetic and thermodynamic results of many SPR studies are of dubious value and that SPR is most useful for a yes/no answer or relative, not quantitative, comparisons in binding studies (66, 105). The need for rigorous control experiments was stressed to rule out any artifacts that lead to a false interpretation of the data. Given these caveats, it is difficult to extract useful kinetic and thermodynamic information from SPR studies alone and unite them to a general model of how TCR/pMHC engagement might correlate with TCR selection, T cell activation, and alloreactivity.

In contrast to SPR, data from equilibrium methods, such as isothermal titration calorimetry (ITC), are much more reliable and straightforward to interpret (33, 66). The heat evolved or absorbed upon interaction of two ligands is directly proportional to the overall reaction enthalpy ΔH. Fitting of a suitable model to the data yields the stoichiometry n and the equilibrium association constant K_a, from which the reaction enthalpy $\Delta G = -RT\ln K_a$ can be derived. The reaction entropy ΔS is calculated from the Gibbs-Helmholtz equation $\Delta G = \Delta H\text{-}T\Delta S$, and, if ΔH is linear over the temperature range studied, the heat capacity ΔC_p can be derived from the temperature dependence of ΔH (65). Thus, ITC has the potential to generate a complete set of thermodynamic parameters for the TCR/pMHC system. Because the measured ΔH values are a composite of individual enthalpies arising from hydrogen and van der Waals bond rearrangement, conformational changes, and proton exchange with the buffer, additional experiments are needed to assess their individual contributions. For instance, proton transfer can be quantified by conducting ITC in different buffers of known protonation enthalpies (6, 15, 30, 35). However, in contrast to SPR, ITC has not widely been used for the study of TCR/pMHC interactions, possibly owing to the need for high protein concentrations in order to detect the small heat changes.

Recently, UC was used to determine low affinities and the state of aggregation of TCR/pMHC and related complexes (5, 70, 88). UC is a primary technique that requires no standards (49, 69). Sedimentation velocity and sedimentation equilibrium experiments give insight into the hydro- and thermodynamic properties of the sample. Since the absorption and interference optics of ultracentrifuges provide a wide range of linearity for detection, sedimentation equilibrium can be used to study intermediate- to low-affinity interactions to yield association constants K_a (10^{-3}–10^{-8} M) and stoichiometries (49). From the temperature dependence of K_a, a complete thermodynamic description can be derived (69). At the same time, UC is uniquely suited to remove ambiguities about whether the sample is a heterogeneous mixture or comprises an interacting system. A possible drawback of ITC and UC in studying TCR/pMHC interactions is that both methods require the soluble domains of the binding partners and the results, therefore, may not reflect the properties of the membrane-bound system where the mobility of the components is restricted to two dimensions.

In the following section, we highlight selected examples using these methods and try to integrate these biophysical results with the structural information available for TCR/pMHC complexes.

Kinetic Properties

TCR/pMHC interactions are of low affinity ($K_d = \sim0.1$–500 μM) and are characterized by slow association and fast dissociation reactions (24). Based on the dissociation of TCR/pMHC complexes being a monomolecular reaction, the dissociation rate constant may be the least error-prone parameter accessible by SPR. Generally, TCR/pMHC complexes exhibit fast dissociation rates in the range of ~0.01–5 s^{-1} corresponding to half-lives of 70–0.1 s (81). Half-lives have been found to correlate with the potency of the T cells bearing the TCR under study (1, 2, 28, 55, 76), although there are exceptions (5, 12, 41, 55). In a recent study, Baker et al. (5) used APLs to repair a packing defect in the TCR/pMHC interface of the A6/HLA-A2/TaxP6A complex (Table 1). By mutation of the peptide residue P6 to alanine, T cell stimulation was abrogated with a concomitant loss of affinity (K_d changed from 1.1 μM to 116 μM as measured by UC) and increase of dissociation rate from ~0.1 s^{-1} to immeasurably fast (by SPR). However, the overall structures of the two complexes barely changed (28, 29). By a stepwise filling of the cavity created by the P6A mutation using chemically modified peptides, T cell stimulation activity was regained, but the half-lives of the TCR/pMHC complexes did not correlate or compensate. However, the corresponding affinity of the mutated peptides for the MHC itself was not measured, leaving open the possibility that the dissociation kinetics as measured by SPR are more complex than anticipated. Alternatively, the different temperatures at which the kinetic (25°C) and T cell assays (37°C) were performed might have led to the observed nonequivalence. Because T cell signaling is an extremely complex process that takes place between two cell membranes and in the context of many costimulatory molecules, it is generally difficult to reliably relate the biophysical data gained from necessarily simplified model systems with biological activity. From this point of view, the good correlation of half-life with T cell stimulatory activity in the majority of cases is rather surprising.

It is a longstanding puzzle and apparent contradiction that despite the low affinity and rapid dissociation of TCR/pMHC complexes, high specificity is observed in T cell signaling. This stems from the fact that T cells need to distinguish low concentrations of nonself peptides (down to several molecules per APC) from a vast excess of self-peptides. To account for these data, several models of TCR signaling have been proposed: allostery, which requires conformational changes for signal transmission across the cell membrane; a kinetic proofreading model that couples TCR/pMHC binding to another biochemical reaction, such as phosphorylation; and cross-linking, which is based on relocation of TCR and signaling molecules to form a supramolecular complex, the immunological synapse. In all models, the dissociation reactions of the TCR/pMHC complexes compete with the rate of the conformational change and the rate of supramolecular complex formation. While a large body of evidence seems to favor the kinetic or cross-linking over the allosteric model [reviewed in (24)], a three-dimensional structure of a quaternary TCR/pMHC/coreceptor/CD3 complex to compare with the individual binary complexes is ultimately needed to completely rule out the latter.

A particularly appealing concept, which provides a means for increased specificity to discriminate between foreign and self-antigens, is the kinetic proofreading model in TCR signaling (55, 83, 93). In this model, a high energy level is maintained by a constant basal stimulation of T cells due to rapid, transient engagement with antigen-presenting cells, which does not lead to activation. A threshold time for productive TCR/pMHC interaction needs to be surpassed in order for the T cell to get activated in a multistep process involving energy-requiring phosphorylation reactions, e.g., of CD3ζ chains (77, 83). Thus, specificity is gained because any interaction that exceeds the threshold time will activate the T cell (53, 118). With some exceptions, the majority of TCR/pMHC systems conform with the activity/kinetic relationship. Thus, the kinetic proofreading model for T cell activation now seems to be generally accepted (45, 75, 94), although it may require adjustment as more data become available (99).

Thermodynamic Properties

Recently, SPR together with ITC was used to rigorously characterize the thermodynamic parameters of two distinct TCR/pMHC interactions, murine F5 TCR/H-2D^b in complex with an influenza nucleoprotein peptide and human TCR JM22/HLA-A2 in complex with an influenza matrix protein peptide (124). By using a low-coupling density to avoid mass transport in the SPR, the data could be fitted by a simple 1:1 binding model to yield reliable values of k_{on}. Measurements were done in a temperature-dependent manner, and the activation enthalpies for association (46 KJ/mol) and dissociation (130 KJ/mol) were calculated from the Arrhenius plots. These large activation enthalpies suggest that conformational changes were required for complex formation (124). This is in line with the crystal structures of liganded and unliganded TCR, where large conformational changes are found in the CDR loops (39, 40), again lending some weight to the importance of conformational changes in TCR/pMHC interactions and, ultimately, in T cell activation. The difference of the activation enthalpies matches the ΔH value for the association reaction that was independently measured by ITC (-82 KJ/mol). Unfortunately, ITC was not used to derive a K_a value for this association or to test for protonation effects during TCR/pMHC association. The TCR/pMHC interaction is exothermic, and from ΔH and the SPR K_d value, an unfavorable ΔS term was calculated. This enthalpy-entropy compensation may well be responsible for the generally low TCR/pMHC affinities. The authors speculate that the reason for the negative ΔS term is not due to the inclusion of water molecules into the TCR/pMHC-binding interface because, by contrast, ordered water molecules should be released upon protein/protein interaction to increase ΔS. Rather than fixing of water molecules, the small activation enthalpy of association argues for conformational adjustments as the likely reason for the negative entropy (12, 124). Once ITC becomes a standard method for immunologists, it will be instructive to see whether other TCR/pMHC interactions share similar thermodynamic footprints, and whether these are affected by, for example, the glycosylation of these cell-surface receptors (101, 102).

A comparison of the crystal structures of a liganded and an unliganded TCR and pMHC reveals conformational changes in both the TCR and the pMHC (39) (J. G. Luz, M. Huang, K. C. Garcia, M. G. Rudolph, L. Teyton & I. A. Wilson, manuscript submitted). Temperature factors of unliganded 2C TCR and H-2K^b indicate that often the CDR loops (39, 40) and the central residues of some bound peptides (103, 109a, 112) are less well ordered. Dramatic changes in both flexibility and conformation are seen with the CDR loops, which therefore may be responsible for the majority of the decrease in entropy. Peptide mobility may also play a significant role, especially for longer peptides that have to bulge out of the peptide-binding groove as a result of their N and C termini being fixed by the MHC (112). Crystal structures of such TCR/pMHC complexes will give insight into the role of peptide-associated conformational changes upon TCR binding.

Recently, with higher-resolution pMHC crystal structures, many water molecules have been assigned in the electron density maps that were not visible in earlier lower-resolution structures. For instance, when the resolution for the H-2K^b-VSV8 and H-2K^b-SEV9 complexes (34) was increased to 1.5 Å and 1.7 Å (M. G. Rudolph & I. A. Wilson, unpublished data), the sphere of hydration was expanded. The recently determined higher-resolution (2.4 Å) 2C TCR/H-2K^{bm3}/dEV8 complex allows for the first time a comparison of interface water molecules with the high-resolution unliganded H-2K^b/dEV8 structure (1.75 Å) (J. G. Luz, M. Huang, K. C. Garcia, M. G. Rudolph, L. Teyton & I. A. Wilson, manuscript submitted). Upon overlay of the two structures, eight water molecules need to be displaced by the 2C TCR, while two water molecules are conserved in both structures and form an integral part of the TCR/pMHC interface, having consequences for the thermodynamics of this interaction. The importance of water in the TCR/pMHC interface is also evidenced by the ~30 ordered water molecules found in the BM3.3/H-2K^b/pBM1 complex (97) and the ~10 water molecules in the HA1.7/HLA-DR4/HA complex interface (48b). Although the precise location of water molecules in crystal structures may depend on the space group and the data collection temperature, the majority of these water molecules should be present in solution. As the concentration of water is 55 M, it is reasonable to assume that water may modify the pMHC surface seen by the TCR and thus can play an important biological part in T cell recognition.

Because water is less ordered at higher temperatures (37°C), the entropic contribution of water release from pMHC by the TCR becomes less prominent at physiological temperatures. The influence of water on ΔS is also dependent on the hydrophobicity of the solvent-exposed pMHC surface and, thereby, specific to the particular MHC and the bound peptide. Clearly, more high-resolution TCR/pMHC and unliganded pMHC structures together with thermodynamic analyses are needed for these comparisons in order to address the possibility and potential role of trapped water molecules in the TCR/pMHC interface. Heat capacity measurements for various TCR/pMHC systems should give further insight into the role of water in TCR/pMHC recognition.

The thermodynamic properties of superantigen binding to MHC molecules were recently investigated using complementary information from SPR and UC. Superantigens (SAG) are bacterial or viral proteins capable of stimulating a large subset (up to 20%) of T cells in a peptide-independent manner. They act on TCR/pMHC class II complexes by cross-linking the β-chain of the TCR with SAG-dependent sites on MHC class II. The result is a massive release of cytokines, such as Il-1, Il-2, TNF-α and TNF-β, leading to toxic-shock syndrome (62). A crystal structure of a ternary complex is still elusive, but binary SAG/pMHC complexes have been determined, showing a great variety of binding modes of the SAG to the $\alpha_1\beta_2$ domain of the pMHC (52, 57, 73, 89). SPR and UC were used to quantify the affinity of *staphylococcal* enterotoxin SAG mutants to the TCR 14.3.d β-chain (70). The K_d values from SPR and UC correlated well (within a factor of two), which may be surprising given the fact that ΔS is directly changed upon immobilization of one binding partner in an SPR experiment. However, the magnitude of ΔS was not quantified in this study. Interestingly, the affinity of the SAG/TCR interaction correlated well with the biological activity (T cell proliferation) of the SAG, which somewhat contrasts with the TCR/pMHC-activity profile (see above).

A key question in T cell signaling is whether the signal delivered by a productive TCR/pMHC interaction traverses the cell membrane by TCR oligomerization or by a cross-linking mechanism. While clustering of TCR/pMHC complexes has been observed (84) and soluble oligomeric pMHC complexes effectively activate T cells (11, 22), the stoichiometry of the signaling-competent TCR/pMHC complex is still unknown. The possibility for higher TCR/pMHC oligomers in solution was previously investigated using light scattering (95) and SPR (1). But the low affinities of the TCRs for pMHC lead to low population of TCR/pMHC complexes in dilute solution, with higher-order oligomers even less populated and difficult to detect. To test the occurrence of higher-order TCR/pMHC oligomers, UC on a high affinity TCR/pMHC complex was used (8). Because no such oligomers were detected, and a number of flaws in the previous studies were evidenced, it was concluded that TCR/pMHC complexes have no tendency to oligomerize in solution. These results are consistent with a lack of specific dimer or oligomer formation in the crystal lattices of TCR and TCR/pMHC complexes. However, the restricted motion of the membrane-bound proteins leaves open the possibility that such assemblies, possibly mediated by CD4 and CD8, may form at the cell surface (44). The affinity of such interactions could be substantially increased on the cell surface as compared to their soluble, truncated versions. Some degree of surface association could then amplify the signals between agonist and antagonist ligands and account for the large biological differences not reflected by either the K_d of the soluble molecules or the small differences in their crystal structures.

FUTURE PERSPECTIVES

Dozens of antibody structures were determined before the full extent of antibody-antigen interactions could be appreciated and general principles that governed antibody-antigen recognition could be gleaned. From a limited number of TCR/pMHC structures, we have concluded that TCRs bind MHC class I and class II in a conserved way, but with some considerable structural variation in the details of the interaction (Figures 1, 2, 3). We have still not uncovered why TCRs adopt such a restricted diagonal orientation with respect to the top surface of the pMHCs. What are the key interactions that guide and preserve this orientation? Examination of the crystal structures of several complexes has failed to reveal a definitive answer, possibly owing to the rather low-affinity interactions that do not leave high-energy footprints that would facilitate such an analysis. Further structures of TCR complexes are needed to derive these basic, general principles of TCR recognition. The question as to how small changes in the interface and in the half-lives of the complexes lead to profound differences in biological outcomes still needs further investigation. So far, the soluble TCR/pMHC complexes, whether in the crystal or as part of other biophysical analyses, are not in their native context on the membrane surface. Nor are they surrounded by the other signaling components of the TCR, such as CD3, or in the vicinity of their coreceptors or costimulatory receptors. Multicomponent complexes of $\alpha\beta$ TCRs with CD3 and CD8 or CD4 must be purified and analyzed structurally in order to understand how subtle changes in the TCR/pMHC interface become amplified on the cell surface. Exciting and dynamic motions of the various receptors have been captured by interference reflection and fluorescence microscopy in the immunological synapse (16, 21, 44, 46, 63, 84, 92, 119). This stable and long-term association is only part of the signaling picture and does not address the short-term or immediate signals that must be generated in the initial encounter complex. However, the combination of X-ray and NMR structure studies with real-time FRET (fluorescence resonance energy transfer) and single-molecule measurements on the cell surface will undoubtedly lead to a most comprehensive understanding of this most important of events in TCR recognition and signaling.

ACKNOWLEDGMENTS

We thank Robyn Stanfield for substantial help with Figures 1, 2, and 3 and advise on calculations; Jens Hennecke, Pjotr Sliz, Don Wiley, Jia-huai Wang, and Ellis Reinherz for coordinates; and Dagmar Klostermeier and William Biddison for critical comments on the manuscript. The authors are supported by NIH AI-42266

(I. A. Wilson), CA-58896 (I. A. Wilson), NIH training fellowship AI-07244 (J. G. Luz), a postdoctoral fellowship of the German Academic Exchange Service (M. G. Rudolph), and the Skaggs Institute.

Visit the Annual Reviews home page at www.annualreviews.org

LITERATURE CITED

1. Alam SM, Davies GM, Lin CM, Zal T, Nasholds W, et al. 1999. Qualitative and quantitative differences in T cell receptor binding of agonist and antagonist ligands. *Immunity* 10:227–37

2. Alam SM, Travers PJ, Wung JL, Nasholds W, Redpath S, et al. 1996. T-cell-receptor affinity and thymocyte positive selection. *Nature* 381:616–20

3. Al-Lazikani B, Lesk AM, Chothia C. 2000. Canonical structures for the hypervariable regions of T cell $\alpha\beta$ receptors. *J. Mol. Biol.* 295:979–95

4. Allison TJ, Winter CC, Fournie J, Bonneville M, Garboczi DN. 2001. Structure of a human $\gamma\delta$ T-cell antigen receptor. *Nature* 411:820–24

5. Baker BM, Gagnon SJ, Biddison WE, Wiley DC. 2000. Conversion of a T cell antagonist into an agonist by repairing a defect in the TCR/peptide/MHC interface: implications for TCR signaling. *Immunity* 13:475–84

6. Baker BM, Murphy KP. 1996. Evaluation of linked protonation effects in protein binding reactions using isothermal titration calorimetry. *Biophys. J.* 71:2049–55

7. Baker BM, Turner RV, Gagnon SJ, Wiley DC, Biddison WE. 2001. Identification of a crucial energetic footprint on the $\alpha 1$ helix of human histocompatibility leukocyte antigen (HLA)-A2 that provides functional interactions for recognition by tax peptide/HLA-A2-specific T cell receptors. *J. Exp. Med.* 193:551–62

8. Baker BM, Wiley DC. 2001. $\alpha\beta$ T cell receptor ligand-specific oligomerization revisited. *Immunity* 14:681–92

9. Belmant C, Espinosa E, Poupot R, Peyrat MA, Guiraud M, et al. 1999. 3-formyl-1-butyl pyrophosphate: a novel mycobacterial metabolite activating human $\gamma\delta$ T cells. *J. Biol. Chem.* 274:32079–84

10. Bodian DL, Jones EY, Harlos K, Stuart DI, Davis SJ. 1994. Crystal structure of the extracellular region of the human cell adhesion molecule CD2 at 2.5 Å resolution. *Structure* 2:755–66

11. Boniface JJ, Rabinowitz JD, Wulfing C, Hampl J, Reich Z, et al. 1998. Initiation of signal transduction through the T cell receptor requires the multivalent engagement of peptide/MHC ligands. *Immunity* 9:459–66

12. Boniface JJ, Reich Z, Lyons DS, Davis MM. 1999. Thermodynamics of T cell receptor binding to peptide-MHC: evidence for a general mechanism of molecular scanning. *Proc. Natl. Acad. Sci. USA* 96:11446–51

13. Borroto A, Mallabiabarrena A, Albar JP, Martinez AC, Alarcon B. 1998. Characterization of the region involved in CD3 pairwise interactions within the T cell receptor complex. *J. Biol. Chem.* 273:12807–16

14. Boyington JC, Motyka SA, Schuck P, Brooks AG, Sun PD. 2000. Crystal structure of an NK cell immunoglobulin-like receptor in complex with its class I MHC ligand. *Nature* 405:537–43

15. Bradshaw JM, Waksman G. 1998. Calorimetric investigation of proton linkage by monitoring both the enthalpy and association constant of binding: application to the interaction of the Src SH2 domain with a high-affinity tyrosyl phosphopeptide. *Biochemistry* 37:15400–7

16. Bromley SK, Burack WR, Johnson KG, Somersalo K, Sims TN, et al. 2001. The immunological synapse. *Annu. Rev. Immunol.* 19:375–96

17. CCP4. 1994. The Collaborative Computational Project Number 4. Suite programs for protein crystallography. *Acta Crystallogr. D* 50:760–63

18. Chien YH, Jores R, Crowley MP. 1996. Recognition by $\gamma\delta$ T cells. *Annu. Rev. Immunol.* 14:511–32

19. Chothia C, Lesk AM. 1987. Canonical structures for the hypervariable regions of immunoglobulins. *J. Mol. Biol.* 196:901–17

20. Claverie JM, Prochnicka-Chalufour A, Bougueleret L. 1989. Implications of a Fab-like structure for the T-cell receptor. *Immunol. Today* 10:10–14

21. Cochran JR, Aivazian D, Cameron TO, Stern LJ. 2001. Receptor clustering and transmembrane signaling in T cells. *Trends Biochem. Sci.* 26:304–10

22. Cochran JR, Cameron TO, Stern LJ. 2000. The relationship of MHC-peptide binding and T cell activation probed using chemically defined MHC class II oligomers. *Immunity* 12:241–50

23. Connolly ML. 1993. The molecular surface package. *J. Mol. Graph.* 11:139–41

24. Davis M, Boniface J, Reich Z, Lyons D, Hampl J, et al. 1998. Ligand recognition by $\alpha\beta$ T cell receptors. *Annu. Rev. Immunol.* 16:523–44

25. Davis MM, Bjorkman PJ. 1988. T-cell antigen receptor genes and T-cell recognition. *Nature* 334:395–402

26. Davis SJ, Schockmel GA, Somoza C, Buck DW, Healey DG, et al. 1992. Antibody and HIV-1 gp120 recognition of CD4 undermines the concept of mimicry between antibodies and receptors. *Nature* 358:76–79

27. Degano M, Garcia KC, Apostolopoulos V, Rudolph MG, Teyton L, Wilson IA. 2000. A functional hot spot for antigen recognition in a superagonist TCR/MHC complex. *Immunity* 12:251–61

28. Ding YH, Baker BM, Garboczi DN, Biddison WE, Wiley DC. 1999. Four A6-TCR/peptide/HLA-A2 structures that generate very different T cell signals are nearly identical. *Immunity* 11:45–56

29. Ding YH, Smith KJ, Garboczi DN, Utz U, Biddison WE, Wiley DC. 1998. Two human T cell receptors bind in a similar diagonal mode to the HLA-A2/Tax peptide complex using different TCR amino acids. *Immunity* 8:403–11

30. Doyle ML, Louie G, Dal Monte PR, Sokoloski TD. 1995. Tight binding affinities determined from thermodynamic linkage to protons by titration calorimetry. *Methods Enzymol.* 259:183–94

31. Fields BA, Malchiodi EL, Li H, Ysern X, Stauffacher CV, et al. 1996. Crystal structure of a T-cell receptor beta-chain complexed with a superantigen. *Nature* 384:188–92

32. Fields BA, Ober B, Malchiodi EL, Lebedeva MI, Braden BC, et al. 1995. Crystal structure of the Vα domain of a T cell antigen receptor. *Science* 270:1821–24

33. Fisher HF, Singh N. 1995. Calorimetric methods for interpreting protein-ligand interactions. *Methods Enzymol.* 259:194–221

34. Fremont DH, Matsumura M, Stura EA, Peterson PA, Wilson IA. 1992. Crystal structures of two viral peptides in complex with murine MHC class I H-2K^b. *Science* 257:919–27

35. Fukada H, Takahashi K. 1998. Enthalpy and heat capacity changes for the proton dissociation of various buffer components in 0.1 M potassium chloride. *Proteins* 33:159–66

36. Gao GF, Tormo J, Gerth UC, Wyer JR, McMichael AJ, et al. 1997. Crystal structure of the complex between human CD8$\alpha\alpha$ and HLA-A2. *Nature* 387:630–34

37. Gao GF, Willcox BE, Wyer JR, Boulter JM, O'Callaghan CA, et al. 2000. Classical and nonclassical class I major histocompatibility complex molecules exhibit

subtle conformational differences that affect binding to CD8 $\alpha\alpha$. *J. Biol. Chem.* 275:15232–38

38. Garboczi DN, Ghosh P, Utz U, Fan QR, Biddison WE, Wiley DC. 1996. Structure of the complex between human T-cell receptor, viral peptide and HLA-A2. *Nature* 384:134–41

39. Garcia KC, Degano M, Pease LR, Huang M, Peterson PA, et al. 1998. Structural basis of plasticity in T cell receptor recognition of a self peptide-MHC antigen. *Science* 279:1166–72

39a. Garcia KC, Degano M, Speir JA, Wilson IA. 1999. Emerging principles for T cell receptor recognition of antigen in cellular immunity. *Rev. Immunogen.* 1:75–90

40. Garcia KC, Degano M, Stanfield RL, Brunmark A, Jackson MR, et al. 1996. An $\alpha\beta$ T cell receptor structure at 2.5 Å and its orientation in the TCR-MHC complex. *Science* 274:209–19

41. Garcia KC, Tallquist MD, Pease LR, Brunmark A, Scott CA, et al. 1997. $\alpha\beta$ T-cell receptor interactions with syngeneic and allogeneic ligands: affinity measurements and crystallization. *Proc. Natl. Acad. Sci. USA* 94:13838–43

42. Garcia KC, Teyton L, Wilson IA. 1999. Structural basis of T cell recognition. *Annu. Rev. Immunol.* 17:369–97

43. Gascoigne NRJ, Zal T, Alam SM. 2001. T-cell receptor binding kinetics in T-cell development and activation. *Exp. Rev. Mol. Med.* http://www-ermm.cbcu.cam. ac.uk/01002502h.htm

44. Gaspar R Jr, Bagossi P, Bene L, Matko J, Szollosi J, et al. 2001. Clustering of class I HLA oligomers with CD8 and TCR: three-dimensional models based on fluorescence resonance energy transfer and crystallographic data. *J. Immunol.* 166:5078–86

45. Germain RN, Stefanova I. 1999. The dynamics of T cell receptor signaling: complex orchestration and the key roles of tempo and cooperation. *Annu. Rev. Immunol.* 17:467–522

46. Grakoui A, Bromley SK, Sumen C, Davis MM, Shaw AS, et al. 1999. Immunological synapse: a molecular machine controlling T cell activation. *Science* 285:221–27

47. Hall D. 2001. Use of optical biosensors for the study of mechanistically concerted surface adsorption processes. *Anal. Biochem.* 288:109–25

48. Hennecke J, Carfi A, Wiley DC. 2000. Structure of a covalently stabilized complex of a human alpha/beta T-cell receptor, influenza HA peptide and MHC class II molecule, HLA-DR1. *EMBO J.* 19:5611–24

48a. Hennecke J, Wiley DC. 2000. T cell receptor-MHC interactions up close. *Cell* 104:1–4

48b. Hennecke J, Wiley DC. 2002. Structure of a complex of the human $\alpha\beta$-T cell receptor HA1.7, influenza HA peptide, and MHC class II molecule, HLA-DR4 (DRA*0101, DRB1*0401)—insight into TCR cross-restriction and alloreactivity. *J. Exp. Med.* In press

49. Hensley P. 1996. Defining the structure and stability of macromolecular assemblies in solution: the re-emergence of analytical ultracentrifugation as a practical tool. *Structure* 4:367–73

50. Huppa JB, Ploegh HL. 1997. In vitro translation and assembly of a complete T cell receptor-CD3 complex. *J. Exp. Med.* 186:393–403

51. Ikemizu S, Sparks LM, van der Merwe PA, Harlos K, Stuart DI, et al. 1999. Crystal structure of the CD2-binding domain of CD58 (lymphocyte function-associated antigen 3) at 1.8 Å resolution. *Proc. Natl. Acad. Sci. USA* 96:4289–94

52. Jardetzky TS, Brown JH, Gorga JC, Stern LJ, Urban RG, et al. 1994. Three-dimensional structure of a human class II histocompatibility molecule complexed with superantigen. *Nature* 368:711–18

53. Kalergis AM, Boucheron N, Doucey MA, Palmieri E, Goyarts EC, et al. 2001. Efficient T cell activation requires an optimal dwell-time of interaction between the

TCR and the pMHC complex. *Nat. Immunol.* 2:229–34

54. Kern PS, Teng MK, Smolyar A, Liu JH, Liu J, et al. 1998. Structural basis of CD8 coreceptor function revealed by crystallographic analysis of a murine CD8 $\alpha\alpha$ ectodomain fragment in complex with H-2K^b. *Immunity* 9:519–30

55. Kersh EN, Shaw AS, Allen PM. 1998. Fidelity of T cell activation through multistep T cell receptor ζ phosphorylation. *Science* 281:572–75

56. Kersh GJ, Kersh EN, Fremont DH, Allen PM. 1998. High- and low-potency ligands with similar affinities for the TCR: the importance of kinetics in TCR signaling. *Immunity* 9:817–26

57. Kim J, Urban RG, Strominger JL, Wiley DC. 1994. Toxic shock syndrome toxin-1 complexed with a class II major histocompatibility molecule HLA-DR1. *Science* 266:1870–74

58. Kim KS, Sun ZY, Wagner G, Reinherz EL. 2000. Heterodimeric CD3$\epsilon\gamma$ extracellular domain fragments: production, purification and structural analysis. *J. Mol. Biol.* 302:899–916

59. Koning F, Maloy WL, Coligan JE. 1990. The implications of subunit interactions for the structure of the T cell receptor-CD3 complex. *Eur. J. Immunol.* 20:299–305

60. Konig R, Shen X, Germain RN. 1995. Involvement of both major histocompatibility complex class II α and β chains in CD4 function indicates a role for ordered oligomerization in T cell activation. *J. Exp. Med.* 182:779–87

61. Koop BF, Rowen L, Wang K, Kuo CL, Seto D, et al. 1994. The human T-cell receptor TCRAC/TCRDC (Cα/Cδ) region: organization, sequence, and evolution of 97.6 kb of DNA. *Genomics* 19:478–93

62. Kotzin BL, Leung DY, Kappler J, Marrack P. 1993. Superantigens and their potential role in human disease. *Adv. Immunol.* 54:99–166

63. Kupfer A, Singer SJ. 1989. Cell biology of cytotoxic and helper T cell functions: immunofluorescence microscopic studies of single cells and cell couples. *Annu. Rev. Immunol.* 7:309–37

64. Kwong PD, Wyatt R, Robinson J, Sweet RW, Sodroski J, Hendrickson WA. 1998. Structure of an HIV gp120 envelope glycoprotein in complex with the CD4 receptor and a neutralizing human antibody. *Nature* 393:648–59

65. Ladbury JE, Chowdhry BZ. 1996. Sensing the heat: the application of isothermal titration calorimetry to thermodynamic studies of biomolecular interactions. *Chem. Biol.* 3:791–801

66. Lakey JH, Raggett EM. 1998. Measuring protein-protein interactions. *Curr. Opin. Struct. Biol.* 8:119–23

67. Lamb JR, Eckels DD, Ketterer EA, Sell TW, Woody JN. 1982. Antigen-specific human T lymphocyte clones: mechanisms of inhibition of proliferative responses by xenoantiserum to human nonpolymorphic HLA-DR antigens. *J. Immunol.* 129:1085–90

68. Lamb JR, Woody JN, Hartzman RJ, Eckels DD. 1982. In vitro influenza virus-specific antibody production in man: antigen-specific and HLA-restricted induction of helper activity mediated by cloned human T lymphocytes. *J. Immunol.* 129:1465–70

69. Laue TM, Stafford WF III. 1999. Modern applications of analytical ultracentrifugation. *Annu. Rev. Biophys. Biomol. Struct.* 28:75–100

70. Leder L, Llera A, Lavoie PM, Lebedeva MI, Li H, et al. 1998. A mutational analysis of the binding of staphylococcal enterotoxins B and C3 to the T cell receptor beta chain and major histocompatibility complex class II. *J. Exp. Med.* 187:823–33

71. Li H, Lebedeva MI, Llera AS, Fields BA, Brenner MB, Mariuzza RA. 1998. Structure of the Vδ domain of a human $\gamma\delta$ T-cell antigen receptor. *Nature* 391:502–6

72. Li H, Lebedeva MI, Ward ES, Mariuzza RA. 1997. Dual conformations of a T cell

receptor Vα homodimer: implications for variability in Vα Vβ domain association. *J. Mol. Biol.* 269:385–94

73. Li Y, Li H, Dimasi N, McCormick JK, Martin R, et al. 2001. Crystal structure of a superantigen bound to the high-affinity, zinc-dependent site on MHC class II. *Immunity* 14:93–104

74. Lipschultz CA, Li Y, Smith-Gill S. 2000. Experimental design for analysis of complex kinetics using surface plasmon resonance. *Methods* 20:310–18

75. Lord GM, Lechler RI, George AJ. 1999. A kinetic differentiation model for the action of altered TCR ligands. *Immunol. Today* 20:33–39

76. Lyons DS, Lieberman SA, Hampl J, Boniface JJ, Chien Y, et al. 1996. A TCR binds to antagonist ligands with lower affinities and faster dissociation rates than to agonists. *Immunity* 5:53–61

77. MacGlashan D Jr. 2001. Signaling cascades: escape from kinetic proofreading. *Proc. Natl. Acad. Sci. USA* 98:6989–90

78. Machius M, Cianga P, Deisenhofer J, Ward ES. 2001. Crystal structure of a T cell receptor Vα11 (av11s5) domain: new canonical forms for the first and second complementarity determining regions. *J. Mol. Biol.* 310:689–98

79. Maenaka K, Juji T, Nakayama T, Wyer JR, Gao GF, et al. 1999. Killer cell immunoglobulin receptors and T cell receptors bind peptide-major histocompatibility complex class I with distinct thermodynamic and kinetic properties. *J. Biol. Chem.* 274:28329–34

80. Manolios N, Letourneur F, Bonifacino JS, Klausner RD. 1991. Pairwise, cooperative and inhibitory interactions describe the assembly and probable structure of the T-cell antigen receptor. *EMBO J.* 10:1643–51

81. Margulies DH. 1997. Interactions of TCRs with MHC-peptide complexes: a quantitative basis for mechanistic models. *Curr. Opin. Immunol.* 9:390–95

82. McDonald IK, Thornton JM. 1994. Satis-

fying hydrogen bonding potential in proteins. *J. Mol. Biol.* 238:777–93

83. McKeithan TW. 1995. Kinetic proofreading in T-cell receptor signal transduction. *Proc. Natl. Acad. Sci. USA* 92:5042–46

84. Monks CR, Freiberg BA, Kupfer H, Sciaky N, Kupfer A. 1998. Three-dimensional segregation of supramolecular activation clusters in T cells. *Nature* 395:82–86

85. Moody DB, Besra GS, Wilson IA, Porcelli SA. 1999. The molecular basis of CD1-mediated presentation of lipid antigens. *Immunol. Rev.* 172:285–96

86. Morita CT, Beckman EM, Bukowski JF, Tanaka Y, Band H, et al. 1995. Direct presentation of nonpeptide prenyl-pyrophosphate antigens to human γδ T cells. *Immunity* 3:495–507

87. Morton TA, Myszka DG, Chaiken IM. 1995. Interpreting complex binding kinetics from optical biosensors: a comparison of analysis by linearization, the integrated rate equation, and numerical integration. *Anal. Biochem.* 227:176–85

88. Natarajan K, Boyd LF, Schuck P, Yokoyama WM, Eliat D, Margulies DH. 1999. Interaction of the NK cell inhibitory receptor Ly49A with H-2D^d: identification of a site distinct from the TCR site. *Immunity* 11:591–601

89. Petersson K, Håkansson M, Nilsson H, Forsberg G, Svensson LA, et al. 2001. Crystal structure of a superantigen bound to MHC class II displays zinc and peptide dependence. *EMBO J.* 20:3306–12

90. Plaksin D, Chacko S, Navaza J, Margulies DH, Padlan EA. 1999. The X-ray crystal structure of a Vα2.6Jα38 mouse T cell receptor domain at 2.5 Å resolution: alternate modes of dimerization and crystal packing. *J. Mol. Biol.* 289:1153–61

91. Pullen JK, Hunt HD, Horton RM, Pease LR. 1989. The functional significance of two amino acid polymorphisms in the antigen-presenting domain of class I MHC molecules. Molecular dissection of K^{bm3}. *J. Immunol.* 143:1674–79

92. Qi SY, Groves JT, Chakraborty AK. 2001. Synaptic pattern formation during cellular recognition. *Proc. Natl. Acad. Sci. USA* 98:6548–53

93. Rabinowitz JD, Beeson C, Lyons DS, Davis MM, McConnell HM. 1996. Kinetic discrimination in T-cell activation. *Proc. Natl. Acad. Sci. USA* 93:1401–5

94. Regner M. 2001. Cross-reactivity in T-cell antigen recognition. *Immunol. Cell Biol.* 79:91–100

95. Reich Z, Boniface JJ, Lyons DS, Borochov N, Wachtel EJ, Davis MM. 1997. Ligand-specific oligomerization of T-cell receptor molecules. *Nature* 387:617–20

96. Reinherz EL, Tan K, Tang L, Kern P, Liu J, et al. 1999. The crystal structure of a T cell receptor in complex with peptide and MHC class II. *Science* 286:1913–21

97. Reiser JB, Darnault C, Guimezanes A, Gregoire C, Mosser T, et al. 2000. Crystal structure of a T cell receptor bound to an allogeneic MHC molecule. *Nat. Immunol.* 1:291–97

98. Rich RL, Myszka DG. 2000. Advances in surface plasmon resonance biosensor analysis. *Curr. Opin. Biotechnol.* 11:54–61

99. Rosette C, Werlen G, Daniels MA, Holman PO, Alam SM, et al. 2001. The impact of duration versus extent of TCR occupancy on T cell activation: a revision of the kinetic proofreading model. *Immunity* 15:59–70

100. Rowen L, Koop BF, Hood L. 1996. The complete 685-kilobase DNA sequence of the human β T cell receptor locus. *Science* 272:1755–62

101. Rudd PM, Elliott T, Cresswell P, Wilson IA, Dwek RA. 2001. Glycosylation and the immune system. *Science* 291:2370–76

102. Rudd PM, Wormald MR, Stanfield R, Huang M, Mattsson N, et al. 1999. Roles for glycosylation in the cellular immune system. *J. Mol. Biol.* 293:351–66

102a. Rudolph MG, Huang M, Teyton L,

Wilson IA. 2001. Crystal structure of an isolated Vα domain of the 2C T cell receptor. *J. Mol. Biol.* 314:1–8

103. Rudolph MG, Speir JA, Brunmark A, Mattsson N, Jackson MR, et al. 2001. The crystal structures of K^{bm1} and K^{bm8} reveal that subtle changes in the peptide environment impact thermostability and alloreactivity. *Immunity* 14:231–42

103a. Rudolph MG, Wilson IA. 2002. The specificity of TCR/pMHC interaction. *Curr. Opin. Immunol.* 14:52–56

104. Sakihama T, Smolyar A, Reinherz EL. 1995. Oligomerization of CD4 is required for stable binding to class II major histocompatibility complex proteins but not for interaction with human immunodeficiency virus gp120. *Proc. Natl. Acad. Sci. USA* 92:6444–48

105. Schuck P. 1997. Use of surface plasmon resonance to probe the equilibrium and dynamic aspects of interactions between biological macromolecules. *Annu. Rev. Biophys. Biomol. Struct.* 26:541–66

106. Schwartz JCD, Zhang XW, Fedorov AA, Nathenson SG, Almo SC. 2001. Structural basis for co-stimulation by the human CTLA-4/B7-2 complex. *Nature* 410:604–8

107. Sha WC, Nelson CA, Newberry RD, Pullen JK, Pease LR, et al. 1990. Positive selection of transgenic receptor-bearing thymocytes by K^b antigen is altered by K^b mutations that involve peptide binding. *Proc. Natl. Acad. Sci. USA* 87:6186–90

108. Sheriff S, Hendrickson WA, Smith JL. 1987. Structure of myohemerythrin in the azidomet state at 1.7/1.3 Å resolution. *J. Mol. Biol.* 197:273–96

109. Sherman LA, Chattopadhyay S. 1993. The molecular basis of allorecognition. *Annu. Rev. Immunol.* 11:385–402

109a. Sliz P, Michielin O, Cerottini JC, Luescher I, Romero P, Karplus M, Wiley DC. 2001. Crystal structures of two closely related but antigenically distinct HLA-A2/melanocyte-melanoma tumor-antigen peptide complexes. *J. Immunol.* 167:3276–84

110. Sloan-Lancaster J, Allen PM. 1996. Altered peptide ligand-induced partial T cell activation: molecular mechanisms and role in T cell biology. *Annu. Rev. Immunol.* 14:1–27

111. Speir JA, Garcia KC, Brunmark A, Degano M, Peterson PA, et al. 1998. Structural basis of 2C TCR allorecognition of H-2L^d peptide complexes. *Immunity* 8:553–62

112. Speir JA, Stevens J, Joly E, Butcher GW, Wilson IA. 2001. Two different, highly exposed, bulged structures for an unusually long peptide bound to rat MHC class I RT1-A^a. *Immunity* 14:81–92

113. Stamper CC, Zhang Y, Tobin JF, Erbe DV, Ikemizu S, et al. 2001. Crystal structure of the B7-1/CTLA-4 complex that inhibits human immune responses. *Nature* 410:608–11

114. Sun ZJ, Kim KS, Wagner G, Reinherz EL. 2001. Mechanisms contributing to T cell receptor signaling and assembly revealed by the solution structure of an ectodomain fragment of the CD3εγ heterodimer. *Cell* 105:913–23

115. Tallquist M, Yun T, Pease L. 1996. A single T cell receptor recognizes structurally distinct MHC/peptide complexes with high specificity. *J. Exp. Med.* 184:1017–26

116. Tissot AC, Ciatto C, Mittl PR, Grutter MG, Pluckthun A. 2000. Viral escape at the molecular level explained by quantitative T-cell receptor/peptide/MHC interactions and the crystal structure of a peptide/MHC complex. *J. Mol. Biol.* 302:873–85

117. Tormo J, Natarajan K, Margulies DH, Mariuzza RA. 1999. Crystal structure of a lectin-like natural killer cell receptor bound to its MHC class I ligand. *Nature* 402:623–31

118. Van Den Berg HA, Rand DA, Burroughs NJ. 2001. A reliable and safe T cell repertoire based on low-affinity T cell receptors. *J. Theor. Biol.* 209:465–86

119. van der Merwe AP, Davis SJ, Shaw AS, Dustin ML. 2000. Cytoskeletal polarization and redistribution of cell-surface molecules during T cell antigen recognition. *Sem. Immunol.* 12:5–21

120. van Raaij MJ, Chouin E, van der Zandt H, Bergelson JM, Cusack S. 2000. Dimeric structure of the coxsackievirus and adenovirus receptor D1 domain at 1.7 Å resolution. *Struct. Fold. Des.* 8:1147–55

121. Wang J, Lim K, Smolyar A, Teng M, Liu J, et al. 1998. Atomic structure of an αβ T cell receptor (TCR) heterodimer in complex with an anti-TCR fab fragment derived from a mitogenic antibody. *EMBO J.* 17:10–26

122. Wang J, Meijers R, Xiong Y, Liu J, Sakihama T, et al. 2001. Crystal structure of the human CD4 N-terminal two domain fragment complexed to a class II MHC molecule. *Proc. Natl. Acad. Sci. USA* 98:10799–804

122a. Wang J, Reinherz EL. 2000. Structural basis of cell-cell interactions in the immune system. *Curr. Opin. Struct. Biol.* 10:656–61

123. Wang JH, Smolyar A, Tan K, Liu JH, Kim M, et al. 1999. Structure of a heterophilic adhesion complex between the human CD2 and CD58 (LFA-3) counterreceptors. *Cell* 97:791–803

124. Willcox BE, Gao GF, Wyer JR, Ladbury JE, Bell JI, et al. 1999. TCR binding to peptide-MHC stabilizes a flexible recognition interface. *Immunity* 10:357–65

125. Wilson IA, Garcia KC. 1997. T cell receptor structure and TCR complexes. *Curr. Opin. Struct. Biol.* 7:839–48

126. Wolan DW, Teyton L, Rudolph MG, Villmow B, Bauer S, et al. 2001. Crystal structure of the murine NK cell-activating receptor NKG2D at 1.95 Å. *Nat. Immunol.* 2:248–54

127. Wu H, Kwong PD, Hendrickson WA. 1997. Dimeric association and segmental variability in the structure of human CD4. *Nature* 387:527–30

Annu. Rev. Biophys. Biomol. Struct. 2002. 31:151–75
DOI: 10.1146/annurev.biophys.31.082901.134259
Copyright © 2002 by Annual Reviews. All rights reserved

PIP$_2$ AND PROTEINS: Interactions, Organization, and Information Flow

Stuart McLaughlin,[1] Jiyao Wang,[1] Alok Gambhir,[1] and Diana Murray[2]

[1]Department of Physiology and Biophysics, HSC, SUNY Stony Brook, New York 11794-8661; email: SMCL@epo.som.sunysb.edu
[2]Department of Microbiology and Immunology, Weill Medical College of Cornell University, 1300 York Avenue, Box 62, New York, New York 10021

Key Words phosphatidylinositol 4,5-bisphosphate, phosphoinositides, signal transduction, second messengers

■ **Abstract** We review the physical properties of phosphatidylinositol 4,5-bisphosphate (PIP$_2$) that determine both its specific interactions with protein domains of known structure and its nonspecific electrostatic sequestration by unstructured domains. Several investigators have postulated the existence of distinct pools of PIP$_2$ within the cell to account for the myriad functions of this lipid. Recent experimental work indicates certain regions of the plasma membrane—membrane ruffles and nascent phagosomes—do indeed concentrate PIP$_2$. We consider two mechanisms that could account for this phenomenon: local synthesis and electrostatic sequestration. We conclude by considering the hypothesis that proteins such as MARCKS bind a significant fraction of the PIP$_2$ in a cell, helping to sequester it in lateral membrane domains, then release this lipid in response to local signals such as an increased concentration of Ca^{++}/calmodulin or activation of protein kinase C.

CONTENTS

INTRODUCTION

Phosphatidylinositol 4,5-bisphosphate, abbreviated as PI(4,5)P$_2$ or PIP$_2$, is the major polyphosphoinositide in mammalian cells. Other recent reviews (29, 30, 32, 48a, 53, 55, 56, 70, 83, 97a, 100, 106) and a monograph (28) discuss the functions of phosphoinositides in cells, as well as their production by different kinases and their breakdown by phosphatases and phosphoinositide-specific phospholipase Cs (PLCs). This review focuses on the biophysics of PIP$_2$ and how it interacts with proteins in the plasma membrane.

Early studies established the role of PIP$_2$ as the source of two second messengers in the cell (16), diacylglycerol (DAG) and inositol 1,4,5-trisphosphate (IP$_3$), a topic that we will not consider in detail. Subsequent studies have shown that PIP$_2$ has a host of functions in cells related to its ability to interact with different proteins. Indeed, Cantley (24) suggests its role in IP$_3$-induced Ca^{++} release in higher eukaryotes is a relatively late adaptation to its original role as a lipid anchor. It is now well documented that PIP$_2$ is important in the attachment of the cytoskeleton to the plasma membrane, exocytosis, endocytosis, membrane trafficking, and the activation of enzymes. This has led several reviewers to ask how one lipid can play so many different roles and to suggest that there are different pools of PIP$_2$ in the plasma membrane (e.g., 49, 70, 97a). New tools for visualizing phosphoinositides in living cells have revealed that PIP$_2$ and other phosphoinositides are in fact distributed nonuniformly in the plasma membrane.

In a perceptive recent review on targeting by membrane lipids, Hurley & Meyer (53) note that "a picture has emerged of a restless subclass of signaling proteins that spend a significant fraction of their time diffusing through the cytosol in search of binding partners." Although many of these signaling proteins indeed move only by passive diffusion, the remarkable feature of signal transduction pathways, including those that involve PIP$_2$, is that the flow of information from the surface to the interior of the cell resembles an elegantly choreographed ballet rather than a collection of uncoordinated random walks. But what choreographs this diffusional "dance to the music of time" (87)? We argue that cells utilize several biophysical mechanisms to facilitate this flow of information. We refer to these concepts as "cheap tricks," a term coined by the distinguished physiologist Knut Schmidt-Nielsen (94) to describe how countercurrent exchangers function passively (i.e., without a direct input of energy) in a number of different organ systems. This physiological cheap trick minimizes, for example, the loss of heat from the leg of a wading bird or flipper of a seal, helps the mammalian kidney to concentrate urine, and thus explains why a desert rat need never take a drink of water. We discuss cheap tricks that act at the molecular or biophysical rather than at the organ systems level.

The three tricks we describe in this review are well known to membrane biophysicists, but cell biologists or biochemists studying signal transduction may be less familiar with biophysical principles. In this spirit, we refer a reader unfamiliar with the fundamentals of diffusion theory to Berg's pithy, lucid, and still timely introduction to this topic in *Random Walks in Biology* (14). Berg's discussion of the diffusional mechanism by which a ligand revisits a surface explains, for example, why only a small fraction of a cell need be covered by receptors to effectively capture a ligand; subsequent theoretical and experimental studies extend Berg's discussion [e.g., (62, 63) and references therein].

Cheap trick #1: Reduction of dimensionality or local concentration effect. Consider, for example, a phosphoinositide-specific phospholipase C-δ (PLCδ) enzyme (91) diffusing randomly through the cytoplasm of a cell: When its pleckstrin homology (PH) domain encounters a PIP₂ in the plasma membrane, it binds to PIP₂ with sufficiently high affinity and specificity to anchor the protein to the membrane (65). This confines the catalytic site of PLCδ to the surface phase, which Guggenheim defines as a thin (few nm) region of the aqueous phase adjacent to the membrane (10). In the surface phase, the catalytic site experiences a ≈1000-fold higher concentration of PIP₂ than if it was diffusing throughout the cytoplasm of a cell, which greatly facilitates PLCδ's ability to hydrolyze PIP₂ when it is activated by an increase in intracellular Ca^{++}. This reduction of dimensionality—or more appropriately, local concentration effect—is well understood at a biophysical level (1, 15, 61, 71, 74).

Membrane anchoring and the local concentration effect are important for all major proteins in the calcium/phosphoinositide second messenger signal transduction pathway. For example, acyl and prenyl chains anchor G proteins to the plasma membrane; PH and other domains anchor PLCs; C1 and C2 domains reversibly anchor protein kinase C (PKC); and a myristate and a cluster of basic residues reversibly anchor MARCKS (myristoylated alanine-rich C kinase substrate). Of course the domains that anchor the protein to the membrane may serve other functions: The PH domain of PLCδ contributes to its preferential localization at the plasma versus internal membranes; the C1 and C2 domains on PKC are involved in the activation of the enzyme as well as membrane targeting (54). As discussed below, it is now well established that PIP₂ often serves to activate as well as merely anchor proteins to the plasma membranes. In other words, it can act as a second messenger as well as a passive membrane anchor.

PHYSICAL/CHEMICAL PROPERTIES OF PIP$_2$ AND ITS CONCENTRATION IN CELLS

Orientation of the Head Group

Figure 1 illustrates the chemical structures and space-filling models of phosphatidylcholine (PC), cholesterol, and PIP$_2$. In PC and other common phospholipids, the glycerol backbone is approximately perpendicular to, and the head group parallel to, the plane of the membrane as illustrated here (43). The orientation of the head group of PIP$_2$ with respect to the membrane surface is unknown. We show it as perpendicular to the plane of the membrane, in agreement with studies of the structure of phosphatidylinositol (21, 113). Note that the potentially erect structure and large size of the PIP$_2$ head group implies that it may protrude further into the aqueous phase than a typical phospholipid.

Charge of PIP$_2$

Cholesterol is a neutral molecule and PC is a zwitterion that also has zero net charge, as indicated in Figure 1. The net charge on PIP$_2$, however, depends on a number of factors such as the local pH and its interaction with proteins. NMR experiments show that the pK values for the first protonation of the 4 and 5 position phosphates of PIP$_2$ (in a PC/PIP$_2$ 99:1 vesicle) are about 6.7 and 7.7 [(107) confirmed by A. McLaughlin & S. McLaughlin]. Thus at pH 7.0, ~1 proton is bound and the net charge on PIP$_2$ might be expected to be −4 (Figure 1). However, the electrophoretic mobility of a PC/PIP$_2$ vesicle formed in 100 mM KCl, pH 7.0 suggests the net charge on PIP$_2$ is only −3 (101, 110); presumably both a K^+ and a H^+ ion are bound to the lipid. It seems likely the K^+ ion will be displaced when PIP$_2$ binds

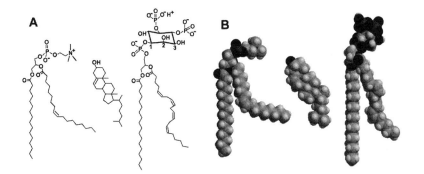

Figure 1   (*a*) Chemical structures of the most prevalent phospholipid (POPC), sterol (cholesterol), and polyphosphoinositide (PIP$_2$) in mammalian cell membranes. The size of the inositol ring of PIP$_2$ is approximately doubled for clarity. (*b*) Molecular models of 1-palmitoyl-2-oleoyl-3-phosphatidylcholine, POPC; cholesterol and 1-stearoyl-2-arachidonyl-3-phosphatidylinositol 4,5-bisphosphate, PIP$_2$. A typical phospholipid in a bilayer occupies an area of 70 Å^2 (79); cholesterol occupies 40 Å^2.

to a protein, although this must be determined in each case. The proton bound to PIP_2 may also be displaced upon binding to a protein, so the charge on PIP_2 could be -3, -4, or -5.

Partial Charges on Lipids

The distribution of the partial charges on PC and other common phospholipids has been determined by ab initio quantum mechanical calculations, but similar calculations have not been performed for PIP_2. The dearth of information about both the orientation of the head group and the distribution of partial charges within the PIP_2 molecule severely limits the types of theoretical calculations that can be performed with this important lipid.

Concentration of PIP₂ in a Typical Mammalian Cell

We assume the cell is a sphere of radius 10 μm and that PIP_2 is confined to the plasma membrane. If all the phospholipids in the plasma membrane of this hypothetical cell (e.g., phosphatidylcholine, phosphatidylethanolamine, PIP_2) were dissolved in the cytoplasm, they would be present at an effective concentration of $\approx$1 mM. If we assume PIP_2 comprises 1% of the phospholipid in the plasma membrane of our hypothetical cell, as it does in human erythrocytes (37, 46), the effective concentration of PIP_2 in the cell is $\approx$10 μM. The recent studies using constructs of PH domains linked to green fluorescent protein (GFP) provide more direct information about the concentration and location of PIP_2 in a mammalian cell. Fluorescent (52, 98, 99, 105, 108) constructs of the PH domain from PLCδ are localized on the plasma membrane, whereas the PH domain from pleckstrin is found in the cytoplasm (65). In vitro the PH domain from PLCδ binds PIP_2 with a K_d of 2 μM, whereas the PH domain from pleckstrin binds PIP_2 with a K_d of 30 μM (65). If we assume the K_d values are the same in the test tube and the cell, then 2 μM $< [PIP_2]_a < 30$ μM, where $[PIP_2]_a$ is the effective concentration of PIP_2 that is accessible to the PH domains. This range is consistent with our calculation of a total effective concentration of $\approx$10 μM but, as discussed below, does not imply that all the PIP_2 in the plasma membrane is free.

The relative concentration of the other phosphoinositides in cells is considered elsewhere; $PI(4,5)P_2$ comprises >99% of the doubly phosphorylated phosphoinositides in a mammalian cell according to (106). We next consider how the PIP_2 located on the cytoplasmic leaflet of the plasma membrane anchors and, in some cases, activates different proteins.

DOMAINS/PROTEINS THAT BIND PIP₂

Domains of Known Structure

Figure 2a (see color insert) shows ribbon diagrams of three structurally diverse domains that bind PIP_2: the PLCδ-PH domain (36), the CALM N-terminal ENTH domain (38), and the radixin FERM domain (47). Either IP_3 or the head group of PIP_2 is shown in each binding pocket with the 1-phosphate facing down; the domains are thus presumably in the orientation they have when they bind to PIP_2 in a bilayer (e.g., Figure 1). Figure 2b illustrates how two Lys residues of PLCδ-PH form hydrogen bonds with both the 4- and 5-phosphates.

PH DOMAINS   As described in many recent reviews [(65) and references therein], PH domains comprise about 120 amino acids; their function is generally to bind to phosphoinositides. The PH domain of PLCδ (PLCδ-PH), for example, binds to PIP_2 with a $K_d = 2$ μM, as measured with PC/PIP_2 vesicles using calorimetry (66), a BIAcore sensor chip (50), or a PLCδ-PH-GFP construct and a centrifugation assay (A. Gambhir & S. McLaughlin, unpublished data). Intact PLCδ binds with a similar K_d (26, 91), an affinity sufficiently strong to anchor the protein to the plasma membrane. The mechanism by which PLCδ-PH and several other PH domains bind phosphoinositides is revealed by crystal structures of the domains with bound IP_3 (36, 65, 81). The 4- and 5-phosphates form several hydrogen bonds with residues in PLCδ-PH, holding the lipid head group in a classical "lock and key" complex. Specifically, Lys^{30} and Lys^{57} form bonds with both phosphates simultaneously (Figure 2b) "clamping the 4- and 5-phosphates in the binding pocket" (36). PLCδ-PH increases the surface pressure of a mixed lipid monolayer when it binds PIP_2, which shows it penetrates the polar head group region (K. N. J. Burger, personal communication). PLCδ-PH binds about 10-fold more strongly to IP_3 than to PIP_2, which complicates the use of PLCδ-PH-GFP constructs to determine the subcellular location of PIP_2. For example, translocation of PLCδ-PH-GFP from membrane to cytosol upon activation of PLC could be due to either a decrease in the level of PIP_2 in the membrane or an increase in the level of IP_3 in the cytosol, an issue that is still unresolved (50, 105, 108).

As discussed elsewhere (65), many of the ≈250 PH domains bind only weakly, and with little specificity, to phosphoinositides: They do not bind phosphoinositides with sufficient avidity to provide a stable membrane anchor on their own. How then do they anchor a protein to the membrane if this is indeed their main function? The PH domain could cooperate with additional membrane-binding sites on the protein or the protein could oligomerize so that more than one PH domain contributes to the binding; signal transduction proteins almost certainly use both schemes (65).

Cheap trick #2: Two domains are better than one. Many signal transduction molecules use two or more domains/motifs to bind to membranes; the membrane-binding energies of the individual domains often simply add (binding constants multiply), as discussed elsewhere (23, 31, 44, 77). Why do signal transduction molecules use multiple domains with low membrane affinities rather than one domain with a high affinity to anchor themselves to the plasma membrane? Multiple membrane–anchoring sites offer at least three advantages. First, they may promote lateral organization or sequestration of the molecules: Proteins with ≥2 saturated acyl chains, such as GAP43 (9), are concentrated in the detergent-insoluble membrane fraction (DIGs) and may be directed laterally to putative cholesterol-enriched rafts in the unperturbed membrane (22, 60, 95). Second, they offer greater possibilities for reversible binding: Dynamin may form oligomers where the n PH domains in the oligomer bind to n PIP$_2$ (65). Thus membrane binding can be controlled through oligomerization without changing the level of PIP$_2$ in the membrane. Third, multiple binding sites provide a mechanism for synergy/coincidence detection: The C1 and C2 domains of PKC require DAG and Ca^{++}, respectively, to bind to membranes—concomitant membrane binding of the C1 and C2 domains removes the pseudosubstrate region of PKC from its binding site and activates the enzyme (54).

Synergy/coincidence counting can also occur when PIP$_2$-binding motifs act in concert with other membrane-binding domains to anchor and simultaneously activate proteins. For example, activation of the Wiskott Aldrich syndrome protein (WASP) family, which is involved in regulating the actin cytoskeleton (35, 75, 82, 86), occurs when it binds PIP$_2$ together with the prenylated, membrane-bound, low-molecular-weight G protein Cdc42 (25). Fawcett & Pawson (35) suggest that "perhaps N-WASP is a 'coincidence detector' because when it binds to activated Cdc42 it becomes destabilized and primed such that only a small amount of a coincident signal—in this case PIP$_2$—is needed for it to become fully activated." The factor(s) that increase the level of PIP$_2$ in the membrane to produce the coincident signal are not well understood.

ENTH DOMAINS   Proteins in the epsin family share a conserved region, the epsin N-terminal homology (ENTH) domain, that binds PIP$_2$. Two recent structural studies provide details of how the ENTH domains of epsin (57) and the AP180 homolog CALM (38) may bind to PIP$_2$ in membranes. The structure of the CALM N-terminal domain, a superhelix of nine major alpha helices, is illustrated in Figure 2 with a bound headgroup of PIP$_2$. The PIP$_2$-binding site in CALM (X-ray structure) is unusual in that it consists of an exposed cluster of lysines that do not form a binding pocket and, curiously, appear to be different from the PIP$_2$-binding site in epsin (NMR structure).

Epsin and CALM regulate assembly of the clathrin lattice, and binding of PIP$_2$ to epsin is necessary for endocytosis (45, 70). Several other proteins that are involved in either recruiting receptors to clathrin-coated pits (e.g., AP-2, β-arrestin) or the final pinching-off process from the plasma membrane (e.g., dynamin) also bind PIP$_2$. Finally, dephosphorylation of PIP$_2$ by synaptojanin to form PI(4)P causes disassembly of the clathrin coat. Tsujishita et al. (102) recently obtained the crystal structure of a synaptojanin and provide an excellent discussion of how the binding pocket could accommodate a phosphoinositide.

FERM DOMAINS   Members of the ezrin/radixin/moesin or ERM family, which help link actin to the plasma membrane, contain an N-terminal FERM (4.1 and ERM) domain that binds to the C-terminal region of the protein. Upon binding to PIP$_2$, the FERM domain is released from the C-terminal autoinhibitory domain, allowing the protein to interact with other proteins, such as CD44, and link actin filaments to the plasma membrane (47, 103). Figure 2a shows the radixin FERM domain bound to IP_3 (47). The PIP_2-binding pocket in the FERM domain is formed from a basic cleft between two subdomains: The cleft is located on a positively charged, relatively flat surface, which should facilitate interaction of the FERM domain with the surface of a negatively charged membrane. The 4-phosphate of PIP_2 intrudes into the cleft, but the 5-phosphate does not; in contrast, both the 4- and 5-phosphates are buried in the pocket of the PH domain of PLCδ, as shown in Figure 2b. This probably explains the ability of radixin to bind moderately strongly to PI4P as well as to PIP_2 (47).

OTHER PIP_2-BINDING DOMAINS   Several other domains of known structure bind PIP_2: The Tubby domain is a new structure with a basic pocket that binds PIP_2 (93); the PX domains contained in many different proteins (75a, 81, 93a) generally bind phosphoinositides that contain a phosphate at the 3 position, but one also binds $PI(4,5)P_2$.

Several important PIP_2-binding proteins have clusters of basic/aromatic residues of relatively undefined structure that interact with PIP_2. For example, although phospholipase D (PLD) contains a PH domain, the PIP_2-binding site responsible for activation has been localized to a different region of the protein containing a conserved cluster of basic/aromatic residues (96); the structure of PLD is unknown. The structure of the actin-binding protein gelsolin was recently determined: Tuominen et al. (104) studied the binding of fluorescently labeled PIP_2 to gelsolin and to peptides corresponding two putative PIP_2-binding regions that contained clusters of basic/aromatic residues. They found that PIP_2 bound more strongly to the native protein than to either of the two peptides. We obtained similar results with peptides corresponding to the cluster of seven basic residues in N-WASP that apparently binds PIP_2 (88): A peptide corresponding to this region binds weakly to PC/PIP_2 vesicles (J. Wang & S. McLaughlin, unpublished data). The weak binding of the basic peptides from gelsolin and N-WASP to PC/PIP_2 vesicles suggests that the structural context of the binding region is important in determining the affinity of a cluster of basic residues for phosphoinositides.

Experiments in several laboratories over the past decade with many different hydrophilic (i.e., lacking aromatic residues) peptides containing a small cluster of basic residues (<7 Lys or Arg) have failed, to our knowledge, to identify peptides where addition of 1% PIP_2 significantly increases (>100-fold) the partition coefficient of the peptide onto a vesicle in physiological salt solutions. Included in this list are myristoylated and nonmyristoylated basic peptides corresponding to the basic N-terminal regions of Src (23) and CAP23 (J. Wang & S. McLaughlin, unpublished data) and a peptide corresponding to the basic C-terminal region of Kras4B (67).

THE ROLE OF STRUCTURE   The data accumulated to date with these small hydrophilic basic peptides suggest that a structured domain, one that can form multiple hydrogen bonds with the phosphates of the phosphoinositide (e.g., Figure 2b), is

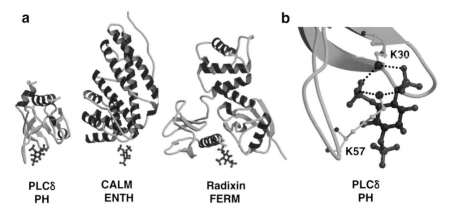

Figure 2 (*a*) Ribbon diagrams of three domains showing their interaction with IP_3 or the head group of PIP_2. Helices, *blue*; β-sheets, *green*; loops, *cyan*; oxygens on IP_3, *red*. (*b*) Detail of the binding pocket of the PH domain of PLCδ showing the two hydrogen bonds that K30 and K57 each make with the 4- and 5-phosphates.

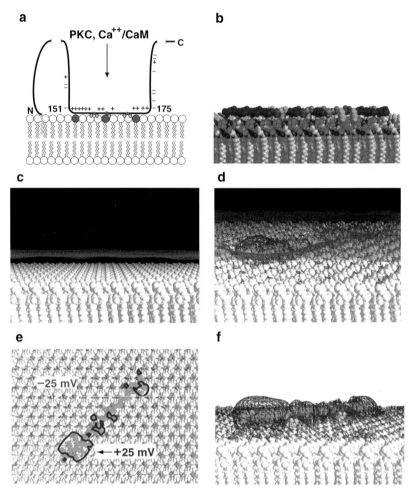

Figure 4 (*a*) Cartoon of MARCKS bound to a bilayer. The myristate (*orange*) inserts hydrophobically into the membrane, and the 13 basic residues (*blue + signs*) in the effector domain interact with acidic lipids (3 *red balls* indicate PIP₂). Five Phe residues (*cyan*) insert into the bilayer. Phosphorylation of 3 Ser (*purple*) by PKC or binding of Ca⁺⁺/calmodulin displaces the effector domain from the bilayer. (*b*) Molecular model of the effector domain of MARCKS bound to a bilayer. Basic residues, *blue*; Ser phosphorylated by PKC, *purple*; Phe, *cyan*. (*c*) Electrostatic equipotential profile (-25 mV = kT/e profile shown in *red*) adjacent to a PC/PS (2:1) bilayer in 100 mM monovalent salt as calculated from the nonlinear Poisson-Boltzmann equation (84). (*d*) Electrostatic potential profiles produced by the binding of a MARCKS effector domain peptide to a PC/PS 2:1 bilayer. The -25 mV equipotential profile is shown in *red*, the +25 mV potential profile in *blue*. (*e*) Simple model to illustrate electrostatic sequestration of PIP₂ by MARCKS. (*f*) MARCKS effector domain adsorbed to a PC/PIP₂ bilayer showing that it captures electrostatically several PIP₂ (*yellow*: two are visible on the front of the peptide). The +25 mV equipotential profile is shown in *blue*, the -25 mV equipotential profile in *red*.

required to anchor a protein firmly to a single PIP$_2$ in the plasma membrane. It seems even more likely that structure is required for specificity. For example, the biologically important 3-phosphorylated phosphoinositides bind with high specificity to several structured domains (e.g., PH, PX, and FYVE domains) (75a, 81, 93a). In contrast, small unstructured molecules, such as neomycin (6) or a peptide corresponding to the MARCKS effector domain that contains 13 basic residues (110), exhibit no specificity between PI(3,4)P$_2$ and PI(4,5)P$_2$, although they bind to PIP$_2$-containing bilayers with high affinity.

If unstructured clusters of basic residues on proteins are located near the membrane-solution interface, however, they could well be involved in sequestering PIP$_2$ laterally in the membrane. The process by which a basic motif binds to a membrane [reviewed in (76)], and the simpler process by which a basic motif located at the interface uses electrostatics to laterally reorganize multivalent lipids such as PIP$_2$, involve different combinations of forces.

Unstructured Domains

THE UNSTRUCTURED BASIC EFFECTOR REGION OF MARCKS BINDS WITH HIGH AFFINITY TO VESICLES CONTAINING PIP$_2$ The MARCKS protein is a puzzle: It is present at high concentration ($\approx 10 \ \mu$M) and is the major PKC substrate in many cell types, but its function is unknown (2, 18). The mechanism by which this unstructured protein binds to membranes containing acidic lipids is well understood (Figure 4a, see color insert) and has been reviewed in detail elsewhere (7, 74). Binding requires both the hydrophobic insertion of the N-terminal myristate (orange) into the bilayer and electrostatic interaction of a conserved cluster of basic residues (blue "+" signs), termed the effector domain, with acidic lipids. As illustrated in Figure 4b, the 25 residue effector domain contains 13 basic (blue) and 5 aromatic (cyan) residues; it also contains the 3 serine (purple) residues phosphorylated by PKC and binds with nM affinity to calcium/calmodulin (Ca^{++}/CaM) (7, 74). The myristate alone cannot anchor the protein to the plasma membrane, so abrogation of the electrostatic interaction with the membrane by binding to Ca^{++}/CaM or phosphorylation by PKC translocates MARCKS from membrane to cytosol in many cell types. This myristoyl/electrostatic switch mechanism (7, 74) has been demonstrated in both phospholipid vesicles and cells, most directly with GFP-MARCKS (80). Although the physiological concentration of monovalent lipids in the plasma membrane provides sufficient electrostatic attraction to anchor the protein, recent work has shown the effector domain binds PIP$_2$ with high affinity. Physiological concentrations of both the intact protein and a peptide corresponding to the effector domain inhibit PLC-catalyzed hydrolysis of PIP$_2$ in phospholipid vesicles. The inhibition occurs because the effector domain sequesters PIP$_2$ away from the catalytic domain of PLC, as shown by direct binding measurements (110). Incorporating 1% PIP$_2$ into PC vesicles increases the binding of the effector domain peptide by four orders of magnitude. For comparison, 100-fold higher concentrations of PC/PIP$_2$ vesicles are required to bind the same fraction of the PH domain of PLCδ.

HOW DOES THE UNSTRUCTURED BASIC EFFECTOR DOMAIN OF MARCKS BIND WITH SUCH HIGH AFFINITY TO PIP_2 ON A BILAYER SURFACE?   It uses cheap trick #2, binding several (probably three) PIP_2 to form an electroneutral complex (110) as demonstrated most directly by recent electron spin resonance (ESR) experiments with spin-labeled PIP_2 (D. Cafiso, personal communication). Small basic hydrophilic peptides with <7 basic residues presumably do not bind with high affinity to PC/PIP_2 membranes because they cannot form complexes with >1 PIP_2. Several lines of evidence support the conclusion that local electrostatic interactions drive this high-affinity binding of the MARCKS effector domain: Raising the salt concentration screens the binding; $PI(4,5)P_2$ and $PI(3,4)P_2$ bind with the same affinity, indicating it is independent of the chemical nature of the phosphoinositide; and peptides with 13 Lys or 13 Arg residues bind with the same affinity as the MARCKS effector domain peptide (110).

FUNCTIONS OF PIP_2

Figure 3 summarizes some of the well-established functions of PIP_2; we discuss these only briefly because they have been considered in detail in other reviews (29, 30, 32, 53, 55, 56, 70, 83, 100, 106).

Production of Second Messengers

Receptor-mediated activation of PLC catalyzes hydrolysis of PIP_2 to produce the second messengers DAG and IP_3 (16). IP_3 releases Ca^{++} from intracellular stores (17, 27), whereas DAG remains in the membrane and helps activate PKC by binding to its C1 domain (54). More recently it has been recognized that PIP_3, which can be formed from phosphorylation of PIP_2 by a PI3 kinase, is also an authentic second messenger that functions as a membrane anchor for a number of proteins (32). It is easy to understand how the products of PI3 kinases, such as PIP_3, function as second messengers. Their level in a quiescent cell is low (106); signaling to a

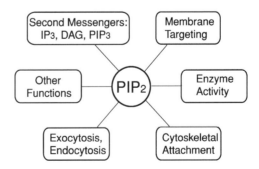

Figure 3 Functions of phosphatidylinositol 4,5-bisphosphate (PIP_2). See text for discussion.

PI3 kinase can thus produce a large increase in the level of the 3-phosphorylated lipid in the membrane, which can be recognized by a binding domain with a high specificity for that lipid. In contrast to DAG, IP_3, and PIP_3, where the level of messenger can increase dramatically, the overall concentration of PIP_2 in the plasma membrane is unlikely to increase significantly, making it less clear how PIP_2 itself acts as a second messenger (53) to activate actin-binding proteins such as the WASP and ERM families, and enzymes such as PLD.

Membrane Targeting

In some cases it is not necessary for the concentration of PIP_2 to increase for it to function effectively as a membrane anchor. The PH domain of PLCδ was the first PIP_2-binding domain to be understood in atomic detail, and the local concentration effect (cheap trick #1) explains why targeting is important with this enzyme. The enzyme is activated not by translocation to the membrane but by an increase in the intracellular $[Ca^{++}]$: Membrane anchoring simply facilitates interaction of the catalytic domain of PLCδ with its membrane-bound substrate PIP_2 (91). TUBBY, in contrast, is apparently anchored to the plasma membrane to prevent it from interacting with its target molecules in the nucleus: Hydrolysis of PIP_2 produces translocation of TUBBY from membrane, allowing it to diffuse to the nucleus (24, 93). In many other cases, PIP_2 acts as a second messenger and activates proteins.

Enzyme Activation

We consider only one example, a major PIP_2 synthesis pathway in mammalian cells. The PI4P 5-kinases (PIP kinases) produce PIP_2 mainly by phosphorylating PI4P; they are strongly activated by phosphatidic acid (PA) (5, 40, 49, 52). PA is produced by PLD, which requires PIP_2 for activation (68). Thus the potential exists for a positive feedback loop. Actually, several complicated positive and negative feedback loops involving PIP_2 control the activation of PIP kinases (32, 34, 89). There is also evidence the enzymes involved in these control mechanisms may be concentrated together in specific regions of the plasma membrane, such as membrane ruffles (52).

Cytoskeletal Attachment

Many actin-binding proteins bind to PIP_2 and are activated by this lipid. We mentioned that PIP_2 induces conformational changes in N-WASP and the ERM proteins [more extensive lists are considered elsewhere (49, 97)]. The possibility that a local increase in the free concentration of PIP_2 acts as a signal for anchoring actin has been discussed widely, and the importance of PIP_2 in cytoskeletal attachment was demonstrated directly by elegant experiments using laser tweezers (90). Decreasing the level of PIP_2 produced a dramatic release of the cytoskeleton from the membrane (90).

Exocytosis, Endocytosis, and Membrane Traffic

This topic has been reviewed recently (30, 70, 97a) and there is no lack of candidate PIP_2-binding molecules that could be involved in exocytosis and clathrin-mediated endocytosis. Several investigators have stressed the importance of understanding the lateral organization of PIP_2 in the membrane and the role it might play in these functions. With respect to exocytosis, Martin notes that immunocytochemical studies from his lab using PC12 cells reveal "plasma membrane rafts of PIP_2 that colocalize with secretory granules" (70). With respect to endocytosis, "the focal assembly of clathrin lattices implies that there may be PIP_2 rich patches in the plasma membrane" (45). The mechanism(s) by which these putative PIP_2-enriched rafts or patches are assembled and maintained is unclear.

Other Functions

Space limitations prevent us from discussing the many other functions of PIP_2 [e.g., regulation of ion channels (48a), binding of scaffolding proteins]. How does one simple lipid do all these different jobs? We consider the possibility there are separate pools of PIP_2 in the plasma membrane.

EVIDENCE FOR THE LATERAL ORGANIZATION OF PIP_2 IN THE PLASMA MEMBRANE

The older literature contains hints that much of the PIP_2 in the plasma membrane is not free. For example, microvesicles released from erythrocytes after a variety of treatments contain only about half the fraction of polyphosphoinositides (mainly PIP_2) seen in the original erythrocyte membranes (46). Other studies suggest different metabolic pools of PIP_2 may exist in cells [see discussion in (49, 108)]. PIP_2 is concentrated in the noncaveolar DIGs fraction of the plasma membrane (85, 111), which suggests an association with putative cholesterol-rich rafts in the unperturbed membrane (22, 60, 95). Because PIP_2 has a polyunsaturated chain (Figure 1), it is unlikely it partitions spontaneously into rafts by itself (22, 33).

Recently, researchers have developed new tools to study the location of PIP_2 in living cells more directly (11, 98, 108). Botelho et al. (20) used fluorescent chimeras of PH domains to show that PIP_2 is concentrated in the nascent phagosomes of macrophages. This elegant, tightly reasoned paper showed the localized accumulation of PLCδ-PH-GFP is transient; the chimera dissociated rapidly once the phagosomes pinched off from the membrane. Several factors could, in principle, decrease the level of PIP_2, but the concomitant appearance of the hydrolysis product DAG (detected by a fluorescent C1 domain chimera) indicates that PLC-catalyzed hydrolysis is at least partially responsible for reducing the concentration of PIP_2 in the phagosomes. Are these transient changes in the level of PIP_2 important? Their observation that neomycin or overexpression of PLCδ-PH inhibits phagocytosis suggests these transient changes in the level of PIP_2 are required for phagocytosis. Botelho et al. (20) discuss the (still imperfectly understood) roles that PIP_2,

PLC, PKC, and other enzymes could play in phagocytosis. They also showed that a PIP kinase involved in the synthesis of PIP$_2$ migrates to the nascent phagosome, then dissociates shortly after completion of phagocytosis. In a subsequent report, they used GFP constructs of PH domains that bind PIP$_3$ (e.g., Akt) to show PIP$_3$ also accumulates in and is sharply restricted to the phagosomal cup (69). The accumulation is transient: PIP$_3$ disappears within 2 min of phagosomal sealing, probably because of the action of the phosphatase SHIP1.

Two other groups have used fluorescent constructs of PLCδ-PH to show transient increases in the concentration of PIP$_2$ in a different region of cells, membrane ruffles. When HeLa cells were stimulated with epidermal growth factor, PLCδ-PH-GFP first translocated to the ruffles then dispersed as the membrane ruffles disappeared (52). The localization of PLCδ-PH-GFP at the ruffles coincided with the presence of a PIP kinase (52), as was observed with the phagosomes. A PLCδ-PH-EGFP chimera has also been shown to be concentrated in the membrane ruffles of NIH-3T3 fibroblasts (99).

The PH-GFP chimeras, of course, are not perfect indicators of PIP$_2$ (11). Holz et al. (51), for example, minimized potential artifacts by using two PIP$_2$ indicators, fluorescent neomycin (6) and PLCδ-PH-GFP, in their study of exocytosis. Fortunately, they produced similar results. Thus the available evidence strongly suggests that PIP$_2$ is concentrated in nascent phagosomes and membrane ruffles, but how?

MECHANISMS THAT COULD CONCENTRATE PIP₂ IN THE PLANE OF THE PLASMA MEMBRANE: SYNTHESIS OR SEQUESTRATION?

We first note that the concentration of PIP$_2$ in a submicroscopic region of the plasma membrane is unlikely to change significantly in response to enhanced local synthesis of PIP$_2$ by a PIP kinase. Put simply, PIP$_2$ will diffuse away faster than it can be produced. Consider, for example, a lateral domain of diameter 100 nm with a single PIP kinase enzyme at the center producing PIP$_2$ at a rate of 100 per sec. The Einstein relation (14), $t = x^2/4D$, gives the average time t to diffuse a distance x in the two-dimensional surface, where D is the diffusion coefficient. For PIP$_2$, D should be $\approx 10^{-8}$ cm^2 s^{-1} (48, 109), so a newly synthesized PIP$_2$ will diffuse away from the domain in <1 ms: Synthesis cannot keep up with diffusion over short distances. More specifically, it is unlikely that local synthesis could produce an accumulation of PIP$_2$ in the putative cholesterol-enriched rafts if they have dimensions <100 nm.

In contrast, local synthesis can and does produce significant gradients of 3-phosphorylated phosphoinositides in the plasma membrane as a whole, and a number of recent reports demonstrate these gradients are important in chemoreception [see references in (48)]. Haugh et al. (48) demonstrated the existence of these gradients in fibroblasts using evanescent wave microscopy and a GFP construct of the Akt PH domain; they also provided a theoretical model that accounts for the gradients.

The accumulation of PIP_2 (and PIP_3) in lateral membrane domains of intermediate size (e.g., nascent phagosomes, ruffles; size $1–10$ μm) by a local synthesis mechanism is certainly possible theoretically, but as discussed critically by Marshall et al. (69), it is difficult to reconcile a simple local synthesis model with the experimental observation that PIP_3 is confined sharply to the phagosomal cup. They considered a more complicated synthesis model in which phosphatases were concentrated at the rim of the cup to hydrolyze escaping PIP_3, but they were unable to obtain experimental support for this model.

What other mechanisms might account for the enhanced local concentration of phosphoinositides in ruffles and phagosomes? One alternative possibility is that specific proteins can act as "buffers," binding and passively concentrating PIP_2 (and PIP_3) in these lateral membrane domains. Such proteins would have to satisfy three criteria: be concentrated in the domains, be present at a sufficiently high concentration to sequester PIP_2 (≥ 10 μM), and have a high affinity for PIP_2. One protein that satisfies these criteria is MARCKS: It is concentrated in the ruffles of fibroblasts (78) and the forming phagosomes of macrophages (4) possibly because of its interaction with actin. Its concentration is comparable to that of PIP_2 (3, 18), and its basic effector domain binds PIP_2 with high affinity (8, 110). [As an aside, we note that the PIP_2 electrostatically associated with the effector domain of MARCKS (e.g., Figure 4f) is accessible to PLCδ-PH-GFP. Concentrations of the MARCKS effector domain peptide that bind >90% of the PIP_2 in a PC/PIP_2 vesicle, have no significant effect on the binding of a PLCδ-PH-GFP construct (A. Gambhir & S. McLaughlin, unpublished observation).

Cheap trick #3: Electrostatic sequestration. A well-understood example of electrostatic sequestration is the binding of charged solutes to membranes because of their nonspecific electrostatic accumulation in the diffuse double layer adjacent to a charged surface. Helmholtz clearly appreciated the qualitative aspects of the phenomenon in the nineteenth century (and the electrostatic double layer is still often approximated as a capacitor with a thickness equal to the Debye length: $1/\kappa = 1$ nm for a 0.1 M solution). Gouy and Chapman combined the Poisson and Boltzmann equations to describe the double layer quantitatively in the early twentieth century. Their model, which predicts the electrostatic potential falls with distance x from the surface as $\exp(-\kappa x)$, describes accurately the electrostatic sequestration of small ions adjacent to phospholipid bilayers (72, 73). For example, the Boltzmann relation predicts, and experiments with membrane-bound pH indicators confirm, that the concentration of a monovalent cation (i.e., a H^+ ion) in the aqueous phase at the surface is enhanced 10-fold over its value in the bulk solution if the surface potential is -60 mV. The effect is much more dramatic for multivalent ions, such as charged basic peptides: Their nonspecific accumulation can be calculated from the first principles of physics using detailed atomic-level models of membranes and peptides in conjunction with the Poisson and Boltzmann relations (12, 13). One calculates the Gibbs surface excess, the integral of the excess concentration of the charged peptide over distance from the surface (76). This is the number of peptides bound per unit area, which can be compared with experimental data. There is satisfactory agreement between theoretical predictions and experimental results, as reviewed elsewhere (76).

We consider the hypothesis that MARCKS uses cheap trick #3, nonspecific electrostatic sequestration, to accumulate laterally a significant fraction of the PIP_2 in a cell. Specifically, the cluster of basic residues in the MARCKS effector domain produces a significantly positive local electrostatic potential, which enhances the local two-dimensional concentration (i.e., number per unit area) of a trivalent lipid such as PIP_2 by the Boltzmann factor (see cheap trick #3). Figure 4 illustrates various features of this model. Figures 4a,b show the orientation of the MARCKS effector domain with respect to the bilayer. Monovalent acidic lipids [e.g., phosphatidylserine (PS)] comprise about 20%–40% of the phospholipids on the cytoplasmic leaflet of a plasma membrane in a mammalian cell. Figure 4c shows the -25 mV electrostatic equipotential profile adjacent to a 2:1 PC/PS membrane in 100 mM monovalent salt (76, 84). Although the discrete nature of the monovalent fixed charges (i.e., PS) produces a slight undulation in the potential profile, to a good approximation the -25 mV surface may be regarded as flat and located about 1 nm from the surface, exactly as predicted by much simpler Gouy-Chapman theory. Figure 4d shows how binding of the MARCKS effector domain modifies this potential. Although the positive charges on the peptide are screened by the counterions in the aqueous solution and the monovalent acidic lipids in the membrane, they nevertheless produce a positive potential in the neighborhood of the peptide, as illustrated by the $+25$ mV equipotential profile shown in blue. It is apparent from Figure 4d that a cluster of basic residues confined to the membrane-solution interface can act as a basin of attraction for multivalent acidic lipids.

To illustrate this more quantitatively, we ask the following questions. What are the average potentials the 3 negative charges on PIP_2 experience when the lipid is far from the peptide and when it is close to the peptide? These charges, located about 0.5 nm from the surface of the bilayer (Figure 1 and Figure 4f), are within the -25 mV equipotential surface (shown in Figure 4c). They experience a potential more negative than -25 mV when the lipid is far (i.e., >1 nm laterally) from the peptide. The 3 charges on a PIP_2 located within the blue mesh surrounding the peptide (Figure 4d) experience a potential more positive than $+25$ mV. For simplicity, we assume there is a neighborhood around the basic peptide where the potential experienced by PIP_2 is uniformly $+25$ mV and that outside this region the PIP_2 experiences a potential of -25 mV as shown in Figure 4e. If we also assume (incorrectly) that the PIP_2 does not perturb the potential in the neighborhood of the peptide when it is sequestered, the Boltzmann relationship predicts PIP_2 will be concentrated laterally by a factor of $\exp(-ze\Delta\psi/kT)$, where $\Delta\psi$ is the difference in potential (50 mV), z is the valence on the PIP_2 (-3), and $kT/e = 25$ mV.

Thus, the simple electrostatic sequestration model predicts that PIP_2 is concentrated by a factor of $\exp(6) = 400$ in this neighborhood of the peptide. As

MARCKS and PIP_2 are present at similar concentrations, and PIP_2 comprises about 1% of the phospholipids, this order of magnitude calculation predicts a significant fraction of the PIP_2 in the membrane should be sequestered by MARCKS. Work in progress on a more realistic theoretical treatment takes into account the perturbation of the potential by PIP_2. Figure 4f shows preliminary calculations for PIP_2 (yellow) sequestered adjacent to a single MARCKS effector domain peptide (green) in an otherwise electrically neutral PC membrane, showing local regions of negative potential around the PIP_2 and local regions of positive potential around the basic residues.

The simple electrostatic sequestration model illustrated in Figure 4 is consistent with the available experimental data obtained by both biophysicists and cell biologists. Physiological levels of MARCKS (10 μM) or its effector domain peptide are predicted to sequester a significant fraction of the PIP_2 in a phospholipid vesicle, even in the presence of a large excess of monovalent acidic lipids. Biophysical experiments on model membranes over the past few years show that this concentration of protein or peptide does in fact inhibit PLC-catalyzed hydrolysis and that this inhibition is due to the electrostatic sequestration of PIP_2 by the effector domain (8, 110). Cell biology experiments show colocalization of MARCKS and PIP_2 antibodies in fixed cells (64). Cell biology experiments provide other important indications that MARCKS sequesters a significant fraction of the PIP_2 in a cell: Overexpression of MARCKS produces a concomitant increase in the level of PIP_2 in the cell, which is the expected response if the cell maintains a constant concentration of free PIP_2 (64). The main caveat here is that the degree to which electrostatic sequestration occurs with MARCKS may depend on the cell type; the relative concentration of MARCKS and PIP_2 has not been determined accurately in most cells.

One interesting feature of the electrostatic sequestration mechanism sketched in Figure 4 is that MARCKS can bind PIP_2 globally and release it locally. Binding of Ca^{++}/CaM or phosphorylation by PKC releases the basic effector domain from the membrane (7, 74, 80). It is easy to demonstrate in phospholipid vesicles that translocation of the effector domain from membrane to solution by PKC or Ca^{++}/CaM releases bound PIP_2: Specifically, it reverses the inhibition of the PLC-catalyzed hydrolysis (76, 110). It is much harder to demonstrate that PIP_2 is reversibly sequestered with MARCKS in a living cell: Laux et al. (64) provided the best evidence to date by showing colocalization of MARCKS and PIP_2 in fixed cells using PIP_2 antibodies, but experiments on living cells with some of the new technologies discussed below are obviously necessary to test critically the reversible sequestration hypothesis. A corollary of the reversible sequestration model, if it can be confirmed in living cells, is that local increases in $[Ca^{++}]$, which are controlled tightly (17), could produce local increases in the free concentration of PIP_2 in the membrane. Specifically, the increase in local $[Ca^{++}/CaM]$ would produce a local release of PIP_2 sequestered by the MARCKS effector domain.

It remains to be determined experimentally whether local synthesis or electrostatic sequestration is more important in concentrating PIP_2 in nascent phagosomes and membrane ruffles. Some experiments (69) strongly suggest that local synthesis and degradation is important in the appearance/disappearance of phosphoinositides in phagosomes, e.g., the "appearance of PIP_3 coincides with the equally localized disappearance of PIP_2 from the base of the cup." But these authors also discuss why local synthesis alone does not account for several features of the accumulation of the phosphoinositides in phagosomes (69). Because both PIP kinases and MARCKS are concentrated in nascent phagosomes and membrane ruffles, both mechanisms might be in play. What is the advantage of combining local synthesis and local sequestration? For a given rate of PIP_2 synthesis in a lateral membrane domain, the analysis of Haugh et al. (48) shows that a 10-fold-larger concentration gradient will be obtained if the diffusion coefficient is lowered 10-fold. If 90% of the PIP_2 in the lateral domain is bound to MARCKS or other proteins, the effective local diffusion coefficient of PIP_2 will be 10-fold lower (e.g., 59), and 10-fold more PIP_2 will be accumulated in the lateral domain.

The MARCKS effector domain is not unique: Other proteins have basic regions with similar sequences, and some are also present at high concentrations. For example, MacMARCKS (2, 18); adducin (58), which may function in ruffle formation (41); a *Drosophila*-scaffolding protein, DAKAP200 (92); and the N-methyl-D-aspartate (NMDA) receptor (112) all have basic regions similar to the MARCKS effector domain. The net positive charge in these effector regions is 12, 11, 10, and 9, respectively. Peptides corresponding to these regions bind PIP_2 with significant affinity: The binding affinity to a PC/PIP_2 (99:1) vesicle correlates with charge on the peptide and decreases 100-fold as the net charge on the peptide decreases from 13 for MARCKS to 9 for the NMDA peptide (J. Wang & S. McLaughlin, unpublished data). Additional work is needed to determine if these proteins also bind PIP_2 in the cell and, if so, whether this binding is biologically important. The NMDA receptor is particularly interesting because it functions as a Ca^{++} channel, and Ca^{++}/CaM binds to the effector region when Ca^{++} flows through the channel (112).

GAP43, MARCKS, AND CAP23: DOES THE GMC GANG HANG OUT IN RAFTS?

Caroni and colleagues have pointed out striking parallels between MARCKS and two neuronal proteins, GAP43 (a growth-associated protein) and CAP23 (a cytoskeletal-associated protein). They coined the term GMC family for these proteins. Although the GMC proteins have no sequence similarity, they share important physical traits (39). For example, they lack any α-helix structure and resemble extended rods, a structure consistent with their highly acidic nature; their N-termini contain either a myristate or two palmitates (GAP43) that insert into the bilayer; and they have a conserved basic region that is phosphorylated by PKC and can bind Ca^{++}/CaM (CAP23 and MARCKS) and actin. The proteins share biological as well as physical properties. Frey et al. (39) used knockin mice to show that GAP43 can largely rescue the phenotypical abnormalities caused by the absence of CAP23. CAP23 and GAP43 together can induce spinal axon regeneration, so they may have interesting clinical applications (19). Based on their experimental observations that PIP_2 colocalizes with GMC proteins in micrometer-size domains when cells are fixed in certain ways, Laux et al. (64) recently proposed a provocative, and potentially important, hypothesis: All GMC proteins are localized in small cholesterol-enriched domains or rafts in unfixed cells, all bind PIP_2, and thus localize PIP_2 to the putative rafts.

The two saturated chains on GAP43 should help localize it to cholesterol-enriched rafts, and previous work has shown that it is concentrated in the detergent-resistant or DIGs fraction of the plasma membrane (9). Proteins with a single saturated acyl chain (i.e., on CAP23, MARCKS, or a mutant GAP43 with one palmitate), however, are not generally present in DIGs, and a single acyl chain is generally considered incapable of targeting a protein to the putative rafts (22). The Laux et al. (64) experiments can be reconciled with the previous DIGs/raft work by noting that they were done under conditions where the GMC proteins were presumably chemically cross-linked into supramolecular assemblies that effectively had multiple saturated acyl chains. Recent work by Dietrich et al. (33) showed that cross-linking a saturated phospholipid analog indeed increases its partitioning into large cholesterol-enriched domains that are visible in a supported monolayer.

The biological significance of the results emerges if one postulates actin, rather than chemical, cross-linking of GMC proteins in specific regions of the cell (e.g., MARCKS in the nascent phagosome and membrane ruffles): The cross-linked GMC proteins might nucleate the formation of cholesterol-enriched rafts in those regions. The recent observation that the diffusion coefficient of a disaturated lipid analog was reduced in the phagosome is consistent with this scenario (69). The postulated connection between the GMC proteins and cholesterol-enriched rafts (64), in our opinion, is important and needs to be evaluated using new tools on living cells. The suggestion that all the GMC proteins sequester PIP_2 and thus act as pipmodulins (64) is also interesting. There is good biophysical evidence that MARCKS can sequester PIP_2 in model systems, but the interaction of PIP_2 with the neuronal proteins CAP23 and GAP43 has not been similarly investigated in any detail. In contrast to MARCKS, overexpression of these two proteins does not produce a heightened level of PIP_2 in cells, which implies they may be less important than MARCKS in acting as buffers to control the level of free cellular PIP_2 (64).

NEW TECHNOLOGIES

Many new techniques are available to examine the location of PIP_2 in living cells and model membranes. GFP constructs of domains that bind with high affinity to specific phosphoinositides are now used widely by cell biologists and should continue to provide important new information. Fluorescent and spin-labeled analogs of PIP_2 have been important tools for model membrane studies, but hydrolysis of these molecules would be a problem in cells; a nonhydrolyzable fluorescent analog of PIP_2 would be extremely useful for examining more directly the distribution of PIP_2 in living cells. Fluorescence resonance energy transfer (FRET) microscopy with GFP-PH domain constructs has already provided useful information in cells (105) and has great potential for examining the possible localization of PIP$_2$ in submicroscopic domains such as rafts. Evanescent wave or total internal reflection fluorescence microscopy (TIRFM) [see references in (109)] has already been used to examine gradients of phosphoinositides in cells (48). We suspect that single molecule fluorescence measurements on living cells will prove to be increasingly valuable in phosphoinositide research, and the technique has been used to provide evidence for rafts in cell membranes (95). Laser tweezer measurements allow the direct determination of the force by which PIP$_2$ attaches the cytoskeleton to the plasma membrane (90). With respect to model membrane systems, computational studies (76) and biophysical measurements on PIP$_2$ are now in progess in different laboratories using laser tweezers (42), NMR, ESR, fluorescence correlation spectroscopy, and other approaches. They should help tease out the physical mechanisms by which proteins interact with phosphoinositides. Thus we are looking forward to the next several years of phosphoinositide research, as they are sure to be exciting ones.

CODA

Of course we have not answered the most important question we posed in the Introduction: How does order emerge from diffusional chaos in the many signal transduction systems that exist in a cell? We hope, however, that the biophysical cheap tricks we have described will help cell biologists to discover how PIP$_2$ acts as its own second messenger and choreographs the diffusional dance of so many other signal transduction molecules; in Yeats' words, to "know the dancer from the dance."

ACKNOWLEDGMENTS

This work was supported by National Institutes of Health Grant GM24971 and National Science Foundation Grant MCB9729538 to S. McLaughlin.

Visit the Annual Reviews home page at www.annualreviews.org

LITERATURE CITED

1. Adam G, Delbrück M. 1968. Reduction of dimensionality in biological diffusion processes. In *Structural Chemistry and Molecular Biology*, ed. A Rich, N Davidson, pp. 198–215. San Francisco: Freeman

2. Aderem A. 1992. The MARCKS brothers: a family of protein kinase C substrates. *Cell* 71:713–16

3. Albert KA, Nairn AC, Greengard P. 1987. The 87-kDa protein, a major specific substrate for protein kinase C: purification from bovine brain and characterization. *Proc. Natl. Acad. Sci. USA* 84:7046–50

4. Allen LA, Aderem A. 1995. A role for MARCKS, the α isozyme of protein kinase C and myosin I in zymosan

phagocytosis by macrophages. *J. Exp. Med.* 182:829–40

5. Anderson RA, Boronenkov IV, Dough-man SD, Kunz J, Loijens JC. 1999. Phos-phatidylinositol phosphate kinases, a mul-tifaceted family of signaling enzymes. *J. Biol. Chem.* 274:9907–10

6. Arbuzova A, Martushova K, Hangyas-Mihalyne G, Morris AJ, Ozaki S, et al. 2000. Fluorescently labeled neomycin as a probe of phosphatidylinositol-4,5-bisphosphate in membranes. *Biochim. Biophys. Acta* 1464:35–48

7. Arbuzova A, Murray D, McLaughlin S. 1998. MARCKS, membranes, and calmo-dulin: kinetics of their interaction. *Bio-chim. Biophys. Acta* 1376:369–79

8. Arbuzova A, Wang L, Wang J, Hangyas-Mihalyne G, Murray D, et al. 2000. Mem-brane binding of peptides containing both basic and aromatic residues. Experimental studies with peptides corresponding to the scaffolding region of caveolin and the ef-fector region of MARCKS. *Biochemistry* 39:10330–39

9. Arni S, Keilbaugh SA, Ostermeyer AG, Brown DA. 1998. Association of GAP-43 with detergent-resistant membranes re-quires two palmitoylated cysteine resi-dues. *J. Biol. Chem.* 273:28478–85

10. Aveyard R, Haydon DA. 1973. *An Intro-duction to the Principles of Surface Chem-istry.* Cambridge, UK: Cambridge Univ. Press

11. Balla T, Bondeva T, Varnai P. 2000. How accurately can we image inositol lipids in living cells? *Trends Pharmacol. Sci.* 21:238–41

12. Ben-Tal N, Honig B, Miller C, McLaugh-lin S. 1997. Electrostatic binding of pro-teins to membranes: theoretical prediction and experimental results with charybdo-toxin and phospholipid vesicles. *Biophys. J.* 73:1717–27

13. Ben-Tal N, Honig B, Peitzsch RM, Denisov G, McLaughlin S. 1996. Bind-ing of small basic peptides to membranes containing acidic lipids: theoretical mod-els and experimental results. *Biophys. J.* 71:561–75

14. Berg HC. 1983. *Random Walks in Biol-ogy.* Princeton: Princeton Univ. Press

15. Berg HC, Purcell EM. 1977. Physics of chemoreception. *Biophys. J.* 20:193–219

16. Berridge MJ, Irvine RF. 1984. Inositol trisphosphate, a novel second messen-ger in cellular signal transduction. *Nature* 312:315–21

17. Berridge MJ, Lipp P, Bootman MD. 2000. The versatility and universality of calcium signalling. *Nat. Rev. Mol. Cell Biol.* 1:11–21

18. Blackshear PJ. 1993. The MARCKS fam-ily of cellular protein kinase C substrates. *J. Biol. Chem.* 268:1501–4

19. Bomze HM, Bulsara KR, Iskandar BJ, Ca-roni P, Skene JH. 2001. Spinal axon regen-eration evoked by replacing two growth cone proteins in adult neurons. *Nat. Neu-rosci.* 4:38–43

20. Botelho RJ, Teruel M, Dierckman R, An-derson R, Wells A, et al. 2000. Localized biphasic changes in phosphatidylinositol-4,5-bisphosphate at sites of phagocytosis. *J. Cell Biol.* 151:1353–68

21. Bradshaw JP, Bushby RJ, Giles CC, Saun-ders MR. 1999. Orientation of the head-group of phosphatidylinositol in a model biomembrane as determined by neutron diffraction. *Biochemistry* 38:8393–401

22. Brown DA, London E. 2000. Structure and function of sphingolipid- and choles-terol-rich membrane rafts. *J. Biol. Chem.* 275:17221–24

23. Buser CA, Sigal CT, Resh MD, McLaugh-lin S. 1994. Membrane binding of myris-tylated peptides corresponding to the NH$_2$-terminus of Src. *Biochemistry* 33:13093–101

24. Cantley LC. 2001. Transcription. Translo-cating tubby. *Science* 292:2019–21

25. Chen F, Ma L, Parrini MC, Mao X, Lopez M, et al. 2000. Cdc42 is required for PIP$_2$-induced actin polymerization and early development but not for cell viability. *Curr. Biol.* 10:758–65

26. Cifuentes ME, Honkanen L, Rebecchi MJ. 1993. Proteolytic fragments of phosphoinositide-specific phospholipase C-δ_1. Catalytic and membrane binding properties. *J. Biol. Chem.* 268:11586–93

27. Clapham DE. 1995. Calcium signaling. *Cell* 80:259–68

28. Cockcroft S, ed. 2000. *Biology of Phosphoinositides*. New York: Oxford Univ. Press. 341 pp.

29. Cockcroft S, De Matteis MA. 2001. Inositol lipids as spatial regulators of membrane traffic. *J. Membr. Biol.* 180:187–94

30. Cremona O, De Camilli P. 2001. Phosphoinositides in membrane traffic at the synapse. *J. Cell Sci.* 114:1041–52

31. Crothers DM, Metzger H. 1972. The influence of polyvalency on the binding properties of antibodies. *Immunochemistry* 9:341–57

32. Czech MP. 2000. PIP₂ and PIP₃: complex roles at the cell surface. *Cell* 100:603–66

33. Dietrich C, Volovyk AN, Levi M, Thompson NL, Jacobson K. 2001. Partitioning of Thy-1, GM1 and cross-linked phospholipid analogs into lipid rafts reconstituted in supported model membrane monolayers. *PNAS* 98:10642–47

34. Donaldson JG, Jackson CL. 2000. Regulators and effectors of the ARF GTPases. *Curr. Opin. Cell Biol.* 12:475–82

35. Fawcett J, Pawson T. 2000. Signal transduction. N-WASP regulation—the sting in the tail. *Science* 290:725–26

36. Ferguson KM, Lemmon MA, Schlessinger J, Sigler PB. 1995. Structure of the high affinity complex of inositol trisphosphate with a phospholipase C pleckstrin homology domain. *Cell* 83:1037–46

37. Ferrell JE Jr, Huestis WH. 1984. Phosphoinositide metabolism and the morphology of human erythrocytes. *J. Cell Biol.* 98:1992–98

38. Ford MG, Pearse BM, Higgins MK, Vallis Y, Owen DJ, et al. 2001. Simultaneous binding of PtdIns(4,5)P2 and clathrin by AP180 in the nucleation of clathrin lat-

tices on membranes. *Science* 291:1051–55

39. Frey D, Laux T, Xu L, Schneider C, Caroni P. 2000. Shared and unique roles of CAP23 and GAP43 in actin regulation, neurite outgrowth, and anatomical plasticity. *J. Cell Biol.* 149:1443–54

40. Fruman DA, Meyers RE, Cantley LC. 1998. Phosphoinositide kinases. *Annu. Rev. Biochem.* 67:481–507

41. Fukata Y, Oshiro N, Kaibuchi K. 1999. Activation of moesin and adducin by Rho-kinase downstream of Rho. *Biophys. Chem.* 82:139–47

42. Galneder R, Kahl V, Arbuzova A, Rebecchi M, Radler JO, McLaughlin S. 2001. Microelectrophoresis of a bilayer-coated silica bead in an optical trap: application to enzymology. *Biophys. J.* 80:2298–309

43. Gennis RB. 1989. *Biomembranes: Molecular Structure and Function*. New York: Springer. 533 pp.

44. Ghomashchi F, Zhang X, Liu L, Gelb MH. 1995. Binding of prenylated and polybasic peptides to membranes: affinities and intervesicle exchange. *Biochemistry* 34:11910–18

45. Gillooly DJ, Stenmark H. 2001. Cell biology. A lipid oils the endocytosis machine. *Science* 291:993–94

46. Hagelberg C, Allan D. 1990. Restricted diffusion of integral membrane proteins and polyphosphoinositides leads to their depletion in microvesicles released from human erythrocytes. *Biochem. J.* 271:831–34

47. Hamada K, Shimizu T, Matsui T, Tsukita S, Hakoshima T. 2000. Structural basis of the membrane-targeting and unmasking mechanisms of the radixin FERM domain. *EMBO J.* 19:4449–62

48. Haugh JM, Codazzi F, Teruel M, Meyer T. 2000. Spatial sensing in fibroblasts mediated by 3′ phosphoinositides. *J. Cell Biol.* 151:1269–80

48a. Hilgemann DW, Feng S, Nasuhoglu C. 2001. The complex and intriguing lives of PIP$_2$ with ion channels and transporters. *Science's STKE.* http://stke.science mag.org/cgi/content/full/OC_sigtrans; 2001/111/re19

49. Hinchliffe KA, Ciruela A, Irvine RF. 1998. PIPkins1, their substrates and their products: new functions for old enzymes. *Biochim. Biophys. Acta* 1436:87–104

50. Hirose K, Kadowaki S, Tanabe M, Takeshiba H, Iino M. 1999. Spatiotemporal dynamics of inositol 1,4,5-trisphosphate that underlies complex Ca^{2+} mobilization patterns. *Science* 284:1527–31

51. Holz RW, Hlubek MD, Sorensen SD, Fisher SK, Balla T, et al. 2000. A pleckstrin homology domain specific for phosphatidylinositol 4,5-bisphosphate (PtdIns-4,5-P$_2$) and fused to green fluorescent protein identifies plasma membrane PtdIns-4,5-P$_2$ as being important in exocytosis. *J. Biol. Chem.* 275:17878–85

52. Honda A, Nogami M, Yokozeki T, Yamazaki M, Nakamura H, et al. 1999. Phosphatidylinositol 4-phosphate 5-kinase alpha is a downstream effector of the small G protein ARF6 in membrane ruffle formation. *Cell* 99:521–32

53. Hurley JH, Meyer T. 2001. Subcellular targeting by membrane lipids. *Curr. Opin. Cell Biol.* 13:146–52

54. Hurley JH, Misra S. 2000. Signaling and subcellular targeting by membrane binding domains. *Annu. Rev. Biophys. Biomol. Struct.* 29:49–79

55. Irvine R. 2000. Nuclear lipid signaling. *Science's STKE:* http://www.stke.org/cgi/content/full/OC_sigtrans;2000/48/re1

56. Irvine RF, Schell MJ. 2001. Back in the water: the return of the inositol phosphates. *Nat. Rev. Mol. Cell Biol.* 2:327–38

57. Itoh T, Koshiba S, Kigawa T, Kikuchi A, Yokoyama S, Takenawa T. 2001. Role of the ENTH domain in phosphatidylinositol-4,5-bisphosphate binding and endocytosis. *Science* 291:1047–51

58. Joshi R, Gilligan DM, Otto E, McLaughlin T, Bennett V. 1991. Primary structure

and domain organization of human alpha and beta adducin. *J. Cell Biol.* 115:665–75

59. Junge W, McLaughlin S. 1987. The role of fixed and mobile buffers in the kinetics of proton movement. *Biochim. Biophys. Acta* 890:1–5

60. Kenworthy AK, Petranova N, Edidin M. 2000. High-resolution FRET microscopy of cholera toxin B-subunit and GPI-anchored proteins in cell plasma membranes. *Mol. Biol. Cell* 11:1645–55

61. Kholodenko BN, Hoek JB, Westerhoff HV. 2000. Why cytoplasmic signalling proteins should be recruited to cell membranes. *Trends Cell Biol.* 10:173–78

62. Lagerholm BC, Starr TE, Volovyk ZN, Thompson NL. 2000. Rebinding of IgE Fabs at haptenated planar membranes: measurement by total internal reflection with fluorescence photobleaching recovery. *Biochemistry* 39:2042–51

63. Lagerholm BC, Thompson NL. 1998. Theory for ligand rebinding at cell membrane surfaces. *Biophys. J.* 74:1215–28

64. Laux T, Fukami K, Thelen M, Golub T, Frey D, Caroni P. 2000. GAP43, MARCKS, and CAP23 modulate PI(4,5)P$_2$ at plasmalemmal rafts, and regulate cell cortex actin dynamics through a common mechanism. *J. Cell Biol.* 149:1455–72

65. Lemmon MA, Ferguson KM. 2000. Signal-dependent membrane targeting by pleckstrin homology (PH) domains. *Biochem. J.* 350:1–18

66. Lemmon MA, Ferguson KM, O'Brien R, Sigler PB, Schlessinger J. 1995. Specific and high-affinity binding of inositol phosphates to an isolated pleckstrin homology domain. *Proc. Natl. Acad. Sci. USA* 92:10472–76

67. Leventis R, Silvius JR. 1998. Lipid-binding characteristics of the polybasic carboxy-terminal sequence of K-ras4B. *Biochemistry* 37:7640–48

68. Liscovitch M, Chalifa V, Pertile P, Chen CS, Cantley LC. 1994. Novel function of phosphatidylinositol 4,5-bisphosphate as

a cofactor for brain membrane phospholipase D. *J. Biol. Chem.* 269:21403–6

69. Marshall JG, Booth JW, Stambolic V, Mak T, Balla T, et al. 2001. Restricted accumulation of phosphatidylinositol 3-kinase products in a plasmalemmal subdomain during Fc gamma receptor-mediated phagocytosis. *J. Cell Biol.* 153:1369–80

70. Martin TF. 2001. PI(4,5)P₂ regulation of surface membrane traffic. *Curr. Opin. Cell Biol.* 13:493–99

71. McCloskey MA, Poo MM. 1986. Rates of membrane-associated reactions: reduction of dimensionality revisited. *J. Cell Biol.* 102:88–96

72. McLaughlin S. 1977. Electrostatic potentials at membrane-solution interfaces. *Curr. Top. Membr. Trans.* 9:71–144

73. McLaughlin S. 1989. The electrostatic properties of membranes. *Annu. Rev. Biophys. Biophys. Chem.* 18:113–36

74. McLaughlin S, Aderem A. 1995. The myristoyl-electrostatic switch: a modulator of reversible protein-membrane interactions. *Trends Biochem. Sci.* 20:272–76

75. Millard TH, Machesky LM. 2001. The Wiskott-Aldrich syndrome protein (WASP) family. *Trends Biochem. Sci.* 26:198–99

75a. Misra A, Miller GJ, Hurley JH. 2001. Recognizing phosphatidylinositol 3-phosphate. *Cell* 107:559–62

76. Murray D, Arbuzova A, Honig B, McLaughlin S. 2002. The role of electrostatic and nonpolar interactions in the association of peripheral proteins with membranes. *Curr. Top. Membr.* 52:271–301

77. Murray D, Hermida-Matsumoto L, Buser CA, Tsang J, Sigal C, et al. 1998. Electrostatics mediates the membrane association of Src: theory and experiment. *Biochemistry* 37:2145–59

78. Myat MM, Anderson S, Allen LH, Aderem A. 1997. MARCKS regulates membrane ruffling and cell spreading. *Curr. Biol.* 7:611–14

79. Nagle JF, Tristram-Nagle S. 2000. Structure of lipid bilayers. *Biochim. Biophys. Acta* 1469:159–95

80. Ohmori S, Sakai N, Shirai Y, Yamamoto H, Miyamoto E, et al. 2000. Importance of protein kinase C targeting for the phosphorylation of its substrate, myristoylated alanine-rich C-kinase substrate. *J. Biol. Chem.* 275:26449–57

81. Overduin M, Cheever ML, Kutateladze TG. 2001. Signaling with PIs: its better than binary. *Mol. Interv.* 1:14–23

82. Pantaloni D, Le Clainche C, Carlier MF. 2001. Mechanism of actin-based motility. *Science* 292:1502–6

83. Payrastre B, Missy K, Giuriato S, Bodin S, Plantavid M, Gratacap M. 2001. Phosphoinositides: key players in cell signalling, in time and space. *Cell Signal* 13:377–87

84. Peitzsch RM, Eisenberg M, Sharp KA, McLaughlin S. 1995. Calculations of the electrostatic potential adjacent to model phospholipid bilayers. *Biophys. J.* 68:729–38

85. Pike LJ, Miller JM. 1998. Cholesterol depletion delocalizes phosphatidylinositol bisphosphate and inhibits hormone-stimulated phosphatidylinositol turnover. *J. Biol. Chem.* 273:22298–304

86. Pollard TD, Blanchoin L, Mullins RD. 2000. Molecular mechanisms controlling actin filament dynamics in nonmuscle cells. *Annu. Rev. Biophys. Biomol. Struct.* 29:545–76

87. Powell A. 1995. *A Dance to the Music of Time: First Movement.* Chicago: Univ. Chicago Press. 726 pp.

88. Prehoda KE, Scott JA, Dyche Mullins R, Lim WA. 2000. Integration of multiple signals through cooperative regulation of the N-WASP-Arp2/3 complex. *Science* 290:801–6

89. Randazzo PA, Nie Z, Miura K, Hsu VW. 2000. Molecular aspects of the cellular activities of ADP-ribosylation factors. *Sci. STKE* 59:1–15

90. Raucher D, Stauffer T, Chen W, Shen K, Guo S, et al. 2000. Phosphatidylinositol 4,5-bisphosphate functions as a second

messenger that regulates cytoskeleton-plasma membrane adhesion. *Cell* 100: 221–28

91. Rebecchi MJ, Pentyala SN. 2000. Structure, function, and control of phosphoinositide-specific phospholipase C. *Physiol. Rev.* 80:1291–335

92. Rossi EA, Li Z, Feng H, Rubin CS. 1999. Characterization of the targeting, binding, and phosphorylation site domains of an A kinase anchor protein and a myristoylated alanine-rich C kinase substrate-like analog that are encoded by a single gene. *J. Biol. Chem.* 274:27201–10

93. Santagata S, Boggon TJ, Baird CL, Gomez CA, Zhao J, Shan WS, et al. 2001. G-protein signaling through tubby proteins. *Science* 292:2041–50

93a. Sato TK, Overduin M, Emr SC. 2001. Location, location, location: membrane targeting directed by PX domains. *Science* 294:1881–85

94. Schmidt-Nielsen K. 1972. *How Animals Work*. Cambridge, UK: Cambridge Univ. Press. 114 pp.

95. Schutz GJ, Kada G, Pastushenko VP, Schindler H. 2000. Properties of lipid microdomains in a muscle cell membrane visualized by single molecule microscopy. *EMBO J.* 19:892–901

96. Sciorra VA, Rudge SA, Prestwich GD, Frohman MA, Engebrecht J, Morris AJ. 1999. Identification of a phosphoinositide binding motif that mediates activation of mammalian and yeast phospholipase D isoenzymes. *EMBO J.* 18:5911–21

97. Sechi AS, Wehland J. 2000. The actin cytoskeleton and plasma membrane connection: PtdIns(4,5)P2 influences cytoskeletal protein activity at the plasma membrane. *J. Cell Sci.* 113:3685–95

97a. Simonson A, Wurmser AE, Emr SD, Stenmark H. 2001. The role of phosphoinositides in membrane transport. *Curr. Opin. Cell Biol.* 13:485–92

98. Stauffer TP, Ahn S, Meyer T. 1998. Receptor-induced transient reduction in plasma membrane PtdIns(4,5)P$_2$ concentration monitored in living cells. *Curr. Biol.* 8:343–46

99. Tall E, Spector I, Pentyala SN, Bitter I, Rebecchi MJ. 2000. Dynamics of phosphatidylinositol 4,5-bisphosphate in actin-supported structures. *Curr. Biol.* 10: 743–46

100. Toker A. 1998. The synthesis and cellular roles of phosphatidylinositol 4,5-bisphosphate. *Curr. Opin. Cell Biol.* 10: 254–61

101. Toner M, Vaio G, McLaughlin A, McLaughlin S. 1988. Adsorption of cations to phosphatidylinositol 4,5-bisphosphate. *Biochemistry* 27:7435–43

102. Tsujishita Y, Guo S, Stolz LE, York JD, Hurley JH. 2001. Specificity determinants in phosphoinositide dephosphorylation: crystal structure of an archetypal inositol polyphosphate 5-phosphatase. *Cell* 105: 379–89

103. Tsukita S, Yonemura S. 1999. Cortical actin organization: lessons from ERM (ezrin/radixin/moesin) proteins. *J. Biol. Chem.* 274:34507–10

104. Tuominen EK, Holopainen JM, Chen J, Prestwich GD, Bachiller PR, et al. 1999. Fluorescent phosphoinositide derivatives reveal specific binding of gelsolin and other actin regulatory proteins to mixed lipid bilayers. *Eur. J. Biochem.* 263:85–92

105. van der Wal J, Habets R, Varnai P, Balla T, Jalink K. 2001. Monitoring agonist-induced phospholipase C activation in live cells by fluorescence resonance energy transfer. *J. Biol. Chem.* 276:15337–44

106. Vanhaesebroeck B, Leevers SJ, Ahmadi K, Timms J, Katso R, et al. 2001. Synthesis and function of 3-phosphorylated inositol lipids. *Annu. Rev. Biochem.* 70:535–602

107. van Paridon PA, De Kruijff B, Ouwerkerk R, Wirtz KW. 1986. Polyphosphoinositides undergo charge neutralization in the physiological pH range: a 31P-NMR study. *Biochim. Biophys. Acta* 877:216–19

108. Varnai P, Balla T. 1998. Visualization of phosphoinositides that bind pleckstrin

homology domains: calcium- and agonist-
induced dynamic changes and relationship to myo-[3H]inositol-labeled phosphoinositide pools. *J. Cell Biol.* 143:
501–10

109. Wagner ML, Tamm LK. 2001. Reconstituted syntaxin 1A/SNAP25 interacts with
negatively charged lipids as measured by
lateral diffusion in planar supported bilayers. *Biophys. J.* 81:266–75

110. Wang J, Arbuzova A, Hangyas-Mihalyne
G, McLaughlin S. 2001. The effector
domain of myristoylated alanine-rich C
kinase substrate binds strongly to phosphatidylinositol 4,5-bisphosphate. *J. Biol.
Chem.* 276:5012–19

111. Waugh MG, Lawson D, Tan SK, Hsuan JJ.
1998. Phosphatidylinositol 4-phosphate
synthesis in immunoisolated caveolae-
like vesicles and low buoyant density
non-caveolar membranes. *J. Biol. Chem.*
273:17115–21

112. Zhang S, Ehlers MD, Bernhardt JP, Su
CT, Huganir RL. 1998. Calmodulin mediates calcium-dependent inactivation of
N-methyl-D-aspartate receptors. *Neuron*
21:443–53

113. Zhou C, Garigapati V, Roberts MF.
1997. Short-chain phosphatidylinositol
conformation and its relevance to phos-
phatidylinositol-specific phospholipase
C. *Biochemistry* 36:15925–31

Annu. Rev. Biophys. Biomol. Struct. 2002. 31:177–206
DOI: 10.1146/annurev.biophys.31.101101.140910

NMR STUDIES OF LIPOPROTEIN STRUCTURE

Robert J. Cushley and Mark Okon
*Department of Molecular Biology and Biochemistry, Simon Fraser
University, Burnaby V5A 1S6, British Columbia, Canada;
e-mail: cushley@sfu.ca; mark@otter.biochem.ubc.ca*

Key Words protein structure, apolipoproteins, conformation, heteronuclear 3D

■ **Abstract** Early NMR structural studies of serum lipoproteins were based on ^{1}H, ^{13}C, ^{31}P, and ^{2}H studies of lipid components. From the early studies information on composition, lipid chain dynamics and order parameters, and monolayer organization resulted. More recently, selective or complete isotopic labeling techniques, combined with multidimensional NMR spectroscopy, have resulted in structural information of apoprotein fragments. Finally, use of heteronuclear three- and four-dimensional experiments have yielded solution structures and protein-lipid interactions of intact apolipoproteins C-I, C-II, and A-I.

CONTENTS

INTRODUCTION

As the title suggests this is not a comprehensive review of all NMR studies involving, or related to, lipoproteins but, rather, reports a narrower focus only involving NMR studies yielding information on the actual structure of lipoproteins. A few examples of the broader aspects, not reported in detail, might include the review

1056-8700/02/0609-0177$14.00 **177**

by Smith et al., who utilized relaxation times (T2) of a signal attributed to lipoprotein(a) to indicate stages of cancer development (75), the many studies on classifying lipoproteins in serum, usually by ^{1}H NMR (9), or the recent studies on putative binding site peptides of the human low-density lipoprotein receptor (20, 25).

NMR of lipoproteins spawned several eras. First, the early ^{1}H and ^{13}C NMR of lipoproteins identified mostly the mobile fatty acid chains of the lipoprotein lipid components while ^{31}P and ^{15}N studies characterized the phospholipid headgroups. A series of ^{2}H NMR studies were used to measure organizational order of lipids in both the lipoprotein core and the outer monolayer. Second, more recent work progressed to two-dimensional NMR studies of peptide fragments of apolipoproteins in lipid-mimetic solutions, or use of labeled groups incorporated into lipoproteins to probe local structure. Last, there are the recent reports of multidimensional NMR of intact apolipoproteins, which have yielded solution structures of the apolipoproteins themselves.

Human Serum Lipoprotein Composition

There are four major classes of lipoproteins based on their differing buoyant densities. The two larger particles, chylomicrons and very-low-density lipoproteins (VLDL), facilitate triglyceride transport. Chylomicra are metabolized rapidly. The two smaller complexes, low-density lipoproteins (LDL) and high-density lipoproteins (HDL), participate in cholesterol transport. Lipoproteins are quasi-spherical particles consisting of a core of triglycerides and/or cholesteryl esters surrounded by an outer monolayer of cholesterol and phospholipids. Embedded in the surface are the apolipoproteins A, B, C, D, E, and F. The apolipoproteins are important for lipoprotein stability, binding, and catabolism. In addition to their basic structural roles, several apolipoproteins function as cofactors for enzymes in lipoprotein metabolism and direct the lipoprotein particle to specific tissues by interacting with cell receptors. A short summary of lipoprotein composition is given in Table 1. [A good review of the lipoproteins is due to the late Peter J. Dolphin (26).]

Cardiovascular disease is the primary cause of death in the industrialized countries of the world claiming about 500,000 lives yearly in the United States alone. High blood cholesterol is one of the major risk factors. Rapid buildup of cholesteryl esters in the aortic intimal layer and the subsequent appearance of fatty streaks is the first clinical sign (stage I) of atherosclerosis. LDL cholesterol levels in blood are positively correlated with risk of cardiovascular disease, hence LDL is termed the "bad" lipoprotein. On the other hand, HDL plasma concentrations have been inversely correlated with the risk of atherosclerosis (57). The process by which HDL lowers cholesterol has been termed reverse cholesterol transport. In this process, HDL transports cholesterol from the peripheral tissues, including the vessel wall, to the liver for excretion from the body (5, 26). The ratio of LDL cholesterol to HDL cholesterol is a significant clinical test defining an individual's risk of heart disease. New cholesterol guidelines have just been published in the *Journal of the American Medical Association* (45). The publication noted that, by lowering blood levels of LDL, heart disease is cut by up to 40%. The new guidelines raise the minimum level of "good" HDL from 35 mg/dl to 40 mg/dl. ApoA-I

TABLE 1   Lipoprotein properties and composition[a]

Particles	HDL	LDL	VLDL	Chylomicrons
Density (g/mL)	1.063–1.21	1.019–1.063	0.93–1.006	0.93–1.006
Particle size (nm)	4–10	18–25	30–80	75–120
Protein (%)	50	20	10	1
Major	A-I	B	B	C-III
Minor	A-II, C-I, C-II, C-III, E		C-I, C-II, C-III, E	B, C-I, C-II, D, E
Phospholipid (%)	30	24	19	4
Cholesterol (%)	18	45	19	6
Triglyceride (%)	5	10	50	90

[a]Data from references (2, 34, 72, 97).

is responsible for the formation of HDL and for the reverse transport of cholesterol as cholesteryl esters from peripheral tissues to the liver for re-utilization or elimination by conversion to bile acids (32).

VLDL are heterogeneous quasi-spherical particles, 25–70 nm in diameter, composed of a hydrophobic core, mainly triglycerides, and a surface monolayer of phospholipid and cholesterol into which are imbedded the apolipoproteins B, E, and C (C-I, C-II, and C-III) (70). The C proteins compose approximately 40%–60% of the total protein content of VLDL; however, because the particle is 90% lipid, only small amounts of the apoCs can be isolated from normal serum. VLDL are lipolysed to form LDL.

LDL particles range from 18 to 25 nm in diameter, with an average diameter of 22 nm. The core is composed mainly of cholesteryl ester molecules, with smaller amounts of triglycerides. The surface monolayer of phospholipids contains a single copy of apoB-100, a 500,500-molecular-weight protein. The particles also contain unesterified cholesterol, which is distributed between the core and the surface. The main phospholipid components are phosphatidylcholine and sphingomyelin. A detailed picture of a LDL particle is given in the recent review by Hevonoja et al. (39). In that review the authors present a three-layer model of a LDL particle. The model divides the surface region into an outer surface layer consisting mainly of the phospholipid headgroups and an interfacial layer consisting of interdigitated core and surface lipids. The core is confined to molecules that are not in direct contact with the surface monolayer.

HDL (Figure 1) are small spherical particles, 4–10 nm in diameter, with a core of mainly cholesteryl esters (70). The particles are further divided by density gradient sedimentation into HDL$_3$ (4–8.5 nm) and HDL$_2$ (8.5–10 nm). The main proteins are apoA-I and apoA-II, with lesser amounts of apoproteins C-I, C-II, C-III, and E. HDL has been shown to be inversely related to incidences of cardiovascular disease. Thus, increased plasma levels of HDL are believed to offer protection against vascular lipid accumulation. While the initial observations of this effect

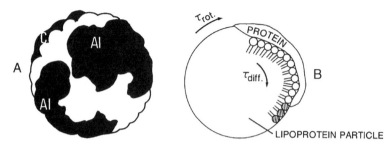

Figure 1 (*A*) Stylized drawing of a high density lipoprotein (HDL) particle and (*B*) cross section of a lipoprotein particle showing the phospholipid monolayer and an apolipoprotein. The times τ_{rot} and τ_{diff} correspond to τ_t and τ_d in Equation 1.4, (Appendix I, follow the Supplemental Material link on the Annual Reviews homepage at http://www.annualreviews.org/).

were based on measurement of the cholesterol content of HDL, it is evident that the apoprotein moiety of this lipoprotein plays an important role in directing its synthesis, modification, and subsequent catabolism. Appreciable homologies exist between the apolipoproteins, supporting the contention they derived from a single gene (46).

Studies of monolayers formed from LDL and HDL_3 phospholipids, with and without cholesterol, demonstrated that LDL surface lipids form a more closely packed monolayer than those of HDL_3 (40). The denser packing was attributed to the higher content of saturated phosphatidylcholine in LDL and to the higher sphingomyelin and cholesterol contents. Saturated phospholipids form more condensed monolayers than do unsaturated phospholipids, and sphingomyelin forms more condensed monolayers than do phosphatidylcholines (40, 41, 49). Also, cholesterol has a stronger condensing effect on LDL phospholipids due to the higher degree of saturation in the acyl chains (40). The studies suggest that surface molecular packing and lipid composition influence the binding of apoA-I to the particles. Because they alter biological function, all these interactions may play an important role in the development of atherosclerosis. Other studies point to the symbiotic nature and delicate balance of the components in the lipoprotein complex. For instance, modulation of the core triglyceride or phospholipid content of LDL alters the conformation of apoB and its binding to receptors (7, 8). A brief discusion of only those human serum apolipoproteins for which high-resolution structural studies have been determined follows.

Apolipoprotein A-I

Fifty percent of the mass of human HDL is protein, of which 70% is apoA-I. The mature form of the protein, present at 1-1.2 g/l, is a single polypeptide chain of 243 amino acids with a molecular weight of 28,083. ApoA-I is the major activator of lecithin: cholesterol acyltransferase, the plasma enzyme responsible for the synthesis of the majority of cholesterol esters via transesterification of the sn-2 fatty acid from phosphatidylcholine to the hydroxyl group of cholesterol. The apolipoprotein forms disc-like particles with phospholipids containing cholesterol, which are good substrates for lecithin:cholesterol acyltransferase. These particles become spherical HDL as their cores are filled with cholesteryl esters. During this process, the structure of apoA-I must change as evidenced by immunogenic sites that were exposed on the discoidal particles but become masked on spherical particles, and new sites appear (10). ApoA-I has also been suggested as a probable ligand for the HDL receptor (1) and in cholesterol efflux (17, 96).

Apolipoprotein A-I is hydrophobic, aggregates in solution, and has two 11- and eight 22-residue repeats of amphiphilic helices that are believed responsible for the lipid-binding properties of the protein (73).

Class C Apolipoproteins (C-I and C-II)

The C class of exchangeable apolipoproteins are representative of an important class of proteins. Their short, straight chain sequences make them ideal candidates for a study of apoprotein conformation by multidimensional NMR. They are minor components of HDL and VLDL; nevertheless, they exert a significant influence on lipid metabolism. While the physiological role of C apolipoproteins has not been as extensively elucidated as the A class, a number of roles for those apoproteins have been confirmed. The C proteins apparently behave like apoE in that they have a carboxyl terminus that is amphipathic, i.e., lipid binding, and an amino terminus that performs the physiological role.

ApoC interacts with other apolipoproteins as evidenced by the apoC inhibition of clearance of apoE-rich particles in tissue (86) and inhibition of said particles binding to apoB/E (LDL) receptors (74). The mechanism by which C apolipoproteins bind to the lipoprotein particles, and the structural details of binding, are not well understood. Binding has been proposed to occur via defects in the phospholipid surface (5) or by protein-protein interactions (3).

APOC-I   Mature human apoC-I, comprising 57 amino acids, is the smallest member of the human plasma apolipoprotein family. ApoC-I stabilizes lipoprotein structure, activates metabolic enzymes, and is involved in receptor recognition (5). The amphipathic helical regions mediate lipid binding, activate lecithin: cholesterol acyltransferase, disrupt apoE-mediated receptor interactions, and inhibit cholesterol ester transfer protein.

ApoC-I self-associates in aqueous solution above pH 3, and the conformational changes that accompany the self-association are significant (63).

APOC-II   ApoC-II is a 79–amino acid straight chain peptide whose sequence was found from both chemical analysis of the protein and its DNA. It contains no carbohydrate (apoC-III, also 79 amino acids in length, is the only one of the C class of apolipoproteins to contain carbohydrate). ApoC-II activates lipoprotein lipase, which hydrolizes tri- and diglycerides, phosphatidylcholines, and phosphatidylethanolamines in chylomicra and VLDL. It is specific for the sn-1 position.

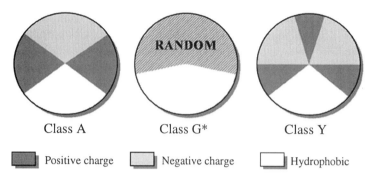

Figure 2   Distribution of amino acid residues in class A, G*, and Y amphipathic helices. The circles are simplified helical wheel representations, i.e., they depict the radial distribution of charged and neutral amino acids around the long axis of amphipathic helices. Reproduced with permission from the thesis of R. Storjohann (78) and adopted from Segrest et al. (73).

The structure of the apoC-II/lipoprotein lipase complex is not known. Thus, the mechanism of action and the precise role of apoC-II are unclear except to note that apoC-II does not increase the binding of lipoprotein lipase to the lipoprotein particle (56).

Structural Motif of Apolipoproteins

Amphipathic α-helical structures have the polar and charged amino acids on one face, which is exposed to the aqueous medium, and the nonpolar amino acid residues on the other face, which interacts with the hydrophobic medium. The lipid-associating domains of the serum apolipoproteins have been proposed to consist of tandem repeats of 11- and 22-residue amphipathic helices (73). The three types of amphipathic helix motifs in serum lipoproteins are shown in Figure 2. Experimentally the apoprotein secondary structures have been inferred from circular dichroism, immunological studies, and from predictive methods based on primary sequence. The secondary structure of apoA-I is predicted to have eight 22-mer and two 11-mer repeats, meaning up to 70% of the total secondary structure would be helices. Interestingly, circular dichroic studies of apoA-I in HDL or reconstituted in lipids gives only 55% helix. NMR structural studies of apoA-I, below, address this discrepancy.

LIPOPROTEIN STRUCTURE

Lipids

Much information on lipoprotein structure has come from physical techniques such as NMR, differential scanning calorimetry (24), X-ray diffraction (4, 6, 44), and neutron diffraction (43).

The majority of NMR investigations have utilized ^{13}C to investigate the motional properties of lipids and are summarized in the review by Hamilton & Morrissett (36). The ^{13}C NMR technique allows a wide range of lipid resonances to be studied and has proved useful in demonstrating the anisotropic nature of the motions of the steroid ring of both cholesterol and cholesteryl esters. Nevertheless, the amount of novel information provided by ^{13}C NMR is small. In general, the chemical shifts and T1 values of most resonances are the same in lipoproteins and in simple model systems. More importantly, the fatty acyl resonances of the different lipids are not resolved. What ^{13}C NMR does clearly demonstrate is that the lipid components of lipoproteins possess a great deal of motional freedom.

The M. C. Phillips group took a different approach. They labeled the majority of apoB-100 lysine residues in human LDL via reductive methylation with [^{13}C]formaldehyde. The resulting ^{13}C spectra gave two different lysine N-[13]CH$_3$ chemical shifts reflecting the native conformation of apoB associated with lipid (48). The same technique was used with apoE, resulting in a similar result, i.e., there were two pools of apoE lysine in HDL (51).

^{2}H and ^{31}P NMR are excellent methods for determining order and orientation in lipoproteins because the quadrupolar and chemical-shielding tensors are only partially averaged owing to the lipoprotein particle size (Appendix I, follow the Supplemental Material link on the Annual Reviews homepage at http://www.annualreviews.org/). Yeagle et al. (92) reported approximately 20% of the phospholipid in LDL was immobilized so not seen in the ^{31}P spectrum, the missing intensity being attributed to interaction between the phospholipids and apoB. Finer et al. (33) and Lund-Katz & Phillips (50) reported similar findings using ^{13}C NMR. In a later study, Yeagle et al. (93) reported there were no immobilized phospholipid headgroups in HDL. Using lanthanide shifts, the authors concluded all mobile phospholipid headgroups are on the surface of the particle in contact with the aqueous medium, the ^{31}P nuclear Overhauser effect (NOE) enhancement being due to the choline N-methyl protons.

^{31}P NMR studies showed that the smaller lipoproteins, HDL$_2$ and HDL$_3$, have larger chemical shift anisotropy (CSA) values (70 ppm and 150 ppm) in comparison to those of the larger lipoproteins, VLDL and LDL (50 ppm) (30). The residual ^{31}P CSA values for LDL and VLDL were similar to those for phospholipid bilayers. The large CSA values in HDL particles were explained in terms of different headgroup conformations, with headgroup orientations moving progressively out of the surface plane, HDL$_3$ headgroup being approximately perpendicular to the particle surface. Such conformations may arise from (*a*) different packing constraints of phospholipid molecules in the smaller particles or (*b*) through possible lipid-protein interactions. Activation energies for phosphate group reorientation, determined from temperature-dependent [31]P T$_1$ measurements, argue against long-lived interactions between phospholipids and proteins in lipoproteins.

Cushley et al. (23) showed that at 25°C phospholipid diffusion in the monolayer of LDL is approximately one order of magnitude slower than in HDL$_2$ and HDL$_3$. The presence of cholesterol, interdigitated between the phospholipids in the lipoprotein surface monolayer, undoubtedly explains some of the slower diffusion in LDL and VLDL compared to the HDLs; however, the much slower diffusion rate in LDL was attributed mostly to surface-core interactions.

To delineate the organization of lipids in HDL, LDL, and VLDL, a series of ^{2}H NMR studies of incorporated selectively deuterated lipids were mounted. The acyl chains in the HDL$_3$ surface monolayer have a deuterium order parameter (plateau region) of $S_{CD} = 0.4$, determined from ^{2}H NMR studies of incorporated selectively deuterated palmitic acids (66). (The plateau region refers to positions C1-C(N/2) of a C(N) acyl chain, i.e., C1–C9 of stearic acid. Deuterium order parameters are essentially constant in the plateau region, decreasing montonically thereafter toward the end of the chain). This is approximately 1.5–2 times higher than in phospholipid bilayers and is significantly higher than in VLDL or LDL (18). Futhermore, in LDL and VLDL there are two different regions of order, one of which (comprising 10%–20% of the phospholipid) possesses extremely low order. To study core organization, cholesteryl oleate, selectively deuterated along the acyl chain, was incorporated into LDL from microemulsion donor particles using plasma transfer proteins (80). Temperature-dependent ^{2}H NMR spectra of the C-2′ and C-5′ deuterons in the plateau region of the acyl chain revealed the presence of two spectral components, corresponding to regions of high and low order in the core. At 25°C, two values of S_{CD} (0.20 and 0.12) were calculated for the C-2′ and C-5′ deuterons. Thus, as was demonstrated for the monolayer of LDL and VLDL, two regions of different core order were found. Based on ^{2}H NMR studies of selectively deuterated cholesteryl palmitate in HDL, the authors demonstrated that the ester adopts an extended conformation in the core (65). This would make penetration of esters into the monolayer likely. The order parameters of esters in the HDL core were significantly higher ($S_{CD} = 0.35$ for deuterons C-2′ to C-6′) than in LDL, and only one domain was detected. Fenske et al. (31) demonstrated a direct effect of core components on the phospholipid monolayer in reconstituted HDL.

Apoproteins

STRUCTURES AND LIPID INTERACTIONS OF LIPOPROTEIN FRAGMENTS   Solution structures of lipid-binding fragments of human serum apolipoproteins A-I, A-II, C-I, C-II, and E have been determined from distance geometry calculations of 2D NOE restraints. Short peptides are mainly unstructured in water but become helical in SDS or dodecylphosphocholine (DPC) solution. Spectra in the presence of these lipid-mimetic compounds provided restraints, which resulted in high-resolution conformations of apolipoprotein segments, gave insights into the apoprotein-lipid complex, and provided useful information for optimization of NMR techniques for structural studies of intact apolipoproteins. Figure 3 is a typical proton NOESY spectrum—that of the 46-residue fragment apoA-I(142-187) in DPC-d$_{38}$ micellar solution.

In summarizing the results of structural studies of short apolipoprotein peptide fragments, A-I, A-II, and two C-I peptides are class A amphipathic helices (Figure 2) in SDS, DPC, and lysophosphatidylcholine (15, 67, 83). The headgroup

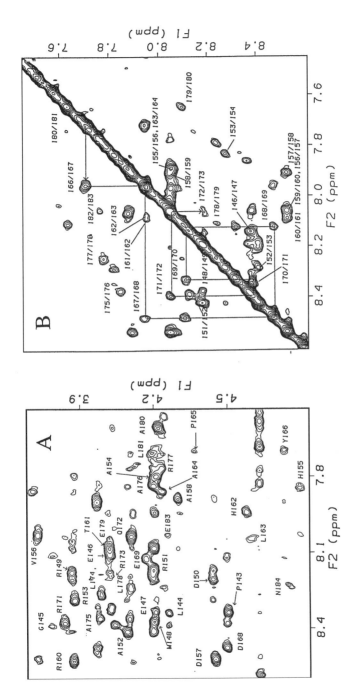

Figure 3 The fingerprint and amide regions of the 600-MHz ^{1}H NOESY spectrum of apoA-I(142–187) (5 mM) in aqueous solution (H$_2$O/D$_2$O, 9:1) of DPC-d_{38} (τ_m = 80 ms) at 37°C and pH 4.9 (peptide/lipid molar ratio = 1:60). H$^\alpha$-H^N region (A) and H^N-H^N region (B) cross peaks are labeled. The intraresidue, sequential, and selected medium-range connectivities are assigned. For clarity, only the sequential assignments for residues 166–172 were constructed in B. Reproduced with permission from (82).

charge of SDS, DPC, and lysophosphatidylcholine are -1, zero, and $+1$. Because the headgroup charge does not appear to affect the bound conformation, the Cushley group proposed that (*a*) hydrophobic interactions between apolipoprotein side chains and the micellar lipid chains are most important in apolipoprotein binding to the micelle surface; (*b*) intermolecular NOEs observed between cationic side chains in apoA-I(166-185) and SDS alkyl chains imply that the binding of lipid to the amphipathic helix is achieved initially via electrostatic interactions of individual SDS molecules; (*c*) apoE(263-286) in SDS micelles is a helix-bend-helix structural motif ($\sim 120°$ bend) rather than the pure α-helix previously proposed. The forces causing the bend were attributed to a pair of aromatic residues in apoE(263-286) that stabilize the loose N-terminal helix, leading to the proposal that, of the hydrophobic side chains leading to lipid binding, it is the aromatic side chains that are especially important; and (*d*), the high-resolution structures determined for apolipoprotein A-I, A-II, C-I, C-II, and E peptides have "debunked" the snorkel hypothesis for lysine side chain orientation (73).

Lycksell et al. (52) reported the 2D NMR of residues 50–79 of apoC-II, followed by the calculated three-dimensional (3D) structure (60). The authors did not investigate the 30-residue segment in lipid complexes but rather in the helix promoter hexafluoropropane. Storjohann et al. (79) determined the conformation of apoC-II(44-79) in SDS and DPC solutions. The structure consists of two helical lipid-binding domains, residues 50–58 and 67–75, connected by a less-structured seven-residue linker (Figure 4*A*). The C terminus, K76-G77-G78-E79, forms a well-defined loop, which is surprising as ends of the other lipoprotein fragments are unstructured, a process referred to as "fraying." The structures are similar in hexafluoropropane, DPC, and SDS, although hexafluoropropane is not as good a substitute for lipids.

In Figure 4*B* the interhelical domain is shown with the consensus Y63 side chain orientation, i.e., the orientation most resembling the average orientation, shown. From these detailed structures Storjohann et al. (79) suggested that the role of the interhelical sequence may be to extend away from the lipoprotein surface in order to project Y63 into the apoC-II-binding site of lipoprotein lipase. The C-terminal helix, residues 67–75, has an amphipathic moment (28) of 0.78 kcal/mol. Because it is so well defined in the NMR calculations, this C-terminal helix probably remains anchored to the lipoprotein surface in the presence of lipoprotein lipase. In that case, the NMR evidence favors the surface penetration model of lipoprotein lipase activation (47).

The conformation of the 46-residue fragment from apoA-I, apoA-I(142-187), elucidated by distance geometry calculations of NMR restraints, is composed of two well-defined helical regions, 146–162 and 168–182, separated by a less well-defined, flexible hinge (82). In both SDS and DPC, the peptide, on average, adopts similar curved amphipathic conformations with all the hydrophobic residues on the concave face (Figure 5).

The similarity in conformation in either SDS or DPC suggests that the hydrophobic interactions determine peptide conformation in the micelle. However, electrostatic interactions between positively charged side chains in apoA-I(142-187)

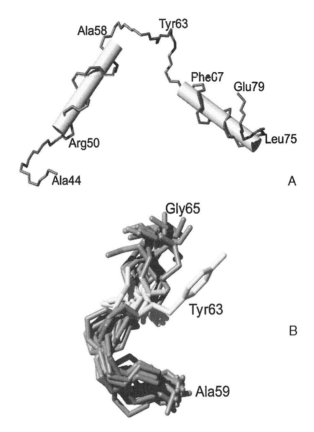

Figure 4   The structure of apoC-II(44-79). (*A*) Backbone conformation, with helical regions indicated by cylindrical rods. (*B*) Backbone conformation of the interhelical domain, residues 59–65. Tyr63 is shown in white. The side chain conformation of a single Tyr63, representative of the major side chain conformation, is shown. Reproduced with permission from (79). The high-resolution, NMR-derived structure of apoC-II(44-79) provides insight into its biological function. For instance, the enzyme lipoprotein lipase, which is activated by apoC-II, is activated equally well by the C-terminal third of apoC-II. Residues 76–79 are important for the binding of apoC-II to lipoprotein lipase (19), whereas Y63 has been proposed to be directly involved in activation from mutation studies (76).

and negatively charged SDS headgroups may initiate binding. NOE crosspeaks between SDS alkyl chains and the side chains of arginines, histidines, and lysine suggested that these amino acids are located in the interface of the peptide/SDS complexes in a class A amphipathic helical motif. The authors proposed a model for apoA-I(142-187)/lipid complexes, wherein the amphipathic helix-hinge-helix structural motif straddles the micelle. The hydrophobic face is more easily envisioned when only the concensus hydrophobic side chain orientation, i.e., the side

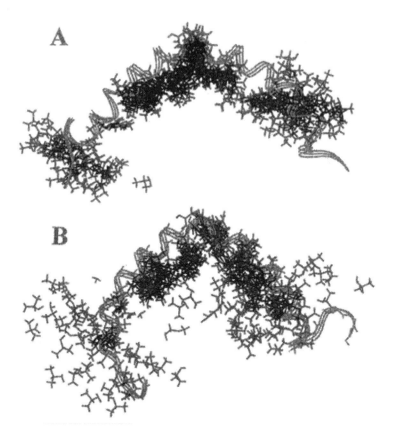

Figure 5 Ribbon representation of the structure of apoA-I(142-187) in DPC (*A*) or in SDS (*B*), The ribbon defines the backbone of the average of the 29 best structures calculated. The N terminus of each structure is on the left. Only the hydrophobic side chains of all structures in the ensemble are given. The hydrophobic side chains show a high population on the concave face, although it is more pronounced for those in the N-terminal helix than in the C-terminal helix, which is less well defined. Reproduced with permission from (82).

chain orientation resembling the average, is shown (Figure 6). The flexible hinge would allow either helix to lift off the lipoprotein surface to interact with lecithin: cholesterol acyltransferase.

X-ray Crystallography

X-ray of the lipoproteins is difficult owing to the liquid crystalline nature of the particles. Also, free human serum apolipoproteins all self-associate in the absence of lipids because of the large areas of the hydrophobic faces. High-resolution

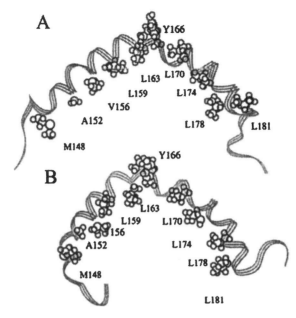

Figure 6   Ribbon representation of the structure of apoA-I(142-187) in DPC (*A*) or in SDS (*B*) with only the hydrophobic side chains resembling the average side chain orientation shown for clarity. Reproduced with permission from (82).

structures from X-ray crystallography have been determined for the insect apolipo-protein apoLp-III and the N-terminal fragment of human apoE, which is the receptor-binding domain. Both proteins were characterized by up-down helical bundles, a four-helix bundle with unusually long helices for the apoE fragment (85), and a five-helix bundle for apoLp-III (13). The bundles were organized so that the hydrophobic helical faces were oriented to the center while the hydrophilic faces were directed toward the aqueous phase. Preliminary X-ray diffraction analysis of apoC-I crystals has been reported (84). These crystals were formed with inclusion of 17% 2-methyl-2,4-pentanediol and 0.25% octyl-β-D-1-thioglucopyranoside, meaning the structure may not equate to that expected in lipid complexes, but it may resemble that found in solution.

Recently, Borhani et al. determined the X-ray crystal structure of the deletion mutant apoA-I(44-243), i.e., where the N-terminal amino acid residues 1–43 are absent (11). The X-ray structure consists of four molecules in the asymmetric unit, each molecule structure consisting "almost entirely of a pseudocontinuous, amphipathic α-helix." The four apoA-I(44-243) molecules associate via their hydrophobic faces to form an antiparallel four-helix bundle with an elliptical ring shape. The crown-shaped pseudocontinuous helix is radically different from the conformation of apoA-I proposed in 1979 by Edelstein et al. (27) from primary sequence analysis and circular dichroism studies. Their structural representation

(27), which has persisted until the recent X-ray work, envisioned a molecule where the tandem repeats form a series of tightly packed antiparallel α-helices linked by short, tight turns (12, 27, 59, 64, 77).

The apoA-I(44-243) crystal structure was determined in the absence of lipid, and the helical bundle arrangement is similar to the crystal structures of insect apo Lp-III and the receptor-binding N-terminal domain of human apoE mentioned above. Thus, none of these protein crystal structures were determined in the presence of lipids. It is certain that the presence of lipids will alter the helical bundle arrangement found for apoA-I, apoLp-III, and the apoE fragment by X ray.

In the next section, solution structures of intact apolipoproteins derived from NMR studies are presented. An evaluation on the use of SDS and DPC micelles as models of lipoprotein structure is necessary at this point.

NMR studies of lipid-associating proteins are often conducted in the presence of SDS or DPC, which serve as models for a membrane environment (37, 55). SDS and DPC micelles are approximately 5 nm in diameter, which is similar in size to the pre-βHDL and to the smallest HDL$_3$; hence, they are likely to yield an apolipoprotein conformation resembling the one present in HDL. DPC has the same headgroup as phospholipids; however, as discussed below, lipoprotein structures are similar in both SDS and DPC. One should run spectra in both DPC and in SDS because binding to the micelle could be stronger in one or the other, and either one might give better resolved NMR spectra.

A number of papers have proposed that SDS and DPC may be used interchangeably to model the lipoprotein environment. Similar structures were obtained for the LCAT activator LAP-20 in the presence of both SDS and DPC (14). Figure 4C of that paper superimposed the NMR-derived average backbone structures that clearly show the identity. For an apoA-II peptide, similar helical contents were calculated from convex constraint analysis of the CD spectra (55% helix in SDS; 45% helix in DPC) (15). The structure of apoA-I(166-187) in SDS and DPC is even more striking (83). Figure 5D of that paper shows that not only do the helical backbones superimpose but also most of the side chains, which, on average, adopt similar orientations. Finally, similar average, curved helix-hinge-helix structures were found for the longer apoA-I fragment, apoA-I(142-186) (82). In both SDS and DPC micelles, curved helix-hinge-helix structures were calculated from the NMR restraints, with the hydrophobic residues occupying the concave face, indicating that hydrophobic interactions dominate. There are some differences in the structures, however. Occasionally, charged side chains have different orientations in the two lipids, and the structure of the hinge in apoA-I(142-186) is slightly different. Monomeric SDS molecules bind to apoA-I(142-187), whereas zwitterionic DPC does not interact with the peptide until the critical micelle concentration is attained (82). On the whole, there is remarkable similarity because the major interaction between apolipoprotein fragments and lipids is the hydrophobic effect; hence, the differently charged headgroups, zwitterionic DPC and negatively charged SDS, play a lesser role. One is still faced with the question of how well do SDS or DPC micelles mimic lipoproteins. However, one cannot yet obtain

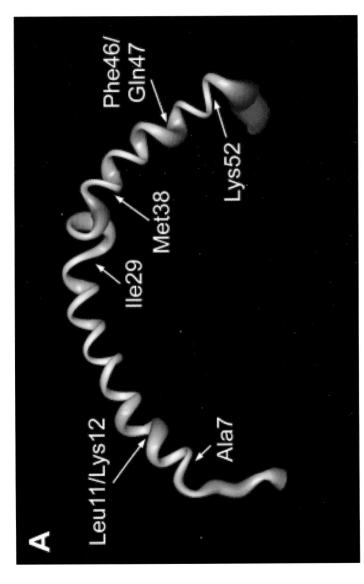

Figure 8 Ribbon representation of the backbone structure of apoC-I that is closest to the mean coordinates of 18 calculated structures. The width and color of the ribbon is modified to reflect the circular variance of the torsion angle ψ. *Red* shading and greater widths indicate poorly defined regions. The circular variance provides a measure of the spread of dihedral angle ψ. The amino acid labels mark the locations of the N- and the C-terminal helices and the positions of highest circular variance within them, which are also the sites of bends. Reproduced with permission from (69).

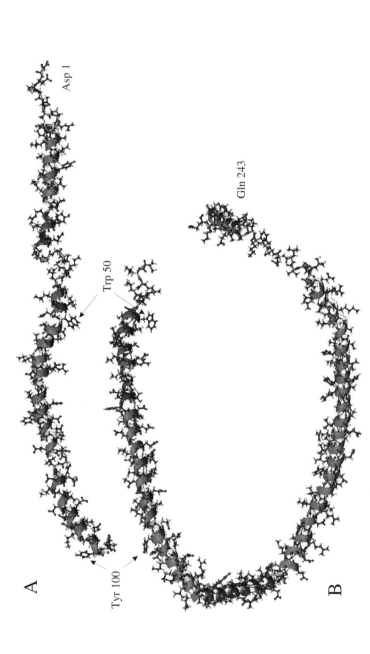

Figure 13 Comparison of NMR and crystal apoA-I tertiary structures represented by MOLMOL (42). (*A*) Calculated apoA-I NMR structure of region 1–102 (one of 20 calculated structures) from the set of NOE-restraints derived from 3D ^{15}N-edited NOESY-HSQC spectra of apoA-I and predicted by TALOS backbone angles (M. Okon & R.J. Cushley, unpublished data). (*B*) ApoA-I(44-243) crystal structure representing one monomer (A1001) of the four-helix bundle determined from X-ray data by Borhani et al. (11).

high-resolution multidimensional NMR spectra of even the smallest lipoprotein with the limitations of currently available technology. Thus, for studying lipid-bound apolipoproteins, the use of micelles seems to be the best possible compromise. Note, for instance, the multitude of model lipoprotein systems using unilamellar phospholipid vesicles, which are even worse than micelles.

NMR SPECTROSCOPY OF INTACT APOLIPOPROTEINS

Because of their unique properties, free apolipoproteins, at the concentration necessary for NMR, form oligomers in aqueous solution by self-association. For instance, that reduced apoA-II forms up to hexamers at high concentration, which do not separate in SDS-polyacrylamide gel electrophoresis (G. Wang & R. J. Cushley, unpublished data). That is, once the oligomers form they are difficult to break up, even with high concentrations of SDS. The authors developed a method to defeat the known self-association of the apolipoproteins. The sample is diluted in SDS, or DPC, and then lyophilized. When the sample is redissolved at NMR concentrations the apolipoprotein does not self-associate.

Structures of Intact Apolipoproteins

Apolipoprotein C-I

From well-resolved ^{1}H NOESY and TOCSY spectra, the structure of apoC-I in the presence of SDS was calculated from 685 NOE-based distance restraints, including 264 interresidue restraints (69). A schematic summary of cross-peaks observed in the NOESY spectrum of apoC-I in SDS is given in Figure 7. The figure shows strong and medium sequential $H_i^N-H_{i+1}^N$ and $H_i^\alpha-H_{i+1}^N$ NOE cross-peaks; strong, medium, and weak $H_i^\alpha-H_{i+3}^N$ cross-peaks; and many medium and weak $H_i^\alpha-H_{i+3}^N$ and $H_i^\alpha-H_{i+4}^N$ cross-peaks. The presence of strong to medium [(i)–(i + 1)] and medium to weak [(i)–(i + 2), (i)–(i + 3), and (i)–(i + 4)] NOEs are indicative of a helical structure.

Detailed 3D structures were calculated by distance geometry–simulated annealing and restrained molecular dynamics methods based on 685 NOE-derived distance restraints. ApoC-I adopts two lipid-binding amphipathic helical regions in the presence of SDS, spanning residues L8 to K30 and R39 to E52. The RMSDs are 1.56 ± 0.32 Å for S6–K30 and 1.92 ± 0.63 Å for L34–E53. Both helical regions are amphipathic with the positively charged residues located at the interface and the negatively charged residues forming a ridge on the polar face (with the exception of E19, which is located at the interface). This is a classical A2 helix. In an A2 amphipathic helix the positively charged amino acid residues are located at the polar-nonpolar interface, and the negatively charged amino acid residues are located at the center of the polar face (Figure 2).

The spatial orientation of the two helices with respect to each other is not well defined, as the intervening hinge is flexible. The N-terminal helix undergoes

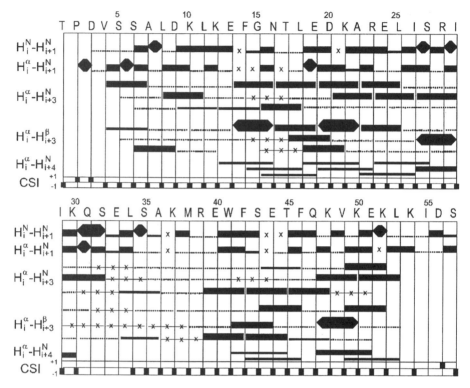

Figure 7 Connectivity diagram of interresidue NOE contacts for apoC-I in SDS-d_{25} solution. The intensity of the NOE connectivity is indicated by the thickness of the *solid black bars*. *Dashed lines* indicate potential NOE cross-peaks, which may be hidden or ambiguous due to resonance overlap. *Crosses* and *lines with crosses* indicate absent NOE cross peaks. The amino acid sequence and residue number is indicated in the top line. The line labeled CSI is the chemical shift index of H^α. Reproduced with permission from (69).

conformational exchange at a second flexible bend, or hinge, situated between K12 and G15. The average backbone structure of apoC-I in SDS is presented in Figure 8 (see color insert).

Prior to the structure determination of apoC-I, the N-terminal 38-residue peptide apoC-I(1-38) was synthesized, and its solution conformation was determined in SDS (68). ApoC-I(1-38) adopts a helical structure between residues V4 and K30 and an extended C terminus from Q31 when associated with SDS. It even includes the hinge at K12 to G15. The region K12–G15 undergoes slow conformational exchange as indicated by broad amide H^N line widths, large temperature coefficients, and fast exchange (<2 h) of H^N with deuterium. The mobility of K12–G15 is reflected in the poorly defined dihedral angles of K12 and E13 in the calculated ensemble of structures. The different mobility of both helices appears to be related to side chain composition, rather than length of the amphipathic helix, and may play a role in the function of apoC-I as an activator of lecithin: cholesterol acyltransferase.

INTERACTION OF APOC-I WITH LIPIDS   Lipid binding of apoC-I is facilitated by having two amphipathic helices (69). Previous studies indicated that the formation of an active, stable amphipathic helical structure in an apoC-I fragment depends on the presence of both the N-terminal and the C-terminal helical regions. In apoC-I, three major lipid-binding sites composed of hydrophobic amino acid side chains were identified: (*a*) L8, L11, F14, and L18; (*b*) L25, I26, and I29, both in the N-terminal helix; and (*c*) L34, M38, W41, F42, F46, and V49 in the C-terminal helix. The positively charged side chains of lysines and arginines exclusively appear as pairs at the edge of these hydrophobic clusters and possibly enhance stability of the amphipathic helix with respect to the lipid surface.

The average structure of apoC-I(1-38) is curved toward its hydrophobic face by a kink, or bend, in the long helical axis defined by the nonhelical dihedral angle of K12/E13 of 125° and a bend of 150° centered at K21. The curvature in the calculated average conformation of apoC-I(1-38) is consistent with the size of a small HDL particle (4 nm). Because apoC-I is distributed between the small HDL and larger VLDL particles (diameter 25–70 nm), the presence of the flexible K12–G15 region may act as a hinge that allows the lipid-binding domain to easily adapt to either particle size.

Apolipoprotein C-II

Just recently, MacRaild et al. (53) determined the structure and protein-detergent interactions of ^{15}N-labeled apoC-II in the presence of SDS micelles using circular dichroism and heteronuclear NMR techniques. ApoC-II contains approximately 60% α-helix as determined by circular dichroism. NMR reveals the first 12 residues of apoC-II to be largely disordered, with the rest of the protein forming a predominantly helical structure. Three regions of helical conformation, residues 16–36, 50–56, and 63–77, are well-defined by NMR-derived constraints, with the intervening regions showing more loosely defined helical conformation. There is evidence of structural heterogeneity in the NMR, which suggests the possibility of more than one conformation present. Although bends have been observed in the structures of several other apolipoprotein lipid-binding helices, they are exclusively oriented toward the hydrophobic face. A pronounced bend in the N-terminal helix is found at the aromatic residues Y25 and W26. In contrast to apoC-I and other apolipoprotein fragments mentioned above, the bend makes the hydrophobic face convex rather than concave. It was suggested that the convex hydrophobic face of the apoC-II N terminus is responsible for the preference of apoC-II for the less-curved lipid surfaces of the larger lipoproteins such as VLDL. The structure of apoC-II agrees well with the structures determined previously for peptides corresponding to residues 50–79 in hexafluoropropane (60) and residues 44–79 in SDS (79), including the loop formed by residues 76–79. The only difference noted was that the C-terminal helix in the intact protein extends toward the N terminus as far as residue 63, whereas for apoC-II(44-79) in SDS, it lost definition at residue 67.

The C-terminal helix has two hydrophobic clusters, with the hydrophobic moment of residues 59–67 making an angle of 111° with the hydrophobic moment of residues 71–75. The authors suggested these misaligned hydrophobic clusters may play a role in lipoprotein lipase activation by disrupting the lipoprotein surface, allowing lipoprotein lipase access to the triacylglycerol core of the lipoprotein, or the misalignment allows one hydrophobic cluster to bind to the lipoprotein surface while the other cluster interacts with lipoprotein lipase.

Apolipoprotein A-I

The solution structure determination of apolipoprotein A-I, a 28K-molecular-weight protein, by NMR is a formidable challenge. Primary sequence analysis, circular dichroism, and the recent X-ray structure of apoA-I(44-243) (11) indicate the secondary structure of apoA-I is highly helical with little or no β structure. This results in a narrow chemical shift dispersion for the amide and C_α-proton resonances. Also, to achieve the amount of helical content found in the lipoproteins requires lipid. Thus, a lipid-containing solution must be present in order to mimic the lipoprotein environment.

The structure of apoA-I, and of an apoA-I deletion mutant apoA-I(1-186) (61), was determined from heteronuclear multidimensional NMR spectra of [u-^{13}C, u-^{15}N]apoA-I and [u-^{13}C, u-^{15}N, u-50% ^{2}H]apoA-I(1-186) in the presence of SDS-d$_{25}$. The labeled apoA-Is included the N-terminal extension Met-Arg-Gly-Ser-(His)$_6$-Met and were expressed in a bacterial medium. The backbone resonances were assigned from a combination of triple-resonance data (HNCO, HNCA, HN(CO)CA, HN(CA)CO, and HN(COCA)HA) and intraresidue and sequential NOEs (3D and 4D ^{13}C- and ^{15}N-edited NOESY). The NMR experiments are summarized in Table 2. Details of these experiments can be found in Okon et al. (61).

For apoA-I, the amide proton (H^N) resonances are confined to a spectral region of only 1.57 ppm, extending from 7.20 to 8.77 ppm, with 95% of all H^N resonances within a 1.1 ppm range (7.5–8.5 ppm). Also, essentially all of the H$^\alpha$ resonances are found in a narrow 0.5 ppm range (between 3.9–4.4 ppm). Another consequence of having almost exclusively α-helical structures is the strong value of sequential $d_{NN}(i, i+1)$ connectivities and the small value of $^3J_{HNC\alpha}$ (<6 Hz). Because the proton line widths are large ($\Delta\nu = 15$–30 Hz) due to complexation with the SDS micelles, experiments such as TOCSY are of little value in determining amino acid spin systems in apoA-I. The wide range of H^N signal intensities, strong overlaps in ^{15}N/^{1}H HSQC spectra, and narrow range of secondary chemical shifts made it difficult to define internuclear distances from 3D ^{15}N-filtered NOESY spectra of apoA-I.

For apoA-I in the SDS micelle, transverse relaxation times of ^{13}C$^\alpha$ nuclei were extremely short (<4ms); therefore, the most sensitive experiments were those where magnetization was mainly on ^{15}N during the pulse sequence (HNCO, HN(CO)CA, HNCA). For partly deuterated apoA-I(1-186), the ^{13}C$^\alpha$ nuclei coupled

TABLE 2 Summary of NMR
experiments

Experiment

3D:
    ^{15}N-edited TOCSY-HSQC[a]
    ^{15}N-edited NOESY-HSQC[b]
    ^{15}N/^{15}N-edited NOESY-HSQC[c]
    HNCO[d]
    HNCA[d]
    HN(CO)CA[d]
    HN(CA)CO[e]
    HN(COCA)HA[f]
    CBCA(CO)NH[f]

4D:
    ^{15}N/^{15}N-edited NOESY[g]
    ^{15}N/^{13}C-edited NOESY[h]
    ^{15}N/^{13}C'-edited NOESY-HNCO[i]

---

[a](54).
[b](94).
[c](29).
[d](35).
[e]Experiment based, in part, on (35).
[f](62).
[g]Experiment based, in part, on (21).
[h](58).
[i]Experiment based, in part, on (95).

to deuterium had longer transverse relaxation times, and additional intraresidual H^N-N-C' correlations were obtained from the HN(CA)CO spectrum.

The ^{13}C' and ^{13}C$^\alpha$ assignments were obtained by the superposition of HNCO and HN(CA)CO spectra [for 50% deuterated apoA-I(1-186)] and HN(CO)CA and HNCA spectra (Figure 9) (60a). In many cases these kinds of correlations between adjacent amino acid residues were not sufficient for unambiguous assignment, and additional NOE information was used from the ^{15}N-edited NOESY/HSQC spectra.

To resolve the overlapped peaks, the series of 4D experiments listed in Table 2 were used, and several 3D experiments were run at several temperatures. Figure 10 shows a 2D slice from the 4D ^{15}N/^{15}N-edited NOESY/HSQC spectrum of apoA-I.

The secondary structure of apoA-I in SDS-d$_{25}$ complexes was determined from the ^{1}H, ^{13}C, and ^{15}N chemical shift values using the Chemical Shift Index (87–91) and the Torsion Angle Likelihood Obtained from Shift and sequence similarity (TALOS) program (22). The Chemical Shift Index is determined from the difference between measured and random coil chemical shifts (87). TALOS uses shift data for three consecutive residues, the triplet, and compares it with similar triplets

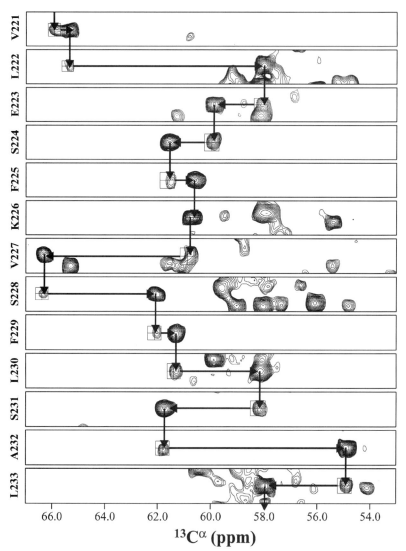

Figure 9   Two-dimensional $^{13}C^{\alpha}$ strip plots taken from the 3D HNCA spectrum for the region from Val 221 to Leu 233 of apoA-I in SDS. The larger intraresidue and smaller interresidue cross peaks between backbone nuclei are evident. The *boxes* indicate the cross peak positions in the HN(CO)CA spectrum. By superimposing the strips the "sequential walk" is illustrated by the arrows.

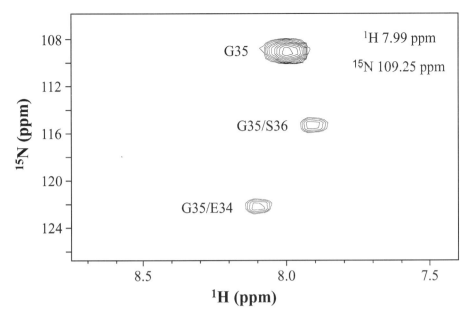

Figure 10   Two-dimensional slice taken from the 4D ^{15}N/^{15}N-edited NOESY/HSQC spectrum of apo A-I (1-243) (pH 6.5, 40°C). Slice is for residue G35 at a ^{1}H chemical shift of 7.99 ppm and ^{15}N chemical shift of 107.6 ppm. Cross peaks with S36 and E34 are observed.

in a database. The ten best matches of phi and psi angles to a given triplet, their averages, and standard deviations are tested for consistency. The TALOS database contains 20 proteins with high-resolution crystal structures (3032 triplets). Four kinds of chemical shifts (^{1}H$^{\alpha}$, ^{13}C$^{\alpha}$, ^{13}C', and ^{15}N) were used for prediction of phi and psi backbone torsion angles using TALOS. The resulting apoA-I(1-186) structure can be found in Okon et al. (61). The secondary structure of apoA-I in SDS predicted by consensus between Chemical Shift Index values and TALOS is given in Figure 11 (60a).

The average backbone torsion angles among all well defined α-helices with $\Phi_{\text{aver}} = -63$ and $\Psi_{\text{aver}} = -42$ degrees. In Figure 11 the helices are defined by the flat sections, which become even clearer from perusing the bottom plot that gives the RMS deviation. The peaks in the plot represent regions with no well-defined structure and coincide with gaps in the Chemical Shift Index plot (not shown). These regions occur between, and overlap with, the helical repeats predicted by Segrest and coworkers (73), although both Segrest's structure and the crystal structure of Borhani et al. (11) appear continuous.

ApoA-I in lipid-mimetic solution is composed of α-helical segments 8–32, 45–64, 67–77, 83–87, 90–97, 100–118, 122–140, 146–162, 167–205, 210–216, and 221–239. In one of the 22mer helical repeats, residues 78–82 are also unstructured. On the other hand, helical repeats 7 and 8 appear to constitute a single, unbroken

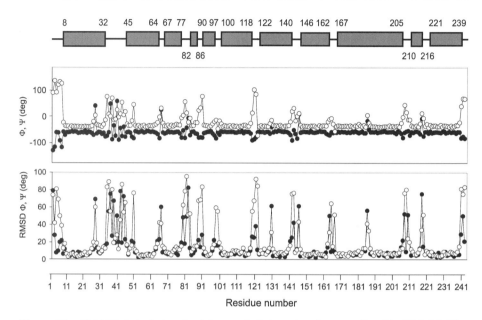

Figure 11 Phi (*filled circles*) and psi (*open circles*) angle values predicted by TALOS. The average backbone torsion angles among all well-defined α-helices (RMSD $\leq$ 8 degrees) are $\Phi_{aver} = -63.2 \pm 2.0$ and $\Psi_{aver} = -41.9 \pm 2.1$ degrees.

helix. A long, disordered region, residues 33–44, separates the region N-terminal from the main protein body and is clearly evident in Figure 11. It was suggested that such a structure would provide a flexible link allowing the N-terminal end to lift off the lipoprotein surface for binding to cell surfaces or receptors (61).

The NMR-derived secondary structure of apoA-I in lipid-mimetic solution is presented in Figure 12. It is compared with the previously determined NMR-derived structure of apoA-I(1-186) (61), the structure predicted by Segrest and coworkers from primary sequence (73), and an apoA-I monomer unit from the lipid-free four-helix bundle determined from X-ray data by Borhani et al. (11). The secondary structures are similar except there are longer nonstructured segments between helical repeats in solution structures. As stated above, the X-ray structure, as well as the structure predicted by Segrest and coworkers, is a continuous helix, whereas the structure predicted by Nolte & Atkinson from primary sequence (59) includes short, tight turns between helical repeats 1–2, 3–4, 4–5, 5–6, and 6–7 and longer turns between repeats 7–8 and 9–10.

The structures of apoA-I and apoA-I(1-186) (61) are similar except around P121. The $^{13}C^\alpha$ chemical shift of E120 undergoes an approximately 3.5 ppm upfield in apoA-I compared to apoA-I(1-186). Such a large shift, together with upfield $^{13}C^\alpha$ shifts of 1.2 ppm for both V119 and L122, indicates a more extended structure around P121 in apoA-I. The $^{13}C^\alpha$ signal of E120 is also sensitive to pH.

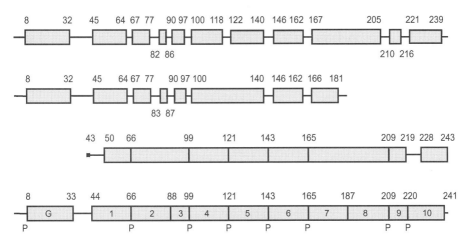

Figure 12   Comparison of apoA-I secondary structures. From top to bottom: NMR solution structure of apoA-I in the presence of SDS-d_{25}, NMR solution structure of apoA-I(1-186) in the presence of SDS-d_{25}, X-ray structure of lipid-free apoA-I(43-243), and predicted apoA-I structure showing the amphipathic helical repeats (73). Proline residues at the beginning of helical repeats are indicated by "P." In the predicted structure (*bottom*), the numbers within the *shaded box* refer to the helical repeat number, with "G" standing for the G* class N-terminal helix.

The NMR evidence strongly suggests apoA-I undergoes a conformational change around P121 as conditions vary. TALOS predicts a V119 conformational change from helical in apoA-I(1-186) to extended in apoA-I. Existence of a mobile domain composed of residues 99–143 was predicted from epitope mapping of apoA-I in lipid-free and lipid-bound forms (16).

TERTIARY ORGANIZATION OF APOA-I   The chemical shift range for signals from apoA-I amino acid side chains is also quite narrow, with almost all side chain chemical shifts equal to their random coil values. The terminal methyl group signals of leucine and valine mainly occur between 0.8 and 1.1 ppm, indicating the absence of strong ring current shifts, which could be expected for aliphatic side chains situated near aromatic side chains in a folded protein structure. This indicates there are no intramolecular or intermolecular helix-helix interactions, thus suggesting poor (if any) tertiary organization of apoA-I structure and absence of apoA-I dimerization in the complex with SDS.

In support of the contention that there are no oligomers of apoA-I in the SDS complex, SDS-polyacrylamide gel electrophoresis of both [u-^{13}C, u-^{15}N, u-50% ^{2}H]apoA-I(1-186) and [u-^{13}C; u-^{15}N]apoA-I samples used for NMR spectroscopy indicated they are monomers in SDS solution. In addition, we did not see extremely broadened sets of peaks in any of our NMR spectra. Broad signals are expected in the presence of dimers, and especially tetramers, of a 28-kD protein in solution.

Figure 13 (see color insert) shows the comparison of the 3D structure of residues 1–102 of apoA-I based on the NMR data with the structure of the region of Borhani's X-ray structure with which it overlaps, i.e., residues 44–102. The tertiary apoA-I organization in solution coincides remarkably well with the structure obtained from crystal data in the region of residues 50–101. Both structures are elongated and the orientations of side chains are similar, in spite of the fact that no lipid is present in the crystal. Also of note is the fact that in the four-helix bundle crystal structure for apoA-I, there were intermolecular helix-helix interactions detected but no intramolecular ones. Comparison of 20 calculated NMR structures for the segment 1–102 shows that there is little or no flexibility in the unstructured region 64–67, thus helical repeats 1 and 2 effectively constitute one long helix due to binding properties of each helix. However, the set of NOE restraints is not complete for this region. It should be mentioned here that the apoA-I crystal structure analyzed by MOLMOL is not a continuous helix [as described in Figure 12 of Borhani's paper (11)]. MOLMOL analysis reveals turns in the regions 64–65, 118–119, 141–143, 202–207, 211–212, and 240–243 for the set of four apoA-I molecules in the four-helix bundle, and the MOLMOL-derived apoA-I crystal structure becomes much closer to the NMR-derived apoA-I secondary structure (Figure 12, *top*). On the other hand, NMR apoA-I secondary structure derived from only secondary shifts (Figure 12, *top*) and NMR apoA-I tertiary structure of region 1–102 derived both from secondary shifts and NOE-restraints (Figure 13A) are similar; the main difference being that helix 1 started at residue 9 (not at residue 8) in the latter structure.

CONCLUDING REMARKS

By using [15]N- and ^{13}C-labeled apolipoproteins obtained via expression and multidimensional heteronuclear NMR techniques, it is possible to determine apolipoprotein structures in lipid-mimetic solution. With nearly complete sets of chemical shifts, we can now identify individual residues in the sequence. Coupled with the use of selective enrichment of residues or point mutations using recombinant technology, these approaches should result in our determining residues and conformations of apolipoproteins responsible for lipid binding and/or enzyme activation and determine the solution NMR structures of these modified peptides.

The big advantage of NMR methods, opposed to X-ray techniques, is that system dynamics can be measured from NOE and relaxation data. To use apolipoprotein A-I as an example, NMR could provide sufficient structural details, not yet available, of the apoA-I/lecithin:cholesterol acyl transferase activation complex and information on binding dynamics (from ^{1}H, ^{13}C, and ^{15}N relaxation rates) to provide conformational details that might explain apolipoprotein activation of enzymes and interactions with lipids.

Finally, it is possible to introduce into apoA-I the naturally occurring mutations, Pro143→Arg, Pro165→Arg, and Pro143→Glu, which target the proposed functional domain of the apolipoprotein, and determine how the structural features of the mutant apoproteins differ in lipid complexes by multidimensional NMR.

ACKNOWLEDGMENTS

This work was supported by grants to R. J. Cushley by the Heart and Stroke Foundation of British Columbia & Yukon and from the Natural Science and Engineering Research Council of Canada (NSERC). R. J. Cushley would especially like to thank the many students and postdoctoral fellows whose work over the years contributed to this review.

Visit the Annual Reviews home page at www.annualreviews.org

LITERATURE CITED

1. Acton S, Rigotti A, Landschulz KT, Xu S, Hobbs HH, Krieger M. 1996. Identification of scavenger receptor SR-BI as a high density lipoprotein receptor. *Science* 271:518–20

2. Alaupovic P. 1996. Significance of apolipoproteins for structure, function, and classification of plasma lipoproteins. *Methods Enzymol.* 263:32–60

3. Assmann G, Brewer HB. 1974. Lipid-protein interactions in high density lipoproteins. *Proc. Natl. Acad. Sci. USA* 71:989–93

4. Atkinson D, Deckelbaum RJ, Small DM, Shipley GG. 1977. Structure of human plasma low-density lipoproteins: molecular organization of the central core. *Proc. Natl. Acad. Sci. USA* 74:1042–46

5. Atkinson D, Small DM. 1986. Recombinant lipoproteins: implications for structure and assembly of native lipoproteins. *Annu. Rev. Biophys. Biophys. Chem.* 15:403–56

6. Atkinson D, Small DM, Shipley GG. 1980. X-ray and neutron scattering studies of plasma lipoproteins. *Ann. NY Acad. Sci.* 348:284–98

7. Aviram M, Bierman EL, Chait A. 1988. Modification of low density lipoprotein by lipoprotein lipase or hepatic lipase induces enhanced uptake and cholesterol accumulation in cells. *J. Biol. Chem.* 263:15416–22

8. Aviram M, Lund-Katz S, Phillips MC, Chait A. 1988. The influence of the trigly-ceride content of low density lipoprotein on the interaction of apolipoprotein B-100 with cells. *J. Biol. Chem.* 263: 16842–48

9. Bathen TF, Engan T, Krane J, Axelson D. 2000. Analysis and classification of proton NMR spectra of lipoprotein fractions from healthy volunteers and patients with cancer or CHD. *Anticancer Res.* 20:2393–408

10. Bergeron J, Frank PG, Scales D, Meng QH, Castro G, Marcel YL. 1995. Apolipoprotein A-I conformation in reconstituted discoidal lipoproteins varying in phospholipid and cholesterol content. *J. Biol. Chem.* 270:27429–38

11. Borhani DW, Rogers DP, Engler JA, Brouillette CG. 1997. Crystal structure of truncated human apolipoprotein A-I suggests a lipid-bound conformation. *Proc. Natl. Acad. Sci. USA* 94:12291–96

12. Brasseur R, De Meutter J, Vanloo B, Goormaghtigh E, Ruysschaert JM, Rosseneu M. 1990. Mode of assembly of amphipathic helical segments in model high-density lipoproteins. *Biochim. Biophys. Acta* 1043:245–52

13. Breiter DR, Kanost MR, Benning MM, Wesenberg G, Law JH, et al. 1991. Molecular structure of an apolipoprotein determined at 2.5 Å resolution. *Biochemistry* 30:603–8

14. Buchko GW, Treleaven WD, Dunne SJ, Tracey AS, Cushley RJ. 1996. Structural studies of a peptide activator of human

lecithin: cholesterol acyl transferase. *J. Biol. Chem.* 271:3039–45

15. Buchko GW, Wang G, Pierens GK, Cushley RJ. 1996. Conformational studies of an amphipathic peptide corresponding to human apolipoprotein A-II residues 18-30 with a C-terminal lipid binding motif EWLNS. *Int. J. Pept. Protein Res.* 48:21–30

16. Calabresi L, Meng QH, Castro GR, Marcel YL. 1993. Apolipoprotein A-I conformation in discoidal particles: evidence for alternate structures. *Biochemistry* 32:6477–84

17. Castro GR, Fielding CJ. 1988. Early incorporation of cell-derived cholesterol into pre-beta-migrating high-density lipoprotein. *Biochemistry* 27:25–29

18. Chana RS, Treleaven WD, Cushley RJ, Steinbrecher UP. 1990. Dynamic structure of the lower density lipoproteins. I. Incorporation of high levels of labelled lipids into very low and low density lipoproteins. *Biochem. Cell Biol.* 68:180–88

19. Cheng Q, Blackett P, Jackson KW, McConathy WJ, Wang CS. 1990. C-terminal domain of apolipoprotein CII as both activator and competitive inhibitor of lipoprotein lipase. *Biochem. J.* 269:403–7

20. Clayton D, Brereton IM, Kroon PA, Smith R. 2000. Three-dimensional NMR structure of the sixth ligand-binding module of the human LDL receptor: comparison of two adjacent modules with different ligand binding specificities. *FEBS Lett.* 479:118–22

21. Clore GM, Kay LE, Bax A, Gronenborn AM. 1991. Four-dimensional 13C/13C-edited nuclear Overhauser enhancement spectroscopy of a protein in solution: application to interleukin-1 beta. *Biochemistry* 30:12–18

22. Cornilescu G, Delaglio F, Bax A. 1999. Protein backbone angle restraints from searching a database for chemical shift and sequence homology. *J. Biol. NMR* 13:289–302

23. Cushley RJ, Treleaven WD, Parmar YI,

Chana RS, Fenske DB. 1987. Surface diffusion in human serum lipoproteins. *Biochem. Biophys. Res. Commun.* 146:1139–45

24. Deckelbaum RJ, Shipley GG, Small DM. 1977. Structure and interactions of lipids in human plasma low density lipoproteins. *J. Biol. Chem.* 252:744–54

25. Dolmer K, Huang W, Gettins PG. 1998. Characterization of the calcium site in two complement-like domains from the low-density lipoprotein receptor-related protein (LRP) and comparison with a repeat from the low-density lipoprotein receptor. *Biochemistry* 37:17016–23

26. Dolphin PJ. 1985. Lipoprotein metabolism and the role of apolipoproteins as metabolic programmers. *Can. J. Biochem. Cell Biol.* 63:850–69

27. Edelstein C, Kezdy FJ, Scanu AM, Shen BW. 1979. Apolipoproteins and the structural organization of plasma lipoproteins: human plasma high density lipoprotein-3. *J. Lipid Res.* 20:143–53

28. Eisenberg D, Weiss RM, Terwilliger TC. 1982. The helical hydrophobic moment: a measure of the amphiphilicity of a helix. *Nature* 299:371–74

29. Ernst RR, Boentges S, Schmidt M. 1996. Part 6. Multidimensional spectroscopy: concepts. In *Encyclopedia of Nuclear Magnetic Resonance*, pp. 3129-33. New York: Wiley

30. Fenske DB, Chana RS, Parmar YI, Treleaven WD, Cushley RJ. 1990. Structure and motion of phospholipids in human plasma lipoproteins. A ^{31}P NMR study. *Biochemistry* 29:3973–81

31. Fenske DB, Parmar YI, Treleaven WD, Chana RS, Cushley RJ. 1987. Lipid-lipid interactions in reconstituted high density lipoproteins studied by deuterium magnetic resonance. *Biochemistry* 27:4491–500

32. Fielding CJ, Fielding PE. 1995. Molecular physiology of reverse cholesterol transport. *J. Lipid Res.* 36:211–28

33. Finer EG, Henry R, Leslie RB, Robertson

RN. 1975. NMR studies of pig low- and high-density serum lipoproteins. Molecular motions and morphology. *Biochim. Biophys. Acta* 380:320–27

34. Gofman JW, Lindgren FT, Elliott H. 1949. Ultracentrifugal studies of lipoproteins in human serum. *J. Biol. Chem.* 179:973–79

35. Grzesiek S, Bax A. 1992. Improved 3D triple-resonance NMR techniques applied to a 31-kDa protein. *J. Magn. Reson.* 96:432–40

36. Hamilton JA, Morrissett JD. 1986. Nuclear magnetic resonance studies of lipoproteins. *Methods Enzymol.* 128:472–515

37. Henry GD, Sykes BD. 1994. Methods to study membrane protein structure in solution. *Methods Enzymol.* 239:515–35

38. Herzfeld J, Griffin RG, Haberkorn RA. 1978. Phosphorus-31 chemical-shift tensors in barium diethyl phosphate and urea-phosphoric acid: model compounds for phospholipid head-group studies. *Biochemistry* 17:2711–18

39. Hevonoja T, Pentikainen MO, Hyvonen MT, Kovanen PT, Ala-Korpela M. 2000. Structure of low density lipoprotein (LDL) particles: basis for understanding molecular changes in modifed LDL. *Biochim. Biophys. Acta* 1488:189–210

40. Ibdah JA, Lund-Katz S, Phillips MC. 1989. Molecular packing of high-density and low-density lipoprotein surface lipids and apolipoprotein A-I binding. *Biochemistry* 28:1126–33

41. Ibdah JA, Phillips MC. 1988. Effects of lipid composition and packing on the adsorption of apolipoprotein A-I to lipid monolayers. *Biochemistry* 27:7155–62

42. Koradi R, Billeter M, Wüthrich K. 1996. MOLMOL: a program for display and analysis of macromolecular structures. *J. Mol. Graph.* 14:51–55

43. Laggner P, Kostner GM, Rakusch U, Worcester D. 1981. Neutron small angle scattering on selectively deuterated human plasma low density lipoproteins.

The location of polar phospholipid headgroups. *J. Biol. Chem.* 256:11832–39

44. Laggner P, Muller KW. 1978. The structure of serum lipoproteins as analysed by X-ray small-angle scattering. *Q. Rev. Biophys.* 11:371–425

45. Lauer S, Fontanarosa PB. 2001. Updated guidelines for cholesterol management. *JAMA* 285:2508–9

46. Li WH, Tanimura M, Luo C, Datta S, Chan L. 1988. The apolipoprotein multigene family: biosynthesis, structure, structure-function relationships, and evolution. *J. Lipid Res.* 29:245–71

47. Lobo LI, Wilton DC. 1997. Effect of lipid composition on lipoprotein lipase activity measured by a continuous fluorescence assay: effect of cholesterol supports an interfacial surface penetration model. *Biochem. J.* 321:829–35

48. Lund-Katz S, Ibdah JA, Letizia JY, Thomas MT, Phillips MC. 1988. A ^{13}C NMR characterization of lysine residues in apolipoprotein B and their role in binding to the low density lipoprotein receptor. *J. Biol. Chem.* 263:13831–38

49. Lund-Katz S, Laboda HM, McLean LR, Phillips MC. 1988. Influence of molecular packing and phospholipid type on rates of cholesterol exchange. *Biochemistry* 27:3416–23

50. Lund-Katz S, Phillips MC. 1986. Packing of cholesterol molecules in human low-density lipoprotein. *Biochemistry* 25:1562–68

51. Lund-Katz S, Weisgraber KH, Mahley RW, Phillips MC. 1993. Conformation of apolipoprotein E in lipoproteins. *J. Biol. Chem.* 268:23008–15

52. Lycksell PO, Ohman A, Bengtsson-Olivecrona G, Johansson LB, Wijmenga SS, et al. 1992. Sequence specific 1H-NMR assignments and secondary structure of a carboxy-terminal functional fragment of apolipoprotein CII. *Eur. J. Biochem.* 205:223–31

53. MacRaild AC, Hatters DM, Howlett GJ, Gooley PR. 2001. NMR structure of

human apolipoprotein C-II in the presence of sodium dodecyl sulfate. *Biochemistry* 40:5414–21

54. Marion D, Ikura M, Tschudin R, Bax A. 1989. Application of homonuclear single-quantum spectroscopy to the NMR study of proteins. *J. Magn. Reson.* 85:393–99

55. McDonnell PA, Opella SJ. 1993. Effect of detergent concentration on multidimensional solution NMR spectra of membrane proteins in micelles. *J. Magn. Reson.* B102:120–25

56. McLean LR, Demel RA, Socorro L, Shinomiya M, Jackson RL. 1986. Mechanism of action of lipoprotein lipase. *Methods Enzymol.* 129:738–63

57. Miller GJ, Miller NE. 1975. Plasma-high-density-lipoprotein concentration and development of ischaemic heart-disease. *Lancet* 1:16–19

58. Muhandiram DR, Xu GY, Kay LE. 1993. An enhanced-sensitivity pure absorption gradient 4D ^{15}N, ^{13}C-edited NOESY experiment. *J. Biomol. NMR* 3:463–70

59. Nolte RT, Atkinson D. 1992. Conformational analysis of apolipoprotein A-I and E-3 based on primary sequence and circular dichroism. *Biophys. J.* 63:1221–39

60. Ohman A, Lycksell PO, Graslund A. 1993. A refined three-dimensional solution structure of a carboxy terminal fragment of apolipoprotein CII. *Eur. Biophys. J.* 22:351–57

60a. Okon M, Frank PG, Marcel YL, Cushley RJ. 2002. Heteronuclear NMR studies of human serum apolipoprotein A-I. Part I. Secondary structure in lipid-mimetic solution. *FEBS Lett.* In press

61. Okon M, Frank PG, Marcel YL, Cushley RJ. 2001. Secondary structure of human apolipoprotein A-I(1-186) in lipid-mimetic solution. *FEBS Lett.* 487:390–96

62. Olejniczak ET, Xu RX, Petros AM, Fesik S. 1992. A general method for assigning NMR spectra of denatured proteins using 3D HC(CO)NH-TOCSY triple resonance experiments. *J. Magn. Reson.* 100:444–50

63. Osborn JC, Bonzart TJ, Brewer HB. 1977.

Self-association of apo-C-I from the human high density lipoprotein complex. *J. Biol. Chem.* 252:5756–60

64. Palgunachari MN, Mishra VK, Lund-Katz S, Phillips MC, Adeyeye SO, et al. 1996. Only the two end helixes of eight tandem amphipathic helical domains of human apo A-I have significant lipid affinity. Implications for HDL assembly. *Atheroscler. Thromb. Vasc. Biol.* 16:328–38

65. Parmar YI, Gorrissen H, Wassall SR, Cushley RJ. 1983. Molecular motion and conformation of cholesteryl esters in reconstituted high density lipoprotein by deuterium magnetic resonance. *J. Biol. Chem.* 258:2000–4

66. Parmar YI, Gorrissen H, Wassall SR, Cushley RJ. 1985. Chain dynamics of selectively deuterated fatty acids in high-density lipoproteins studied by deuterium NMR. *Biochemistry* 24:171–76

67. Rozek A, Buchko GW, Cushley RJ. 1995. Conformation of two peptides corresponding to human apolipoprotein C-I residues 7-24 and 35-53 in the presence of sodium dodecyl sulfate by CD and NMR spectroscopy. *Biochemistry* 34:7401–8

68. Rozek A, Buchko GW, Kanda P, Cushley RJ. 1997. Conformational studies of the N-terminal lipid-associating domain of human apolipoprotein C-I by CD and ^{1}H NMR. *Protein Sci.* 6:1858–68

69. Rozek A, Sparrow JT, Weisgraber KH, Cushley RJ. 1999. The structure of human apolipoprotein C-I determined by NMR in a lipid-mimetic environment. *Biochemistry* 38:14475–84

70. Scanu AM, Edelstein C, Shen BW. 1982. Lipid-protein interactions in plasma lipoproteins. Model: high density lipoprotein. In *Lipid-Protein Interactions*, ed. PC Jost, OH Griffith, pp. 259–316. New York: Wiley

71. Seelig J. 1978. ^{31}P nuclear magnetic resonance and the head group structure of phospholipids in membranes. *Biochim. Biophys. Acta* 515:105–40

72. Segrest JP, Garber DW, Brouillette CG,

Harvey SC, Anantharamaiah GM. 1994. The amphipathic alpha helix: a multifunctional structural motif in plasma apolipoproteins. *Adv. Protein Chem.* 45:303–69

73. Segrest JP, Jones MK, De Loof H, Brouillette CG, Venkatachalapathi YV, Anantharamaiah GM. 1992. The amphipathic helix in the exchangeable apolipoproteins: a review of secondary structure and function. *J. Lipid Res.* 33:141–66

74. Sehavek E, Eisenberg S. 1991. Mechanisms of inhibition by apolipoprotein C of apolipoprotein E-dependent cellular metabolism of human triglyceride-rich lipoproteins through the low density lipoprotein receptor pathway. *J. Biol. Chem.* 266:18259–67

75. Smith ICP, Princz EJ, Saunders JK. 1990. Magnetic resonance spectroscopy in cancer research. *Can. Assoc. Radiol. J.* 41:32–38

76. Smith LC, Voyta JC, Catapano AL, Kinnunen PK, Gotto AM Jr, Sparrow JT. 1980. Activation of lipoprotein lipase by synthetic fragments of apolipoprotein C-II. *Ann. NY Acad. Sci.* 348:213–23

77. Sparks DL, Davidson WS, Lund-Katz S, Phillips MC. 1993. Effect of cholesterol on the charge and structure of apolipoprotein A-I in recombinant high density lipoprotein particles. *J. Biol. Chem.* 268:23250–57

78. Storjohann R. 1998. *Structure of a biologically active fragment of human serum apolipoprotein C-II in the presence of sodium dodecyl sulfate and dodecylphosphocholine determined by NMR spectroscopy.* MSc thesis. Simon Fraser Univ. 119 pp.

79. Storjohann R, Rozek A, Sparrow JT, Cushley RJ. 2000. Structure of a biologically active fragment of human serum apolipoprotein C-II in the presence of sodium dodecyl sulfate and dodecylphosphocholine. *Biochim. Biophys. Acta* 1486:253–64

80. Treleaven WD, Parmar YI, Gorrissen H, Cushley RJ. 1986. Orientational order of cholesteryl oleate in low-density lipoprotein observed by ^{2}H-NMR. *Biochim. Biophys. Acta* 877:198–210

81. Valic MI, Gorrissen H, Cushley RJ, Bloom M. 1979. Deuterium magnetic resonance study of cholesteryl esters in membranes. *Biochemistry* 18:854–59

82. Wang G, Sparrow JT, Cushley RJ. 1997. The helix-hinge-helix structural motif in human apolipoprotein A-I determined by NMR spectroscopy. *Biochemistry* 36:13657–66

83. Wang G, Treleaven WD, Cushley RJ. 1996. Conformation of human serum apolipoprotein A-I(166-185) in the presence of sodium dodecyl sulfate or dodecylphosphocholine by ^{1}H-NMR and CD. Evidence for specific peptide-SDS interactions. *Biochim. Biophys. Acta* 1301:174–84

84. Weisgraber KH, Newhouse YM, McPherson A. 1994. Crystallization and preliminary X-ray analysis of human plasma apolipoprotein C-I. *J. Mol. Biol.* 236:382–84

85. Wilson C, Wardell MR, Weisgraber KH, Mahley RW, Agard DA. 1991. Three-dimensional structure of the LDL receptor-binding domain of human apolipoprotein E. *Science* 252:1817–22

86. Windler E, Chao Y, Havel RJ. 1980. Determinants of hepatic uptake of triglyceride-rich lipoproteins and their remnants in the rat. *J. Biol. Chem.* 255:5475–80

87. Wishart DS, Bigam CG, Holm A, Hodges RS, Sykes BD. 1995. 1H, 13C and 15N random coil NMR chemical shifts of the common amino acids. I. Investigations of nearest-neighbor effects. *J. Biomol. NMR* 5:67–81

88. Wishart DS, Nip AM. 1998. Protein chemical shift analysis: a practical guide. *Biochem. Cell. Biol.* 76:153–63

89. Wishart DS, Sykes BD. 1994. The 13C chemical-shift index: a simple method for the identification of protein secondary structure using 13C chemical-shift data. *J. Biomol. NMR* 4:171–80

90. Wishart DS, Sykes BD, Richards FM.

1991. Relationship between nuclear magnetic resonance chemical shift and protein secondary structure. *J. Mol. Biol.* 222: 311–33

91. Wishart DS, Sykes BD, Richards FM. 1992. The chemical shift index: a fast and simple method for the assignment of protein secondary structure through NMR spectroscopy. *Biochemistry* 31:1647–51

92. Yeagle PL, Langdon RG, Martin RB. 1977. Phospholipid-protein interactions in human low density lipoprotein detected by ^{31}P nuclear magnetic resonance. *Biochemistry* 16:3487–91

93. Yeagle PL, Martin RB, Pottenger L, Langdon RG. 1978. Location and interactions of phospholipid and cholesterol in human low density lipoprotein from ^{31}P nuclear magnetic resonance. *Biochemistry* 17:2707–10

94. Zhang O, Kay LE, Olivier JP, Forman-Kay JD. 1994. Backbone ^{1}H and ^{15}N resonance assignments of the N-terminal SH3 domain of drk in folded and unfolded states using enhanced-sensitivity pulsed field gradient NMR techniques. *J. Biomol. NMR* 4:845–58

95. Zhang W, Smithgall TE, Gmeiner WH. 1996. Separation of NOEs from degenerate amide protons in ^{13}C/^{15}N-Labeled proteins using a 3D [13]C'-edited NOESY-H(N)CO experiment. *J. Magn. Reson. B* 111:305–9

96. Zhao Y, Sparks DL, Marcel YL. 1996. Specific phospholipid association with apolipoprotein A-I stimulates cholesterol efflux from human fibroblasts. Studies with reconstituted sonicated lipoproteins. *J. Biol. Chem.* 271:25145–51

97. Zubay G. 1993. *Biochemistry.* Iowa: Brown Publishers

Annu. Rev. Biophys. Biomol. Struct. 2002. 31:207–33
DOI: 10.1146/annurev.biophys.31.082901.134329
Copyright © 2002 by Annual Reviews. All rights reserved

THE α-HELIX AND THE ORGANIZATION AND GATING OF CHANNELS

Robert H. Spencer[1] and Douglas C. Rees[2]

[1]*Department of Pharmacology, Merck Research Laboratories, West Point, Pennsylvania 19486; e-mail: rob_spencer@merck.com*
[2]*Division of Chemistry and Chemical Engineering 147-75CH, Howard Hughes Medical Institute, California Institute of Technology, Pasadena, California 91125; e-mail: dcrees@caltech.edu*

Key Words   ion channels, membrane proteins, transmembrane helices, conformational changes

■ **Abstract**   The structures of an increasing number of channels and other α-helical membrane proteins have been determined recently, including the KcsA potassium channel, the MscL mechanosensitive channel, and the AQP1 and GlpF members of the aquaporin family. In this chapter, the orientation and packing characteristics of bilayer-spanning helices are surveyed in integral membrane proteins. In the case of channels, α-helices create the sealed barrier that separates the hydrocarbon region of the bilayer from the permeation pathway for solutes. The helices surrounding the permeation pathway tend to be rather steeply tilted relative to the membrane normal and are consistently arranged in a right-handed bundle. The helical framework further provides a supporting scaffold for nonmembrane-spanning structures associated with channel selectivity. Although structural details remain scarce, the conformational changes associated with gating transitions between closed and open states of channels are reviewed, emphasizing the potential roles of helix-helix interactions in this process.

CONTENTS

INTRODUCTION

Few discoveries have had a greater, or longer-lasting, impact on the field of protein structure and function than the α-helix, first unveiled by Linus Pauling 50 years ago (74). This is particularly true in the study of membrane proteins, where the

α-helix provides an exquisite solution to the problem of satisfying the hydrogen-bonding potential of the peptide bond in the apolar environment of the bilayer. (The β-sheet, Pauling's "other" secondary structure (73), also provides a solution to this problem adopted by outer-membrane proteins such as porins that are beyond the scope of this review.) Prior to any detailed structural understanding of membrane proteins or even of the membrane itself, it was anticipated that membrane-spanning proteins would be predominantly helical, based on observations that the α-helix content of polypeptides increases significantly in nonaqueous solvents (87). These predictions were subsequently confirmed through Henderson & Unwin's observation of seven rod-like features in the initial electron crystallographic studies of bacteriorhodopsin (37) and, ultimately, at high resolution in the structure of the photosynthetic reaction center by Deisenhofer et al. (18). Our present understanding of the primary and secondary structure organization of these integral membrane proteins can be summarized by the statements that the bilayer-spanning residues consist primarily of apolar amino acids and that these residues are predominantly found in the α-helical conformation.

Channels constitute a functionally important class of membrane proteins that mediate the transmembrane passage of ions and other small molecules in their thermodynamically favorable direction [reviewed in (1, 38)]. These macromolecular pores establish the basis for synaptic transmission, cell signaling, volume regulation, and many other critical physiological processes via their characteristic properties of ion selectivity, conductance, and gating. Channels may be highly selective for a particular molecular species (e.g., potassium, sodium, glycerol), or more permissive to a general class of molecules or ions such as anions, or they may even be completely nonselective. The structural basis for channel specificity has been established in greatest detail for the K^+ channel (22) and more recently for the aquaporin family (30, 66). The conductance of a channel specifies the number of molecules that can pass through the channel per unit time and depends on the geometry of the permeation pathway and the energetic profile for passage through the channel. In many cases, the conductance of a channel is regulated or gated by the conformational switching of the protein structure between "open" and "closed" states. The conformational sensitivity of channels to external influences is at the heart of the ability of these molecules to function as signal transducers. This behavior represents a fascinating biophysical challenge for understanding how the protein structure is coupled to these environmental cues.

Crystallographic analyses of the KcsA (22), MscL (11), AQP1 (66), and GlpF (30) channels have provided the first detailed views of their molecular organization (Figure 1). These channels represent a diverse cross section of channel activities: KcsA is a potassium ion–specific channel, MscL is a mechanosensitive channel that is most likely associated with protection against osmotic shock, and GlpF and AQP1 are members of the aquaporin family. Not coincidentally, the channels whose structures have been established by X-ray crystallography (KcsA, MscL, and GlpF) have all been isolated from prokaryotes, which reflects the great advantages (at present) of bacterial systems for the expression and purification of appropriate

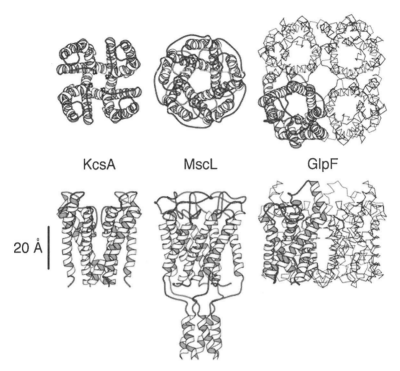

Figure 1   Structures of the KcsA (22), MscL (11), and GlpF (30) channels viewed parallel (*top*) and perpendicular (*bottom*) to the membrane normal. One of the four subunits in the GlpF tetramer is highlighted as a ribbons diagram in each view, with the Cα backbones of the remaining subunits traced in thinner lines. The vertical bar on the left indicates 20 Å. The molecular figures in this article were prepared with MOLSCRIPT (48).

quantities of naturally less-abundant membrane proteins for crystallization trials. As evidenced from the structures, the bilayer-spanning region of these channels is formed from a collection of α-helices oriented such that the helix axes tend to be aligned along the membrane normal. The helices are packed together to form a sealed barrier that separates the hydrocarbon region of the bilayer from the permeation pathway for solutes. These structures provide a molecular framework for addressing functional properties of channels. For example, the structures of the KcsA and aquaporin family channels provide fundamental insights into the chemical basis for channel selectivity. In both systems, specificity is achieved through nonhelical structures in the center of the respective channels that form the "selectivity filter" responsible for selective binding of the appropriate molecular species. The structure of the KcsA channel has also permitted theoretical analyses of channel conductance that take into account the geometry of the permeation pathway, along with electrostatic and binding interactions that shape the energy landscape as the solute traverses the channel (81). Still to be established is the structural basis for the coupling of channel structure to environmental changes, in particular the issues of how the sensing occurs and how the protein conformation switchs between closed and open states. For channels such as MscL that have open states of large conductance, these conformational changes must be dramatic and clearly must involve rearrangements in the helix-helix packing interactions.

As these initial studies demonstrate, the α-helix provides the central structural element for channel construction. This chapter explores implications of this α-helical framework for the conformation and gating transitions of channels. After a brief introduction to gating, a more-detailed analysis of α-helices in membranes will be presented, followed by a discussion of structurally characterized channels.

GATING

The simplest model for conformational gating treats the channel as exhibiting two conformational states, closed (C) and open (O)

$$C \overset{K(V,\, c,\, P,\, etc.)}{\leftrightarrow} O.$$

The equilibrium constant between these states is sensitive to the values of environmental parameters such as membrane potential (V), ligand concentrations (c), and tension applied to the bilayer (P). By convention, this equilibrium is written such that the left-hand side is favored under resting conditions. For example, the closed state of K^+ channels and MscL are stabilized by $\sim$10 kcal/mole relative to the open state (38, 96). In response to appropriate changes in the environment, however, the equilibrium will shift toward the open state. Conformational changes between the closed and open states can formally be accomplished through many mechanisms. For voltage-gated channels, altered charge distributions between the open and closed states can couple protein conformation to changes in the membrane potential; for ligand-gated ion channels, changes in ligand affinity can shift the equilibrium between closed and open (or desensitized) states; for mechanosensitive channels, changes in membrane tension can differentially stabilize open and closed states that vary in cross-sectional areas. The steepness of the response provides a measure of the cooperative nature of the transition between states. Although this model clearly is an oversimplification of real systems, because detailed electrophysiological studies of ion channels have demonstrated the existence of multiple closed and open states, it does provide a useful basis for addressing the conformational basis of channel gating.

This description of channel gating may be treated within the framework of the Monod-Wyman-Changeux (MWC) model for allosteric systems (12, 65). In the MWC formalism, allosteric systems are considered to be composed of a symmetric arrangement of subunits that exist in two states, R and T, with different properties;

conventionally, the R and T states represent the active and inactive states. The equilibrium between these states may be shifted through the binding of ligands and other effectors that have different affinities for the two states:

$$T \overset{1/L}{\leftrightarrow} R.$$

Typical values of the resting state ratio of (R)/(T) are in the range of 10^{-3} to 10^{-6} (33, 76), so that the T state is favored in the absence of ligands by $\sim$5–10 kcal/mole—comparable to the energetic difference between open and closed states of channels. (Note, this equilibrium constant corresponds to the inverse of the allosteric constant L defined by MWC.) The binding of substrates and allosteric activators increases activity by shifting the equilibrium toward the more-active R state, whereas allosteric inhibitors stabilize the less-active T state. A critical insight from this model is that the cooperativity characteristic of allosteric systems reflects their oligomeric construction. A key assumption of the MWC treatment is that the oligomer remains symmetric, so that it behaves as a two-state system (R or T). This has the important consequence that the structure and ligand-binding properties of each subunit depend only on the quaternary state of the system and not on how many ligand molecules are bound. Again, although this model is overly simplistic, it does capture the essence of many real systems.

In view of the parallels between gated channels and allosteric enzymes, the general types of conformational changes associated with gating are anticipated to resemble those observed for allosteric systems (33, 61, 76). Switching between the R and T states can involve changes in both quaternary and tertiary levels of structural organization. Quaternary structural changes result in alteration of subunit-subunit interactions, which can achieve global rearrangements that effectively propagate ligand-binding events over large distances from the ligand-binding sites. These changes typically involve switching between alternate close-packed and interdigitated configurations of the polypeptide chain at the subunit-subunit surfaces. Tertiary structural changes primarily involve rearrangements within subunits. Although these can be more localized than quaternary changes, alterations in domain-domain interfaces can also be comparable to rearrangements of subunit-subunit interfaces and consequently can involve large-scale rearrangements. Order-disorder transitions that result in the folding or unfolding of part of the polypeptide chain have also been associated with allostery (33, 61). Many of the general types of gating models proposed for ion channels [see (38)] have counterparts in structurally characterized transitions in allosteric systems; for example, alterations in subunit-subunit interactions between closed and open states correspond to quaternary structure changes, whereas gating models descriptively designated "swinging door," "slider," "tethered-ball," and "ball-and-chain" involve tertiary structure changes.

Gerstein et al. (32) have identified and documented two major types of conformational changes that can occur within domains "hinge" and "shear." Hinge motions involve larger-scale movement in residues not constrained by packing interactions due to a few large changes in the main chain torsion angles of spatially adjacent residues, which represent the hinge. In view of the close-packed nature of membrane-spanning domains, hinge motions in channels would seem more relevant for conformational changes involving the extramembrane regions. In contrast, shear motions involve more-localized changes between close-packed segments that do not involve repacking of interfaces or deformation of the main chain. An important feature of proteins exhibiting shear motions is that they may be considered to have a "layered architecture," and conformational changes proceed through the sliding of adjacent layers. Of significance for our channel discussion, helices are an important component of these layers. The helices most commonly found in sliding interfaces are usually crossed, as opposed to more nearly (anti)parallel. Gerstein et al. (32) speculate that the smaller interface between crossed helices, relative to more parallel arrangements, can better accommodate the structural changes associated with shear motions.

CHANNEL STRUCTURE AND FUNCTION

Characteristics of α-Helices in Membrane Proteins

As a reference point for our discussion of channel structure and function, some general characteristics of α-helices in membrane proteins are briefly reviewed. This discussion builds extensively on Bowie's insightful analysis of helix-helix interactions in membrane proteins (8). Given the still small number of channel structures, the present analysis is based on a larger set of helical membrane protein structures, both channel and nonchannel, that contains 15 proteins with a total of 139 membrane-spanning helices (Table 1). Although the energetic principles driving the structural organization of membrane proteins are not explicitly discussed, engaging expositions of this relevant and fundamentally important topic may be found in recent reviews by White & Wimley (105), Popot & Engelman (77), and Fleming (27). A discussion of the consequences of deviations from noncanonical α-helical geometries for membrane protein structure and function may be found in (80a, 102).

To begin, we define a coordinate system for membrane proteins using the convention that the membrane normal is oriented along the z-axis, with the origin corresponding to the center of the membrane-spanning region and the positive z-axis pointing toward the outside of the cell (Figure 2). Because the membrane-spanning region cannot be experimentally defined, with the exception of a few proteins such as bacteriorhodopsin that have been studied by electron crystallography in their native membranes, it is necessary to identify this region through computational methods. For proteins that are oligomeric (including most of the proteins in Table 1), the direction of the rotation axis relating identical or homologous subunits is taken to correspond to the membrane normal. For the remaining structures, the direction of the membrane normal is defined such that the overall tilt of the helix axes from the normal is minimized. In this coordinate frame, the membrane-spanning region is assigned following the approach of Deisenhofer &

TABLE 1 Proteins used in the analyses of membrane-spanning helices that are described in the text

PDB	TM	N	Protein	Ref.
1occ	28	2	bovine cytochrome *c* oxidase	(101)
1qle	22	1	*Paracoccus denitrificans* cytochrome *c* oxidase	(43)
1bgy	13	2	bovine cytochrome bc_1	(42)
2prc	11	1	*Rhodopseudomonas viridis* photosynthetic reaction center	(18)
1aij	11	1	*Rhodobacter sphaeroides* photosynthetic reaction center	(90)
1eul	10	1	rabbit calcium ATPase	(99)
1brx	7	3	*Halobacterium salinarium* bacteriorhodopsin	(59)
1e12	7	3	halorhodopsin	(47)
1f88	7	1	bovine rhodopsin	(69)
1fx8	6	4	*E. coli* glycerol facilitator GlpF	(30)
1fum	6	1	*E. coli* fumarate reductase	(41)
1qla	5	2	*Wolinella succinogenes* fumarate reductase	(51)
1kzu	2	9	*Rhodopseudomonas acidophila* light harvesting complex	(63)
1bl8	2	4	*Streptomyces lividans* K$^+$ channel KcsA	(22)
1msl	2	5	*Mycobacterium tuberculosis* mechanosensitive MscL	(11)

PDB denotes identifier for the coordinates in the Protein Data Bank (5, 97); TM is the number of unique membrane-spanning helices in each structure; and N denotes the copy number of identical subunits in the likely functional unit.

Michel (19), who characterized the relative apolarity of the protein surface by the fraction of the accessible surface area contributed by carbon atoms. The origin is then assigned as the midpoint of the region with the greatest average surface apolarity.

As seen in Figure 3, helical membrane proteins exhibit a 20 Å–wide region with >90% of the surface area contributed by carbon atoms. This same region is also characterized by the presence of few potentially charged side chains. Adjacent to this central region, the apolarity of the protein surface tapers down over a 10 Å–wide band to the ~55% contribution typical of water-accessible surfaces, while the number of charged side chains increases sharply in this same region. Hence, based on surface apolarity, membrane proteins exhibit a 40 Å–wide band composed of a 20 Å–wide central region with flanking 10 Å–wide stripes that presumably correspond to the hydrocarbon and headgroup regions of the membrane bilayer. The 20 Å width of the most apolar band of the membrane-spanning surface corresponds well with the region of minimum-charge density identified in experimentally determined electron-density distributions for membrane bilayers (105) and with the region of maximum probability for the distribution of carbon atoms in the hydrocarbon chains of phospholipids (67). These studies have also

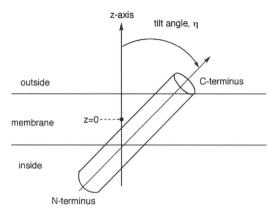

Figure 2 Definition of the coordinate system used in this article for the analysis of helix properties, including the orientation of the membrane normal along the z-axis, assignment of the membrane center to $z = 0$, and the convention used to define the helix tilt angle, η.

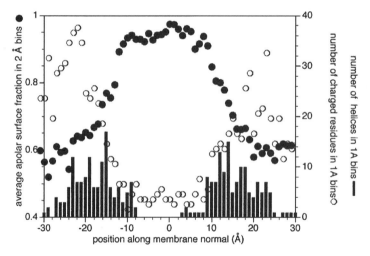

Figure 3 Variations with position in the apolarity of the protein surface and in the distribution of charged residues and helix termini, relative to the membrane, for the proteins listed in Table 1. The fractions of the accessible surface area contributed by carbon atoms are indicated by filled circles (●), as calculated in 2 Å slabs perpendicular to the membrane normal and averaged over all proteins. The numbers of side chains of potentially charged residues (Arg, Asp, Glu, His, and Lys) are represented by open circles (o), as calculated in 1 Å intervals along z, while the histogram indicates the number of membrane-spanning helices that terminate in 1 Å bins centered at the indicated z value. The residues in each helix were identified with the program STRIDE (29). The positions of charged side chains were assigned from locations of the Cζ, Cγ, Cδ, Cγ, and Nζ atoms for Arg, Asp, Glu, His, and Lys, respectively.

positioned the maximum of the probability distribution for the phosphate head-groups to be approximately 40 Å apart, which coincides with the transition of the average polarity of the protein surface to that typical of water-soluble surfaces.

The high average hydrophobicity of the protein surface is consistent with the apolar nature of the lipid-exposed residues in integral membrane proteins. This hydrophobicity analysis may also be extended to include interior residues, by using surface area calculations to identify residues in the membrane-spanning helices that are either lipid-exposed (surface) or lipid-inaccessible (interior). For this calculation, residues were used that had Cαs positioned between -10 Å $\leq z \leq 10$ Å in the membrane-spanning helices of the proteins in Table 1. Surface residues were identified as exposing at least 20% of the total surface area for a given type of amino acid. This classification resulted in 33% and 67% of the residues assigned to the surface and interior classes. The average residue hydrophobicities of these two classes were evaluated with the hydrophobicity scale defined by Eisenberg et al. (24), where the extreme values are set by arginine and isoleucine at -1.76 and $+0.73$. For the proteins in Table 1, the average hydrophobicities of the interior and surface residues are calculated to be $+0.23$ and $+0.41$. Hence, while the interior and surface residues of membrane proteins are, on average, both apolar, the lipid-exposed surface residues tend to be more apolar. Furthermore, the interior residues of membrane proteins have comparable hydrophobicities to the interior residues of water-soluble proteins. This analysis is completely consistent with observations reported on earlier membrane protein structures (79, 104). One implication of this behavior is that it should be possible to solubilize membrane proteins by replacement of lipid-exposed residues with polar amino acids (80); the design, preparation, and characterization of solubilized forms of phospholamban have recently been described (28, 57).

The positioning of bilayer-spanning helices within the membrane may be assessed from the locations of the helix termini with respect to the membrane coordinate system described in Figure 2. For the purposes of this analysis, the helix boundaries were assigned by the program STRIDE (29); occasional irregularities in helix geometries can lead to the assignment of two helices within one membrane-spanning stretch. The length of the 139 membrane-spanning helices in Table 1 averages 26 ± 6 residues. When the positions of the termini for the helices along the membrane normal are projected onto the apolarity distribution (Figure 3), the clear trend is that most helices span the 20 Å–wide apolar region and end in the headgroup regions (104). Few helices, however, span the complete 40 Å distance across the membrane from one headgroup-aqueous interface to the other. Of significance for later discussion, the amino-terminal ends of 76 helices $(0.547 = 76/139 \equiv P_N)$ are positioned on the cytoplasmic side.

The axes of membrane-spanning helices are not randomly oriented within the membrane, but rather tend to be aligned perpendicular to the bilayer plane. Bowie (8) observed that, on average, the helix axes are tilted $\sim 21°$ relative to the membrane normal. Similar trends are observed in the present survey, with the helix tilt averaging $23° \pm 10°$ when the direction of the polypeptide chain across the membrane is ignored. The tilt-angle distribution for the proteins in Table 1,

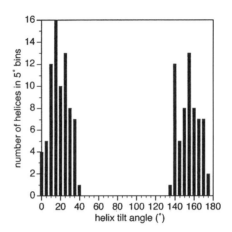

Figure 4   Histogram of the tilt angle of the helix axis with respect to the membrane normal for the proteins listed in Table 1, tabulated in 10° bins. Tilt angles between 0°–90° and 90°–180° correspond to helices with their N-terminal (76 helices) or C-terminal (63 helices) ends closest to the cellular interior. For this calculation, the tilt angle was calculated from the transformation required to superimpose an ideal helix oriented along the z-axis onto those residues located within the 20 Å–wide apolar area (Figure 3) of membrane-spanning helices. Similar, but not identical, results (not shown) were obtained for the entire helical stretches owing to the presence of kinks and other irregular regions.

including the directionality of the polypeptide chain across the bilayer, is illustrated in Figure 4. Longer helices do not appear to be more (or less) tilted than their shorter counterparts (data not shown).

Both the interhelical-crossing angle and the distance of closest approach characterize the packing together of two helices (13). In this survey, these parameters were evaluated with the program PROMOTIF (40) for the α-helical residues within the 20 Å–wide nonpolar surface region of the proteins listed in Table 1. As discussed by Bowie (8), helix-helix interactions with nearly parallel helix axes are much more favored in membrane proteins than in water-soluble proteins (Figure 5A). Parallel orientations result in more extensive helix-helix interfaces (7), which may contribute to the more efficient packing density that has been reported for membrane proteins (23, 31). A preference for small residues, particularly Gly, at helix interfaces (23, 44, 54, 82, 83) should also contribute to the packing efficiency of membrane proteins.

Although the preference for helix axes to be parallel reflects the strong tendency of helices to be oriented along the membrane normal, it is not the entire story because left-handed packing arrangements are more abundant than right-handed ones (8, 52). Specifically, the observed distributions indicate an excess of left-handed interactions, with interhelical-crossing angles at $+20°$ and $-160°$ and a deficit of

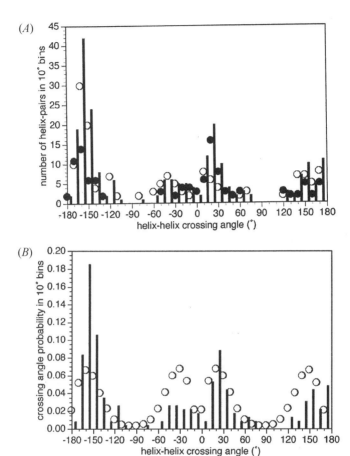

Figure 5 (A) Histogram of the 226 interhelical-crossing angles calculated with PROMOTIF (40) for the membrane-spanning helices in Table 1. The open (o) and closed (•) circles represent helical pairs separated by <10 Å (135 helices) and >10 Å (91 helices). The distributions were tabulated in 10° bins, centered at the indicated values. Helical segments within the 20 Å–wide apolar region of the membrane (Figure 3) were used for this calculation; 21 of these helix contacts occurred between different protomers within an oligomer. (B) Histogram of the observed interhelical-crossing angle probability distribution with the expected (o) distribution superimposed, evaluated in 10° bins. The observed distribution was obtained from the results of Figure 5A, divided by the total number of helical pairs in the data set (226 helices). The expected distribution was derived assuming the random pairing of helices obeying the tilt-angle distribution in Figure 4, allowing free rotation of the helices about the membrane normal.

right-handed interactions at $-30°$ and $+150°$ relative to the frequencies expected (Figure 5*B*) for random pairings of helices with the observed tilt-angle distribution (Figure 4). In addition to the preference for left-handed packing arrangements, there is also a clear preference for antiparallel arrangements (8), which occur in $94/135 = 0.696$ of the helix pairs separated by less than 10 Å. This is significantly more frequent than expected from random considerations because, for the orientations of helices in this database, the expected fraction for antiparallel arrangements is calculated to be $0.496 (= 2 \times P_N \times (1 - P_N))$—close to that actually observed for helix pairs separated by more than 10 Å $(0.528 = 48/91)$.

In all channels characterized to date, the permeation pathway for solutes through the membrane is lined by helices. For symmetric, oligomeric proteins that have the permeation pathway generated by one helix per subunit, the tilt of the helix with respect to the membrane normal, η, the interhelical-crossing angle, α, and the minimum pore radius, R_0, are not all independent. With perfectly regular helices modeled as cylinders of diameter d and exact N-fold rotational symmetry, the variation in minimum pore radius with helix tilt may be shown to be

$$R_0 = \frac{d}{2} \left(\tan \eta \cot \left(\frac{\alpha}{2} \right) - 1 \right), \tag{1}$$

where

$$\cos \alpha = \cos^2 \eta + \sin^2 \eta \cos \theta, \tag{2}$$

and $\theta = 2\pi/N$. The dependence of R_0 on η is illustrated in Figure 6 for different numbers of subunits in an oligomer. For perfectly regular helices and ideal oligomeric symmetry, an increase in pore radius requires an increase in helical tilt. At least for tetramers and pentamers, significant changes in pore radius only occur as the helix tilt exceeds $\sim$40°. Not surprisingly, for a given helix tilt, the pore radius increases with the number of helices lining the permeation pathway. It has been noted, for example, that pentameric channels tend to have larger pore diameters and poorer ion selectivity than channels formed from four subunits (38). This simple analysis further suggests that formation of a pore of any diameter is essentially impossible from three ideal helices.

Real Channels

LIGAND-GATED CHANNELS: THE NICOTINIC ACETYLCHOLINE RECEPTOR   The nicotinic acetylcholine receptor (nAChR) isolated from the muscle-derived electric organ of the *Torpedo* ray provided the first visual evidence of the three-dimensional structure of an ion channel (100). Organized as a heteropentamer $(\alpha_2 \beta \gamma \delta)$ of homologous subunits that are each predicted to contain four transmembrane segments (designated M1 to M4), this receptor is the classic representative of a superfamily of phylogenetically related proteins including the glycine, γ-aminobutyric acid, and serotonin receptors [reviewed in (14, 53)]. Three-dimensional views of this receptor reconstructed from electron microscopic images, including the

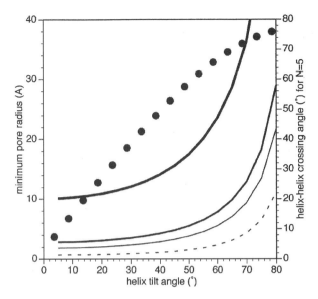

Figure 6   Dependence of the minimum pore radius R_0 on the helix tilt angle for ideal, oligomeric channels with one helix per subunit lining the permeation pathway. R_0 values (Å, left-hand axis) are calculated as a function of tilt angle using Equations 1 and 2 for $N = 3$ (*dotted line*), 4 (*thin line*), 5 (*medium line*), and 10 (*dark line*). Circles (●, right-hand axis) indicate the interhelical-crossing angles calculated as a function of tilt angle for $N = 5$ from Equation 2. A helix diameter $d = 9$ Å was used in these calculations.

recent analysis at 4.6 Å resolution (64), provided the first structural evidence of an hourglass-shaped pore coursing through the central axis of the receptor complex, with the narrowest region localized approximately midway through the membrane. The permeation pathway is lined by five α-helices that pack together in a right-handed bundle. Based upon a variety of data gathered from biochemical, electrophysiological, and mutagenesis experiments, the pore region is most probably lined by residues contributed by the M2 transmembrane segments from each subunit, with each M2 segment adopting an α-helical structure. The constricted region of the channel has been proposed to function as the physical gate, perhaps formed by a thin ring of apolar side chains that regulate ionic flux through the transbilayer pore. Although the exact identities of the residues involved in forming the physical channel gate are uncertain, a series of conserved leucine residues have been implicated [(50); reviewed in (14)]. Consistent with the hypothesis that this constriction or kink in the M2 helices regulates the ion-conduction pathway, Unwin observed conformational changes within this region upon flash-freezing the receptor after brief exposure to acetylcholine (103). Evidence from cysteine mutagenesis studies differs from this interpretation

(3), however, highlighting the need for further increases in the resolution of the current structural model.

The recent crystal structure determination of a soluble acetylcholine-binding protein (AChBP) from snails (9) represents an important advance in characterizing the binding of ligands in this system. AChBP forms a stable homopentamer of subunits homologous to the ligand-binding domain of nAChR; significantly, AChBP binds agonists and competitive antagonists of nAChR (36a). The AChBP subunit adopts an immunoglobin-like fold, with ligand-binding sites located at the subunit-subunit interfaces, sites that seemed to be blocked by the binding of a neurotoxin, α-bungarotoxin (36a). From the location of a buffer molecule believed to serve as an acetylcholine mimic, the molecular details of the binding site have been defined. In particular, the binding site is rich in aromatic residues, as anticipated (14), that interact with quaternary amine-containing agonists through cation-pi interactions (21). The gating mechanism(s) by which ligand binding is coupled to changes in the transmembrane domain remain obscure, and future developments on this system are eagerly awaited.

SELECTIVITY AND VOLTAGE-GATING: K^+ CHANNELS   The regulation and maintenance of an electrochemical potential across the plasma membrane are vital to all living cells and provide the energy required for driving many metabolic and cellular functions, most classically exemplified in the case of nerve and muscle firing. Voltage-sensitive K^+ channels (Kv) not only play a critical role in controlling the resting membrane potential but also affect the duration and amplitude of signaling events (action potentials) based upon their gating and inactivation properties, as well as other factors (e.g., unitary conductance and level of expression). Due to the extensive study of Kv channels at the biophysical, biochemical, molecular, and atomic levels over the past decade and a half, we have gained a clearer understanding of structure-activity relationships within these proteins in regard to ion selectivity, subunit assembly, interactions with blockers, activation and gating, inactivation, and many other important questions.

Organized as tetramers of identical or related subunits (60, 86), the conduction pathway for K^+ ions runs parallel to the fourfold central axis of the channel, as clearly evidenced in the crystal structure of the prokaryotic K^+ channel, KcsA, by MacKinnon and coworkers (22). Each subunit within a Kv channel, as epitomized by the *Shaker* channel from *Drosophila*, is thought to have six membrane-spanning helices (designated S1 to S6), with the highly conserved interconnecting loop between S5 and S6 playing a predominant role in ion selectivity. The molecular organization of this region of the potassium channel was established by the structural analysis of KcsA (22). Each subunit of KcsA contains two membrane-spanning helices, corresponding to S5 and S6 in Kv channels, with the intervening segment containing the pore helix and a loop-forming structure, which functions as the selectivity filter. The permeation pathway through the membrane is formed by the second transmembrane helix (corresponding to S6). These helices are tilted $\sim 35°$ from the membrane normal, and pack against their counterparts from

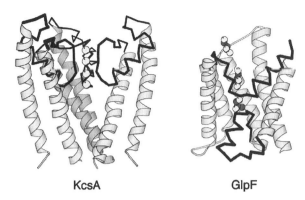

KcsA   GlpF

Figure 7   Structures of KcsA (*left*) (22) and GlpF (*right*) (30) emphasizing the location of nonmembrane-spanning elements responsible for channel selectivity. The transmembrane helices are represented as ribbons, whereas the nonmembrane-spanning regions are depicted as solid traces. The positions of three potassium and one water in the selectivity filter of KcsA (*left*) and three glycerol molecules in the permeation pathway of GlpF (*right*) are indicated by CPK models. For clarity, one subunit of the KcsA tetramer has been removed, while only one subunit of GlpF is displayed, with the first and last transmembrane helices omitted.

adjacent subunits to form a right-handed bundle with interhelical-crossing angles of −51°. The S5 and S6 helices provide the framework that positions the residues in the interconnecting loops responsible for ion selectivity. Significantly, the KcsA structure has provided physical evidence for the mechanism of ion selectivity, illustrating the coordination of dehydrated K^+ ions by backbone carbonyl atoms within the selectivity filter (22) (Figure 7). Based on the sequence similarity with the Kv channels, the structure of the KcsA channel most probably serves as a good model for the structure of the pore region in Kv channels.

Although we do not yet have a complete crystallographic model of a Kv channel, several pieces of structural information provide other clues as to some of the pertinent functional elements of the extramembrane components. A region N-terminal to the first transmembrane helix of the Kv channels, known as T1, although not absolutely required for channel function (45), appears to participate in the specificity of subunit assembly (58, 85) and is also involved in the docking with modulatory Kv β-subunits (35, 84). The tetrameric structure of the isolated T1 domain suggests that the respective T1 regions from each subunit might co-assemble together below the cytoplasmic face of the channel pore (49). However, it was initially unclear how this structure might be compatible with biophysical data on the accessibility of the N-terminal "inactivation ball" to the cytoplasmic side of the pore. In support of this model, the structure of the T1 domain together with a modulatory β-subunit, which is known to contain an inactivation ball, has recently been solved (35). By combining this and other structural information with biochemical and biophysical evidence, it is suggested that the inactivation particle may gain access to the pore through a gap or window between the T1 and transmembrane domains (35, 46, 88, 106). Following initial interaction with the cytoplasmic channel surface, it is proposed that the inactivation particle subsequently enters the pore as an extended peptide and binds in a cavity adjacent to the selectivity filter, thereby blocking the channel (108). Because the overall quaternary structure appears to remain intact, these gating transitions are based on changes in the tertiary structure of the channel.

Although it is uncertain as to whether the subunit associations in the T1 domain rearrange or dissociate during channel gating in vivo, locking this domain together does not greatly affect channel gating (46). Additionally, replacing acidic residues within the linker region between the transmembrane and T1 domains (S1-T1) with neutral or basic residues decreases the rate of inactivation apparently by altering electrostatic interactions with the inactivation gate (35). The inactivation gate and several small-molecule inhibitors physically interact with the cytoplasmic side of the transmembrane pore (20, 108); because the opening through the center of the assembled T1 domain is too small and too basic to accommodate these molecules, the experimental evidence seems to support the model of lateral openings leading from the cytoplasm to the channel pore. Intriguingly, structural information for the ligand-gated and mechanosensitive channels also appear to exhibit similar openings beneath their respective transmembrane pores (11, 64), suggesting that this structural feature has been conserved throughout ion channel evolution and may play a valuable functional role.

Based on abundant electrophysiological and spectroscopic data, the transduction of membrane potential changes to conformational movements in Kv channels is likely mediated by the fourth transmembrane helix (S4), the "voltage-sensor," which contains a regular series of basic residues repeated at every fourth position. Additionally, negatively charged residues within the second and third transmembrane helices (S2 and S3) have been demonstrated to form salt bridges with the basic amino acids in the S4 helix, suggesting that these interactions stabilize and coordinate the structural rearrangements between the closed and open states (26, 70, 98). In order to better understand the dynamics involved in the movement of the S4 helix during activation gating, a multitude of techniques have been employed [reviewed in (6, 39)] and together suggest that during activation there is a rotation of the S4 helix and also a change in its helical tilt angle relative to the membrane. However, the mechanics involved in transducing movements in the voltage sensor into physical removal of a barrier within the ion permeation pathway is still unknown. This process could involve separation of the S5 and S6 helices at the base of the pore, as suggested in the pH-dependent gating of KcsA (16). At the current level of understanding, these alterations may be the consequence of shear-type motions (32) that result in the repositioning of helices around the pore.

SELECTIVITY AND FACILITATED DIFFUSION: AQUAPORINS   The flux of water and other small solutes across the membrane must be carefully controlled to maintain the appropriate osmotic balance within the cell. Members of the aquaporin

(AQP) family are widely distributed through a diverse set of organisms and include highly specific water-conducting channels [reviewed in (25)], as well as glycerol-conducting channels such as the *Escherichia coli* glycerol facilitator, GlpF. Organized as tetramers of identical subunits, the quaternary structure of the AQP proteins seems reminiscent to that of the K^+ channel proteins. However, unlike the K^+ channels, each AQP subunit within the tetramer is capable of functioning as an independent channel pore. The conductance of some members of the AQP family are regulated by pH or phosphorylation.

The amino acid sequences of AQP family members show clear evidence for sequence duplication between the amino- and carboxyl-terminal halves of the channel, including a characteristic Asn-Pro-Ala (NPA) signature sequence found in each segment. Structures of the AQP family have recently been determined for the *E. coli* GlpF channel by X-ray crystallography at 2.2 Å resolution (30) and for the red blood cell AQP1 by electron microscopy at 3.8 Å resolution (66). These studies reveal that each subunit has six transmembrane helices threaded across the membrane, along with two half-helices (Figure 1). The membrane-spanning helices are tilted by an average of ∼33° and form a right-handed helical bundle that provides the supporting scaffold for the two half-helices that enter from each side of the bilayer. The sequence duplication is reflected in the presence of an internal quasi-twofold axis in the plane of the membrane that relates the two structurally equivalent parts of the channel. In particular, the two conserved NPA motifs interact through the prolines across the interface surrounding this axis.

An exciting aspect of the GlpF structure is the presence of three glycerol molecules that identify the permeation pathway and establish the selectivity mechanism of this channel for glycerol (30). The challenge faced by the GlpF channel is to allow the passage of glycerol while absolutely discriminating against all ions including OH^- and H^+ (67a). The channel conducts both larger and smaller solutes that are chemically similar to glycerol but with different conductances that reflect stereo- and enantioselectivity (30). As noted by the authors, this is not unlike the challenge faced by potassium channels that must selectively allow the passage of dehydrated potassium ions through its pore. The half-membrane-spanning helices in GlpF play a key role in its selectivity, particularly the Asn residues in the NPA motifs at the amino-terminal end of each helix, as well as the residues in the loop leading into these helices. Analogous to the KcsA channel, these residues can be considered to form the selectivity filter of the GlpF channel (Figure 7). Carbonyl groups from residues in this region form a hydrogen-bonding network on one side of the channel that can interact with the OH groups of glycerol and associated water molecules. The opposing side of the permeation pathway is lined with apolar groups that can participate in van der Waals contacts with the carbon atoms of glycerol. The amphipathic nature of the surface of the permeation pathway helps to select molecules, including the linear poly-alcohols termed alditols, that are similar to glycerol and share the characteristic of having a polar side and an apolar side. Furthermore, the apolar component of the permeation pathway likely serves to discriminate against ions and other charged molecules. Finally, the tight packing of this region prevents expansion of the pore necessary to permit the passage of larger molecules. As with the K^+ channel, the overall selectivity of aquaporin channels appears to reflect an energetic balance between competing repulsive and attractive forces.

MECHANOSENSITIVE CHANNELS: MscL   The typically higher concentration of osmolytes within a bacterial cell relative to the surrounding environment provides a driving force for water flux into the cytoplasm. The resultant increase in volume of the cytoplasm creates a turgor pressure that counteracts this flux due to the expansion of the cytoplasmic membrane against the cell wall. Moderate turgor pressure provides the mechanical force for the expansion of the cell wall and is critical for bacterial growth. However, upon a sudden decrease in the osmolarity of the surrounding medium, water rapidly moves into the cells, increasing the turgor pressure to the point of cell rupture. Based upon the work of Kung et al. and others, it appears that nearly all eubacteria express mechanosensitive channels within the cytoplasmic membrane (4, 55, 94) that are sensitive to membrane tension, and more recent work extends these observations to archaea (36).

The prokaryotic MscL, or mechanosensitive channel of large-conductance, provides a simplified paradigm for ion channels specialized in the transduction of mechanical stimuli (e.g., sound, touch, gravity, pressure) into an electrochemical response. First characterized by Kung et al. in *E. coli* following isolation of a stretch-activated channel, MscL exhibits a large conductance of $\sim$2.5 nS with no ionic selectivity and was subsequently cloned and shown to function as a homomultimer (93). The crystal structure of MscL from *Mycobacterium tuberculosis* (11) provided clear evidence of the pentameric structure of this channel and demonstrated that the protein is organized as two helical domains, one intramembrane and one cytoplasmic (Figure 1). The membrane domain is composed of ten transmembrane helices, two from each subunit, whereas the cytoplasmic domain is organized as a left-handed bundle containing one helix from each subunit. The transmembrane helices are tilted by $\sim$35°, with respect to the membrane normal with the amino-terminal–most helix of each subunit (the inner helix) lining the permeation pathway. These inner helices pack together in a right-handed fashion with a crossing angle of $\sim$−43° to form the pore. This arrangement of helices around the permeation pathway is similar to that observed for KcsA, despite the opposite threadings of the polypeptide chains through the membranes, and the differences in oligomeric states (78). A generally consistent view of the MscL channel organization has been provided by recent site-directed spin label studies (75). The narrowest region of the pore occurs near the cytoplasmic side of the membrane domain, where the side chain of Val[21] is positioned directly into the ion-conduction pathway, in effect, occluding permeation of solutes through the pore. A critical role for Val[21] in the gating of MscL has been demonstrated through mutagenesis studies (68). Other residues flanking this region, as well as more distantly located positions such as in the extracellular loop, have also been shown to have modulatory effects on the gating mechanism (2, 34, 62, 94, 107), which may reflect their roles in the transition to the open state (91).

Although significant structural rearrangements are necessary to account for the conductance properties of MscL in the open state, it is not obvious how the transmembrane and cytoplasmic domains structurally rearrange upon sensing membrane tension. With an estimated pore diameter of $\sim$30–40 Å (15), the conformational changes associated with the closed-to-open transition of MscL must be substantial. Assuming that all the subunits in the channel are equivalent in the open state, an increase in pore radius necessarily requires some combination of an increased number of helices lining the pore and/or an increased tilt of helices lining the pore (Figure 6). An early model for the open state of MscL is based on the former possibility and invokes an alteration of inner and outer helices to create a 10-helix barrel-stave–type channel with the α-helices nearly parallel to the membrane normal (15, 89). The conformational rearrangement associated with this transition could plausibly involve the coordinated movement of adjacent pairs of inner and outer helices that are nearly antiparallel because these types of helix-helix interfaces tend to be more stable (32). Attempts to generate explicit models of this type, however, have suggested that a substantial number of hydrophobic residues may be exposed to water in the open state, which would be energetically unfavorable (92). An alternative mechanism for increasing the number of helices, by increasing the number of subunits in the oligomer, appears unlikely in view of the observations of Sukharev et al. that the MscL oligomer is not in dynamic equilibrium with monomers (95).

Recently, a detailed proposal for the open state of MscL has been developed by Sukharev & Guy, based on modeling studies combined with disulfide trapping and electrophysiological characterizations (91, 92). In this model (Figure 8), the symmetry of MscL is assumed to follow MWC-type postulates and is conserved in both closed and open states. The structural rearrangements for forming a large $\sim$30 Å pore in the open state involve increasing the helical tilt from 35° (closed) to 70° (open); the inner helix lines the permeation pathway in both states. In the open-state model, the interhelical-crossing angle between adjacent inner helices increases from -43° to -68°. Both the tilt and the helix crossing angle are essentially unprecedented in structurally characterized membrane proteins (Figures 4 and 5A), although of course, they are proposed to exist in a form that is significantly less stable than the closed state under resting conditions. Rather than the side chains of Val[21] in the inner helices serving as the gate, Sukharev & Guy propose that the real gate is a five-helix bundle containing the highly conserved amino-terminal residues of each subunit. These residues are not observed in the crystal structure, however, presumably due to disorder or other types of conformational heterogeneity. Experimental support for the Sukharev & Guy model is provided by the ability to stabilize an open state of MscL through disulfide-bond formation between specifically incorporated cysteines that should be spatially adjacent only in the open state. Due to the role of protein dynamic effects (10) and the influence of the membrane location of the cysteines on the rate of disulfide formation (17), however, it would appear difficult to derive quantitative distance constraints from these experiments. Nevertheless, this general approach has many attractive

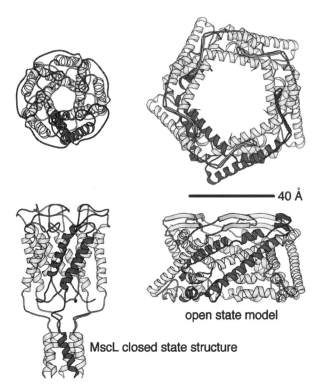

Figure 8   Comparisons of the structures of MscL as observed crystallographically in the closed state (*left*) (11) and as modeled in the open state by Sukharev & Guy (*right*) (91, 92). Views down the membrane normal (*top*) and in the plane of the membrane (*bottom*) are provided. One subunit is highlighted in each structure for clarity. The increased tilt of the membrane-spanning helices in the open-state model, along with the increased helical length necessary to span the bilayer in the open-state model, are evident. The dark horizontal line (*right*) indicates 40 Å.

features that could ultimately help lead to preparation and characterization of a stable open state for structural studies.

CONCLUSIONS

The α-helix unquestionably serves as the dominant element in the structural organization of the membrane-spanning region of channels and many other proteins. Generalizing from the presently available structures of the KcsA, MscL, AQP1, and GlpF channels, as well as the overall properties of helices in membrane proteins, it appears that

1. The most-nonpolar region of the membrane-exposed surface is 20 Å wide (Figure 3), compared to the overall thickness of the bilayer ($\sim$40 Å), which should have implications for the electrostatic barrier to movement of ions across the membrane [for examples, see (56, 71, 72)].

2. The permeation pathways of channels are formed from helices that are tilted $\sim$30°–40° with respect to the membrane normal, which is relatively steep for membrane-spanning helices (Figure 4). The pore-forming helices are packed in right-handed bundles with a relatively steep interhelical-crossing angle ($\sim$−40°) (Figure 5A) that creates a funnel-like architecture with a defined point of constriction.

3. The determinants of channel selectivity are provided by nonmembrane-spanning elements supported within the helical bundle (Figure 7).

4. The conformational changes associated with channel gating can involve pronounced quaternary structure rearrangements of the pore-forming helices, as well as changes in tertiary structure involving these helices and extramembrane components of channels. At the high tilt angles observed for the pore-forming helices, the minimum pore diameter is particularly sensitive to changes in helix tilt (Figure 6).

The role of the α-helix as the workhorse for ion channels reflects both the common elements of this motif, which are determined by the properties of the polypeptide backbone, as well as the infinite variations that can be incorporated through the particular choice of side chains dictated by the amino acid sequence. Hence, the same basic structural framework can be tailored for a myriad of specific functional purposes. From the available structures, common themes are emerging concerning the role of α-helices in the organization of the resting states of various channels. The greatest outstanding challenges in our structural understanding of channels are to realize how rearrangements of this basic framework can be triggered and the mechanisms by which these changes occur.

ACKNOWLEDGMENTS

Discussions with Randal Bass, Kaspar Locher, Pavel Strop, Allen Lee, Margaret Barclay, Dennis Dougherty, Henry Lester, and Chris Miller are greatly appreciated. This work was supported in part by NIH grant GM62532.

NOTE ADDED IN PROOF

Recent advances in the structural characterization of channels and transporters have been provided by the crystal structure determinations of a KcsA potassium channel-Fab complex [(108a); with an accompanying analysis of the energetics of ion conductance (5a, 65a)] and of the *E. coli* MsbA transporter, a member of the ATP-binding cassette family (10a). Movements of the inner helices between the closed and open states of KcsA have been characterized by site-directed spin labeling studies (58a). The X-ray crystal structure of AQP1 has been reported at 2.2 Å resolution (90a).

Visit the Annual Reviews home page at www.annualreviews.org

LITERATURE CITED

1. Aidley DJ, Stanfield PR. 1996. *Ion Channels*. Cambridge: Cambridge Univ. Press. 307 pp.
2. Ajouz B, Berrier C, Besnard M, Martinac B, Ghazi A. 2000. Contributions of different extramembranous domains of the mechanosensitive ion channel MscL to its response to membrane tension. *J. Biol. Chem.* 275:1015–22
3. Akabas MH, Kaufmann C, Archdeacon P, Karlin A. 1995. Identification of acetylcholine receptor channel-lining residues in the entire M2 segment of the alpha subunit. *Neuron* 13:919–27
4. Batiza AF, Rayment I, Kung C. 1999. Channel gate! Tension, leak and disclosure. *Structure* 7:R99–103
5. Berman HM, Westbrook J, Feng Z, Gilliland G, Bhat TN, et al. 2000. The Protein Data Bank. *Nucleic Acids Res.* 28:235–42
5a. Bernèce S, Roux B. 2001. Energetics of ion conduction through the K⁺ channel. *Nature* 414:73–77
6. Bezanilla F. 2000. The voltage sensor in voltage-dependent ion channels. *Physiol. Rev.* 80:555–92
7. Bowie JU. 1997. Helix angle packing preferences. *Nat. Struct. Biol.* 4:915–17
8. Bowie JU. 1997. Helix packing in membrane proteins. *J. Mol. Biol.* 272:780–89
9. Brejc K, van Dijk WJ, Klaassen RV, Schuurmans M, van der Oost J, et al. 2001. Crystal structure of an ACh-binding protein reveals the ligand-binding domain of nicotinic receptors. *Nature* 411:269–76
10. Butler SL, Falke JJ. 1996. Effects of protein stabilizing agents on thermal backbone motions: a disulfide trapping study. *Biochemistry* 35:10595–600
10a. Chang G, Roth CB. 2001. Structure of MsbA from *E. coli*: a homolog of the multidrug resistance ATP binding cassette (ABC) transporters. *Science* 293:1793–800
11. Chang G, Spencer RH, Lee AT, Barclay MT, Rees DC. 1998. Structure of the MscL homolog from *Mycobacterium tuberculosis*: a gated mechanosensitive ion channel. *Science* 282:2220–26
12. Changeux JP, Edelstein SJ. 1998. Allosteric receptors after 30 years. *Neuron* 21:959–80
13. Chothia C, Levitt M, Richardson D. 1981. Helix to helix packing in proteins. *J. Mol. Biol.* 145:215–50
14. Corringer P-J, Le Novere N, Changeux J-P. 2000. Nicotinic receptors at the amino acid level. *Annu. Rev. Pharmacol. Toxicol.* 40:431–58
15. Cruickshank CC, Minchin RF, LeDain AC, Martinac B. 1997. Estimation of the pore size of the large-conductance mechanosensitive ion channel of *Escherichia coli*. *Biophys. J.* 73:1925–31
16. Cuello LG, Romero RG, Cortes DM, Perozo E. 1998. pH-dependent gating in the *Streptomyces lividans* K⁺ channel. *Biochemistry* 37:3229–36
17. Czerski L, Sanders CR. 2000. Thiol modification of diacylglycerol kinase: dependence upon site membrane disposition and reagent hydrophobicity. *FEBS Lett.* 472:225–29
18. Deisenhofer J, Epp O, Miki K, Huber R,

Michel H. 1985. Structure of the protein subunits in the photosynthetic reaction center of *Rhodopseudomonas viridis* at 3 Å resolution. *Nature* 318:618–24

19. Deisenhofer J, Michel H. 1989. The photosynthetic reaction centre from the purple bacterium *Rhodopseudomonas viridis*. *EMBO J.* 8:2149–70

20. del Camino D, Holmgren M, Liu Y, Yellen G. 2000. Blocker protection in the pore of a voltage-gated K^+ channel and its structural implications. *Nature* 403:321–25

21. Dougherty DA. 1996. Cation-pi interactions in chemistry and biology: a new view of benzene, phe, tyr and trp. *Science* 271:163–68

22. Doyle DA, Cabral JM, Pfuetzner RA, Kuo A, Gulbis JM, et al. 1998. The structure of the potassium channel: molecular basis of K^+ conduction and selectivity. *Science* 280:69–77

23. Eilers M, Shekar SC, Shieh T, Smith SO, Fleming PJ. 2000. Internal packing of helical membrane proteins. *Proc. Natl. Acad. Sci. USA* 97:5796–801

24. Eisenberg D, Weiss RM, Terwilliger TC, Wilcox W. 1982. Hydrophobic moments and protein structure. *Faraday Symp. Chem. Soc.* 17:109–20

25. Engel A, Fujiyoshi Y, Agre P. 2000. The importance of aquaporin water channel protein structures. *EMBO J.* 19:800–6

26. Fedida D, Hesketh J. 2001. Gating of voltage-dependent potassium channels. *Prog. Biophys. Mol. Biol.* 75:165–99

27. Fleming KG. 2000. Riding the wave: structural and energetic principles of helical membrane proteins. *Curr. Opin. Biotechnol.* 11:67–71

28. Frank S, Kammerer RA, Hellstern S, Pegoraro S, Stetefeld J, et al. 2000. Toward a high-resolution structure of phospholamban: design of soluble transmembrane domain mutants. *Biochemistry* 39:6825–31

29. Frishman D, Argos P. 1995. Knowledge-based protein secondary structure assignment. *Proteins Struct. Funct. Genet.* 23:566–79

30. Fu D, Libson A, Miercke LJW, Weitzman C, Nollert P, et al. 2000. Structure of a glycerol-conducting channel and the basis for its selectivity. *Science* 290:481–86

31. Gerstein M, Chothia C. 1999. Proteins in motion. *Science* 285:1682–83

32. Gerstein M, Lesk AM, Chothia C. 1994. Structural mechanisms for domain movements in proteins. *Biochemistry* 33:6739–49

33. Goldsmith EJ. 1996. Allosteric enzymes as models for chemomechanical energy transducing assemblies. *FASEB J.* 10:702–8

34. Gu LQ, Liu WH, Martinac B. 1998. Gating pattern for the G14E site-directed mutant of the large mechanosensitive ion channel (MscL) of *Escherichia coli* characterized by a continuous spectrum of subconductance levels. *Biophys. J.* 74:A324

35. Gulbis JM, Zhou M, Mann S, MacKinnon R. 2000. Structure of the cytoplasmic β subunit—T1 assembly of voltage-dependent K^+ channels. *Science* 289:123–27

36. Hamill OP, Martinac B. 2001. Molecular basis of mechanotransduction in living cells. *Physiol. Rev.* 81:685–740

36a. Harel M, Kasher R, Nicolas A, Guss JM, Balass M, et al. 2001. The binding site of acetylcholine receptor as visualized in the X-ray structure of a complex between α-bungarotoxin and a mimotope peptide. *Neuron* 32:265–75

37. Henderson R, Unwin PNT. 1975. Three-dimensional model of purple membrane obtained by electron microscopy. *Nature* 257:28–32

38. Hille B. 2001. *Ionic Channels of Excitable Membranes*. Sunderland, MA: Sinauer. 853 pp.

39. Horn R. 2000. A new twist in the saga of charge movement in voltage-dependent ion channels. *Neuron* 25:511–14

40. Hutchinson EG, Thornton JM. 1996. PROMOTIF—a program to identify and analyze structural motifs in proteins. *Protein Sci.* 5:212–20

41. Iverson TM, Luna-Chavez C, Cecchini G, Rees DC. 1999. Structure of the *Escherichia coli* fumarate reductase respiratory complex. *Science* 284:1961–66

42. Iwata S, Lee JW, Okada K, Lee JK, Iwata M, et al. 1998. Complete structure of the 11-subunit bovine mitochrondrial cytochrome bc_1 complex. *Science* 281: 64–71

43. Iwata S, Ostermeier C, Ludwig B, Michel H. 1995. Structure at 2.8 Å resolution of cytochrome *c* oxidase from *Paracoccus denitrificans. Nature* 376: 660–43

44. Javadpour MM, Eilers M, Groesbeek M, Smith SO. 1999. Helix packing in polytopic membrane proteins: role of glycine in transmembrane helix association. *Biophys. J.* 77:1609–18

45. Kobertz WR, Miller C. 1999. K$^+$ channels lacking the 'tetramerization' domain: implications for pore structure. *Nat. Struct. Biol.* 6:1122–25

46. Kobertz WR, Williams C, Miller C. 2000. Hanging gondola structure of the T1 domain in a voltage-gated K$^+$ channel. *Biochemistry* 39:10347–52

47. Kolbe M, Besir H, Essen L-O, Oesterhelt D. 2000. Structure of the light-driven chloride pump halorhodopsin at 1.8 Å resolution. *Science* 288:1390–96

48. Kraulis PJ. 1991. Molscript—a program to produce both detailed and schematic plots of protein structures. *J. Appl. Crystallogr.* 24:946–50

49. Kreusch A, Pfaffinger PJ, Stevens CF, Choe S. 1998. Crystal structure of the tetramerization domain of the Shaker potassium channel. *Nature* 392:945–48

50. Labarca C, Nowak M, Zhang H, Tang L, Deshpande P, Lester H. 1995. Channel gating governed symmetrically by conserved leucine residues in the M2 domain of nicotinic receptors. *Nature* 376:514–16

51. Lancaster CRD, Kröger A, Auer M, Michel H. 1999. Structure of fumarate reductase from *Wolinella succinogenes* at 2.2 Å resolution. *Nature* 402:377–85

52. Langosch D, Heringa J. 1998. Interaction of transmembrane helices by a knobs-into-holes packing characteristic of soluble coiled coils. *Proteins Struct. Funct. Genet.* 31:150–59

53. Leite J, Cascio M. 2001. Structure of ligand-gated ion channels: critical assessment of biochemical data supports novel topology. *Mol. Cell. Neurosci.* 17: 777–92

54. Lemmon MA, Engelman DM. 1994. Specificity and promiscuity in membrane helix interactions. *Q. Rev. Biophys.* 27:157–18

55. Levina N, Tötemeyer S, Stokes NR, Louis P, Jones MA, Booth IA. 1999. Protection of *Escherichia coli* cells against extreme turgor by activation of MscS and MscL mechanosensitive channels: identification of genes required for MscS activity. *EMBO J.* 18:1730–37

56. Levitt DG. 1978. Electrostatic calculations for an ion channel. I. Energy and potential profiles and interactions between ions. *Biophys. J.* 22:209–19

57. Li H, Cocco MJ, Steitz TA, Engelman DM. 2001. Conversion of phospholamban into a soluble pentameric helical bundle. *Biochemistry* 40:6636–45

58. Li M, Jan YN, Jan LY. 1992. Specification of subunit assembly by the hydrophilic amino-terminal domain of the Shaker potassium channel. *Science* 257: 1225–30

58a. Liu Y-S, Sompornpisut P, Perozo E. 2001. Structure of the KcsA channel intracellular gate in the open state. *Nat. Struct. Biol.* 8:883–87

59. Luecke H, Richter HT, Lanyi JK. 1998. Proton transfer pathways in bacteriorhodopsin at 2.3 Å resolution. *Science* 280:1934–37

60. MacKinnon R. 1991. Determination of the subunit stoichiometry of a voltage-activated potassium channel. *Nature* 350:232–35

61. Mattevi A, Rizzi M, Bolognesi M. 1996. New structures of allosteric proteins reveal remarkable conformational changes. *Curr. Opin. Struct. Biol.* 6:824–29

62. Maurer JA, Elmore DE, Lester HA, Dougherty DA. 2000. Comparing and contrasting *Escherichia coli* and *Mycobacterium tuberculosis* mechanosensitive channels (MscL)—new gain of function mutations in the loop region. *J. Biol. Chem.* 275:22238–44

63. McDermott G, Prince SM, Freer AA, Hawthornthwaite-Lawless A, Papiz MZ, et al. 1995. Crystal structure of an integral membrane light-harvesting complex from photosynthetic bacteria. *Nature* 374:517–21

64. Miyazawa A, Fujiyoshi Y, Stowell M, Unwin N. 1999. Nicotinic acetylcholine receptor at 4.6 Å resolution: transverse tunnels in the channel wall. *J. Mol. Biol.* 288:765–86

65. Monod J, Wyman J, Changeux JP. 1965. On the nature of allosteric transitions: a plausible model. *J. Mol. Biol.* 6:306–29

65a. Morais-Cabral JH, Zhou Y, MacKinnon R. 2001. Energetic optimization of ion conduction rate by the K^+ selectivity filter. *Nature* 414:37–42

66. Murata K, Mitsuoka K, Hirai T, Walz T, Agre P, et al. 2000. Structural determinants of water permeation through aquaporin-1. *Nature* 407:599–605

67. Nagle JF, Tristram-Nagle S. 2000. Lipid bilayer structure. *Curr. Opin. Struct. Biol.* 10:474–80

67a. Nollert P, Harries WEC, Fu D, Miercke LJW, Stroud RM. 2001. Atomic structure of a glycerol channel and implications for substrate permeation in aqua(glycerol)porins. *FEBS Lett.* 504:112–17

68. Ou XR, Blount P, Hoffman RJ, Kung C.

1998. One face of a transmembrane helix is crucial in mechanosensitive channel gating. *Proc. Natl. Acad. Sci. USA* 95:11471–75

69. Palczewski K, Kumasake T, Hori T, Behnke CA, Motoshima H, et al. 2000. Crystal structure of rhodopsin: a G protein–coupled receptor. *Science* 289:739–45

70. Papazian DM, Shao XM, Seoh S-A, Mock AF, Huang Y, Wainstock DH. 1995. Electrostatic interactions of S4 voltage sensor in *Shaker* K^+ channel. *Neuron* 14:1293–301

71. Parsegian A. 1969. Energy of an ion crossing a low dielectric membrane: solutions to four relevant electrostatic problems. *Nature* 221:844–46

72. Partenskii MB, Jordan PC. 1992. Theoretical perspectives on ion-channel electrostatics—continuum and microscopic approaches. *Q. Rev. Biophys.* 25:477–510

73. Pauling L, Corey RB. 1951. Configurations of polypeptide chains with favored orientations around single bonds: two new pleated sheets. *Proc. Natl. Acad. Sci. USA* 37:729–40

74. Pauling L, Corey RB, Branson HR. 1951. The structure of proteins: two hydrogen-bonded helical configurations of the polypeptide chain. *Proc. Natl. Acad. Sci. USA* 37:205–11

75. Perozo E, Kloda A, Cortes DM, Martinac B. 2001. Site-directed spin-labeling analysis of reconstituted MscL in the closed state. *J. Gen. Physiol.* 118:193–206

76. Perutz M. 1990. *Mechanisms of Cooperativity and Allosteric Regulation in Proteins.* Cambridge: Cambridge Univ. Press

77. Popot J-L, Engelman DM. 2000. Helical membrane protein folding, stability, and evolution. *Annu. Rev. Biochem.* 69:881–922

78. Rees DC, Chang G, Spencer RH. 2000. Crystallographic analyses of ion channels: lessons and challenges. *J. Biol. Chem.* 275:713–16

79. Rees DC, DeAntonio L, Eisenberg D. 1989. Hydrophobic organization of membrane proteins. *Science* 245:510–13

80. Rees DC, Komiya H, Yeates TO, Allen JP, Feher G. 1989. The bacterial photosynthetic reaction center as a model for membrane proteins. *Annu. Rev. Biochem.* 58:510–13

80a. Riek RP, Rigoutsos I, Novotny J, Graham RM. 2001. Non-α-helical elements modulate polytopic membrane protein architecture. *J. Mol. Biol.* 306:349–62

81. Roux B, Berneche S, Im W. 2000. Ion channels, permeation and electrostatics: insights into the function of KcsA. *Biochemistry* 39:13295–306

82. Russ WP, Engelman DM. 2000. The GxxxG motif: a framework for transmembrane helix-helix association. *J. Mol. Biol.* 296:911–19

83. Senes A, Gerstein M, Engelman DM. 2000. Statistical analysis of amino acid patterns in transmembrane helices: the GxxxG motif occurs frequently and in association with β-branched residues at neighboring positions. *J. Mol. Biol.* 296:921–36

84. Sewing S, Roeper J, Pongs O. 1996. Kv beta 1 subunit binding specific for *Shaker*-related potassium channel alpha subunits. *Neuron* 16:455–63

85. Shen NV, Pfaffinger PJ. 1995. Molecular recognition and assembly sequences involved in K$^+$ channel subunit proteins. *Neuron* 14:625–33

86. Sheng M, Laiao YJ, Jan YN, Jan LY. 1993. Presynaptic A-current based on heteromultimeric K$^+$ channels detected *in vivo*. *Nature* 365:72–75

87. Singer SJ. 1962. The properties of proteins in non-aqueous solvents. *Adv. Protein Chem.* 17:1–68

88. Sokolova O, Kolmakova-Partensky L, Grigorieff N. 2001. Three-dimensional structure of a voltage-gated potassim channel at 2.5 nm resolution. *Structure* 9:215–20

89. Spencer R, Chang G, Rees DC. 1999. Feeling the pressure: structural insights into a gated mechanosensitive channel. *Curr. Opin. Struct. Biol.* 9:448–54

90. Stowell M, McPhillips TM, Rees DC, Soltis SM, Abresch E, Feher G. 1997. Light-induced structural changes in photosynthetic reaction center: implications for mechanism of electron-proton transfer. *Science* 276:812–16

90a. Sui H, Han B-G, Lee JK, Walian P, Jap BK. 2001. Structural basis of water-specific transport through the AQP1 water channel. *Nature* 414:872–78

91. Sukharev S, Betanzos M, Chiang C-S, Guy HR. 2001. The gating mechanism of the large mechanosensitive channel MscL. *Nature* 409:720–24

92. Sukharev S, Durell SR, Guy HR. 2001. Structural models of the MscL gating mechanism. *Biophys. J.* 81:917–36

93. Sukharev SI, Blount P, Martinac B, Blattner FR, Kung C. 1994. A large-conductance mechanosensitive channel in *E. coli* encoded by *mscl* alone. *Nature* 368:265–68

94. Sukharev SI, Blount P, Martinac B, Kung C. 1997. Mechanosensitive channels of *Escherichia coli*: the MscL gene, protein, and activities. *Annu. Rev. Physiol.* 59:633–57

95. Sukharev SI, Schroeder MJ, McCaslin DR. 1999. Stoichiometry of the large conductance bacterial mechanosensitive channel of *E. coli*. A biochemical study. *J. Membr. Biol.* 171:183–93

96. Sukharev SI, Sigurdson WJ, Kung C, Sachs F. 1999. Energetic and spatial parameters for gating of the bacterial large conductance mechanosensitive channel, MscL. *J. Gen. Physiol.* 113:525–39

97. Sussman J, Lin D, Jiang J, Manning N, Prilusky J, et al. 1998. Protein Data Bank (PDB): database of three-dimensional structural information of biological macromolecules. *Acta Crystallogr. D* 54:1078–84

98. Tiwari-Woodruff SK, Schulteis CT,

Mock AF, Papazian DM. 1997. Electrostatic interactions between transmembrane segments mediate folding of *Shaker* K^+ channel subunits. *Biophys. J.* 72:1489–500

99. Toyoshima C, Nakasako M, Nomura H, Ogawa H. 2000. Crystal structure of the calcium pump of sarcoplasmic reticulum at 2.6 Å resolution. *Nature* 405:647–55

100. Toyoshima C, Unwin N. 1988. Ion channel of acetylcholine receptor reconstructed from images of postsynaptic membranes. *Nature* 336:247–50

101. Tsukihara T, Aoyama H, Yamashita E, Tomizaki T, Yamaguchi H, et al. 1996. The whole structure of the 13-subunit oxidized cytochrome *c* oxidase at 2.8 Å. *Science* 272:1136–44

102. Ubarretxena-Belandia I, Engelman DM. 2001. Helical membrane proteins: diversity of functions in the context of simple architecture. *Curr. Opin. Struct. Biol.* 11:370–76

103. Unwin N. 1995. Acetylcholine receptor channel imaged in the open state. *Nature* 373:37–43

104. Wallin E, Tsukihara T, Yoshikawa S,

von Heijne G, Elofsson A. 1997. Architecture of helix bundle membrane proteins: an analysis of cytochrome *c* oxidase from bovine mitochondria. *Protein Sci.* 6:808–15

105. White SH, Wimley WC. 1999. Membrane protein folding and stability: physical principles. *Annu. Rev. Biophys. Biomol. Struct.* 28:319–65

106. Yi BA, Jan LY. 2000. Taking apart the gating of voltage-gated K^+ channels. *Neuron* 27:423–25

107. Yoshimura K, Batiza A, Schroeder M, Blount P, Kung C. 1999. Hydrophilicity of a single residue within MscL correlates with increased channel mechanosensitivity. *Biophys. J.* 77:1960–72

108. Zhou M, Morais-Cabral JH, Mann S, MacKinnon R. 2001. Potassium channel receptor site for the inactivation gate and quaternary amine inhibitors. *Nature* 411:657–61

108a. Zhou Y, Morais-Cabral JH, Kaufman A, MacKinnon R. 2001. Chemistry of ion coordination and hydration revealed by a K^+ channel-Fab complex at 2.0 Å resolution. *Nature* 414:43–48

Annu. Rev. Biophys. Biomol. Struct. 2002. 31:235–56
DOI: 10.1146/annurev.biophys.31.082901.134215

THE LINKAGE BETWEEN PROTEIN FOLDING AND FUNCTIONAL COOPERATIVITY: Two Sides of the Same Coin?

Irene Luque, Stephanie A. Leavitt, and Ernesto Freire

*Department of Biology, The Johns Hopkins University, Baltimore, Maryland 21218;
e-mail: ef@jhu.edu*

Key Words   protein stability, cooperativity, allosterism, ligand binding, thermodynamics, calorimetry

■ **Abstract**   During the course of their biological function, proteins undergo different types of structural rearrangements ranging from local to large-scale conformational changes. These changes are usually triggered by their interactions with small-molecular-weight ligands or other macromolecules. Because binding interactions occur at specific sites and involve only a small number of residues, a chain of cooperative interactions is necessary for the propagation of binding signals to distal locations within the protein structure. This process requires an uneven structural distribution of protein stability and cooperativity as revealed by NMR-detected hydrogen/deuterium exchange experiments under native conditions. The distribution of stabilizing interactions does not only provide the architectural foundation to the three-dimensional structure of a protein, but it also provides the required framework for functional cooperativity. In this review, the statistical thermodynamic linkage between protein stability, functional cooperativity, and ligand binding is discussed.

CONTENTS

INTRODUCTION

The study of the forces and mechanisms that stabilize protein structures has attracted the attention of scientists since the early years of the twentieth century [see comments by Edsall (10) and paper by Hsien Wu reprinted in same issue (81)]. The initial studies of protein stability were limited to descriptions of the integrity and activity of proteins when subjected to several perturbations such as heat, pH, and chemicals. The thermodynamic description of protein stability was solidly established in the mid-1950s by the seminal work of Schellman (68). By the mid-1960s, the folding of proteins was acknowledged to be a highly cooperative process, with folding/unfolding behavior that could be described in terms of the so-called Two-State Hypothesis (49). According to this view, which has been the predominant view until today, the thermodynamic stability of a protein can be considered in terms of an equilibrium process that involves only two states, the denatured and the native states. Within this framework, the inherent cooperativity of protein structures dictates that partially folded structures have negligible probabilities and never become significantly populated. In their pioneering work Lumry and coworkers (48, 49) elaborated a series of experimental tests aimed at evaluating the validity of the two-state hypothesis in specific cases. These tests are still in use today and include the comparison of denaturation profiles obtained with different physical observables and the comparison of the enthalpy changes measured directly by calorimetry or indirectly by a van't Hoff analysis. In either test, if the results obtained with different observables or the van't Hoff and calorimetric enthalpies are identical, it is concluded that the transition obeys the two-state model. With the development of modern calorimetry, the thermodynamic parameters that determine the stability of many proteins have been measured (see 66 for a recent compilation). With few exceptions, the temperature denaturation of most single-domain globular proteins conforms to the two-state model as originally proposed in the early 1970s by Privalov and coworkers (63).

The two-state view has dominated our thinking about protein stability for the past thirty years. Accordingly, if it were possible to measure the stability of a protein using every one of its amino acid residues as a probe, one should obtain the same value or order for each. The development of NMR-detected hydrogen/deuterium exchange under native conditions (e.g., 3, 5, 8, 9, 28, 35, 36, 39, 52, 64, 70, 75, 80) has provided such an opportunity because this technique allows estimation of the individual stability of a large number of residues in a protein. The results of these studies, repeated for many proteins, indicate that under native conditions not all the residues in a protein exhibit the same stability and that significant variations could be found between different regions in a single-domain protein. According to these experiments, under native conditions proteins do not obey the two-state model, and consequently they cannot be considered as single cooperative units.

The protein view generated from hydrogen/deuterium exchange under native conditions and pioneered by Englander and coworkers (3, 5, 12, 35, 36, 52, 53) appeared to be at odds with the classical two-state view; however, the two sets of results are consistent with each other and together provide a more comprehensive picture of the conformational equilibrium in proteins. A picture in which the cooperative regime observed under native conditions is different from the one observed under denaturing conditions, but connected through known functional responses of the Gibbs energy to different physical or chemical perturbations.

PROTEIN STABILITY

Measuring Stability by Denaturation

The traditional methods for measuring protein stability do so by introducing a chemical or physical perturbation that induces protein denaturation. By far the most widely used agents are the chemical denaturants, urea and guanidinium hydrochloride (GdmHCl), and temperature. These agents induce denaturation because they affect differently the Gibbs energy of the various states that are accessible to a protein. As an example, we consider the simple situation of an equilibrium between three states (the native state N, the denatured state D, and an arbitrary intermediate state I) and its response to the addition of a chemical denaturant. Following standard practice, we assume that the Gibbs energy at any denaturant concentration ($\Delta G(D)$) is a linear function of the concentration of denaturant (23):

$$\Delta G(D) = \Delta G(0) - m \times [\text{Denaturant}], \tag{1}$$

where $\Delta G(0)$ is the Gibbs energy in the absence of denaturant, and m is the denaturant dependence of the Gibbs energy.

Figure 1, panel A illustrates the case in which the denaturant equally affects the Gibbs energy of the three states. In this case denaturation does not occur because the relative Gibbs energies between states remain the same. The addition of the denaturant only causes a shift in the absolute magnitude of the Gibbs energy. In Figure 1, panel B, the dependence of the Gibbs energy is assumed to be higher for the intermediate and even higher for the denatured state. In this case the addition of the denaturant first induces a transition to the intermediate state and then a second

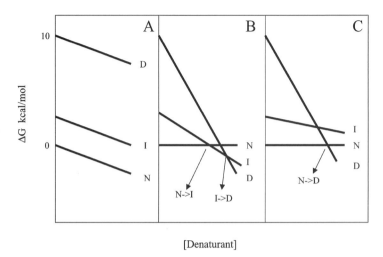

[Denaturant]

Figure 1 Schematic depiction of the denaturant dependence of the Gibbs energy for three different states of a protein. This figure illustrates the effects of different denaturant dependencies for each state on the denaturation process. The outcomes are discussed in the text.

transition to the denatured state at higher denaturant concentrations. In Figure 1, panel C, the denaturant dependence of the Gibbs energy for the intermediate has been assumed to be not as pronounced as in panel B. In this case the addition of denaturant induces a single transition from the native to the denatured state, and the intermediate never becomes significantly populated.

The Nature of the Equilibrium

The example in Figure 1 indicates that the addition of a denaturant agent not only induces denaturation but also affects the nature of the equilibrium between states. In Figure 1, the equilibrium under native conditions (i.e., in the absence of denaturant) is the same in all three cases, and it predominantly involves the equilibrium between the native state and the intermediate, which is close in Gibbs energy to the native state ($\sim$2.5 kcal/mol). Depending on the denaturant dependence of the Gibbs energy of the various states, different situations can be observed in the transition region. Some of them are depicted in Figure 1. However, it is straightforward to generate other possible denaturation scenarios. The situation depicted in Figure 1, panel C, is particularly interesting because it generates a two-state transition between the native and denatured states, and it yields the correct thermodynamic parameters between those states but fails to produce a correct picture of the equilibrium existing under native conditions. These examples illustrate that a characterization of the conformational equilibrium derived from denaturation experiments cannot be extrapolated to the situation existing under native conditions.

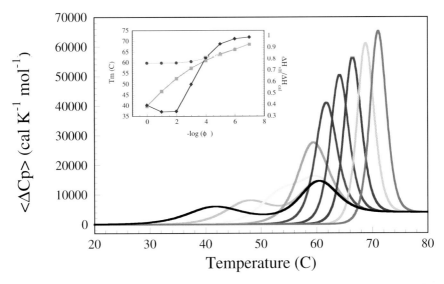

Figure 6 Simulated heat capacity profiles for Model 1 in the absence of ligands. The intrinsic domain stability parameters used in the simulation are ΔH_1 = 100 kcal·mol⁻¹, Tm_1 = 60 °C, ΔCp_1 = 2000 cal·K⁻¹·mol⁻¹ for the first domain and ΔH_2 = 60 kcal·mol⁻¹, Tm_2 = 40 °C, ΔCp_2 = 2000 cal·K⁻¹·mol⁻¹ for the second domain. In these and all simulations in this paper, the Tms are defined as the temperatures at which half of the population of a given domain is unfolded. Shown are the expected thermograms for interaction constants, ϕ, of 1 (*black*), 1 x 10⁻¹ (*green*), 1 x 10⁻² (*yellow*), 1 x 10⁻³ (*orange*), 1 x 10⁻⁴ (*red*), 1 x 10⁻⁵ (*magenta*), 1 x 10⁻⁶ (*purple*), 1 x 10⁻⁷ (*light blue*), and 1 x 10⁻⁸ (*dark blue*). The corresponding values for the $\Delta H_{vH}/\Delta H_{cal}$ ratio (*blue*) and Tms for each domain (most stable domain in *red* and least stable domain in *orange*) as a function of the strength of the interaction are shown in the insert.

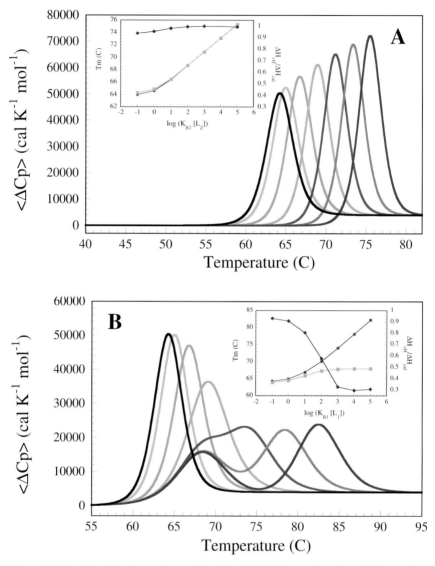

Figure 7 Simulated heat capacity profiles for Model 1 as a function of the product
(K_B·[L]), where K_B is the binding constant and [L] the concentration of free ligand. The
different curves correspond to K_B·[L] values of 0 (*black*), 1 x 10^{-1} (*yellow*), 1 (*green*), 1 x
10^1 (*brown*), 1 x 10^2 (*orange*), 1 x 10^3 (*red*), 1 x 10^4 (*magenta*), and 1 x 10^5 (*purple*). The
intrinsic stability parameters for each domain are the same as in Figure 6. The interaction
constant between both domains, ϕ, is 1 x 10^{-5} for all the simulations. The effect of binding
to the least and most stable domains is shown in *panels A* and *B*, respectively. The corresponding values for $\Delta H_{vH}/\Delta H_{cal}$ ratio (*blue*) and Tm for each domain (most stable domain
in *red* and least stable domain in *orange*) are shown in the insert.

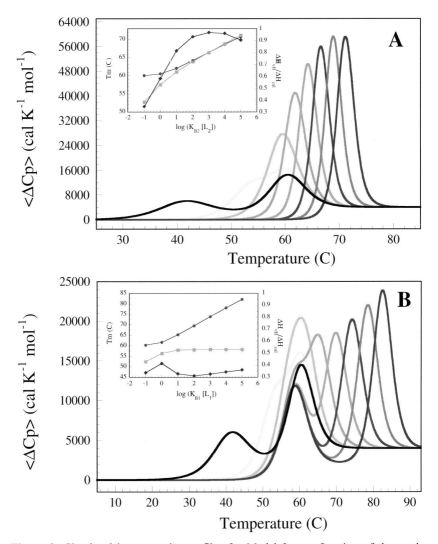

Figure 9 Simulated heat capacity profiles for Model 2 as a function of the product $(K_B \cdot [L])$, where K_B is the binding constant and [L] the concentration of free ligand. The different curves correspond to $K_B \cdot [L]$ values of 0 (*black*), 1 x 10^{-1} (*yellow*), 1 (*green*), 1 x 10^1 (*brown*), 1 x 10^2 (*orange*), 1 x 10^3 (*red*), 1 x 10^4 (*magenta*), and 1 x 10^5 (*purple*). The intrinsic stability parameters for each domain are the same as in Figure 6. The interaction constant, ϕ, between the two domains has been set to 1 for all the simulations (noninteracting domains in the absence of ligand). The coupling parameter between domain cooperativity and binding has been set to 1 x 10^3. The effect of binding to the least and most stable domains is shown in *panels A and B*, respectively. The corresponding values for $\Delta H_{vH}/\Delta H_{cal}$ ratio (*blue*) and Tm for each domain (most stable domain in *red* and least stable domain in *orange*) as a function of the product $(K_B \cdot [L])$ are shown in the inserts.

PROTEIN STABILITY BY HYDROGEN/DEUTERIUM EXCHANGE

The Stability Under Native Conditions

The technique of NMR-detected hydrogen/deuterium exchange in the study of protein stability and folding has been pioneered by Englander and Baldwin (for a recent review see 12). Under equilibrium conditions, hydrogen exchange permits an estimation of the so-called protection factors, which for many residues coincide with their individual stability constants (26). This technique measures the rate of hydrogen/deuterium exchange for individual amides in a protein. By comparing the measured exchange rate (k_{ex}) with the one expected for the same amide when fully exposed to the solvent (k_{in}), it is possible to calculate the protection factor (PF $= k_{ex}/k_{in}$). Amide groups buried from the solvent within the protein structure only become exposed when the regions of the protein that protect them undergo unfolding. This is usually referred to as the "opening reaction." In the kinetic limit known as EX2 (31), the free energy of the opening reaction can be obtained ($\Delta G = -RT \ln PF = -RT \ln(k_{ex}/k_{in})$) for each amide that shows protection in the native state.

If the only opening reaction or unfolding event is the cooperative two-state global unfolding of the protein, then the magnitude of the protection factors must be equal to the equilibrium constant for unfolding. Furthermore, if global unfolding were the only unfolding event, all protected amides would exhibit the same protection and therefore the same stability constants and corresponding ΔG values, which should be equal in magnitude to the macroscopic or global stability constant measured in denaturation experiments. This is not the behavior observed under native conditions.

Different ΔG for Different Regions

More than forty proteins have been studied using NMR-detected hydrogen exchange under native conditions (Figure 2). In all cases, the results indicate that variations in ΔG of several kcal/mol can be observed between different residues. Figure 2 summarizes the range of ΔG values observed for different residues in these proteins. In the figure, the top of the bars denotes the ΔG values for the most protected residues, and the bottom denotes the ΔG values for the less protected. The top values correspond to the ΔG for global unfolding, i.e., solvent exposure of those residues require the complete unfolding of the protein. The lower values, on the other hand, correspond to residues that become exposed to solvent by local unfolding reactions. On average the difference between high and low values is 5.0 kcal/mol with a standard deviation of 2.0 kcal/mol. This is a significant spread, especially considering that the average global ΔG in the set of proteins studied is 8.2 kcal/mol. More importantly perhaps is the fact that ΔG for the least stable regions averages only 3.0 kcal/mol with a standard deviation of 1.9 kcal/mol. The existence of unfolding reactions, which are distinct from global unfolding and characterized by lower than global ΔG values, indicate that under native conditions the

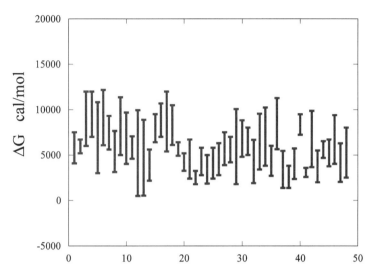

Figure 2 The upper and lower limits of residue stability obtained from hydrogen exchange measurements for the following proteins: [1] ACBP Apo (44); [2] staphylococcal nuclease (47); [3] equine cytochrome c (ox) (53); [4] equine cytochrome c (red) (53); [5] BPTI (38); [6] BPTI (76); [7] ribonuclease S (59); [8] equine lysozyme (55); [9] HEWL (64); [10] HEWL (62); [11] human α-lactalbumin (70); [12] thioredoxin (ox) (34); [13] thioredoxin (red) (34); [14] tendamistat (69); [15] ribonuclease A (59); [16] ribonuclease H (8); [17] ribonuclease T1 (56); [18] ribonuclease T1 (30); [19] CheY (45); [20] CheY (F14N, P110G) (45); [21] chymotrypsin inhibitor (58); [22] spectrin SH3 domain (67); [23] Src SH3 domain (22); [24] C102T Iso-1-cytochrome c (ox) (6); [25] C102T Iso-1-cytochrome c (red) (6); [26] apocytochrome b562 (21); [27] apoflavodoxin II (*Azotobacter vinelandii*) (73); [28] Acyl CoA binding protein (43); [29] T4 lysozyme (2); [30] LysN (1); [31] bovine β-lactoglobulin (65); [32] equine β-lactoglobulin (41); [33] stefin A (monomer) (37); [34] stefin A (dimer) (37); [35] ovomucoid third domain (75); [36] soybean leghemoglobin (54); [37] cardiotoxin III (71); [38] cobrotoxin (71); [39] λ-repressor [6-85 (25)]; [40] transthyretin (46); [41] cold shock protein A (33); [42] myoglobin/CO (7); [43] CD2 (60); [44] anaerobic sensor kinase phosphotransfer domain (32); [45] bovine apo α-lactalbumin (78); [46] bovine holo α-lactalbumin (78); [47] canine milk lysozyme (40); [48] holoflavodoxin II (72).

predominant equilibrium is not between the native and unfolded conformations, but between the native state and the collection of states created by those unfolding reactions.

Convergence of ΔG under Denaturing Conditions

The experimental observation is that the measured ΔG values obtained from hydrogen exchange experiments converge to a single value, which approaches or

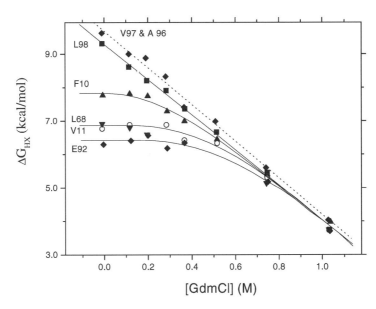

Figure 3 Hydrogen exchange results for different amides in oxidized equine cyto-chrome c as a function of denaturant concentration (4). Shown are the dependencies of the exchange free energy with denaturant for some of the fastest (F10, L68, V11, and E92) and slowest (L98, V97, and A96) amides. The exchange of the faster amides is controlled by local fluctuations at low GdmCl concentrations and is overtaken by global unfolding as the denaturant concentration increases. L98 is a clear example of a residue that only exchanges by global unfolding.

corresponds to the global ΔG value measured at increasing denaturant concentrations (12, 60), and is similar in magnitude to the macroscopic or global stability ΔG measured in denaturation experiments. Figure 3 illustrates the situation for the case of cytochrome c as published by by Bai et al. and Milne et al. (4, 53). The asymptotic behavior of the measured ΔG for each residue reflects the underlying equilibrium between states. Consider, for example, a certain residue that under native conditions becomes exposed to solvent by an unfolding reaction characterized by a ΔG of 2.5 kcal/mol. That same residue can also become exposed to solvent by the global unfolding of the protein (e.g., 10 kcal/mol). If that is the case, under native conditions the probability of exchange via global unfolding is 3×10^5 times smaller than via subglobal reaction (i.e., negligible), and the measured ΔG would be equal to 2.5 kcal/mol and reflect the energetics of the subglobal transition.

There is no relationship between the magnitude of ΔG and the size of the region that becomes unfolded via subglobal unfolding. Structure-based thermodynamic calculations indicate that most partially folded conformations have ΔG values much larger than that of the unfolded state (14, 15, 19, 24). There is a

relationship, however, between the m value obtained from chemical denaturation (urea or GdmHCl) and the surface area that becomes exposed upon unfolding
(57). Accordingly, the initial m values obtained in hydrogen exchange experiments should reflect the extent of the dominant unfolding equilibrium under native conditions. The experimental values are usually small, indicating that the
regions that undergo unfolding are also small and expose little surface area to the
solvent.

Figure 4 illustrates the situation. Panel A shows the expected values for the
observed Gibbs energy per residue associated with a small local unfolding characterized by a ΔG of 2.5 kcal/mol and an m value of 100, in addition to the global
unfolding characterized by a ΔG of 10 kcal/mol and an m value of 3000. It is
clear that a simple process in which a residue can be exposed to solvent by two
opening reactions already captures the general features observed in hydrogen exchange experiments (see Figure 3). The observed ΔG per residue is given in terms
of the probabilities of the states in which the residue is exposed to the solvent
(26).

$$\Delta G_{res} = -RT \ln \left(\frac{\sum P_{res,exposed}}{1 - \sum P_{res,exposed}} \right), \qquad (2)$$

where the summation runs over all the states in which the residue under consideration is exposed to the solvent. The probability of each state is proportional to its
Gibbs energy:

$$P_i = \frac{e^{\frac{-\Delta G_i}{RT}}}{\sum_j e^{\frac{-\Delta G_j}{RT}}}. \qquad (3)$$

More complex situations than the one described in Figure 4, panel A, can
easily be considered by incorporating additional reactions. For example, a given
residue can undergo an additional reaction for being part of a higher-order cooperative structure (e.g., an alpha helix). Figure 4, panel B, depicts that situation
for an additional state characterized by a ΔG of 5.5 kcal/mol and an m value of
1500. The existence of hierarchical layers of cooperative structures (20) immediately creates a large number of possibilities for different residues. For example,
it is possible for another residue to belong to the same higher-order cooperative structure but show a different local behavior. Such a situation is one in
which one residue lies near the center of a helix and another near one of the
ends.

The experimental hydrogen exchange data is consistent with the presence of a
large number of local unfolding reactions scattered throughout the entire protein
molecule. Based on their extremely low m values, these reactions appear to involve few residues and occur independently of each other. The existence of these
reactions indicates that under native conditions proteins do not exist as all-or-none
globally cooperative structures.

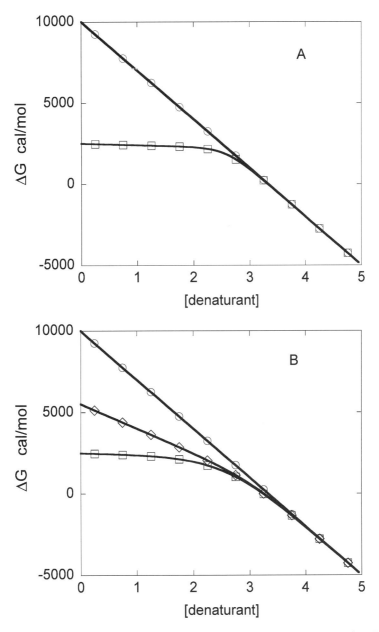

Figure 4 Simulated ΔG per residue as a function of denaturant concentration. *Panel A* illustrates the situation in which a residue unfolds via two separate processes, a small local unfolding characterized by a ΔG of 2.5 kcal/mol and an *m* value of 100, in addition to the global unfolding characterized by a ΔG of 10 kcal/mol and an *m* value of 3000. In *Panel B* an additional state characterized by a ΔG of 5.5 kcal/mol and an *m* value of 1500 has been included. See text for details.

THE STRUCTURAL DISTRIBUTION OF
PROTEIN STABILITY

Low- and High-Stability Regions

In the view that emerges from hydrogen exchange experiments performed under native conditions, proteins must be considered as statistical ensembles created by the occurrence of local unfolding reactions scattered throughout their entire structures. These unfolding reactions may involve only a few amino acids and give rise to a large number of states in which each state is defined by the presence of one or several locally unfolded regions. This collection of states defines the native-state ensemble. The immediate, and perhaps most relevant, consequence of these observations is that the Gibbs energy of stabilization of a protein is not uniformly distributed throughout its three-dimensional structure. There are regions with high-stability constants and regions with low-stability constants (26, 28). A fundamental question arising from those observations relates to the biological implications of the uneven distribution of the structural stability. Is the location of stable and unstable regions a random event, or is it dictated by functional considerations? How are protein function and stability related? An answer to that question requires a way of calculating the stability of individual residues within the protein structure.

Ergodic Algorithms

For any given protein, the structural stability of an individual residue in its native-state conformation is proportional to the fractional amount of time that the residue spends in that conformation compared to other alternative conformations. A highly stable residue will spend most of the time in the native-state conformation, whereas a relatively unstable residue will make excursions into different regions of conformational space. Because under native conditions proteins do not behave in a two-state fashion, these excursions may or may not involve other regions of the protein. In a molecular mechanics sense, the stability of a residue would be defined as the ratio of the fraction of time in which that residue is in the native state relative to the fraction of time in which it is not. Accordingly, the stability of a residue is a statistical quantity reflecting the probability of native versus nonnative conformations. For an "ergodic" system the probabilities obtained for a single molecule by time-averaging are the same as the probabilities obtained by averaging the ensemble of states in a single instant of time. Ergodic algorithms take advantage of the equivalence of time and ensemble averaging.

Hilser and colleagues (26–29) implemented an ensemble-based algorithm (COREX) aimed at estimating from structure the individual stability constants for all the residues in a protein. The algorithm used the crystallographic or NMR structure of a protein as a template to generate states characterized by having some regions unfolded and the remaining regions in the state specified by the native structure. Even though the states in the COREX ensemble are generated by using rather severe restrictive assumptions, it was, nevertheless, able to account quite well for the hydrogen exchange data obtained for several proteins (26–29, 67). The general agreement of the COREX ensemble with the data suggests that, at least under native conditions, proteins do not sample states with other than the native fold and that all states with a measurable probability are native-like and characterized by variable degrees of unfolding, which are the main COREX assumptions. In its original implementation, the COREX algorithm exhaustively generated all possible states created by a sliding window ranging in size from N_{min} to the entire length of the protein. For a reasonable window size ($N_{min} \leq 8$), this approach limited the applicability of COREX to small proteins. Newer implementations of the COREX algorithm use a random sampling technique that allows consideration of proteins of arbitrary size (17, 50).

The Structural Stability of Binding Sites

The COREX algorithm was used in the analysis of 16 nonstructurally homologous proteins for which high-resolution structures of their complexes with specific ligands are available (50). The results of these studies indicated that for the proteins considered in the analysis, the binding sites had a dual stability character and were characterized by the presence of regions with low structural stability and regions with high stability. In most cases the low-stability regions were loops that became stable and covered a significant portion of the ligand upon binding. For enzymes, catalytic residues were usually, but not always, located in regions with high structural stability. This arrangement provides significant advantages for the optimization of binding affinity and also provides a necessary framework for the propagation of binding effects to distal sites such as in allosteric proteins. The analysis clearly indicated that binding sites are not located at random in relation to the structural distribution of the stability of a protein. In particular, the presence of regions of low stability appears to provide a mechanism for eliciting high binding affinity for low-molecular-weight ligands and as an initiation point for the transmission of binding signals to distal sites. The presence of low-stability regions in the binding sites also facilitates the occurrence of long-range cooperative effects. A necessary condition for a ligand to induce a conformational change is that the binding site is not binding competent in the unliganded protein. If the binding site were intrinsically stable, all the states in the native ensemble would be binding competent, and ligand binding will only induce an energy shift without an internal reordering in the ensemble. In that case, the propagation of binding effects would be limited to the immediate neighborhood of the binding site. A ligand-induced redistribution in the probabilities of conformational states requires that only a subset of the native ensemble is binding competent. This condition is satisfied when part of the residues that define the binding site exhibit low structural stability or exist in a nonbinding-competent conformation in the unliganded protein. In many cases the presence of low-stability regions provide such a mechanism.

THE LINKAGE BETWEEN PROTEIN
STABILITY AND BINDING

Linkage Equations

The fundamental linkage equations between stability and binding were developed by Wyman (82) 50 years ago. In general, the Gibbs energy of any given protein state, i, is modified by ligand binding as follows:

$$\Delta G_i = \Delta G_i^0 - RT \ln \frac{(1 + K_{B,i}[L])}{(1 + K_{B,0}[L])}, \tag{4}$$

where ΔG_i^0 is the Gibbs energy in the absence of ligand, $K_{B,0}$ is the binding constant to the native state, and $K_{B,i}$ is the binding constant to state i and [L] the free ligand concentration. Equation 4 dictates that protein states are structurally stabilized proportionally to their binding affinity toward a ligand. Equation 4 has usually been applied to the equilibrium between the native and the unfolded state in denaturation experiments or the equilibrium between two different allosteric states (74); however, Equation 4 has general validity and also applies to the ensemble of conformations that define the native state. As discussed above, under native conditions proteins are characterized by the existence of a large number of local unfolding reactions. Many of these reactions involve regions that define binding sites. Accordingly, within the ensemble of states existing under native conditions, some states will have the binding site intact and therefore will be binding competent, whereas other states will have parts of the binding site unfolded and therefore will be unable to bind the ligand. Because all states in the native ensemble are not binding competent, the presence of a ligand will not only induce a shift in the Gibbs energy, but, more importantly, it will induce a redistribution of the population of states. In the presence of a ligand, the probability of each state is given by the equation

$$P_i = \frac{e^{-\frac{\Delta G_i^0}{RT}} \cdot \frac{(1 + K_{B,i}[L])}{(1 + K_{B,0}[L])}}{\sum_j e^{-\frac{\Delta G_j^0}{RT}} \cdot \frac{(1 + K_{B,j}[L])}{(1 + K_{B,0}[L])}}, \tag{5}$$

in which the statistical weight of each state is modified by the ligand linkage term defined in Equation 4.

Propagation of Binding Interactions to Distal Regions

Ligands usually interact with only a small group of residues in a protein; however, their effects often propagate to residues that are not in direct contact with the ligand. The propagation of these binding effects may be limited to regions immediately adjacent to the binding site or may extend to distal regions (11, 13, 51, 77, 79). One of the most remarkable observations is that, even in cases where binding effects propagate to regions far away from the binding site, only a subset of amino acids is affected (79). The propagation of binding effects through only a subset of residues is consistent with the idea of cooperative pathways within the protein structure (16) and that different sites in a protein (e. g., regulatory and catalytic sites in allosteric proteins) communicate with each other through a relatively small number of residues (17, 50). In this regard, Pawlyk & Pettigrew (A. C. Pawlyk & D. W. Pettigrew, personal communication) have recently engineered allosteric regulation into a nonallosteric kinase by transplanting 11 of 502 amino acids of the allosterically regulated *Escherichia coli* glycerol kinase into the nonallosteric enzyme from *Haemophilus influenzae*.

Ligand-mediated coupling between two protein sites requires that the regulatory binding site is not binding competent in the unligated protein. If the binding competent conformation were intrinsically stable, the association of a ligand would further stabilize that conformation without inducing a redistribution in the native-state ensemble. If the binding site were structurally stable in all states, ligand binding would only shift the energy of all states by an equal amount. A ligand-induced redistribution in the probabilities of conformational states requires that only a subset of the native ensemble is binding competent (15). Two circumstances can account for this situation: Either the binding site exists in a stable but different conformation in the absence of ligand or it exhibits low structural stability. Under those circumstances, ligand binding will induce a redistribution in the native ensemble in which states that are only negligibly populated in the absence of ligand become the most significantly populated. Because different states may be characterized by different functional properties, a redistribution in the native ensemble is often reflected in changes in biological activity.

MODELING DOMAIN-DOMAIN INTERACTIONS AND ALLOSTERIC REGULATION

In the following section we present a quantitative discussion of the issue of propagation of binding signals through protein structures. For simplicity, we consider a protein consisting of two different domains whose interactions can be mediated by ligand binding. This situation appears to be common in signal transduction proteins characterized by the presence of different regulatory modules (e.g., SH2 and SH3 domains). The statistical thermodynamic linkage between domain stability, interdomain cooperativity, and ligand binding is presented for two different situations.

Model 1

The thermodynamic behavior of two domains within a protein can be represented in terms of their intrinsic structural stability and a cooperative parameter, ϕ, that

#	State	ΔG	Stat. Weight
0	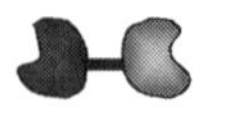	0	1
1	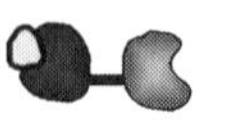	ΔG_{B1}	$K_{B1} \cdot [L_1]$
2		ΔG_{B2}	$K_{B2} \cdot [L_2]$
3		$\Delta G_{B1} + \Delta G_{B2}$	$(K_{B1} \cdot [L_1]) \cdot (K_{B2} \cdot [L_2])$
4		$\Delta G_2 + \Delta g_{int}$	$\phi \cdot K_2$
5		$\Delta G_2 + \Delta g_{int} + \Delta G_{B1}$	$\phi \cdot K_2 \cdot (K_{B1} \cdot [L_1])$
6		$\Delta G_1 + \Delta g_{int}$	$\phi \cdot K_1$
7	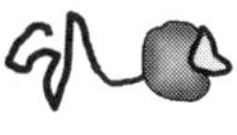	$\Delta G_1 + \Delta g_{int} + \Delta G_{B2}$	$\phi \cdot K_1 \cdot (K_{B2} \cdot [L_2])$
8		$\Delta G_1 + \Delta G_2 + \Delta g_{int}$	$\phi \cdot K_1 \cdot K_2$

Figure 5 Enumeration of the states accessible to Model 1. Each state (*column 1*) is specified in terms of the folding and ligation state of each domain as depicted in *column 2*. The relative Gibbs energies are shown in *column 3*. The statisitical weights (*column 4*) are obtained by calculating the Boltzmann exponent of the Gibbs energies in *column 3*.

accounts for the interactions between the two domains. In addition, either one or both domains may have binding sites for specific ligands. Figure 5 enumerates the different states accessible to this system and tabulates the free energies and statistical weights for the situation in which each of the domains binds a specific ligand, L_1 or L_2. In this model the binding of a ligand to either site does not affect the binding affinity of the second ligand to the other site. There is no ligand-induced conformational change that affects interdomain interactions. Interdomain cooperativity is only given by the ligand-independent interaction parameter ϕ. A total of nine states are available to this model, differing from each other by their ligation state and/or their folding state. The partition function is the sum of the nine statistical weights in Figure 5. In the absence of ligands it reduces to:

$$Q = 1 + \phi \times K_1 + \phi \times K_2 + \phi \times K_1 \times K_2. \tag{6}$$

If the interaction energy between domains is zero and the cooperative parameter $\phi = 1$, then the partition function further reduces to that of two independent domains ($Q = (1 + K_1) \times (1 + K_2)$). The partition function is used to derive experimentally observed quantities using standard statistical thermodynamic relationships (18). Because differential scanning calorimetry (DSC) is the most appropriate technique to identify and quantitate cooperative interactions, we have performed a series of computer simulations aimed at illustrating the effects of different interaction parameters on the expected observed behavior. Figure 6 (see color insert) shows a series of simulated DSC scans as a function of the interaction parameter ϕ. In the absence of any interdomain interactions, the simulated protein is characterized by a low-stability and a high-stability domain with thermal denaturations centered at 40°C and 60°C respectively. The remaining parameters are listed in the figure legend. As the interaction between domains increases and the magnitude of ϕ decreases, the two peaks coalesce into one and the ratio of the van't Hoff to calorimetric enthalpies ($\Delta H_{vH}/\Delta H_{cal}$) approaches unity. In this example, for ϕ values smaller than 10^{-5} the transition satisfies all existing criteria for a two-state transition, i.e., $\Delta H_{vH}/\Delta H_{cal} > 0.95$, as observed for small globular proteins (63).

The effects of specific ligands depend strongly on the magnitude of ϕ and the identity of the targeted domain, i.e., whether the ligand binds to the low-stability or to the high-stability domain. The behavior is illustrated in Figure 7 (see color insert) for a situation in which the folding/unfolding transition in the absence of ligand can be already classified as a two-state transition if it were measured experimentally ($\phi = 10^{-5}$). The effects of the presence of a ligand that binds to the least stable domain are shown in panel A. Only a shift of the transition peak to higher temperatures is observed, indicating that both domains are stabilized by a similar amount. In this case the ligand-induced stabilization effect is effectively transmitted to the other domain. The situation is entirely different for a ligand that binds to the more stable domain (Figure 7, panel B). In this case the presence of increasing concentrations of ligand preferentially shifts that domain, the transition becomes less cooperative as evidenced by a decreasing $\Delta H_{vH}/\Delta H_{cal}$ ratio, and eventually two well-separated peaks become clearly visible in the calorimetric scans. The behavior of the two domains becomes uncoupled from each other as evidenced by the observation that upon increasing ligand concentration, a point is reached at which only the targeted domain is stabilized.

Model 2

In this case the binding of a specific ligand to one of the domains stabilizes a conformation that interacts differently with the other domain. For this example, it can be said that ligand binding induces a conformational change in the first domain and that the "induced" conformation interacts better with the second domain. This model provides a mechanistic approach for the induced fit theory advanced by Koshland in 1963 (see 42 for a recent review). Accordingly, if the second domain is already folded, the effective Gibbs energy of binding will be equal to the sum of the intrinsic binding energy plus the additional energy of interaction with the second domain. This additional interaction does not exist if the second domain is unfolded or does not exist (i.e., it has been removed from the rest of the protein). Figure 8 tabulates the free energies and statistical weights for each of the six states in this model. The partition function is the sum of the statistical weights for the six states. The general behavior of this model will be illustrated for the case in which the two domains are independent of each other in the absence of a ligand and that the binding of a ligand enhances the interactions by 4 kcal/mol (i.e., by a factor of 10^3). Figure 9, panel A, (see color insert) illustrates the situation in which the domain with the binding site is the least stable domain. In this case the low-stability domain is preferentially stabilized at low ligand concentrations; however, at higher concentrations the two peaks coalesce into one and eventually the overall transition becomes a two-state transition and is characterized by $\Delta H_{vH}/\Delta H_{cal} \sim 1$. Only at

#	State	ΔG	Statistical Weight
0	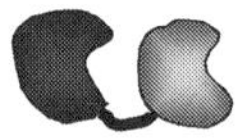	0	1
1	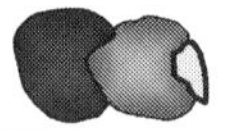	$\Delta G_B + \Delta g_{B,int}$	$k_{B,int} \cdot K_B \cdot [L]$
2	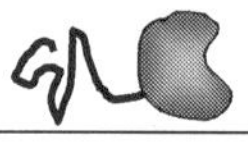	$\Delta G_1 + \Delta g_{int}$	$\phi \cdot K_1$
3	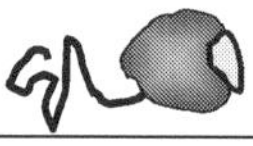	$\Delta G_1 + \Delta G_B + \Delta g_{int}$	$\phi \cdot K_1 \cdot K_B \cdot [L]$
4		$\Delta G_2 + \Delta g_{int}$	$\phi \cdot K_2$
5		$\Delta G_1 + \Delta G_2 + \Delta g_{int}$	$\phi \cdot K_1 \cdot K_2$

Figure 8 Enumeration of the states accessible to Model 2. Each state (*column 1*) is specified in terms of the folding and ligation state of each domain as depicted in *column 2*. The relative Gibbs energies are shown in *column 3*. The statistical weights (*column 4*) are obtained by calculating the Boltzmann exponent of the Gibbs energies in *column 3*.

extreme high concentrations ($K_B[L] > 10^5$) does the transition lose cooperativity and $\Delta H_{vH}/\Delta H_{cal}$ decreases below 0.9. The situation is different if the domain with the binding site is the most stable domain (as illustrated in panel *B*). In this case the transition never approaches two-state behavior. At low ligand concentrations, some stabilization of the least stable domain is observed; however, this effect disappears (at $K_B[L] > 10$ for the parameters in the example) and further addition of ligand only stabilizes the high-stability domain. As in Model 1, the propagation of binding effects from one domain to another is more efficient when binding occurs to the least stable domain.

The simulations presented above validate the conclusion that the propagation of binding effects is more efficient when the binding site is located in a region of low-stability. From a statistical standpoint, binding to a low-stability region induces a more extensive redistribution in the conformational ensemble than binding to a more stable one.

Allosteric Regulation

The propagation of binding interactions to distal sites in the protein provides the basis for fundamental biological phenomena such as allosteric regulation and signal transduction. The examples of ligand-mediated cooperative interactions described above provide some possible scenarios for interdomain communication in proteins. Even though the examples have been presented in terms of domains, the situation is the same if it is framed in terms of subdomains, structural elements, structural motifs, or secondary structure. It is clear that functional cooperativity and protein stability are linked to each other and that this link is mediated by the distribution of stability within different structural elements of a protein and the interactions existing between them. Hydrogen/deuterium exchange experiments performed under native conditions have indeed revealed that the stability of a protein is not uniformly distributed within its structure. If this is the case, the propagation of binding signals should obey precise thermodynamic rules, and the location of allosteric sites should be dictated by thermodynamic stability criteria within the protein. If stability and allosterism are linked to each other, then the structural distribution of protein stability should not be expected to be random because evolutionary pressures would have preferentially selected a distribution that optimizes comunication between regulatory and active sites. Accordingly, the end product of the protein folding process is not only a stable native structure but a structure in which the relative balance and location of stabilizing forces are also dictated by functional requirements.

ACKNOWLEDGMENTS

Supported by grants from the National Institutes of Health GM51362 and GM-57144, and National Science Foundation MCB-9816661. I. Luque is a recipient of a postdoctoral fellowship from the Fundación Ramón Areces, Madrid, Spain.

Parts of this review were presented at the ASBMB Symposium in honor of Daniel E. Koshland, Jr. on March 31, 2001.

Visit the Annual Reviews home page at www.annualreviews.org

LITERATURE CITED

1. Alexandrescu AT, Jaravine VA, Dames SA, Lamour FP. 1999. NMR hydrogen exchange of the OB-fold protein LysN as a function of denaturant: the most conserved elements of structure are the most stable to unfolding. *J. Mol. Biol.* 289:1041–54

2. Anderson DE, Lu J, McIntosh L, Dahlquist FW. 1993. The folding, stability and dynamics of T4 lysozyme: a perspective using nuclear magnetic resonance. In *NMR of Proteins*, ed. GM Clore, AM Gronenborn, pp. 258–304. Boca Raton: CRC

3. Bai Y, Milne JS, Mayne L, Englander SW. 1993. Primary structure effects on peptide group hydrogen exchange. *Proteins* 17:75–86

4. Bai Y, Milne JS, Mayne L, Englander SW. 1994. Protein stability parameters measured by hydrogen exchange. *Proteins* 20:4–14

5. Bai Y, Sosnick TR, Mayne L, Englander SW. 1995. Protein folding intermediates: native-state hydrogen exchange. *Science* 269:192–97

6. Baxter SM, Fetrow JS. 1999. Hydrogen exchange behavior of [U-15N]-labeled oxidized and reduced iso-1-cytochrome *c*. *Biochemistry* 38:4493–503

7. Cavagnero S, Theriault Y, Narula SS, Dyson J, Wright PE. 2000. Amide proton hydrogen exchange rates for sperm whale myoglobin obtained from 15N-1H NMR spectra. *Protein Sci.* 9:186–93

8. Chamberlain AK, Handel TM, Marqusee S. 1996. Detection of rare partially folded molecules in equilibrium with the native conformation of RnaseH. *Nat. Struct. Biol.* 3:782–87

9. Dabora JM, Marqusee S. 1994. Equilib-

rium unfolding of *Escherichia coli* ribonuclease H: characterization of a partially folded state. *Protein Sci.* 3:1401–8

10. Edsall JT. 1995. Hsien Wu and the first theory of protein denaturation (1931). *Adv. Protein Chem.* 46:1–5

11. Engen JR, Gmeiner WH, Smithgall TE, Smith DL. 1999. Hydrogen exchange shows peptide binding stabilizes motions in Hck SH2. *Biochemistry* 38:8926–35

12. Englander SW. 2000. Protein folding intermediates and pathways studied by hydrogen exchange. *Annu. Rev. Biophys. Biomol. Struct.* 29:213–38

13. Finucane MD, Jardetzky O. 1995. Mechanism of hydrogen-deuterium exchange in *trp* repressor studied by ^{1}H-^{15}N NMR. *J. Mol. Biol.* 253:576–89

14. Freire E. 1995. Thermodynamics of partly folded intermediates in proteins. *Annu. Rev. Biophys. Biomol. Struct.* 24:141–65

15. Freire E. 1997. The statistical thermodynamic linkage between conformational and binding equilibrium. *Adv. Protein Chem.* 51:255–79

16. Freire E. 1999. The propagation of binding interactions to remote sites in proteins. Analysis of the binding of the monoclonal antibody D1.3 to lysozyme. *Proc. Natl. Acad. Sci. USA* 96:10118–22

17. Freire E. 2000. Can allosteric regulation be predicted from structure? *Proc. Natl. Acad. Sci. USA* 97:11680–82

18. Freire E, Biltonen RL. 1978. Statistical mechanical deconvolution of thermal transitions in macromolecules. I. Theory and application to homogeneous systems. *Biopolymers* 17:463–79

19. Freire E, Haynie DT, Xie D. 1993. Molecular basis of cooperativity in protein folding.

IV. CORE: a general cooperative folding model. *Proteins* 17:111–23

20. Freire E, Murphy KP. 1991. The molecular basis of cooperativity in protein folding. *J. Mol. Biol.* 222:687–98

21. Fuentes EJ, Wand AJ. 1998. Local dynamics and stability of apocytochrome b562 examined by hydrogen exchange. *Biochemistry* 37:3687–98

22. Grantcharova VP, Baker D. 1997. Folding dynamics of the src SH3 domain. *Biochemistry* 36:15685–92

23. Greene RF Jr, Pace CN. 1974. Urea and guanidine hydrochloride denaturation of ribonuclease, lysozyme, alpha-chymotrypsin, and beta-lactoglobulin. *J. Biol. Chem.* 249:5388–93

24. Haynie DT, Freire E. 1993. Structural energetics of the molten globule state. *Proteins* 16:115–40

25. Hilser VJ, Dowdy D, Oas TG, Freire E. 1998. The structural distribution of cooperative interactions in proteins: analysis of the native state ensemble. *Proc. Natl. Acad. Sci. USA* 95:9903–8

26. Hilser VJ, Freire E. 1996. Structure based calculation of the equilibrium folding pathway of proteins. Correlation with hydrogen exchange protection factors. *J. Mol. Biol.* 262:756–72

27. Hilser VJ, Freire E. 1997. Predicting the equilibrium protein folding pathway: structure-based analysis of staphylococcal nuclease. *Proteins* 27:171–83

28. Hilser VJ, Oas T, Dowdy D, Freire E. 1998. The structural distribution of cooperative interactions in proteins: analysis of the native state ensemble. *Proc. Natl. Acad. Sci. USA* 95:9903–8

29. Hilser VJ, Townsend BD, Freire E. 1997. Structure-based statistical thermodynamic analysis of T4 lysozyme mutants: structural mapping of cooperative interactions. *Biophys. Chem.* 64:69–79

30. Huyghues-Despointes BM, Langhorst U, Steyaert J, Pace CN, Scholtz JM. 1999. Hydrogen-exchange stabilities of RNase T1 and variants with buried and solvent-exposed Ala Gly mutations in the helix. *Biochemistry* 38:16481–90

31. Hvidt A, Nielsen SO. 1966. Hydrogen exchange in proteins. *Adv. Protein Chem.* 21:287–386

32. Ikegami T, Okada T, Ohki I, Hirayama J, Mizuno T, Shirakawa M. 2001. Solution structure and dynamic character of the histidine-containing phosphotransfer domain of anaerobic sensor kinase ArcB from *Escherichia coli. Biochemistry* 40:375–86

33. Jaravine VA, Rathgeb-Szabo K, Alexandrexcu AT. 2000. Microscopic stability of cold shock protein A examined by NMR native state hydrogen exchange as a function of urea and trimethylamine N-oxide. *Protein Sci.* 9:290–301

34. Jeng M-F, Dyson HJ. 1995. Comparison of the hydrogen-exchange behavior of reduced and oxidized Escherichia coli thioredoxin. *Biochemistry* 34:611–19

35. Jeng M-F, Englander SW. 1991. Stable submolecular folding units in a noncompact form of cytochrome *c. J. Mol. Biol.* 221:1045–61

36. Jeng M-F, Englander SW, Elöve GA, Wand AJ, Roder H. 1990. Structural description of acid-denatured cytochrome *c* by hydrogen exchange and 2D NMR. *Biochemistry* 29:10433–37

37. Jerala R, Zerovnik E. 1999. Accessing the global minimum conformation of stefin A dimer by annealing under partially denaturing conditions. *J. Mol. Biol.* 291:1079–89

38. Kim K-S, Fuchs JA, Woodward CK. 1993. Hydrogen exchange identifies native-state motional domains important in protein folding. *Biochemistry* 32:9600–8

39. Kim K-S, Woodward C. 1993. Protein internal flexibility and global stability: effect of urea on hydrogen exchange rates of bovine pancreatic trypsin inhibitor. *Biochemistry* 32:9609–13

40. Kobashigawa Y, Demura M, Koshiba T, Kumaki Y, Kuwajima K, Nitta K. 2000. Hydrogen exchange study of canine milk

lysozyme: stabilization mechanism of the molten globule. *Proteins* 40:579–89

41. Kobayashi T, Ikeguhi M, Sugai S. 2000. Molten globule structure of equine β-lactoglobulin probed by hydrogen exchange. *J. Mol. Biol.* 299:757–70

42. Koshland DE Jr. 1994. The key-lock theory and the induced fit theory. *Angew. Chem. Int. Ed. Engl.* 33:2375–78

43. Kragelund BB, Heinemann B, Knudsen J, Poulsen FM. 1998. Mapping the lifetimes of local opening events in a native state protein. *Protein Sci.* 7:2237–48

44. Kragelund BB, Knudsen J, Poulsen FM. 1995. Local perturbations by ligand binding of hydrogen deuterium exchange kinetics in a four-helix bundle protein, acyl coenzyme A binding protein (ACBP). *J. Mol. Biol.* 1995:695–706

45. Lacroix E, Bruix M, Lopez-Hernandez E, Serrano L, Rico M. 1997. Amide hydrogen exchange and internal dynamics in the chemotactic protein CheY from *Escherichia coli*. *J. Mol. Biol.* 271:472–87

46. Liu K, Cho HS, Hoyt DW, Nguyen TN, Olds P, et al. 2000. Deuterium-proton exchange on the native wild-type transthyretin tetramer identifies the stable core of the individual subunits and indicates mobility at the subunit interface. *J. Mol. Biol.* 303:555–65

47. Loh SN, Prehoda KE, Wang J, Markley JL. 1993. Hydrogen exchange in unligated and ligated staphylococcal nuclease. *Biochemistry* 32:11022–28

48. Lumry R, Biltonen R. 1969. Thermodynamic and kinetic aspects of protein conformations in relation to physiological function. In *Biological Macromolecules: Structure and Stability of Biological Macromolecules*, ed. SN Timasheff, GD Fasman, pp. 65–211. New York: Marcel Dekker

49. Lumry R, Biltonen R, Brandts JF. 1966. Validity of the "two-state" hypothesis for conformational transitions of proteins. *Biopolymers* 4:917–44

50. Luque I, Freire E. 2000. The structural sta-

bilty of binding sites. Consequences for binding affinity and cooperativity. *Proteins* 4:63–71

51. McCallum SA, Hitchens TK, Torborg C, Rule GS. 2000. Ligand-induced changes in the structure and dynamics of a human mu glutathione s-transferase. *Biochemistry* 39:7343–56

52. Milne JS, Mayne L, Roder H, Wand AJ, Englander SW. 1998. Determinants of protein hydrogen exchange studied in equine cytochrome *c*. *Protein Sci.* 7:739–45

53. Milne JS, Xu Y, Mayne LC, Englander SW. 1999. Experimental study of the protein folding landscape: unfolding reactions in cytochrome *c*. *J. Mol. Biol.* 290:811–22

54. Morikis D, Wright PE. 1996. Hydrogen exchange in the carbon monoxide complex of soybean leghemoglobin. *Eur. J. Biochem.* 237:212–20

55. Morozova LA, Haynie DT, Arico-Muendel C, van Dael H, Dobson CM. 1995. Structural basis of the stability of a lysozyme molten globule. *Nat. Struct. Biol.* 2:871–75

56. Mullins LS, Pace CN, Raushel FM. 1997. Conformational stability of ribonuclease T1 determined by hydrogen-deuterium exchage. *Protein Sci.* 6:1387–95

57. Myers JK, Pace CN, Scholtz JM. 1995. Denaturant m values and heat capacity changes: relation to changes in accessible surface areas of protein unfolding. *Protein Sci.* 4:2138–48

58. Neira JL, Itzhaki LS, Otzen DE, Davis B, Fersht AR. 1997. Hydrogen exchange in chymotrypsin inhibitor 2 probed by mutagenesis. *J. Mol. Biol.* 270:99–110

59. Neira JL, Sevilla P, Menendez M, Bruix M, Rico M. 1999. Hydrogen exchange in ribonuclease A and ribonuclease S: evidence for residual structure in the unfolded state under native conditions. *J. Mol. Biol.* 285:627–43

60. Parker MJ, Marqusee S. 2001. A kinetic folding intermediate probed by native state hydrogen exchange. *J. Mol. Biol.* 305:593–602

61. Deleted in proof
62. Pedersen TG, Thomsen NK, Andersen KV, Madsen JC, Poulsen FM. 1993. Determination of the rate constants k1 and k2 of the Linderstrom-Lang model for protein amide hydrogen exchange. A study of the individual amides in hen egg-white lysozyme. *J. Mol. Biol.* 230:651–60
63. Privalov PL, Khechinashvili NN. 1974. A thermodynamic approach to the problem of stabilization of globular protein structure: a calorimetric study. *J. Mol. Biol.* 86:665–84
64. Radford SE, Buck M, Topping KD, Dobson CM, Evans PA. 1992. Hydrogen exchange in native and denatured states of hen egg-white lysozyme. *Proteins* 14:237–48
65. Ragona L, Fogolari F, Romagnoli S, Zetta L, Maubois JL, Molinari H. 1999. Unfolding and refolding of bovine beta-lactoglobulin monitored by hydrogen exchange measurements. *J. Mol. Biol.* 293:953–69
66. Robertson AD, Murphy KP. 1997. Protein structure and the energetics of protein stability. *Chem. Rev.* 97:1251–67
67. Sadqi M, Casares S, Abril MA, Mayorga OL, Conejero-Lara F, Freire E. 1999. The native state conformational ensemble of the SH3 domain from α-spectrin. *Biochemistry* 38:8899–906
68. Schellman JA. 1955. The stability of hydrogen bonded peptide structures in aqueous solution. *C. R. Trav. Lab. Carlsberg Ser. Chim.* 29:230–59
69. Schönbrunner N, Wey J, Engels J, Georg H, Kiefhaber T. 1996. Native-like beta-structure in a trifluoroethanol-induced partially folded state of the all-beta-sheet protein tendamistat. *J. Mol. Biol.* 260:432–45
70. Schulman BA, Redfield C, Peng Z, Dobson CM, Kim PS. 1995. Different subdomains are most protected from hydrogen exchange in the molten globule and native states of human α-lactalbumin. *J. Mol. Biol.* 253:651–57
71. Sivaraman T, Kumar TKS, Tu YT, Peng HJ, Yu C. 1999. Structurally homologous toxins isolated from the Taiwan cobra (naja naja atra) differ significantly in their structural stability. *Arch. Biochem. Biophys.* 363:107–15
72. Steensma E, Nijman MJM, Bollen YJM, de Jager PA, Van den Berg WAM, et al. 1998. Apparent local stability of the secondary structure of *Azotobacter vinelandii* holoflavodoxin II as probed by hydrogen exchange: implications for redox potential regulation and flavodoxin folding. *Protein Sci.* 7:306–17
73. Steensma E, van Mierlo CPM. 1998. Structural characterization of apoflavodoxin shows that the location of the stable nucleus differs among proteins with a flavodoxin-like topology. *J. Mol. Biol.* 282:653–66
74. Straume M, Freire E. 1992. Two-dimensional differential scanning calorimetry: simultaneous resolution of intrinsic protein structural energetics and ligand binding interactions by global linkage analysis. *Anal. Biochem.* 203:259–68
75. Swint-Kruse L, Robertson AD. 1996. Temperature and pH dependence of hydrogen exchange and global stability for ovomucoid third domain. *Biochemistry* 35:171–80
76. Wagner G, Stassinopoulou CI, Wüthrich K. 1984. Amide-proton exchange studies by two-dimensional correlated H NMR in two chemically modified analogs of the basic pancreatic trypsin inhibitor. *Eur. J. Biochem.* 143:431–36
77. Wang F, Blanchard JS, Tang XJ. 1997. Hydrogen exchange/electrospray ionization mass spectrometry studies of substrate and inhibitor binding and conformational changes of *Escherichia coli* dihydrodipicolinate reductase. *Biochemistry* 36:3755–59
78. Wijesinha-Bettoni R, Dobson CM, Redfield C. 2001. Comparison of the structural and dynamical properties of Holo and Apo bovine alpha-lactalbumin by NMR spectroscopy. *J. Mol. Biol.* 307:885–98

79. Williams DC, Benjamin DC, Poljak RJ, Rule GS. 1996. Global changes in amide hydrogen exchange rates for a protein antigen in complex with three different antibodies. *J. Mol. Biol.* 257:866–76

80. Woodward C. 1993. Is the slow-exchange core the protein folding core? *TIBS* 18:359–60

81. Wu H. 1995. Studies on denaturation of proteins XIII. A theory of denaturation. *Adv. Protein Chem.* 46:6–26

82. Wyman J. 1948. Heme proteins. *Adv. Protein Chem.* 4:407–531

Annu. Rev. Biophys. Biomol. Struct. 2002. 31:257–73
DOI: 10.1146/annurev.biophys.31.082901.134439
Copyright © 2002 by Annual Reviews. All rights reserved

THE SEARCH AND ITS OUTCOME:
High-Resolution Structures of Ribosomal Particles from Mesophilic, Thermophilic, and Halophilic Bacteria at Various Functional States

Ada Yonath
Department of Structural Biology, Weizmann Institute of Science, Rehovot 76100, Israel and Max-Planck-Research Unit for Ribosomal Structure, Hamburg 22603, Germany; e-mail: ada.yonath@weizmann.ac.il

Key Words ribosomes, large ribosomal subunit, small ribosomal subunit, flexibility, initiation, antibiotics

■ **Abstract** We determined the high-resolution structures of large and small ribosomal subunits from mesophilic and thermophilic bacteria and compared them with those of the thermophilic ribosome and the halophilic large subunit. We confirmed that the elements involved in intersubunit contacts and in substrate binding are inherently flexible and that a common ribosomal strategy is to utilize this conformational variability for optimizing its functional efficiency and minimizing nonproductive interactions. Under close-to-physiological conditions, these elements maintain well-ordered characteristic conformations. In unbound subunits, the features creating intersubunit bridges within associated ribosomes lie on the interface surface, and the features that bind factors and substrates reach toward the binding site only when conditions are ripe.

CONTENTS

1056-8700/02/0609-0257$14.00

257

INTRODUCTION

Ribosomes are the universal cellular organelles that catalyze the sequential polymerization of amino acids according to the genetic blueprint encoded in the mRNA. They are built of two subunits that associate for performing this task. The larger subunit creates the peptide bonds and provides the path for the progression of the nascent proteins. The smaller subunit has key roles in the initiation of the process, in decoding the genetic message, in discriminating against non- and near-cognate aminoacylated tRNA molecules, in controlling the fidelity of codon-anti-codon interactions, and in mRNA/tRNA translocation. The prokaryotic large ribosomal subunit (50S) has a molecular weight of 1.5×10^6 Dalton and contains two RNA chains with a total of $\sim$3000 nucleotides and $\sim$35 proteins. The small ribosomal subunit (called 30S) has a molecular weight of 8.5×10^5 Dalton and contains one RNA chain of over 1500 nucleotides and $\sim$20 proteins.

Over two decades ago, we initialized a long and demanding search for the determination of the three-dimensional structure of the ribosome by X-ray crystallography (74). The key to high-resolution data was to crystallize homogenous preparations under conditions similar to their in situ environments or to induce a selected conformation after the crystals were formed. Relatively robust ribosomal particles were chosen, assuming that they would deteriorate less during preparation and therefore provide more homogenous starting materials for crystallization.

The first crystals to yield some crystallographic information (e.g., symmetry, unit cell parameters, and resolution) were of the large subunit from *Bacillus stearothermophilus* (71) and *Haloarcula marismortui* (H50S) (39, 66). Shortly afterward, we characterized crystals of the small subunit from *Thermus thermophilus* (T30S) (72). Microcrystals of the same source were grown independently at approximately the same time (64).

An alternative approach was to design complexes containing ribosomes at defined functional stages, such as of the entire ribosome with two tRNA molecules and a short mRNA analog (27). This approach was later adopted, refined, and extended and has led a medium-resolution structure of the ribosome with three tRNA molecules (75). It is interesting that, until recently, the only crystals that led to high-resolution structures worldwide were of these two sources, H50S (4) and T30S (53, 69). As discussed below and in (5, 28), this situation has now changed since we identified a robust ribosome from a mesophilic eubacterium that crystallizes well under mild conditions in the presence and in the absence of antibiotics and substrate analogs.

All ribosomal crystals presented challenging technical problems, resulting from their enormous size, complexity, natural tendency to deteriorate and disintegrate, internal flexibility, and their sensitivity to irradiation. For minimizing the harm caused by the latter, we pioneered crystallographic data collection at cryogenic temperatures (32). This, together with the dramatic advances of the X-ray sources, namely the third-generation synchrotrons equipped with state-of-the-art detectors and increased sophistication in phasing, enabled us, as well as others, to handle most of the technical problems. Consequently, structures of ribosomal particles are currently emerging at an impressive speed (4, 28, 53, 69). This chapter focuses on the functional relevance of one of the characteristic properties of ribosomal particles: their inherent conformational variability.

From the initial stage of our studies, we aimed at the elucidation of the three-dimensional structures of ribosomal particles in functionally relevant conformations. For this aim, we developed two approaches: (*a*) We crystallized and maintained the crystals under close-to-physiological conditions or (*b*) we activated the crystallized subunits and stabilized the so obtained conformation. Although neither of these approaches is simple or routine, we exploited them for the determination of high-resolution, functionally relevant structures of the small and large ribosomal subunits. These structures provide unique tools for the understanding of key questions concerning ribosomal function, mobility, dynamics, and integrity.

FLEXIBILITY, FUNCTIONAL ACTIVITY, AND DISORDER

Among the many crystal types that were obtained by us, the first to diffract to high resolution was that of the large ribosomal subunits from *H. marismortui* (66), the bacterium that lives in the Dead Sea, the lake with the highest salinity in the world. This bacterium withstands the high salinity as well as the elevated temperatures and has developed a sophisticated system to accumulate enormous amounts (3M) of KCl, although the medium contains only mM amounts of it (Table 1) (24). The reasons for the potassium intake are most probably not related to the ribosome function. However, the ribosomes of this bacterium adapted to the bacterial in situ environment, and their functional activity is directly linked to the concentration of potassium ions in the reaction mixture (Figure 1).

Initially, we grew the crystals of the 50S subunits from this bacterium (H50S) under conditions mimicking the interior of the bacteria at their log period. In these experiments, crystals were grown and kept in solutions containing all salts required to maintain a high functional activity of these halophilic ribosomes, including 3 M potassium chloride. Under these conditions, nucleation occurred rapidly and yielded small disordered crystals. Consequently, we developed a procedure for crystallization at the lowest potassium concentration required for maintaining the integrity of the subunits. Once the crystals grew, we transferred them to solutions containing ~3 M KCl, allowing the crystallized particles to rearrange into

TABLE 1 The concentration of ions within the cells of *Haloacula marismortui* [based on (24)]

	Early log	**Late log**	**Stationary**
K in cells:	3.7–5.0 M	3.7–4.0 M	3.7–4.0 M
Na in cells:	1.2–3.0 M	1.6–2.1 M	0.5–0.7 M

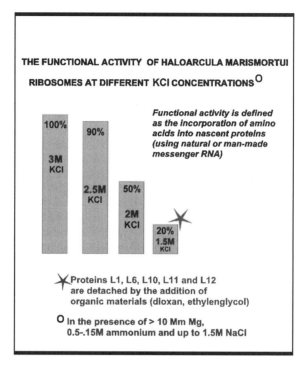

Figure 1   The functional activity of the ribosomes from *H. marismortui* at different potassium concentrations. Activity was checked by the synthesis of polypeptides and by the incorporation of 50S into 70S. In both cases, the ribosomal particles underwent heat activation at 55° for 40 min, and homo- or heteronucleotides served as mRNA chains.

their active conformation and regain their full functional activity. These crystals exhibited functional activity and diffracted well to high resolution (66, 73), but the high potassium concentration within them caused severe problems in the course of structure determination (29, 73). The combination of severe nonisomorphism, apparent twinning, high radiation sensitivity, unstable cell constants, nonuniform mosaic spread, and uneven reflection shape hampered the collection of data usable for structure determination. As these problems became less tolerable at higher resolution, the structure determination under close-to-physiological conditions stalled at resolutions lower than 5 Å (3, 29, 68, 73).

Improved crystals were obtained by drastic reduction (to mM amounts) of the salt concentration in their stabilization solution and by the exchange of high concentration of KCl by relatively low concentration of NaCl. These far-from-physiological conditions yielded a structure at 2.4 Å resolution (4) and even allowed the binding of compounds believed to be substrate analogs, such as CCdA-phosphate-puromycin (47). However, while under the far-from-physiological conditions, these ribosomes are less active in synthesis of proteins (56).

Several regions, including RNA helices and more than four proteins, were not observed in the 2.4 Å map of H50S (4). These were considered to be disordered. Almost all these untraceable regions are known to be heavily involved in the process of protein biosynthesis. Two of the RNA helical elements form intersubunit bridges, "the A-site finger" (H38) and the bridge reaching the decoding center (H69), within the assembled ribosome and interact with the tRNA molecules. The central loop of protein L5 forms the only intersubunit bridge made solely of proteins (together with protein S13 from the small subunit). Two additional proteins (L12 and L10) are involved in the contacts with the translocational factors and in factor-dependent GTPase activity (14), and protein L11 is involved in elongation factor activities (16). Protein L1 is a translational repressor binding mRNA (46), and its absence has a negative effect on the rate of protein synthesis (59).

All four proteins not observed in the 2.4 Å map match the list of proteins that we detached selectively from halophilic ribosomes (20). Furthermore, the low salt conditions used for the stabilization of the crystals are similar to those developed by us for the detachment of the selected proteins, namely the lowering of the salt concentration while adding modest amounts of organic materials. Evidently, these proteins are loosely held by the core of the large subunit, and it may well be that their level of disorder within the crystals allows partial or full removal from the large subunit. These crystals contain unusually large and continuous solvent regions (73) and accommodate materials the size of average ribosomal proteins (A. Bashan & J. Harms, unpublished data). Interestingly, the two major features not seen in the 2.4 Å map of H50S form the lateral protuberances, called the L1 stalk (H76-H78 with their bound protein L1) and the L12 stalk (H43-H44 and their bound proteins L10 and L12), that create the prominent features of the typical shape of the large subunit (Figure 2, see color insert). Electron microscopy (EM), using negative staining, dark field, or cryo-EM reconstruction, readily observed both of them. These protruding stalk elements were also detected in electron density maps obtained from the crystals of H50S grown and maintained under close to physiological conditions (2, 73) albeit at lower resolution.

ARE THE INTERSUBUNIT BRIDGES DISORDERED IN UNBOUND RIBOSOMAL SUBUNITS?

All structural elements assumed to be disordered in the 2.4 Å structure of H50S were clearly detected in the 5.5 Å maps of the assembled 70S ribosome. This stimulated the notion that structural elements that interact with the small subunit or with ribosomal substrates are disordered in the unbound large subunit and may be stabilized in the 70S ribosome by intersubunit interactions or by their contacts with the tRNA molecules (75).

A possible cause for the disorder of the functionally relevant features in the 2.4 Å structure of H50S may be linked to the fact that these ribosomal particles were measured under conditions far from the in vivo situation. Biochemical, functional, and electron-microscopical studies indicate that these features are inherently flexible, but flexibility is not necessarily synonymous with disorder. In many cases, flexible structural elements assume several well-defined conformations, and the switch from one conformation to another is related to their functional states. Detecting large disordered features in the high-resolution structure of H50S may indicate that the ribosomal strategy to avoid subunit association and substrate binding under far-from-physiological conditions is to introduce disorder in the relevant features.

To shed light on this intriguing question, we searched for a robust nonhalophilic bacterium as a potential source for suitable ribosomes. In parallel, we continued our efforts to elucidate the structure of H50S under close-to-physiological conditions. We recently calculated an electron density map from data collected from H50S crystals grown and kept under conditions mimicking the physiological environment of *H. marismortui* (I. Agmon, unpublished data). The resolution (3.6 Å) of our map is somewhat lower than that obtained for the crystals kept under far-from-physiological conditions. Nevertheless, the map is interpretable and enabled a rather detailed comparison between the two structures. The conformations of almost all the proteins in our structure differ to some extent from those observed under far-from-physiological conditions. The larger differences were observed in the locations and the internal order of the termini extensions. Under close-to-physiological conditions, more tails and extensions reach functionally important locations, such as tRNA-binding sites and intersubunit bridges. Also, many of the RNA regions disordered in the 2.4 Å map of H50S (4), such as helices H1, H38, and the L11 arm, are ordered. Thus, it is conceivable that the disorder of the features in the 2.4 Å structure of H50S reflects the strategy that the large subunit developed in order to avoid nonproductive association with the small subunit or with factors and substrates under far from natural conditions.

The search for a suitable mesophilic ribosome was stimulated by several reasons in addition to the apparent disorder of the functional elements of the 2.4 Å structure of H50S. *H. marismortui* is an archaea bearing low compatibility with *Escherichia coli*, the species yielding most of our knowledge on ribosomes. Despite the suitability of the ribosomes from *H. marismortui* for high-resolution crystallography, they have not become a subject of many biochemical studies. Consequently, only a small part of the vast amount of data of ribosomal research accumulated over almost half a century can be related directly to its structure. In addition, the antibiotics from the macrolide family hardly bind to the halophilic ribosomes because a key adenine is a guanine in their 23S RNA. They are also rather resistant to most of the antibiotic agents (40), even under suitable conditions. Thus, it is not surprising that contrary to the wealth of crystallographic information already obtained about binding of factors and antibiotics to the small subunit (9, 11, 12, 49, 50), only complexes of H50S with materials believed to represent substrate analogs were suitable for high-resolution crystallographic studies (47). Furthermore, despite extensive studies exploiting these complexes, the mechanism of the peptidyl-transferase activity is still not understood (5). In contrast to the strict requirements for antibiotics binding, all nucleotides crucial for the catalytic activity in the proposed mechanism

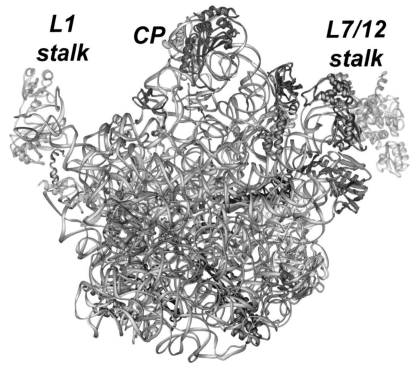

Figure 2 The "crown view" of D50S. The RNA is shown as *gray-blue* ribbons and the proteins are in different colors. For orientation, the L1 arm is on the left, and the L7/12 arm is on the right.

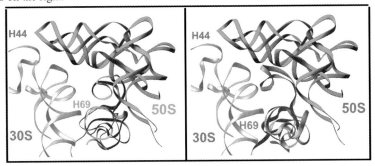

Figure 3 The intersubunit bridge formed by helix H69. In both parts, the small subunit is placed on the left side and the large subunit on the right. Helix H44 of the small subunit is shown in *gray*. The decoding center is on its upper side. Also shown are the docked tRNA molecules (P-site tRNA in *magenta* and A-site tRNA in *green*). Coordinates of the small subunit and the two tRNA sites were taken from (75). For clarity, the mRNA is not shown. The *left box* shows the shape of H69 in the large (50S) subunit, just before the approach of the initiation complex (the small subunit, P-site tRNA, and the initiator mRNA). In this position, H69 interacts with its neighbors in the 50S subunit. The approaching tRNA pushes H69 toward the small subunit until it reaches its bound conformation (in *gold*), as determined in the 70S complex (75).

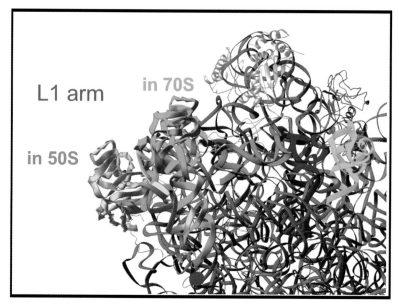

Figure 4 Part of the upper side of the view shown in Figure 2, with the L1 stalk on the left. The flexibility of the L1 arm may be exploited to form a gate for the exiting tRNA molecules. The *gold* feature represents its position in the unbound D50S subunit, and the *green* represents its position in the entire ribosome. *Red* indicates the pivot point. In the complex of the whole ribosome with three tRNA molecules (75), this arm assumes a conformation that may correspond to a "closed-gate," trapping the E-site tRNA (in *magenta*). The conformation seen in the unbound 50S subunit may represent the "open-gate" state.

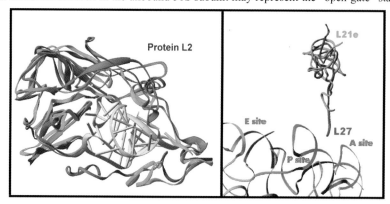

Figure 5 *Left*: Protein L2 (*purple*, in H50S; *green*, in D50S). Helix H66 is shown in *yellow*. Note the remarkable differences in the conformations of parts of the globular domains and of the C-terminal tails. In D50S the latter embraces and stabilizes the RNA helix H66. In H50S, in contrast, it folds backward on itself away from the helix. *Right*: The D50S protein L27 and its tail that extends toward the A- and P-site tRNAs. Protein L27 does not exist in the halophilic ribosome, and its position is occupied by a protein that shows no sequence similarity to L27 (called L21e and shown in *green*). The tail of L21e folds backward, away from the tRNA-binding sites.

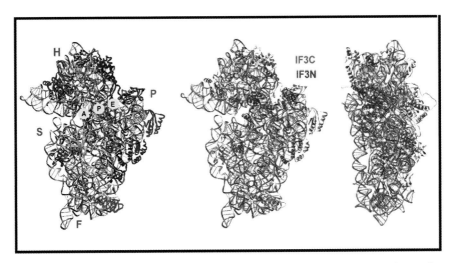

Figure 6 *Left*: The small subunit seen from the interface side (the side facing the large subunit in the 70S ribosome). The RNA is shown as simple ribbons, in *silver*. The proteins are in different colors. The major subdivisions are labeled: H, head; S, shoulder; P, platform; F, foot. The approximate locations of A-, P-, and E-tRNA-binding sites are marked. *Middle*: The same view of the small subunit as on the left, but the entire subunit is drawn in *gray*. The location of IF3 is marked in *red* (for the C-terminal domain, IF3C) and in *blue* (the N-terminal domain, IF3N, and the intersubunit linker). *Right*: Side view of the mall subunit, with its platform pointing toward the reader (obtained by 90° rotation about the long axis of the left and the middle views).

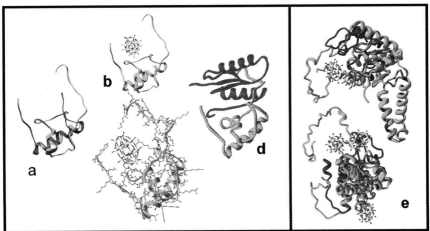

Figure 7 The conformations of proteins L18 (*left*) and L2 (*right*) as detected in the tungstenated (in *green*) and the nontungstenated (*dark blue*) forms of T30S. The W atoms are shown in *red*. (*a*) Superposition of the two structures of protein S18. (*b, c*) The general fold and the specific contacts formed between the terminal tails of protein S18 and the W18 cluster. (*d*) The binding of IF3C to the 30S subunit. Most of the contacts are formed by protein S18. Note the remarkable similarities in IF3C and W18 binding by the tails of S18. (*e*) Superposition of the two structures of protein S2.

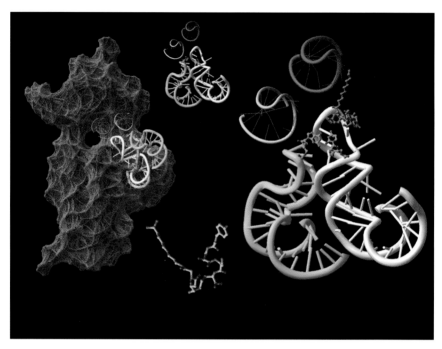

Figure 8 The binding of the universal antibiotic edeine to the small subunit. *Left*: An over-all view (color code of the helical elements as described below). The small subunit is shown at about 75° rotation (around the vertical axis of the particle) compared to the view of the left side of Figure 6. The mRNA channel is clearly seen and the sites of P- (*orange*) and E- (*yellow*) are indicated. *Right*: Close-up of edeine-binding area. H23 is shown in *light green*, and H24 in *white*. Edeine is *pink*, and the newly formed base pair is *green*. The inhibitory action of this antibiotic—interfering with the initiation process by limiting the mobility of the platform—is evident. *Inserts*: *Top*: The edeine-binding region (as shown on the right) in its unbound state. *Bottom*: The chemical formula of edeine.

(47) could be mutated with little or no effect on peptide bond formation in vitro (51) and in vivo (62).

As mentioned above, we identified a robust ribosome from a mesophilic bacterium, *Deinococcus radiodurans* [and determined the 3.0 Å resolution structure of its large subunit (6, 28)]. The ribosome of this source shows a high homology to those of *T. thermophilus* and *E. coli*, and the crystals of its large subunit were grown and maintained under conditions almost identical to the bacterial in situ environment. These crystals, as well as those grown from complexes of these subunits with antibiotics, diffract to higher than 3 Å resolution, are relatively stable in the X-ray beam, and yield crystallographic data of high quality. Thus, they provide an excellent system to investigate antibiotic binding (54), shed light on the mechanism of peptide bond formation, and provide more insight into functional flexibility.

The structure of the large ribosomal subunit from *D. radiodurans*, D50S, as determined by us at 3 Å resolution, is significantly more ordered than that of H50S. Thus, most of the features that are disordered in H50S are well resolved in D50S (6, 28). Among the well-ordered features are the intersubunit bridges to the upper part of the small subunit (formed by helix H38) and to the decoding site (formed by H69), as well as the middle loop of protein L5, which forms the only intersubunit brige formed solely by ribosomal proteins "only protein" bridge. Also well ordered are the L1 arm (helices H76–H78) and the GTPase center (helices H42–H44 and protein L11). All display orientations that differ from those seen in the 5.5 Å structure of the 70S ribosome complex (75), which manifests their inherent flexibility.

Figure 3 (see color insert) demonstrates a feasible sequence of events leading to the creation of the intersubunit bridge, spanning from the large subunit to the decoding center on the small one. Helix H69, which is responsible for this bridge, lies in the unbound 50S subunit on the interface surface and interacts intensively with helix H70. Once the initiation complex, which includes the small subunit and tRNA at the P-site (see below for more detail), approaches the large subunit, the tRNA pushes helix H69 toward the decoding center, and the intersubunit bridge is formed.

The inherent flexibility of the ribosomal features is exploited also for controlling events in translocation. The comparison between the structure of the unbound 50S and the 70S ribosome indicates how the L1 arm facilitates the exit of the tRNA molecules. In the complex of T70S with three tRNA molecules, the L1 stalk interacts with the elbow of E-tRNA, and the exit path for the E-tRNA is blocked by proteins L1 from the large subunit and S7 from the small one (75). In the unbound mesophilic 50S, the L1 arm is tilted ∼30 degrees away from its position in the T70S ribosome (Figure 4, see color insert), and it does not block the presumed exit path of the E-site tRNA. Hence, the mobility of the L1 arm is utilized for facilitating the release of E-site tRNA. Superposition of the structure of the mesophilic unbound 50S on the T70S ribosome allowed the definition of a pivot point for a possible rotation of the L1 arm.

Our structure analysis showed that a similar strategy is taken when protein tails are involved in functional aspects. Almost all ribosomal proteins are built of globular domains with extended tails or loops. Most of the globular domains are located on the solvent side of the particle, with their tails buried in the interior, and stabilize the RNA fold. However, the tails of a few proteins are pointing into the solution and are less engaged in RNA contacts. Some of these may make contributions to the efficient binding of nonribosomal factors participating in the process of protein biosynthesis by using their long tails as tentacles that enhance the correct positioning of the factors [as seen below and in (6, 25, 50)]. It is conceivable that the flexibility of these tails is also used for the reverse path. Once the binding is no longer required, the protein tails can stretch out, or become disordered, and release the compounds.

In general, the protein tails in the ribosomes that were kept close to their physiological environment seem to be more involved in protective interactions and reach closer to the functionally relevant sites than those maintained under nonphysiological conditions. Figure 5 (see color insert) shows examples for both tasks. The tail of protein L2 in the large subunit that was kept under physiological conditions (D50S) encloses and embraces an important RNA feature (H66), whereas the tail of the counterpart in the less physiologically relevant H50S particles folds away from the sensitive area. The second example is protein L27, which is located on the interface side of D50S at the base of the central protuberance (CP) in proximity to the peptidyl-transferase center, consistent with results of immune electron microscopy, protein-protein cross-linking, affinity labeling, chemical probing (57, 70), and footprinting (A. Mankin, personal communication). This protein has been implicated as a constituent of the peptidyl-transferase center of *E. coli* 50S by a variety of experimental observations. These include a deletion mutant that grows much slower than the wild type and shows deficiencies in the peptidyl-transferase activity and impaired enzymatic binding of Phe-tRNA Phe to the A-site. Although we did not resolve termini of four amino acids, in our structure it reaches the proximity of the P- and the A-sites, consistent with the proposal that it contributes to peptide bond formation by facilitating the proper placement of the acceptor end of the A-site tRNA (70). In contrast, the protein placed at the location of L27 in the 2.4 Å structure of H50S (called H21e) folds backward, toward the interior of the subunit, consistent with the hypothesis that the tails of the ribosomal proteins that bind factors and substrates fold away from the action sites when the conditions are not suitable for productive protein biosynthesis.

CONFORMATIONAL MOBILITY: THE KEY FOR SUBUNIT ASSOCIATION, DISSOCIATION, AND THE INITIATION OF PROTEIN BIOSYNTHESIS

The small ribosomal subunit is less stable than the large one. We found that by exposing 70S ribosomes to a potent proteolytic mixture, the 50S subunits remained intact, whereas the 30S subunits were completely digested (18). Similarly, large differences in the integrity of the two subunits were observed when attempting crystallization of entire ribosomes assembled from purified subunits. Crystals obtained from these preparations consisted only of 50S subunits (7), and the supernatant of the crystallization drop did not contain intact small subunits but did show 30S proteins and a fragmented 16S RNA chain. Consequently, among the many ribosome sources that were tested, only the 30S from *T. thermophilus* (T30S) crystallized is suitable for crystallographic studies. Almost a decade was needed to minimize the severe nonisomorphism of this form, and all the procedures developed for increasing the homogeneity of these crystals are based on post-crystallization treatments. Our approach, described below and in (50, 53, 63), is to induce a specific conformation. Other approaches include treatment of the crystal by Co-hexamine (15, 69), a material known to bind specifically to RNA chains and increase their rigidity (13), or by spectinomycin (12), an antibiotic agent that locks the "head" (Figure 6, see color insert) of the small subunit in a particular conformation (43).

The first task of the small subunit is to form the initiation complex; therefore, we assumed that the commonly used heat-activation procedure, developed over 30 years ago (76), induces the conformation required for this task. For obtaining small subunits at that particular conformation, we exposed our T30S crystals to elevated temperatures, according to the routine heat-activation procedure. Once activation was achieved, the conformation of the particles was stabilized (at ambient temperature) by incubation with minute amounts of a heteropolytungstate cluster, W18 (53, 63). The same procedure was employed for complexes of T30S with compounds that facilitate or inhibit protein biosynthesis, mRNA analogs, initiation factors, and antibiotics. Soaking in solutions containing the nonribosomal compounds in their normal binding buffer was performed at elevated temperatures. Once the functional complex was formed, the crystals were treated with the W18 cluster.

The initiation of protein biosynthesis has an important role in governing the accurate setting of the reading frame, as it facilitates the identification of the start codon of the mRNA. In prokaryotes, the initiation complex contains the small subunit, mRNA, three initiation factors (IF1, IF2-GTP, and IF3), and initiator tRNA. IF3 plays multiple roles in the formation of this complex. It influences the binding of the other ligands and acts as a fidelity factor by destabilizing noncanonical codon-anticodon interactions. It also selects the start-mRNA codon (37, 60) and the correct initiator tRNA to be positioned at the P-site (in prokaryotes, the fMET-tRNA). It stabilizes the binding of the fMet-tRNA/IF2 complex to 30S and discriminates against leaderless mRNA chains (42, 61). IF3 also acts as an anti-association factor because it binds with a high affinity to the 30S subunit and shifts the dissociation equilibrium of the 70S ribosome toward free subunits, thus maintaining a pool of 30S (26).

IF3 is a small basic protein of about 20 kD. It consists of C and N terminus domains (IF3C and IF3N) connected by a rather long lysine-rich linker region. The structure of the entire protein has not been determined, but NMR (22, 23) and X-ray structures of the N- and C-terminal domains have been reported (8, 36). The interdomain linker appears as a rigid alpha-helix only in the crystals containing it and IF3N. However, the NMR studies showed that even under physiological conditions, the linker is partially unfolded and displays flexibility (17, 33, 34, 36, 45). Subsequently, the interdomain distances vary between 25 and 65 Å.

Crystals of the complex of T30S with IF3C were produced by heat activation and W18 stabilization. The conformation of the small subunits in this crystal is almost identical to that obtained by heat activation of the isolated particles (50). This indicates that activated and stabilized T30S has the conformation of the small subunit during the initiation phase of protein biosynthesis. It also explains why no major conformational changes were observed between the tungstenated and IF3C-bound 30S subunits, contrary to the conformational changes observed while binding IF3 to isolated 30S (21, 41). We therefore conclude that the conformation of the tungsten-bound 30S ribosomal subunit mimics that of the small subunit at the initiation stage and that the W18 cluster imitates the C-terminal domain of IF3 (Figures 6 and 7, see color inserts). Indeed, in competition experiments, crystals treated with W18 prior to soaking in solutions containing IF3C failed to bind IF3C.

Striking differences in the conformations of the proteins that bind IF3 (S18, S11, and S7) and of those interacting with them, such as protein S2, were detected by comparing the structure of isolated T30S (69) and that bound to IF3C (50). These proteins have tails and extended loops pointing toward the solution, in contrast to the majority of tails of ribosomal proteins that are buried within RNA features. An interesting example is protein S18. Its long terminus tails are more ordered in the tungstenated or IF3C-bound T30S than in the Co-hexamine-treated small subunits. These tails appear to act as tentacles that enhance the binding of IF3C, consistent with the firm binding of this domain to the ribosome (55, 67). They are also capable of binding the IF3C mimic, namely the W18 cluster (Figure 7).

The initiator mRNA in prokaryotes includes, along with the start codon, an upstream purine-rich sequence (SD, Shine-Dalgarno). This pairs with a complementary region in the 16S RNA (anti-SD) at its 3′ end, thus anchoring the mRNA chains. In the high-resolution structures of the 30S subunit, the anti-SD region is located on the solvent side of the platform, the region that also contains a large part of the E- site. Using crystals of T30S in complex with IF3C, IF3C binds to the 30S particle at the upper end of the platform on the solvent side (Figure 6), close to the anti-SD region of the 16S rRNA (50). This location reconfirms the results of NMR and mutagenesis of the IF3 molecule (55) and is compatible with the effect of the double mutations 1503, 1531 (19). It is also consistent with almost all the cross-links, footprints, and protection patterns reported for the *E. coli* system (38, 52).

CONFORMATIONAL MOBILITY GOVERNS SUBUNIT ASSOCIATION AND DISSOCIATION

It has been suggested that the C-terminal domain of IF3 (IF3C) performs many of the tasks assigned to the entire IF3 molecule: preventing the association of the 30S with the 50S subunit and contributing to the dissociation of the entire ribosome (30).

IF3C also influences the formation of the initiation complex. The ability of IF3 to discriminate noncanonical initiation codons, or to verify codon-anticodon complementarity, has been attributed mainly to IF3N (10).

The location of IF3C we observed suggests that the binding of IF3C to the 30S subunit influences the mobility of the platform near the anchoring site of the SD sequence. The binding at this site could affect the conformational mobility of the platform, essential for the association of the two ribosomal subunits to form a productive ribosome, consistent with biochemical observations indicating that IF3C prevents subunit association or promotes dissociation by influencing the conformational dynamics of the subunit. The spatial proximity of the IF3C-binding site to the anti-SD region suggests a connection between them. These interactions could suppress the change in the conformational dynamics induced by IF3, thus allowing subunit association. The connection between the double mutation of G1530/A1531 to A1530/G1531 and the reduced IF3 binding to the 30S subunit, together with the enhanced affinity of IF3 to the 70S ribosomes, supports this hypothesis.

The placement of IF3C on the solvent side of the upper platform sheds light on the initial step of protein biosynthesis, which involves the detachment of the SD sequence. This region is also involved in the displacement of the platform that accompanies the translocation (21), as part of the combined head-platform-shoulder conformational changes. The binding of IF3C and the hybridization of the anti-SD sequence limit the mobility of this region. Upon the detachment of the SD anchor, required at the beginning of the translocation process, the platform may regain its conformational mobility. The bound IF3N leaves a limited, albeit sufficient, space for P-site tRNA, and only small conformational changes are required for simultaneous binding of IF3N, mRNA, and the P-site tRNA. Thus, the influence of IF3N on initiator tRNA binding is based on space-exclusion principles rather than on specific codon-anticodon complementarity rules, as suggested earlier (41).

Only indirect contacts exist between IF3N and IF3C, via the curved connection formed by the interdomain linker that wraps around the platform toward the neck. Various mutations, insertions, and deletions that cause significant modifications in the length of the linker do not have major effects on the efficiency of IF3, which indicates that the linker maintains its flexibility while IF3 is bound to the 30S subunit. Consequently, it can act as a transmitting strap between the two domains and can indirectly affect the conformation of the P-site and induce its specificity (17). Similarly, the structural changes in IF3 could trigger conformational changes within the 30S subunit that are required for initiating the biosynthetic process and may also lead to a suppression of secondary-structure elements in the mRNA. Thus, our placement is consistent with the proposal that the linker maintains its flexibility when IF3 is bound to the 30S subunit and that the flexibility and the ability of the linker region to alter its fold are related to the function of IF3.

Support for the placement of IF3, and for the mechanism inferred from it, is provided by the analysis of the mode of action and the location of edeine (Figure 8, see color insert), a universal antibiotic agent that interferes with the initiation process (1, 48). Edeine is a peptide-like antibiotic agent, produced by a strain of *Bacillus brevis*. It contains a spermidine-type moiety at its C-terminal end and a beta-tyrosine residue at its N-terminal end (35). Using crystals of the complex of edeine with T30S, we found that edeine binds in the solvent side of the platform. It also induces the formation of a new base pair between two helices of the platform. In its position, edeine would not alter IF3C binding but might well affect the binding of the linker and hence the binding of IF3N. At the same time, it could affect the 30S mobility, the interaction of the 3' end with IF3C, and the interaction of the 30S and 50S subunits because it connects the penultimate helix (H44) with the major constituents of the platform. By physically linking these components, edeine can lock the small subunit (Figure 8) and hinder the conformational changes that accompany the translation process (21, 65). Independent studies show that pactamycin, an antibiotic agent that shares a protection pattern with edeine, bridges the same helices linked by the edeine-induced base pair (9). Pactamycin is also known to interfere with the initiation process, and its mode of interaction suggests that it may interfere with the pairing of the SD sequence or prevent it.

The universal effect of edeine on initiation implies that the main structural elements important for the initiation process are conserved in all kingdoms (48). Our results show that the rRNA bases that bind edeine are conserved in chloroplasts, mitochondria, and the three phylogenetic domains. Electron microscopy studies on rat liver 40S in complex with the eukaryotic IF3 located it in a region comparable to our findings (58). In this location, IF3 and its eukaryotic counterpart seem to perform their anti-association activity by affecting the conformational mobility of the small ribosomal subunit: in particular, suppressing the conformational mobility of the platform, essential for association of the two ribosomal subunits. Some aspects of the initiation process of protein biosynthesis were different in eukaryotic and prokaryotic systems (31). Nevertheless, neither indicate different locations of IF3. The consistency between our results and the location of the eukaryotic IF may indicate that the main concepts underlying the initiation process and governing the anti-association properties of the initiation complex have been evolutionarily conserved.

CONCLUDING REMARKS

Ribosomal crystallography, initiated two decades ago, recently yielded an impressive amount of exciting structural information. This chapter relates to characteristics common to all available structures and describes our analyses of selected conformations of the two ribosomal subunits at various functional states. These studies identified the structural elements involved in the dynamics of protein biosynthesis and showed that exploiting inherent flexibility for controlling the functional needs of the ribosome is the general strategy taken by the ribosome. By comparing the structures obtained from conditions far and close to physiological ones, we learned that the ribosome exploits this built-in flexibility as a natural tool for preventing nonproductive binding of factors or intersubunit interactions. This is achieved either by folding the tails of the binding proteins away from the binding sites or by inducing significant disorder, as seen in the 2.4 Å structure of the large ribosomal subunit from *H. marismortui* because it represents a conformation that differs from that of the native particle. Still to be revealed is the high-resolution structure of the entire ribosome and the mechanism of peptide bond formation. The need for additional structures required to answer specific questions is evident. However long-lasting the search has been already, it is not over yet, and the reality of understanding the mechanisms of translation by the ribosome are enticing prospects for the future.

ACKNOWLEDGMENTS

These studies were performed at the Structural Biology Department of the Weizmann Institute, the Max-Planck Research Unit for Ribosomal Structure, and in the Max-Planck Institute for Molecular Genetics in Berlin. Thanks are given J. M. Lehn for indispensable advice; M. Pope for the tungsten clusters; R. Wimmer for recommending the ribosomal source; and M. Wilchek, W. Traub, L. Shimon, and A. Mankin for critical discussions. These studies could not be performed without the cooperation and assistance of the staff of the synchrotron radiation facilities at EMBL and MPG at DESY; ID14/2&4 at EMBL/ESRF and ID19/APS/ANL. The Max-Planck Society, the U.S. National Institutes of Health (GM34360), the German Ministry for Science and Technology (Bundesministerium für Bildung, Wissenschaft, Forschung und Technologie Grant 05-641EA) and the Kimmelman Center for Macromolecular Assembly at the Weizmann Institute provided support. A. Yonath holds the Martin S. Kimmel Professorial Chair.

Visit the Annual Reviews home page at www.annualreviews.org

LITERATURE CITED

1. Altamura S, Sanz JL, Amils R, Cammarano P, Londei P. 1988. The antibiotic sensitivity spectra of ribosomes from the thermoproteales phylogenetic depth and distribution of antibiotic binding sites. *Syst. Appl. Microbiol.* 10:218–25
2. Ban N, Freeborn B, Nissen P, Penczek P, Grassucci RA, et al. 1998. A 9 Å resolution X-ray crystallographic map of the large ribosomal subunit. *Cell* 93:1105–15
3. Ban N, Nissen P, Hansen J, Capel M, Moore P, Steitz TA. 1999. Placement of protein and RNA structures into a 5 Å resolution map of the 50S ribosomal subunit. *Nature* 400:841–47
4. Ban N, Nissen P, Hansen J, Moore PB, Steitz TA. 2000. The complete atomic structure of the large ribosomal subunit at 2.4 Å resolution. *Science* 289:905–20
5. Barta A, Dorner S, Polacek N. 2001. Mechanism of ribosomal peptide bond formation. *Science* 291:203–4
6. Bashan A, Agmon I, Zarivach R, Schlünzen F, Harms J, et al. 2001. *High Resolution Structures of Ribosomal Subunits: Initiation, Inhibition and Conformational Variability*. New York: Cold Spring Harbor. In press
7. Berkovitch-Yellin Z, Bennett WS, Yonath A. 1992. Aspects in structural studies on ribosomes. *CRC Rev. Biochem. Mol. Biol.* 27:403–44

8. Biou V, Shu F, Ramakrishnan V. 1995. X-ray crystallography shows that translational initiation factor IF3 consists of two compact alpha/beta domains linked by an alpha-helix. *EMBO J.* 14:4056–64

9. Brodersen DE, Clemons WM Jr, Carter AP, Morgan-Warren RJ, Wimberly BT, et al. 2000. The structural basis for the action of the antibiotics tetracycline, pactamycin and hygromycin B on the 30S ribosomal subunit. *Cell* 103:1143–54

10. Bruhns J, Gualerzi CO. 1980. Structure-function relationship in *E. coli* initiation factors: role of tyrosine residues in ribosomal binding and functional activity of IF-3. *Biochemistry* 19:1670–76

11. Carter AP, Clemons WM Jr, Brodersen DE, Morgan-Warren RJ, Hartsch T, et al. 2001. Crystal structure of an initiation factor bound to the 30S ribosomal subunit. *Science* 291:498–501

12. Carter AP, Clemons WM Jr, Brodersen DE, Morgan-Warren RJ, Wimberly BT, et al. 2000. Functional insights from the structure of the 30S ribosomal subunit and its interactions with antibiotics. *Nature* 407:340–48

13. Cate JH, Doudna JA. 1996. Metal-binding site in the major groove of a large ribozyme domain. *Structure* 4:1221–29

14. Chandra Sanyal S, Liljas A. 2000. The end of the beginning: structural studies of ribosomal proteins. *Curr. Opin. Struct. Biol.* 10:633–36

15. Clemons WM Jr, Brodersen DE, McCutcheon JP, May JLC, Carter AP, et al. 2001. Crystal structure of the 30S ribosomal subunit from *Thermus thermophilus*: purification, crystallization and structure determination. *J. Mol. Biol.* 310:827–43

16. Cundliffe E, Dixon P, Stark M, Stoffler G, Ehrlich R, et al. 1979. Ribosomes in thiostrepton-resistant mutants of *Bacillus megaterium* lacking a single 50S subunit protein. *J. Mol. Biol.* 132:235–52

17. de Cock E, Springer M, Dardel F. 1999. The inter domain linker of *E. coli* initiation factor IF3: a possible trigger of translation initiation specificity. *Mol. Microbiol.* 32:193–202

18. Evers U, Franceschi F, Boeddeker N, Yonath A. 1994. Crystallography of halophilic ribosome: the isolation of an internal ribonucleoprotein complex. *Biophys. Chem.* 50:3–16

19. Firpo MA, Connelly MB, Goss DJ, Dahlberg AE. 1996. Mutations at two invariant nucleotides in the 3′-minor domain of *E. coli* 16S rRNA affecting translational initiation and initiation factor 3 function. *J. Biol. Chem.* 271:4693–98

20. Franceschi F, Sagi I, Boeddeker N, Evers U, Arndt E, et al. 1994. Crystallography, biochemical and genetics studies on halophilic ribosomes. *Syst. Appl. Microbiol.* 16:697–705

21. Gabashvili I, Grawal RK, Grassucci R, Frank J. 1999. Structure and structural variations of the *E. coli* 30S ribosomal subunit as revealed by three-dimensional cryo-electron microscopy. *J. Mol. Biol.* 286:1285–91

22. Garcia C, Fortier P, Blanquet S, Lallemand J-Y, Dardel F. 1995. ¹H and ¹⁵N resonance assignment and structure of the N-terminal domain of *Escherichia coli* initiation factor 3. *Eur. J. Biochem.* 228:395–402

23. Garcia C, Fortier P, Blanquet S, Lallemand J-Y, Dardel F. 1995. Solution structure of the ribosome-binding domain of *E. coli* translation initiation factor IF3. Homology with U1A protein of the eukaryotic spliceosome. *J. Mol. Biol.* 254:247–59

24. Ginzburg M, Sacks L, Ginzburg BZ. 1970. Ion metabolism in *Halobacterium*. *J. Gen. Physiol.* 55:178–207

25. Gluehmann M, Harms J, Zarivach R, Bashan A, Schlünzen F, Yonath A. 2001. Ribosomal crystallography: from poorly diffracting micro-crystals to high resolution structures. *Methods* In press

26. Grunberg-Manago M, Dessen P, Pantaloni D, Godefroy-Colburn T, Wolfe AD, et al. 1975. Light-scattering studies showing the effect of initiation factors on the reversible

dissociation of *E. coli* ribosomes. *J. Mol. Biol.* 94:461–78

27. Hansen HAS, Volkmann N, Piefke J, Glotz C, Weinstein S, Makowski I, et al. 1990. Crystals of complexes mimicking protein biosynthesis are suitable for crystallographic studies. *Biochim. Biophys. Acta* 1050:1–7

28. Harms J, Schlünzen F, Zarivach R, Bashan A, Gat S, et al. 2001. High-resolution structure of the large ribosomal subunit from a mesophilic eubacterium. *Cell* 107:1–20

29. Harms J, Tocilj A, Levin I, Agmon I, Stark H, et al. 1999. Elucidating the medium-resolution structure of ribosomal particles: an interplay between electron cryomicroscopy and X-ray crystallography. *Struct. Fold Des.* 7:931–41

30. Hershey JW. 1987. Protein synthesis. In *ASM Molecular Biology*, ed. F Neidhardt, J Ingraham, K Low, B Magasanik, M Schaechter, H Umbarger, pp. 613–47. Washington, DC: ASM

31. Hershey JW, Asano K, Naranda T, Vornlocher HP, Hanachi P, Merrick WC. 1996. Conservation and diversity in the structure of translation initiation factor EIF3 from humans and yeast. *Biochimie* 78:903–7

32. Hope H, Frolow F, von Boehlen K, Makowski I, Kratky C, et al. 1989. Cryo crystallography of ribosomal particles. *Acta Crystallogr. B* 345:190

33. Hua YX, Raleigh DP. 1998. Conformational analysis of the inter domain linker of the central homology region of chloroplast initiation factor IF3 supports a structural model of two compact domains connected by a flexible tether. *FEBS Lett.* 433:153–56

34. Hua YX, Raleigh DP. 1998. On the global architecture of initiation factor IF3: a comparative study of the linker regions from the *E. coli* protein and the *Bacillus stearothermophilus* protein. *J. Mol. Biol.* 278:871–78

35. Kurylo-Borowska Z. 1975. Biosynthesis of edeine. II. Localization of edeine synthetase within *Bacillus brevis* Vm4. *Biochim. Biophys. Acta* 399:31–41

36. Kycia JH, Biou V, Shu F, Gerchman SE, Graziano V, et al. 1995. Prokaryotic translation initiation factor IF3 is an elongated protein consisting of two crystallizable domains. *Biochemistry* 34:6183–87

37. La Teana A, Gualerzi CO, Brimacombe R. 1995. From stand-by to decoding site. Adjustment of the mRNA on the 30S ribosomal subunit under the influence of initiation factors. *RNA* 1:772–82

38. Mackeen LA, Kahan L, Wahba AJ, Schwartz I. 1980. Photochemical crosslinking of initiation factor-III to *Escherichia coli* 30S ribosomal-subunits. *J. Biol. Chem.* 255:526–31

39. Makowski I, Frolow F, Shoham M, Wittmann HG, Yonath A. 1987. Single crystals of large ribosomal particles from *H. marismortui* diffract to 6 Å. *J. Mol. Biol.* 193:819–22

40. Mankin AS, Garrett RA. 1991. Chloramphenicol resistance mutations in the single 23S rRNA gene of archaeon *Halobacterium halobium*. *J. Bacteriol.* 173:3559–63

41. McCutcheon JP, Agrawal RK, Philips SM, Grassucci RA, Gerchman SE, et al. 1999. Location of translational initiation factor IF3 on the small ribosomal subunit. *Proc. Natl. Acad. Sci. USA* 96:4301–6

42. Meinnel T, Sacerdot C, Graffe M, Blanquet S, Springer M. 1999. Discrimination by *E. coli* initiation factor IF3 against initiation on non-canonical codons relies on complementarity rules. *J. Mol. Biol.* 290:825–37

43. Moazed D, Noller HF. 1987. Interaction of antibiotics with functional sites in 16S rRNA. *Nature* 327:389–94

44. Moazed D, Samaha RR, Gualerzi C, Noller HF. 1995. Specific protection of 16S rRNA by translational initiation factors. *J. Mol. Biol.* 248:207–10

45. Moreau M, Coch E, Fortier PL, Garcia C, Albaret C, et al. 1997. Heteronuclear NMR studies of *E. coli* translation initiation factor IF3. Evidence that the inter-domain region is disordered in solution. *J. Mol. Biol.* 266:15–22

46. Nikonov S, Nevskaya N, Eliseikina I, Fomenkova N, Nikulin A, et al. 1996. Crystal structure of the RNA binding ribosomal protein L1 from *Thermus thermophilus*. *EMBO J.* 15:1350–59

47. Nissen P, Hansen J, Ban N, Moore PB, Steitz TA. 2000. The structural basis of ribosome activity in peptide bond synthesis. *Science* 289:920–30

48. Odon OW, Kramer G, Henderson AB, Pinphanichakarn P, Hardesty B. 1978. GTP hydrolysis during methionyl-tRNAf binding to 40S ribosomal subunits and the site of edeine inhibition. *J. Biol. Chem.* 253:1807–16

49. Ogle JM, Brodersen DE, Clemons WM Jr, Tarry MJ, et al. 2000. Recognition of cognate transfer RNA by the 30S ribosomal subunit. *Science* 292:897–902

50. Pioletti M, Schlünzen F, Harms J, Zarivach R, Gluhmann M, et al. 2001. Crystal structures of complexes of the small ribosomal subunit with tetracycline, edeine and IF3. *EMBO J.* 20:1829–39

51. Polacek N, Gaynor M, Yassin A, Mankin AS. 2001. Ribosomal peptidyl transferase can withstand mutations at the putative catalytic nucleotide. *Nature* 411:498–501

52. Sacerdot C, de Cock E, Engst K, Graffe M, Dardel F, Springer M. 1999. Mutations that alter initiation codon discrimination by *Escherichia coli* initiation factor IF3. *J. Mol. Biol.* 288:803–10

53. Schlünzen F, Tocilj A, Zarivach R, Harms J, Glühmann M, et al. 2000. Structure of functionally activated small ribosomal subunit at 3.3 angstrom resolution. *Cell* 102:615–23

54. Schlünzen F, Zarivach R, Harms J, Bashan A, Tocilj A, et al. 2001. Structural basis for the interaction of five antibiotics with the peptidyl transferase center in eubacteria. *Nature* 413:814–21

55. Sette M, Spurio R, Van Tilborg P, Gualerzi CO, Boelens R. 1999. Identification of the ribosome binding sites of translation initiation factor IF3 by multidimensional heteronuclear NMR spectroscopy. *RNA* 5:82–92

56. Shevack A, Gewitz HS, Hennemann B, Yonath A, Wittmann HG. 1985. Characterization and crystallization of ribosomal practical from *H. marismortui*. *FEBS Lett.* 184:68–73

57. Sonenberg N, Wilchek M, Zamir A. 1973. Mapping of *E. coli* ribosomal components involved in peptidyl transferase activity. *Proc. Natl. Acad. Sci. USA* 70:1423–26

58. Srivastava S, Verschoor A, Frank J. 1992. Eukaryotic initiation factor-III does not prevent association through physical blockage of the ribosomal-subunit interface. *J. Mol. Biol.* 226:301–4

59. Subramanian AR, Dabbs ER. 1980. Functional studies on ribosomes lacking protein L1 from mutant *Escherichia coli*. *Eur. J. Biochem.* 112:425–30

60. Sussman JK, Simons EL, Simons RW. 1996. *E. coli* translation initiation factor 3 discriminates the initiation codon in vivo. *Mol. Microbiol.* 21:347–60

61. Tedin K, Moll I, Grill S, Resch A, Graschopf A, et al. 1999. Translation initiation factor 3 antagonizes authentic start codon selection on leaderless mRNAs. *Mol. Microbiol.* 31:67–77

62. Thompson J, Kim DF, O'Connor M, Lieberman KR, Bayfield MA, et al. 2001. Analysis of mutations at residues A2451 and G2447 of 23S rRNA in the peptidyltransferase active site of the 50S ribosomal subunit. *Proc. Natl. Acad. Sci. USA* 98:9002–7

63. Tocilj A, Schlünzen F, Janell D, Gluehmann M, Hansen HAS, et al. 1999. The small ribosomal subunit from *T. thermophilus* at 4.5 Å resolution: pattern fittings and the identification of a functional site. *Proc. Natl. Acad. Sci. USA* 96:14252–57

64. Trakhanov SD, Yusupov MM, Agalarov SC, Garber MB, Ryazantsev SN, et al. 1987. Crystallization of 70S ribosomes and 30S ribosomal subunits from *Thermus thermophilus*. *FEBS Lett.* 220:319–22

65. VanLoock MS, Agrawal RK, Gabashvili I, Frank J, Harvey SC. 2000. Movement of the decoding region of the 16S ribosomal RNA accompanies tRNA translocation. *J. Mol. Biol.* 304:507–15

66. von Boehlen K, Makowski I, Hansen HA, Bartels H, Berkovitch-Yellin Z, et al. 1991. Characterization and preliminary attempts for derivatization of crystals of large ribosomal subunits from *Haloarcula marismortui* diffracting to 3 Å resolution. *J. Mol. Biol.* 222:11–15

67. Weiel J, Hershey JW. 1981. Fluorescence polarization studies of the interaction of *E. coli* protein synthesis initiation factor 3 with 30S ribosomal subunits. *Biochemistry* 20:5859–65

68. Weinstein S, Jahn W, Glotz C, Schlünzen F, Levin I, et al. 1999. Metal compounds as tools for the construction and the interpretation of medium-resolution maps of ribosomal particles. *J. Struct. Biol.* 127:141–51

69. Wimberly BT, Brodersen DE, Clemons WM Jr, Morgan-Warren RJ, Carter AP, et al. 2000. Structure of the 30S ribosomal subunit. *Nature* 407:327–39

70. Wower IK, Wower J, Zimmermann RA. 1998. Ribosomal protein L27 participates in both 50S subunit assembly and the peptidyl transferase reaction. *J. Biol. Chem.* 273:19847–52

71. Yonath A, Bartunik AD, Bartels K, Wittmann HG. 1984. Some X-ray diffraction patterns from single crystals of the large ribosomal subunit from *Bacillus stearothermophilus*. *J. Mol. Biol.* 177:201–6

72. Yonath A, Glotz C, Gewitz HS, Bartels KS, von Bohlen K, et al. 1988. Characterization of crystals of small ribosomal subunits. *J. Mol. Biol.* 203:831–34

73. Yonath A, Harms J, Hansen HAS, Bashan A, Schlünzen F, et al. 1998. Crystallographic studies on the ribosome, a large macromolecular assembly exhibiting severe nonisomorphism, extreme beam sensitivity and no internal symmetry. *Acta Crystallogr. A* 54:945–55

74. Yonath A, Mussig J, Tesche B, Lorenz S, Erdmann V, Wittmann HG. 1980. *Biochem. Int.* 1, 428:31–35

75. Yusupov MM, Yusupova GZ, Baucom A, Lieberman K, Earnest TN, et al. 2001. Crystal structure of the ribosome at 5.5 Å resolution. *Science* 292:883–96

76. Zamir A, Miskin R, Elson D. 1971. Inactivation and reactivation of ribosomal subunits: amino acyl transfer RNA binding activity of the 30S subunit from *E. coli*. *J. Mol. Biol.* 60:347–64

Annu. Rev. Biophys. Biomol. Struct. 2002. 31:275–302
DOI: 10.1146/annurev.biophys.31.101101.140927

PRINCIPLES AND BIOPHYSICAL APPLICATIONS OF LANTHANIDE-BASED PROBES

Paul R. Selvin

Physics Department and Biophysics Group, University of Illinois,
Urbana, Illinois 61801; e-mail: selvin@uiuc.edu

Key Words   fluorescence resonance energy transfer, lanthanide, luminescence

■ **Abstract**   Using luminescent lanthanides, instead of conventional fluorophores, as donor molecules in resonance energy transfer measurements offers many technical advantages and opens up a wide range of new applications. Advantages include farther measurable distances ($\sim$100 Å) with greater accuracy, insensitivity to incomplete labeling, and the ability to use generic relatively large labels, when necessary. Applications highlighted include the study of ion channels in living cells, protein-protein interaction in cells, DNA-protein complexes, and high-throughput screening assays to measure peptide dimerization associated with DNA transcription factors and ligand-receptor interactions.

CONTENTS

INTRODUCTION TO LANTHANIDE LUMINESCENCE AND ITS APPLICATIONS

Luminescent lanthanide chelates have highly unusual spectral characteristics that make them useful nonisotopic alternatives to organic fluorophores, particularly where there are problems of background autofluorescence (40, 53). They are also useful donors in fluorescence (luminescence) resonance energy transfer to measure nanometer conformational changes and binding events (42, 50, 57). In this review we focus on the use of lanthanides in energy transfer experiments.

Fluorescence resonance energy transfer (FRET) is a widely used technique to measure the distance between two points separated by approximately 15–100 Å (10, 12, 16, 49, 51). Measurements can be done under physiological conditions in vitro and especially with genetically encoded dyes, often in vivo as well. The technique relies on a distant-dependent transfer of energy from a donor fluorophore to an acceptor dye. Energy transfer leads to spectral changes, including changes in donor intensity, excited-state lifetime, and photobleaching rates, as well as acceptor changes. By monitoring these changes, the amount of energy transfer can be deduced, and with suitable calibrations one can then infer the distance. FRET has generally relied on organic-based dyes. However, a recent modification of the technique uses a luminescent lanthanide donor to transfer energy to an (organic-based) acceptor dye. Because lanthanide emission is technically not fluorescence (i.e., arising from a singlet-to-singlet transition), this has been called lanthanide-based or luminescence resonance energy transfer (LRET). LRET has a number of technical advantages compared to conventional FRET but relies on the same fundamental mechanism: subject to careful interpretation of various terms. Technical advantages include larger measurable distance range (>100 Å), with significantly greater accuracy and signal to background, and insensitivity to incomplete probe labeling.

First we briefly discuss the luminescent and photophysical characteristics of lanthanides, followed by a brief review of FRET theory and measurement, highlighting those areas where lanthanides differ from conventional probes. We then show a number of applications where LRET has enabled new types of systems to be studied: ion channels in living cells, the molecular motor myosin in vitro and in vivo, and the detection of binding events in high-throughput drug screening assays.

CHARACTERISTICS OF LUMINESCENT LANTHANIDE PROBES

Figure 1 shows four prototypical luminescent lanthanide probes. All contain an organic chromophore, which serves as an antenna or sensitizer, absorbing the excitation light and transferring the energy to the lanthanide ion. An antenna is necessary because of the inherently weak absorbance of the lanthanide ($1 \ M^{-1}$ cm^{-1}, or $10^4 - 10^5 \ M^{-1} \ cm^{-1}$ smaller than conventional organic fluorophores.) The complexes also contain a chelate that serves several purposes, including binding

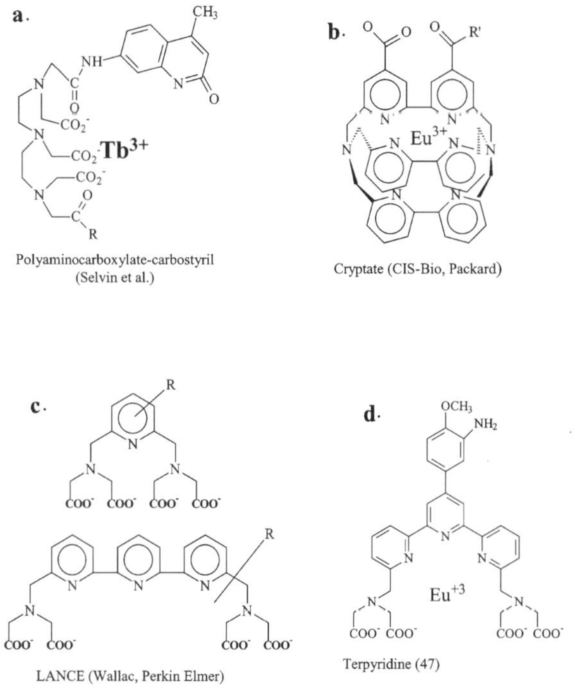

a. Polyaminocarboxylate-carbostyril
(Selvin et al.)

b. Cryptate (CIS-Bio, Packard)

c. LANCE (Wallac, Perkin Elmer)

d. Terpyridine (47)

Figure 1   Structure of representative chelates.

the lanthanide tightly, shielding the lanthanide ion from the quenching effects of water, and acting as a scaffold for attachment of the antenna and a reactive group, the latter for coupling the chelate complex to biomolecules. In the cryptates, LANCE, and terpyridine probes (Figure 1b–d), the antenna is involved in binding the lanthanide; hence logically there is not a clear separation between chelate and antenna, whereas in the polyaminocarboxylate chelates such as DTPA-cs124 (Figure 1a) the DTPA chelate and cs124 antenna are distinct entities. All four sets of probes shown have been used as detection agents to replace either conventional fluorescent probes or radioactive probes [reviewed in (48)] where subpicomolar detection limits have been achieved (13, 21, 43, 47, 54, 64). They have also been used in resonance energy transfer application, which is the focus of this review (2, 6, 9, 17, 23, 25, 29, 34, 41–43, 55, 57, 62). The predominant application of the cryptates (commercialized by CIS-Bio International and Packard Instruments) and LANCE (commercialized by Wallac, now part of Perkin Elmer) have been in binding assays associated with high-throughput screening, whereas the primary application of the polyaminocarboxylate compounds have been in basic studies to measure conformational changes. However, all such chelates can be used in both applications. We focus on the polyaminocarboxylate chelates such as DTPA-cs124.

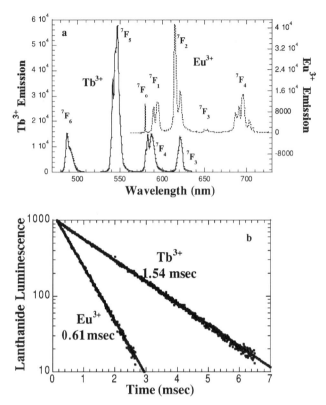

Figure 2   (*a*) Emission spectra and (*b*) lifetime of Tb^{3+}- and Eu^{3+}-DTPA-cs124.

Figure 2*a* shows the emission spectra and Figure 2*b* shows the excited-state lifetime characteristics of the DTPA-cs124 bound to either terbium or europium. These two are by far the most useful lanthanides. Dy and Sm are the only other two lanthanides that emit in the visible but with much weaker intensity (65). Excitation of the antenna is in the ultraviolet, typically utilizing the convenient nitrogen laser (337 nm), although flash lamps can also be used. Emission is in the green (Tb) and red (Eu). This large Stokes shift enables facile discrimination against excitation light. Eu and Tb emission are sharply spiked in wavelength, with long (msec) excited-state lifetimes. These attributes are important for resonance energy transfer applications (see below). The sharply spiked spectra occur because emission is atomic-like and the chelate shields the atom from broadening effects of the solvent. The long lifetime occurs because the electronic transitions involved in emission are formally forbidden by various selection rules (3). More specifically, emission arises from a 4f to 4f electronic transition and hence is parity forbidden; it also involves a high spin to high spin transition from an $S = 2$ state ($^{5}D_{4}$ for Tb^{3+}, $^{5}D_{0}$ for Eu^{3+}) to an $S = 3$ state ($^{7}F_{J}$, where $J = 0–6$). The high spin nature of the transitions is why emission is formally neither fluorescence (singlet-to-singlet transition) nor phosphorescence (triplet-to-singlet transition). Despite the unusual nature of the atomic states, emission primarily arises from electric dipole transitions (3, 15). This is important because it is the same mechanism used by organic fluorophores. Hence, the electric field produced by a lanthanide donor and by an organic donor have the same distance dependence, i.e., they both decrease as $1/R^3$ for distances $\ll$ wavelength of light. Ultimately, this leads to the same distance dependence, R^{-6}, for resonance energy transfer measurements using either lanthanides or organic donors.

The emission quantum yield for terbium or europium in the chelates is also quite high (15). This is important because the efficiency of energy transfer is proportional to the donor quantum yield (Equations 3 and 5). By lanthanide quantum yield, Q_{Ln}, we mean the probability that the lanthanide will emit a photon given that the lanthanide is excited. This definition is similar to that used with conventional fluorophores, although there is a subtlety. Lanthanide excitation is a two-step process: The antenna absorbs a photon and then passes this energy onto the lanthanide with some finite probability ($\equiv Q_{transfer} \leq 1$) (Figure 3). The lanthanide then emits with some probability, i.e., the quantum yield mentioned above, Q_{Ln}. The overall probability that the lanthanide will emit a photon (Q_{total}), given that an excitation photon was absorbed by the complex (antenna), is

$$Q_{total} = Q_{Ln} \times Q_{transfer}. \tag{1}$$

For organic fluorophores, $Q_{transfer} \equiv 1$ and hence $Q_{total} = Q_{Ln}$. For Tb^{3+} and Eu^{3+} in polyaminocarboxylate chelates such as in Figure 1a, $Q_{transfer} = 0.4$–0.75 and $Q_{total} = 0.1$–0.4 (64). In any case, the efficiency of energy transfer (related to R_o, the distance at which half the donor's energy is transferred to the acceptor, e.g., Equation 5) is proportional to Q_{Ln}, and Q_{total} is only relevant in that it affects the total brightness of the sample.

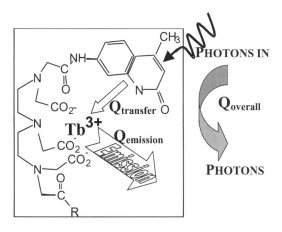

Figure 3   Definition of quantum yields.

In order for the lanthanides to be useful in bioassays, the chelates must have a reactive group for attachment to biomolecules. Fortunately, the standard reactive groups can be coupled to the chelates: Amine-reactive groups such as isothio-cyanates (36) and thiol-reactive groups such as maleimides, bromoacetamides, and pyridyl dithio (8) have been made for the polyaminocarboxylate chelates. The same or similar reactive groups have been made for the LANCE (58) and cryptates (see also www.perkinelmer.com). The reactive groups can, however, lead to more complicated photophysics in that they can interact with the antenna molecules or adopt multiple conformations, leading to multi-exponential lanthanide decays, particularly with terbium (8).

LANTHANIDE-BASED RESONANCE ENERGY TRANSFER

In resonance energy transfer experiments, using lanthanides as donors to transfer energy to organic-based acceptors leads to many technical advantages compared to using all-organic dyes. Because lanthanide emission is not formally fluores-cence, we call the technique lanthanide- or luminescence-resonancy energy trans-fer (LRET), as opposed to FRET, for which we mean energy transfer using organic dyes. Despite the differences, the mechanism of energy transfer is the same in FRET and LRET; hence the underlying theory and formulas can be used, subject to careful interpretation of various terms. Here we quickly review the theory and measurement of FRET and highlight those parts relevant or different in LRET.

FRET and its derivative, LRET, are techniques for measuring the distance be-tween two points that are separated by approximately 15–100 Å. The techniques are valuable because measurements can be made under physiological (or other) conditions with near-Angstrom resolution and with the exquisite sensitivity of flu-orescence measurements. In FRET or LRET, a donor fluorophore is excited and transfers energy to an acceptor fluorophore in a distant-dependent fashion. The classical physics view of this process is that the donor, after being excited, pro-duces an oscillating electric dipole field that decays with distance (R). At distances less than the wavelength of light (λ), the electric field predominantly drops off as R^{-3}. (For $R \gg \lambda$, $E \, \alpha \, R^{-1}$, which is simply the electric part of the propagating field that is the emitted photons.) An acceptor, if nearby and containing energy levels corresponding to the frequencies of the oscillating electric field, can interact with this field and become excited, taking energy. The probability of the acceptor being excited depends on the square of the electric field strength and hence decays as R^{-6} for $R \ll \lambda$, the relevant distance scale in FRET/LRET ($\lambda \approx 500$ nm). Energy transfer also depends on how well the acceptor energy levels match the frequen-cies of the donor (the so-called spectral overlap term, e.g., Equation 6). Finally, energy transfer may also depend on the orientation of the donor and acceptor (the "κ^2" term, e.g., Equations 5 and 7) because the electric field of the donor may be polarized and anisotropic.

The efficiency of energy transfer, E, is defined as the probability that an excited donor will return to the ground state by giving its energy to an acceptor. This can be written as

$$E = k_{et}/(k_{et} + k_{nd}) = 1/(1 + k_{nd}/k_{et}) = 1/(1 + 1/k_{et}\tau_D), \tag{2}$$

where k_{et} is the rate of energy transfer and is distant-dependent, and k_{nd} is the rate of all other donor decay processes, such as the radiative and nonradiative rates of donor decay. These latter processes clearly do not depend on the donor-acceptor distances. The donor lifetime in absence of acceptor is τ_D. Note that E depends on the ratio k_{et} to other processes but does not depend on the absolute donor lifetime. In FRET, donor rates (or lifetimes) and energy transfer rates are in the nanosecond range, whereas in LRET they are in the millisecond range; both can yield similar values of E. As a side point, if the distance between the probes changes slowly on the FRET timescale, but quickly on the LRET timescale, the two techniques can give dramatically different energy transfer efficiencies. Indeed, one signature of such dynamics is if LRET gives a much higher E than FRET (7).

Because the rate of energy transfer depends on the R^{-6} distance between donor and acceptor, Equation 2 can be rewritten as

$$E = 1/\left(1 + R^6/R_o^6\right) \tag{3}$$

or, rearranging,

$$R = R_o(1/E - 1)^{1/6}, \tag{4}$$

where R_o is a constant depending on the spectral properties of the dyes as well as their relative orientation, and it is the distance at which E = 0.5. Consequently, if R_o can be determined or calculated and E measured spectroscopically, then FRET/LRET can be used as a spectroscopic ruler to determine distances (56).

R_o is usually calculated from the spectral properties of donor and acceptor (5):

$$R_o = 0.21\left(Jq_D n^{-4}\kappa^2\right)^{1/6} \text{ (in Angstroms)} \tag{5}$$

$$J = \int \varepsilon_A(\lambda)\, f_D(\lambda)\lambda^4 d\lambda \Big/ \int f_D(\lambda)\, d\lambda \text{ in } \underline{M}^{-1} \text{ cm}^{-1} \text{ nm}^4, \tag{6}$$

where J is the normalized spectral overlap of the donor emission (f_D) and acceptor absorption (ε_A in units of $\underline{M}^{-1}$ cm^{-1}, where $\underline{M}$ is units of Moles/liter), q_D is the quantum efficiency (or quantum yield) for donor emission in the absence of acceptor (q_D = number of photons emitted divided by number of photons absorbed), n is the index of refraction (1.33 for water; 1.29 for many organic molecules), and κ^2 is a geometric factor related to the relative orientation of the transition dipoles of the donor and acceptor and their relative orientation in space. Note that for LRET, q_D in Equation 5 is Q_{Ln} and not Q_{total} (Equation 1). This is because Q_{Ln}, not Q_{total}, determined the strength of the donor's electric field.

The orientation term, κ^2, in R_o, is often a source of uncertainty in FRET measurements. It is defined as

$$\kappa^2 = (\cos\theta_{DA} - 3\cos\theta_D \cos\theta_A)^2, \tag{7}$$

where θ_{DA} is the angle between the donor and acceptor transition dipole moments, and θ_D (θ_A) is the angle between the donor (acceptor) transition dipole moment and the R vector joining the two dyes. By measuring the polarization of donor and acceptor emission, constraints on these angles can often be imposed, reducing—although usually not completely eliminating—the uncertainty in κ^2. κ^2 ranges from 0 if all angles are 90 degrees to 4 if all angles are zero degrees, and it equals 2/3 if the donor and acceptor rapidly and completely rotate during the donor excited-state lifetime (14). If the donor is unpolarized, as is the case for terbium and usually europium (J. G. Reifenberger, G. E. Snyder & P. R. Selvin, manuscript in preparation), and the acceptor is completely rigid and either parallel ($\kappa^2 = 2/3$) or perpendicular ($\kappa^2 = 1/3$) to the radius vector, then $1/3 < \kappa^2 < 2/3$. This limits the worst case error in R_o to -11% $+12\%$ if one simply assumes $\kappa^2 = 2/3$. Furthermore, because the lanthanides have millisecond lifetimes, the acceptor will likely rotate during this time, making κ^2 very close to 2/3. Hence, the error in distances measured via LRET due to the orientation factor is essentially negligible. This in turn makes the distance determination via LRET generally more accurate than FRET because the orientation factor in FRET is often poorly known.

Finally, R_o is also proportional to J, the spectral overlap. The lanthanides have highly spiked emission spectra in regions where several excellent dyes absorb (Figure 2a), e.g., the Tb^{3+} 490 nm emission peak overlaps well with fluorescein, green fluorescent protein, and Alexa 488 absorption; the Tb^{3+} 546 nm peak overlaps with Cy3, tetramethylrhodamine, Alexa 546, and R-phycoerythrin absorption; the Eu 617 nm peak overlaps with Cy5, Alexa 633, and allophycocyanin absorption. Consequently, J for LRET can be unusually large. When combined with a high Q_{Ln}, the R_o in LRET can also be quite large (Table 1).

Measuring E

In Figure 4, an energy transfer experiment between a terbium-labeled DNA and a rhodamine-labeled DNA complement is shown (52). This example highlights various ways of measuring energy transfer. In FRET and LRET there are several ways of measuring E: a reduction in donor intensity in the presence of acceptor because some of the energy is going to the acceptor instead of into donor emission, by a decrease in donor excited-state lifetime because energy transfer to the acceptor is an additional relaxation pathway of the donor's excited state, or by an increase in acceptor fluorescence because the acceptor is receiving energy from the donor and converting this energy into acceptor fluorescence. In LRET, E can also be measured via the sensitized-emission lifetime (see below). In FRET (but not LRET) E can also be measured by an increase in the photostability of the donor in the presence of acceptor because energy transfer to the acceptor decreases the donor's excited-state lifetime, and photobleaching is generally proportional to the amount of time the dye spends in its excited state. Finally FRET and potentially LRET can be measured by an increase in donor intensity following photodestruction of the acceptor (30).

TABLE 1 J-values and R_o for lanthanide chelates and organic dyes

Donor-acceptor pairs*	J-value ($M^{-1}\ cm^{-1}\ nm^4$)	R_o (Å)
Terbium to fluorescein (bound to DNA) ($\varepsilon_{max} = 75k$ @ 492 nm)	9.23×10^{14}	45.0
Terbium to eGFP (free) ($\varepsilon_{max} = 55k$ @ 488 nm)	7.14×10^{14}	43.1
Terbium to TMR (bound to DNA) ($\varepsilon_{max} = 100k$ @ 557 nm)	3.80×10^{15}	57.0
Terbium to Cy3 (free) ($\varepsilon_{max} = 150k$ @ 552 nm)	5.82×10^{15}	61.2
Terbium to R phycoerythrin pH 7.5 (free) ($\varepsilon_{max} = 1960k$ @ 566 nm)	9.60×10^{16}	97.5
Europium to Cy5 (bound to myosin) ($\varepsilon_{max} = 249k$ @ 650 nm)	8.89×10^{15}	55.2
Europium to allophycocyanin pH 7.5 (free) ($\varepsilon_{max} = 700k$ @ 652 nm)	4.01×10^{16}	71.0

*J and R_o calculated for terbium and europium using corrected emission spectra and quantum yields for lanthanide bound to DTPA-cs124 in aqueous solutions ($q_{Tb} = 0.48$; $q_{Eu} = 0.17$). J and R_o in D_2O and in other chelates with same emission spectra can be determined by multiplying by the appropriate quantum yields, found in (64). Other constants: n = 1.33; $\kappa^2 = 2/3$. The emission spectra of Tb^{3+} and Eu^{3+} are insensitive to attachment to biomolecules, although the absorption spectra of the acceptor dye can be somewhat sensitive to attachment. Absorption spectra of R phycoerythrin and allophycocyanin are from Molecular Probes Inc., and Cy-3 from Amersham.

The efficiency of energy transfer (E) is then

$$E = \left(1 - I_{D_A}/I_D\right) = 1 - \tau_{D_A}/\tau_D = 1 - \tau_{A_D}/\tau_D = 1 - \tau_D^{bl}/\tau_{D_A}^{bl}, \qquad (8)$$

where I_{D_A}, τ_{D_A}, and $\tau_{D_A}^{bl}$ are the donor's intensity, excited-state lifetime, and photobleaching time constant in the presence of acceptor, and I_D, τ_D, and τ_D^{bl} are the same parameters in the absence of acceptor. τ_{A_D} is the lifetime of the sensitized emission of acceptor (discussed further below).

Although using absolute intensities, I_{D_A}, I_D, is conceptually straightforward, it involves matching concentrations of two different samples and hence is prone to titration errors. Lifetime measurements avoid this problem and also resolve multiple species with different E's. Figure 4b shows a single-exponential donor-only lifetime that is reduced upon hybridization with an acceptor-containing DNA strand. Starting with a single-exponential donor-only lifetime is not essential but significantly simplifies the analysis of complex donor-acceptor mixtures. Titrating in with substoichiometric amounts of acceptor strand leads to two populations and hence a bi-exponential donor decay: a donor-only unhybridized strand ($\tau_{D_A} = $ 2.1 msec) and donor-acceptor double-stranded DNA ($\tau_{D_A} = 330\ \mu$sec). The amount of energy in the donor-acceptor pair can be calculated in Equation 8 using the

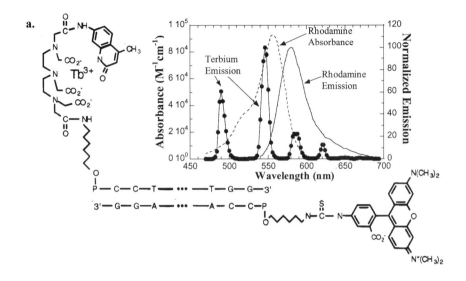

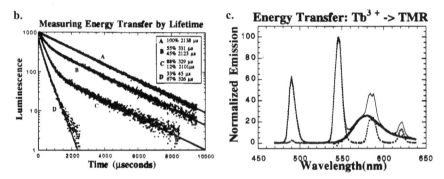

Figure 4 (*a*) DNA hybridization and model system for LRET. (*b*) Lifetime data. (*c*) Spectral data. [Figure adapted from (52)].

330-μsec lifetime and the donor-only lifetime of a terbium DNA hybridized to an unlabeled complementary DNA, which is 2.8 msec (data not shown). The relative populations of the two species can be determined by their pre-exponential amplitudes. Titrating in more acceptor strand increases the amplitude of the short time component but leaves its lifetime unchanged, as expected.

In LRET, E can also be measured by measuring the lifetime of the sensitized emission of acceptor (Figure 4*b*, *curve D*). The donor is excited by a pulse of light, the direct acceptor emission decays in nanoseconds, and any acceptor emission after this initial delay is therefore due only to energy transfer received by the acceptor from the long-lived donor. Its lifetime, τ_{A_D}, will follow the donor's lifetime, τ_{D_A}. Importantly, τ_{A_D} can be measured without contaminating background from either direct acceptor fluorescence via temporal discrimination or from donor emission via spectral discrimination. The latter is possible because the donor is sharply spiked in emission spectra, including regions where the donor is dark yet where the acceptor fluoresces. For example terbium is dark around 520 nm and 570 nm, where fluorescein and tetramethylrhodamine emit, respectively. Consequently, the temporal decay of the acceptor-sensitized emission can be measured with no background, from either donor leakage or direct acceptor leakage. This sensitized-emission lifetime is a powerful advantage of LRET because it only arises from donor-acceptor pairs. In Figure 4b, *curve D*, the sensitized-emisison lifetime closely matches the short component of the donor lifetime; however, it does not have contamination from the donor-only DNA strands. The pre-exponential amplitudes of a sensitized-emission decay correspond to the population of excited acceptors. Hence, in a multi-exponential decay corresponding to a distribution of donor-acceptor pairs, the pre-exponential terms are the product of the individual energy transfer efficiencies and their populations (24). This is in contrast to the donor decay, where the amplitudes are just proportional to populations.

E can also be determined by measuring the increase in fluorescence of the acceptor due to energy transfer and comparing this to the residual donor emission,

$$E = \left[I_{A_D}/q_A\right]/\left[I_{D_A}/q_D + I_{A_D}/q_A\right], \qquad (9)$$

where I_{D_A} is the integrated area under the donor-emission curve in the presence of acceptor, I_{A_D} is the integrated area of the sensitized emission of the acceptor (i.e., not including the fluorescence due to direct excitation of the acceptor by the exciting light source), and q_i is the quantum yield for donor or acceptor. The integrated areas are determined by curve-fitting the spectrum to the sum of a donor-only and acceptor-only spectra. Qualitatively, this equation says that energy transfer takes area under the donor-emission curve to area under the acceptor curve. Because E is defined in terms of excitations, not emissions, these areas are normalized by their quantum yields, which is just the ratio of emissions to excitations. More specifically, the numerator is the number of excitations of the acceptor due to energy transfer. The left-hand term of the denominator is the number of donor excitations that do not lead to energy transfer. The right-hand term is the donor excitations that do lead to energy transfer, i.e., acceptor excitation.

Figure 4c shows the time-delayed emission spectra of the donor and donor-acceptor complex (corresponding to *curve C* in Figure 4b), which can be used to determine the two intensities in Equation 9. The donor-acceptor sample is excited using a short excitation pulse, and emission is detected after a few tens of microseconds delay. This procedure eliminates all prompt fluorescence of the acceptor. It also eliminates any contribution from acceptor-only species, if present, as well as any direct fluorescence from the antenna, both of which have nanosecond lifetimes. The donor-acceptor spectrum is then fit to the sum of a donor and acceptor spectra, with I_{D_A} being the area due to donor emission and I_{A_D} equal to the area under the acceptor emission. Note that the absolute concentrations of the donor-only species, the acceptor-only species, and the donor-acceptor species are irrelevant. In practice, the curve-fitting is done as follows: The donor-only spectra and donor-acceptor spectra are normalized at the 490-nm peak, or at any point where there is no acceptor fluorescence. The donor-only curve is then subtracted from the donor-acceptor spectra, and the difference is the sensitized-emission curve, with area I_{A_D}. This should have the same shape as an acceptor-only emission spectra. I_{D_A} is simply the area under the donor-curve. (Although we always take a donor-only spectra as a control (*dashed line*, Figure 4c), the spectral shape of Tb-DTPA-cs124 does not change under any condition tested; hence a donor-only spectrum taken once is likely to remain unchanged.)

There are two additional points needed to properly use Equation 9. First, the emission spectra must be corrected for wavelength sensitivity of the detector. This is done via conventional means, using an emission source (standard lamp or a dye) whose emission spectra are known (35). Second, the donor and acceptor quantum yields must be measured. Fortunately, we have recently determined the quantum yield of Tb^{3+} and Eu^{3+} in free polyaminocarboxylate chelates (64). The quantum yield of lanthanide chelates bound to biomolecules can then simply be determined by comparing lifetimes to the free chelates. Acceptor quantum yields can be measured by conventional means: intensity or lifetime comparison to standards such as fluorescein [QY $= 0.93$ in 1 N NaOH (61)], or tetramethylrhodamine [QY $= 0.58$ in 10-mM Na-phosphate buffer, pH 7.46, 80-mM NaCl, room temperature (60)], or sulforhodamine 101 [QY $= 1$, lifetime $= 4.36$ nsec, in methanol (33)].

The importance of Equation 9 is that it allows accurate measurement of relatively small amounts of energy transfer (distances $>R_o$). It is also interesting to note, although not widely appreciated, that by combining equations 4, 5, and 9, the calculated distance depends only on the acceptor quantum yield and not on the donor quantum yield:

$$R = C\left[I_{D_A}q_A/I_{A_D}\right]^{1/6}, \tag{10}$$

where C is simply all the constants in R_o except q_D. Finally, Equations 9 and 10 can also be used in conventional FRET, but here the direct excitation of acceptor must first be subtracted off (11).

In summary, the advantages of LRET include large signals (big R_os) with low backgrounds, enabling long distances to be determined with little uncertainty due to orientation factors. Energy transfer can be measured accurately because absolute concentrations do not matter via spectral measurements, and the μsec-msec lifetimes can be measured accurately via temporal measurements. The extent of donor and acceptor incorporation has only a minor effect on LRET measurements because, via sensitized-emission lifetime measurements, donor-only and acceptor-only species do not contribute contaminating backgrounds. This lack of sensitivity to incomplete labeling is particularly important in cellular applications, where 100% labeling and purification cannot usually be achieved.

Instrumentation

The instrumentation used to perform LRET is relatively simple, although slightly more complex than conventional steady-state fluorimeters. The general requirements are a pulsed UV excitation source and time-resolved detection. The pulsed

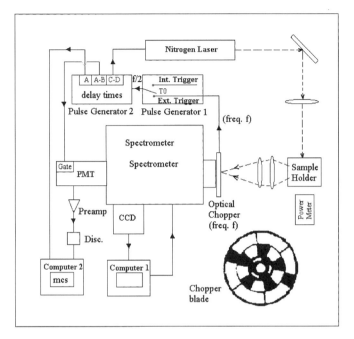

Figure 5   LRET instrumentation. A pulsed nitrogen laser excites the lanthanide sample, and emission is collected by a mechanically chopped spectrometer and CCD for time-delayed spectral measurements, or a spectrometer and electronically gated PMT for excited-state lifetime measurements. [Figure from (63)].

excitation source is usually a nitrogen laser (337 nm, 5-nsec pulse-width typical, 20–50-Hz repetition rate). For lifetime measurements, a photomultiplier tube with suitable color filters and counting electronics is used. For time-delayed spectra, a spectrometer, typically utilizing diffraction gratings, and either a time-gated photomultiplier tube or preferably a CCD, gated either electronically or with a mechanical chopper, are used. A schematic of the instrument built in my laboratory is shown in Figure 5 and details are given elsewhere (63, 64).

APPLICATIONS

The technical advantages of LRET open up many applications. We highlight a few representative examples from my lab, as well as from others.

Ion Channels

We have used LRET to measure conformational changes in the Shaker potassium ion channel, a voltage-gated channel involved in nerve impulses. In many ways this is an extremely demanding use of LRET. The measurement is on a living cell (*Xenopus* oocytes); hence purification of completely labeled donor-acceptor species is not possible. Indeed, a heterogeneous mixture of labeled proteins exists, all in the presence of nonspecific labeling to other membrane components. Furthermore, two distances are expected to exist (see below) and the distance changes (as a function of voltage—see below) are quite small—a few Ångstroms. The technical advantages of LRET help overcome these difficulties.

The channel is a transmembrane protein, consisting of four identical subunits (Figure 6a,b) with fourfold symmetry. Each subunit contains six transmembrane-spanning segments, S1–S6 (Figure 6c). A pore, or channel, is formed at the intersection of the four subunits, which is opened or closed, i.e., gated, depending on the voltage across the cell membrane. At the resting transmembrane potential of approximately -60 mV, the pore is closed. Upon depolarization to approximately 0 mV, the protein undergoes a conformational change that ultimately leads to an opening of the pore, allowing potassium ions to flow from the inside to outside of the cell, down its electrochemical gradient. The flow of potassium ions along with the flow of sodium ions through analogous sodium channel are the electrical currents that form nerve impulses.

One of the transmembrane segments, S4, is known as the "voltage sensor" and contains seven positively charged amino acids. These charges feel a force due to the transmembrane potential or electric field and are likely to move in response to changes in these fields. A second segment, S2, also contains some positively charged residues and likely plays a secondary role in voltage sensing as well.

Fundamental questions remain regarding how the channel senses and responds to voltage. What is the structure of the S4, e.g., is it an alpha helix? How does it sit in the membrane—perpendicular to the membrane or tilted at an angle? How does the S4 move in response to voltage changes? Does it move like a plunger, e.g., moving up and down, perpendicular, or at some angle to the membrane? Or does it rotate like a knob, perhaps with little transmembrane motion? Or is the movement some combination, perhaps like a corkscrew rotating and translating? And finally, how is the motion of S4 coupled to the pore region such that a motion of S4 leads to opening and closing of the pore?

Cysteine-scanning mutagenesis is the most common method for detecting conformational changes in ion channels. The idea is to look at changes in accessibility of engineered cysteines to external-labeling reagents. Labeling of reagents can be detected if they have an effect on ionic or gating currents. (Ionic current is the flow of potassium ions through the pore; gating currents are transient currents created by the movement of the charged residues in the protein, mostly on S4 and S2.) This method, however, is quite indirect since changes in labeling efficiency can be due to several factors and not all sites lead to changes in gating properties. Isacoff et al. (39), and shortly thereafter, Bezanilla and colleagues (5a), introduced the use of fluorescent-labeling reagents to detect conformational changes. Here a fluorophore was attached to an engineered cysteine in S4 and changes in fluorescence with changes in voltage were measured. These fluorescence changes were interpreted as arising from changes in the local environment around the fluorophore, e.g., from a more hydrophic or membrane-like environment to a more water-like

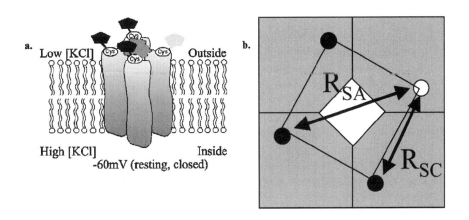

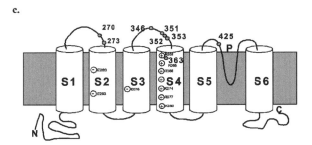

Figure 6 Structure of Shaker potassium ion channel and labeling scheme. (*a*) Side view, (*b*) top view, (*c*) substructure. The channel consists of a central pore (*dark gray* in 6*a*) surrounded by four identical subunits. Each subunit consists of six transmembrane domains (6*c*) and is labeled with either a donor (*black*, 6*a,b*), or acceptor (*light gray*, 6*a*; *white*, 6*b*). Labeling is done such that there are 3 donors (*black*) and only one acceptor (*white*) per channel. Specific labeling is achieved by introducing a unique cysteine in the S3-S4 linker, near S4, which is the voltage sensor.

environment (39). This led Isacoff et al. to postulate a translational, transmembrane movement of the S4, bringing fluorophores buried inside the membrane to a more extracellular region. However, changes in fluorescence are also an indirect measurement of conformational changes. FRET, or LRET, is a much more direct measure (51). In more recent work the Isacoff group (18) used FRET to measure S4 motion, and the Bezanilla and Selvin groups used LRET (6). Both concluded there was a rotation of S4, although based on the LRET methodology, Bezanilla and Selvin concluded there was not a large transmembrane movement, whereas the Isacoff group argued such a motion may exist. A detailed comparison of the two experiments has been published (27). Here we review the LRET experiment.

For labeling the channel, a single engineered cysteine was introduced at various positions in the S3-S4 linker, near the top of the S4. Each channel therefore contains four cysteines, one on each subunit. Conveniently, the Shaker channel does not contain native cysteines that are reactive to extracellularly applied probes. Channels were expressed in *Xenopus* oocytes and labeled with a mixture of donor and acceptor probes, the donor in excess to ensure that most channels contain at most only one acceptor. Under this condition, two different donor-acceptor distances are expected (Figure 6b). A donor sees an acceptor on a contiguous subunit (distance R_{SC}) or on a subunit across the pore (distance R_{SA}). To measure these distances, we focused on measuring the sensitized-emission lifetime. This has the great advantage that those channels containing all donors—the majority of channels—do not contribute signal and can be ignored. (Those containing all acceptors can also be ignored, although this is a small fraction of the channels.) We therefore expect the sensitized-emission lifetime to be bi-exponential, with the shorter lifetime corresponding to the greater E and shorter distance. Figure 7a shows this behavior for a probe labeled at position 346. The two distances are in excellent agreement with the expected Pythagorean relationship. By placing probes at various positions, ranging from 363 near the top of S4 to 346 near the middle of the S3-S4 linker, we found that the intersubunit distances decreased. This implies that S3-S4 (and perhaps S4) is tilted toward the pore as one moves in the extracellular direction.

In FRET, and to a certain extent in LRET, absolute distances are always more difficult to measure than relative distances. However, to check whether our absolute distances were reasonable, we measured distances between residues 425. This residue is found in the crystal structure of the KcsA channel, a (nonvoltage-gated) prokaryotic analog of Shaker containing two transmembranes per subunit, analogous to S5 and S6. We found $R_{SA} = 30$ Å, in excellent agreement with the $C_\alpha - C_\alpha$ 29 Å distance in the crystal structure. Furthermore, after publication of our LRET results, other workers measured distances using "tethered linkers" and found excellent agreement in absolute distances to our results (1). This is in sharp contrast to the FRET results (18), which yielded much larger absolute distances. The latter probably occurred because of uncertainties in donor quantum yields and possibly because of the κ^2 factor.

Next we measured intersubunit distances as a function of voltage. Changes in lifetime and hence distances between site 346 near S4 are shown in Figure 7b. Figure 7c shows a plot of R_{SC} versus voltage, superimposed on gating charge movement. Strikingly, the changes in distance at 346 strongly mirror gating charge movement, implying that the distances we measure at 346 are related to the charge movement in S4 and functioning of the channel. By modeling the distance versus voltage curve, we concluded that a large transmembrane motion did not occur (6). Furthermore, small but statistically significant changes in distance were found at positions 350, 351, and 352, where 351 moved farther apart, 350 remained unchanged, and 352 moved closer together (Figure 8a). The simplest model to account for this nonmonotonic behavior is to postulate that the S3-S4 linker is helical and undergoes a rotation about its long axis (Figure 8b). Because

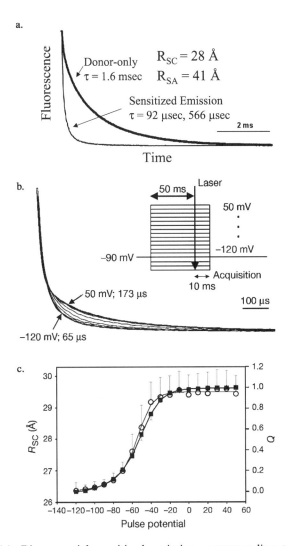

Figure 7 (*a*) Biexponential sensitized emission, corresponding to two donor-acceptor distances, corresponding to distances between subunits across the channel and neighboring subunits. (*b*) Voltage-dependent changes in sensitized emission arising from movement of S346C in the voltage-sensing region of Shaker potassium channel. (*c*) Changes in distance between S346 and amount of charge in S4 moved across membrane potential. The changes in distance closely mirror the charge movement in S4. [Figures from (6)].

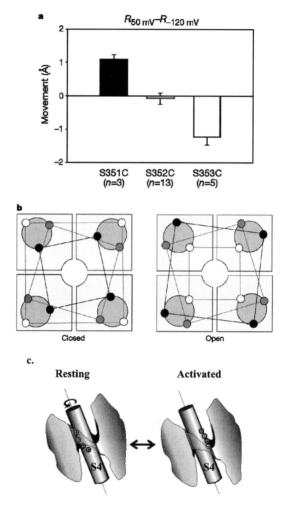

Figure 8 Changes in distance between sites 351–353. These data can be explained by a rotation of a helical segment of the ion channel (*b*), leading to a model where the voltage sensor, S4, may undergo a rotation in response to voltage (*c*). [Adapted from (6, 18)].

the S3-S4 linker distance changes are coupled closely to the charge movement of S4, S4 may also undergo a rotation (Figure 8*c*) in response to voltage. That such small distance changes can be measured is a tribute to the power of LRET, although interpretation of such small distance changes must be made with caution. Interestingly, a rotation in ligand-gated ion channels (26, 28) and a transporter (37) has recently been measured, which suggests that helix rotation may be a general feature of membrane channels.

APPLICATION 2: CONFORMATIONAL CHANGES IN A RNA POLYMERASE SUBUNIT UPON DNA BINDING

Protein-Induced DNA Bends

The Heyduk lab has been active in using LRET to study DNA-protein interactions. In one of their earlier works they used LRET to measure protein-induced DNA bending (25), which is involved in the packaging and regulation of DNA. They used LRET, for example, to measure the bending of a 30mer double-stranded DNA oligomer by a class of proteins known as high-mobility group (HMG) proteins. The DNA was 5'-labeled with europium and Cy5, and distances out to 100 Å were measured with energy transfer efficiencies of less than 3%. This was possible because of LRET's capability to accurately determine lifetimes, especially when the donor is single exponential. The Ebright lab has also recently applied LRET using a terbium chelate to measure 100 Å distances in DNA complexes bent by the CAP protein (32).

Recently, Heyduk and coworkers have used LRET to study conformational changes in RNA polymerase upon binding to DNA and transcription initiation in prokaryotes (4, 23). The first step in transcription initiation in prokaryotes involves recognition of promoter DNA sequence by a multisubunit enzyme RNA polymerase [reviewed in (20)]. One of the subunits, σ^{70}, is involved in the initial recognition of the promoter DNA via direct protein-DNA contacts separated by ~17 base pairs. σ^{70} exists in the cell in two major forms: free and in complex with the remaining RNA polymerase subunits (core polymerase). However, only σ^{70} in complex with the core RNA polymerase is able to specifically recognize promoter DNA, whereas the free σ^{70} does not bind to promoter DNA. Thus, the promoter recognition capabilities of σ^{70} are allosterically regulated by an interaction of σ^{70} with the core polymerase.

LRET experiments were used to investigate the nature of the regulation of σ^{70} promoter DNA-binding activity (4). The idea was to look for conformational differences in σ^{70} in the bound and free form that might affect its DNA-recognition ability. The specific incorporation of the donor (DTPA-Eu-DTPA-AMCA-maleimide) (22) and the acceptor (Cy5 maleimide) into selected domains of σ^{70} was achieved by preparing a set of σ^{70} mutants with pairs of unique reactive cysteine residues engineered into the desired locations. Since both donor and acceptor were thiol-reactive, and both labeling sites were cysteine residues, a mixture of donor-donor, donor-acceptor, and acceptor-acceptor labeling resulted. However, by using LRET, the sensitized emission arising from only the donor-acceptor complex could be measured. Good quality determinations of τ_{ad} were possible in this case even though the donor-acceptor species constituted only approximately 25% of the mixture. This is possible because the donor-only and acceptor-only species do not contribute background signals. Representative LRET data are shown in Figure 9. It would be difficult to perform these measurements with FRET utilizing classical fluorescence probes.

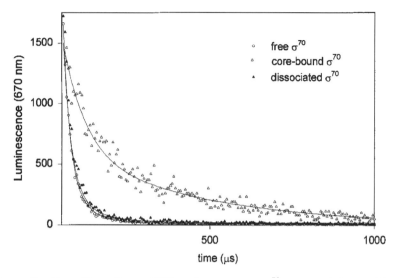

Figure 9   The effect of core RNA polymerase on σ^{70} measured by sensitized-emission lifetime. Thiol-reactive Eu donor and Cy5 acceptor were labeled at positions A59C to R596C in σ^{70}, and sensitized emission of free and core-bound σ^{70} was measured. The increase in sensitized-emission lifetime upon core binding indicates less energy transfer and an increase in distance between these sites. [Figure from Figure 3D of (4)].

Comparison of distances measured for the free σ^{70} and the core-bound σ^{70} revealed that most distances were significantly increased upon binding of σ^{70} to the core polymerase. (DNA was not present in these experiments because σ^{70} binding to the core polymerase is not DNA dependent.) One of the distances measured, between residues 442 and 366, allowed a direct comparison between a distance measured by LRET in solution and a distance between the same residues measured in the crystal structure (38). Excellent agreement between these distances was found—35 Å in the crystal structure versus 38 Å measured via LRET—providing a further validation of LRET results. In total six distances between four sites in the σ^{70} protein were measured, making it possible to build three-dimensional models of the architecture of σ^{70} protein domains in free and core-bound protein.

In conclusion, these DNA and DNA-protein studies were greatly facilitated by LRET's ability to measure long distances and under labeling conditions where only a small fraction of the protein contained both donor and acceptor labels.

APPLICATION 3: MEASURING MOLECULAR INTERACTIONS IN A CELL

Douglas Root has used LRET to study the interaction of the proteins dystrophin and actin in the muscle cell (46). Dystrophin is present in the inner muscle cell membrane and is believed to stabilize muscle fibers by binding to actin filaments and ultimately creating a bridge to the extracellular matrix. This model requires the direct association (close proximity) between dystrophin and actin, and there is significant in vitro evidence for this. However, because some proteins bind in vitro but not in vivo, Root asked the question whether this association is present in the muscle cell.

Root used thin (20 μM) tissue sections of muscle cells and specifically labeled dystrophin with monoclonal antibodies labeled with Tb-DTPA-cs124. Actin was stained with phalloidin-tetramethylrhodamine. This pair was reported to have a R_o of 59 Å, although 56 Å is probably more accurate (e.g., Table 1, which lists values for R_os) (64). In any case, a relatively large R_o is necessary to get reasonable energy transfer because of the large size of antibodies ($\approx$100 Å). If the donor antibody on dystrophin is in close proximity, roughly within R_o, of the acceptor-labeled actin, then energy transfer should be observed. If the distance is large ($\gg R_o$), then no energy transfer is expected.

In fixed tissues donor intensity decreased 40% (in unfixed tissue 60%) in the presence of acceptor, indicating significant energy transfer and therefore a close association between anti-dystrophin antibodies and actin (Figure 10). Sensitized emission (using delayed detection to eliminate prompt acceptor fluorescence) was also observed. In addition, Root measured donor and sensitized-emission lifetime measurements (fitting to a single exponential) and found that the sensitized-emission lifetime (at 568 nm) was similar but somewhat shorter than the donor-lifetime (at 547 nm) [data not presented here, but see (46)]. This indicates that most, but not all, of the anti-dystrophin antibodies had an acceptor nearby. (A comparison of donor lifetime to sensitized-emission lifetime gives information about the

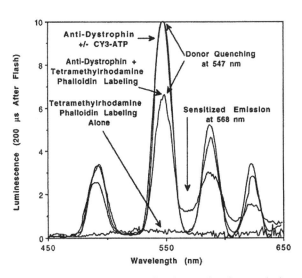

Figure 10   LRET signal indicating molecular proximity between dystrophin and actin in a muscle cell. [Figure from (46)].

distribution of donor-acceptor complexes: Donor-emission measurements are weighted toward those transferring less energy, and sensitized-emission measurements are weighted toward those transferring more energy. For example, if some donors have no acceptors nearby, this will lengthen the average donor lifetime, whereas it does not affect the sensitized-emission lifetime because this latter signal arises only from those complexes that can transfer energy.)

Root also looked at the spatial distribution of the anti-dystrophin antibodies by performing LRET in a microscope. Examining 90-μm diameter regions of the tissue sections, dual-labeled samples yielded a sensitized-emission lifetime of $0.7+/-0.1$ msec, but donor-emission lifetimes were more variable, ranging from 0.7 msec to 1.4 msec. Root suggested that the association for dystrophin for actin may have micro-heterogeneity within the cell.

Finally, Root compared the detection of molecular colocalization using LRET with the conventional technique of immunofluorescence colocalization. In immunofluorescence colocalization, the association of two objects are inferred by staining them with different dyes and looking for spatial overlap of the fluorescence from the two dyes in the microscope. This technique, although widely used, is limited in spatial resolution by conventional diffraction (submicron resolution) and therefore cannot differentiate between a true molecular association (nm scale) and nearby binding (submicron). Root looked for the association of dystrophin with nucleotide-binding proteins. Specifically, he stained muscle sections with the terbium-labeled anti-dystrophin antibody and with ATP bound to the dye Cy3, which is spectrally similar to tetramethylrhodamine. Both were found in the cell periphery by immunofluorescence microscopy, but no energy transfer was found, indicating that they were in the same vicinity but may not be molecularly interacting. Hence, the combination of using lanthanides as donors, which can produce significant energy transfer even with antibodies, and the extra spatial resolution of resonance energy transfer yields a more accurate picture of molecular interactions than conventional immunofluorescence microscopy.

APPLICATION 4: DETECTION OF BINDING IN HIGH-THROUGHPUT SCREENING

Biochemistry, at its fundamental level, is the interaction of macromolecular complexes. The detection of such events, and the ability to alter them through drugs, is essential for basic and applied science. With combinatorial chemical methods, it is now possible to produce millions of proto-drugs, and the ability to screen these rapidly, cheaply, and sensitively is crucial in drug development efforts. LRET has become increasingly popular for this purpose. LRET has several advantages. First, LRET is nonisotopic and hence avoids the health, environmental, and cost problems associated with radioactive assays, which historically have been standard. Second, LRET is homogenous, i.e., requires no separation or wash steps. Third, because LRET can measure fairly long distances, generic labeling reagents, which are often relatively large, can be used. This has the enormous advantage of being able to use one or a few sets of labeling reagents (e.g., antibodies, streptavidin, Protein A) for many different assays. Fourth, the ability to detect relatively small amounts of energy transfer—generally through sensitized emission, which is sensitive to only donor acceptor pairs—enables the analysis of samples that may have only a small percentage of fully labeled donor-acceptor pairs. This is particularly relevant when using complex mixtures such as cell extracts. Finally, LRET can be detected at (sub-) nanomolar concentrations, which minimizes reagent use and is often required if measuring the binding of nanomolar-affinity complexes.

Figure 11a highlights an assay to measure protein-protein interaction using generic reagents (34, 42). Jun and Fos oncogenes produce proteins that form a heterodimer. The dimer can bind to DNA and regulate transcription. Drugs that inhibit this dimerization are of potential therapeutic value. In one screening assay, a 40–amino acid section of Jun and of Fos, both containing the leucine zipper–binding domains responsible for dimerization, was synthesized and labeled with a biotin-avidin-chelate and the large fluorescent phycobiliprotein allophycocanin. Dimerization led to sensitized emission of the APC. Addition of an inhibitor disrupted dimerization and hence decreased APC-sensitized emission. Therefore screening for drugs that inhibit Jun-Fos dimerization can be readily achieved using LRET.

A second example using LRET and generic labels involves monitoring ligand-receptor interactions, which are often the first or early steps in a long biochemical cascade. In Figure 11b, an interleukin 4 (IL-4) ligand is biotinylated and then labeled with an APC-streptavidin (44). The IL-4 receptor (IL-4R) is expressed as a fusion protein with a Fc fragment. A europium-labeled protein-A is then used to label the Fc fragment of the IL-4R. The nanomolar-binding affinity for ligand and receptor is readily measured by changes in APC-sensitized emission.

FINAL REMARKS

New biophysical techniques invariably open up new applications. The development of new probes is leading to a dramatic expansion of the use of fluorescence in general and FRET-based techniques in particular. The most pressing issue is the ability to site-specifically label probes. Temporal and spectral discrimination when using lanthanides in energy transfer measurements help decrease the sensitivity to nonspecific labeling. However, particularly for cellular work, more selective means of attachments for both donors and acceptors are needed. Two different methods, one for donor, and one for acceptor, would be ideal. Genetically encoded dyes such as green fluorescent proteins is one method of selective attachment (56); dyes such as "FLASH," which bind to a highly unusual six–amino acid motif via an arsenic moiety, is another (19); dyes modified to contain Ni, which can then coordinate to a hexahistidine group engineered into a protein, is yet another (31). Using the power of these new labeling methods with the

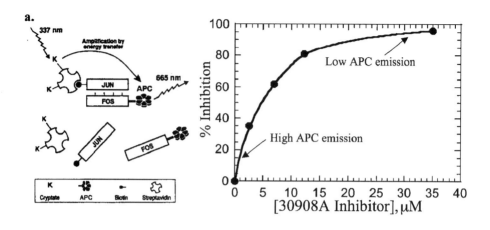

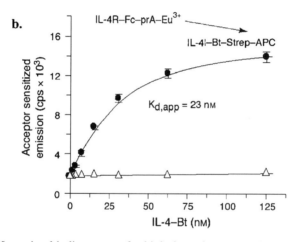

Figure 11   Measuring binding events for high-throughput screening assays using generic labeling reagents. (*a*) Jun-Fos dimerization and inhibition by drug. [Figure adapted from (34, 42)]. (*b*) Ligand-receptor binding in the IL-4 system with an apparent binding constant of 23 nM. [Figure from (44)].

power of lanthanides will likely shed new light on biophysical systems in the near future.

ACKNOWLEDGMENTS

I would like to thank Jeff Reifenberger for generating Table 1. This work was supported by NIH AR44420, NSF 9984841, and through the Material Research Laboratory, University of Illinois, DOE grant DEFG 02-91ER45439.

Visit the Annual Reviews home page at www.annualreviews.org

LITERATURE CITED

1. Blaustein RO, Cole PA, Williams C, Miller C. 2000. Tethered blockers as molecular 'tape measures' for a voltage-gated K+ channel. *Nat. Struct. Biol.* 7:309–11

2. Blomberg K, Hurskainen P, Hemmila I. 1999. Terbium and rhodamine as labels in a homogeneous time-resolved fluorometric energy transfer assay of the B subunit of human chorionic gonadotropin in serum. *Clin. Chem.* 45:855–61

3. Bunzli J-CG. 1989. Luminescent probes. In *Lanthanide Probes in Life, Chemical and Earth Sciences, Theory and Practice*, ed. J-CG Bunzli, GR Choppin, pp. 219–93. New York: Elsevier

4. Callaci S, Heyduk E, Heyduk T. 1999. Core RNA polymerase from *E. coli* induces a major change in the domain arrangement of the sigma 70 subunit. *Mol. Cell* 3:229–38

5. Cantor CR, Schimmel PR. 1980. *Biophysical Chemistry*. San Francisco: Freeman

5a. Cha A, Bezanilla. 1997. Characterizing voltage-dependent conformational changes in the Shaker K+ channel with fluorescence. *Neuron* 19(5):1127–40

6. Cha A, Snyder GE, Selvin PR, Bezanilla F. 1999. Atomic scale movement of the voltage sensing region in a potassium channel measured via spectroscopy. *Nature* 402:809–13

7. Chakrabarty T, Xiao M, Cooke R, Selvin PR. 2000. Structure and dynamics of the myosin dimer measured by fluorescence and luminescence resonance energy transfer. *Biophys. J.* 78:233A

8. Chen J, Selvin PR. 1999. Thiol-reactive luminescent lanthanide chelates. *Bioconjugate Chem.* 10:311–15

9. Chen J, Selvin PR. 2000. Lifetime and color-tailored fluorophores in the micro- to milli-second time regime. *J. Am. Chem. Soc.* 122:657–60

10. Clegg RM. 1995. Fluorescence resonance energy transfer. *Curr. Opin. Biotechnol.* 6:103–10

11. Clegg RM, Murchie AI, Zechel A, Lilley DM. 1993. Observing the helical geometry of double-stranded DNA in solution by fluorescence resonance energy transfer. *Proc. Natl. Acad. Sci. USA* 90:2994–98

12. Coker G III, Chen SY, van der Meer BW. 1994. *Resonance Energy Transfer*. New York: VCH

13. Cooper ME, Sammes PG. 2000. Synthesis and properties of a new luminescent europium(III) terpyridyl chelate. *J. Chem. Soc. Perkin Trans.* 28:1675–700

14. Dale RE, Eisinger J, Blumberg WE. 1979. The orientational freedom of molecular probes. *Biophys. J.* 26:161–94

15. Drexhage KH. 1970. Monomolecular layers and light. *Sci. Am.* 222:108–19

16. Fairclough RH, Cantor CR. 1978. The use of singlet-singlet energy transfer to study macromolecular assemblies. *Methods Enzymol.* 48:347–79

17. Farrar SJ, Whiting PJ, Bonnert TP, McKernan RM. 1999. Stoichiometry of a ligand-gated ion channel determined by fluorescence energy transfer. *J. Biol. Chem.* 274:10100–4

18. Glauner KS, Mannuzzu LM, Gandhi CS, Isacoff EY. 1999. Spectroscopic mapping of voltage sensor movement in the Shaker potassium channel. *Nature* 402:813–17

19. Griffin BA, Adams SR, Tsien RY. 1998. Specific covalent labeling of recombinant protein molecules inside live cells. *Science* 281:269–72

20. Helmann JD, deHaseth PL. 1999. Protein-nucleic acid interactions during open complex formation investigated by systematic alteration of the protein and DNA binding partners. *Biochemistry* 38:5959–67

21. Hemmilä I, Dakubu S, Mukkala V-M, Siitari H, Lövgren T. 1984. Europium as a

label in time-resolved immunofluorometric assays. *Anal. Biochem.* 137:335–43

22. Heyduk E, Heyduk T. 1997. Thiol-reactive luminescent Europium chelates: luminescence probes for resonance energy transfer distance measurements in biomolecules. *Anal. Biochem.* 248:216–27

23. Heyduk E, Heyduk T. 1999. Architecture of a complex between the sigma 70 subunit of *Escherichia coli* RNA polymerase and the nontemplate strand oligonucleotide. Luminescence resonance energy transfer study. *J. Biol. Chem.* 274:3315–22

24. Heyduk T, Heyduk E. 2001. Luminescence energy transfer with lanthanide chelates: interpretation of sensitized acceptor decay amplitudes. *Anal. Biochem.* 289:60–67

25. Heyduk E, Heyduk T, Claus P, Wisniewski JR. 1997. Conformational changes of DNA induced by binding of chironomus high mobility group protein 1a (cHMG1a). *J. Biol. Chem.* 272:19763–70

26. Horenstein J, Wagner DA, Czajkowski C, Akabas MH. 2001. Protein mobility and GABA-induced conformational changes in GABA(A) receptor pore-lining M2 segment. *Nat. Neurosci.* 4:477–85

27. Horn R. 2000. A new twist in the saga of charge movement in voltage-dependent ion channels. *Neuron* 25:511–14

28. Johnson JP Jr, Zagotta WN. 2001. Rotational movement during cyclic nucleotide-gated channel opening. *Nature* 412:917–21

29. Jones SG, Lee DY, Wright JF, Jones CN, Teear ML, et al. 2001. Improvements in the sensitivity of time resolved fluorescence energy transfer assays. *J. Fluoresc.* 11:13–21

30. Jovin TM, Arndt-Jovin DJ. 1989. FRET microscopy: digital imaging of fluorescence resonance energy transfer. Applications in cell biology. In *Microspectrofluorimetry of Single Living Cells*, ed. E Kohen, JS Ploem, JG Hirschberg, pp. 99–117. Orlando: Academic

31. Kapanidis AN, Ebright YW, Ebright RH. 2002. Site-specific incorporation of fluorescent probes into protein: hexahisti-dine-tag-mediated fluorescent labeling using (Ni++: nitrilotriacetic acid)n-fluorochrome conjugates. *J. Am. Chem. Soc.* 123 (48):12123–25

32. Kapanidis AN, Ebright YW, Ludescher RD, Chan S, Ebright RH. 2001. Mean DNA bend angle and distribution of DNA bend angles in the CAP-DNA complex in solution. *J. Mol. Biol.* 312:1–16

33. Karstens T, Kobs K. 1980. Rhodamine B and rhodamine 101 as reference substances for fluorescence quantum yield measurements. *J. Phys. Chem.* 84:1871–72

34. Kolb AJ, Burke JW, Mathis G. 1997. A homogeneous, time-resolved fluorescence method for drug discovery. In *High Throughput Screening: The Discovery of Bioactive Substances*, ed. JP Devlin, pp. 345–60. New York: Marcel Dekker

35. Lakowicz JR. 1999. *Principles of Fluorescence.* New York: Kluwer

36. Li M, Selvin PR. 1997. Amine-reactive forms of a luminescent DTPA chelate of terbium and europium: attachment to DNA and energy transfer measurements. *Bioconjugate Chem.* 8:127–32

37. Loo TW, Clarke DM. 2001. Cross-linking of human multidrug resistance p-glycoprotein by the substrate, tris-(2-maleimidoethyl)amine, is altered by atp hydrolysis. evidence for rotation of a transmembrane helix. *J. Biol. Chem.* 276:31800–5

38. Malhotra A, Severinova E, Darst SA. 1996. Crystal structure of a sigma 70 subunit fragment from *E. coli* RNA polymerase. *Cell* 87:127–36

39. Mannuzzu LM, Moronne MM, Isacoff EY. 1996. Direct physical measure of conformational rearrangement underlying potassium channel gating. *Science* 271:213–16

40. Marriott G, Heidecker M, Diamandis EP, Yan-Marriott Y. 1994. Time-resolved delayed luminescence image microscopy using an europium ion chelate complex. *Biophys. J.* 67:957–65

41. Mathis G. 1993. Rare earth cryptates and homogeneous fluoroimmunoassays with human sera. *Clin. Chem.* 39:1953–59

42. Mathis G. 1995. Probing molecular interactions with homogeneous techniques based on rare earth cryptates and fluorescence energy transfer. *Clin. Chem.* 41:1391–97

43. Mathis G, Socquet F, Viguier M, Darbouret B. 1997. Homogeneous immunoassays using rare earth cryptates and time resolved fluorescence: principles and specific advantages for tumor markers. *Anticancer Res.* 17:3011–14

44. Pope AJ, Haupts UM, Moore KJ. 1999. Homogeneous fluorescence readouts for miniaturized high-throughput screening: theory and practice. *Drug Discov. Today* 4: 350–62

45. Deleted in proof

46. Root DD. 1997. *In situ* molecular association of dystrophin with actin revealed by sensitized emission immuno-resonance energy transfer. *Proc. Natl. Acad. Sci. USA* 94:5685–90

47. Saha AK, Kross K, Kloszewski ED, Upson DA, Toner JL, et al. 1993. Time-resolved fluorescence of a new europium chelate complex: demonstration of highly sensitive detection of protein and DNA samples. *J. Am. Chem. Soc.* 115:11032–33

48. Sammes PG, Yahioglu G. 1996. Modern bioassays using metal chelates as luminescent probes. *Nat. Prod. Rep.* 13:1–28

49. Selvin PR. 1995. Fluorescence resonance energy transfer. *Methods Enzymol.* 246: 300–34

50. Selvin PR. 1996. Lanthanide-based resonance energy transfer. *IEEE J. Quantum Electron.* 2:1077–87

51. Selvin PR. 2000. The renaissance in fluorescence resonance energy transfer. *Nat. Struct. Biol.* 7:730–34

52. Selvin PR, Hearst JE. 1994. Luminescence energy transfer using a terbium chelate: improvements on fluorescence energy transfer. *Proc. Natl. Acad. Sci. USA* 91:10024–28

53. Seveus L, Vaisala M, Hemmila I, Kojola H, Roomans GM, Soini E. 1994. Use of fluorescent europium chelates as labels in microscopy allows glutaraldehyde fixation

and permanent mounting and leads to reduced autofluorescence and good long-term stability. *Microsc. Res. Tech.* 28:149–54

54. Siitari H, Hemmila I, Soini E, Lövgren T, Koistinen V. 1983. Detection of hepatitis B surface antigen using time-resolved fluoroimmunoassay. *Nature* 301:258–60

55. Stenroos K, Hurskainen P, Eriksson S, Hemmila I, Blomberg K, Lindqvist C. 1998. Homogeneous time-resolved IL-2-IL-2R alpha assay using fluorescence resonance energy transfer. *Cytokine* 10:495–99

56. Stryer L, Haugland RP. 1967. Energy transfer: a spectroscopic ruler. *Proc. Natl. Acad. Sci. USA* 58:719–26

57. Stryer L, Thomas DD, Meares CF. 1982. Diffusion-enhanced fluorescence energy transfer. *Annu. Rev. Biophys. Bioeng.* 11: 203–22

58. Takalo H, Mukkala V-M, Mikola H, Liitti P, Hemmila I. 1994. Synthesis of europium(III) chelates suitable for labeling of bioactive molecules. *Bioconjugate Chem.* 5:278–82

59. Tsien RY. 1998. The green fluorescent protein. *Annu. Rev. Biochem.* 67:509–44

60. Vamosi G, Gohlke C, Clegg R. 1996. Fluorescence characteristics of 5-carboxytetramethylrhodamine linked covalently to the 5′ end of oligonucleotides: multiple conformers of single-stranded and double-stranded dye-DNA complexes. *Biophys. J.* 71:972–94

61. Weber G, Teale FWJ. 1957. Determination of the absolute quantum yield of fluorescent solutions. *Trans. Faraday Soc.* 53:646–55

62. Xiao M, Li H, Snyder GE, Cooke RG, Yount R, Selvin PR. 1998. Conformational changes between the active-site and regulatory light chain of myosin as determined by luminescence resonance energy transfer: the effect of nucleotides and actin. *Proc. Natl. Acad. Sci. USA* 95:15309–14

63. Xiao M, Selvin PR. 1999. An improved instrument for measuring time-resolved lanthanide emission and resonance energy transfer. *Rev. Sci. Inst.* 70:3877–81

64. Xiao M, Selvin PR. 2001. Quantum yields of luminescent lanthanide chelates and far-red dyes measured by resonance energy transfer. *J. Am. Chem. Soc.* 123:7067–73

65. Xu YY, Pettersson K, Blomberg K, Hemmila I, Mikola H, Lövgren T. 1992. Simultaneous quadruple-label fluorometric immunoassay of thyroid-stimulating hormone, 17 alpha-hydroxyprogesterone, immunoreactive trypsin, and creatine kinase MM isoenzyme in dried blood spots. *Clin. Chem.* 38:2038–43

Annu. Rev. Biophys. Biomol. Struct. 2002. 31:303–19
DOI: 10.1146/annurev.biophys.31.082901.134202

SINGLE-PARTICLE IMAGING OF MACROMOLECULES BY CRYO-ELECTRON MICROSCOPY

Joachim Frank

Howard Hughes Medical Institute, Health Research Inc at the Wadsworth Center, and Department of Biomedical Sciences, State University of New York at Albany, Empire State Plaza, P.O. Box 509, Albany, New York 12201-0509; e-mail: joachim@wadsworth.org

Key Words molecular machines, ribosome, spliceosome, three-dimensional reconstruction, transcription complex

■ **Abstract** Cryo-electron microscopy (cryo-EM) of biological molecules in single-particle (i.e., unordered, nonaggregated) form is a new approach to the study of molecular assemblies, which are often too large and flexible to be amenable to X-ray crystallography. New insights into biological function on the molecular level are expected from cryo-EM applied to the study of such complexes "trapped" at different stages of their conformational changes and dynamical interactions. Important molecular machines involved in the fundamental processes of transcription, mRNA splicing, and translation are examples for successful applications of the new technique, combined with structural knowledge gained by conventional techniques of structure determination, such as X-ray crystallography and NMR.

CONTENTS

PERSPECTIVES AND OVERVIEW

As more and more structures of proteins are being solved by X-ray crystallography and NMR, and the availability of genomic information is starting to facilitate a systematic exploration of sequence and structure data, the focus of structural biology increasingly moves to the interactions of macromolecules in the cell. The complexes formed in these interactions have been termed macromolecular machines [see (5)], a term that attempts to capture the dynamic nature, processivity, and high precision of these localized interactions, as well as the involvement of multiple ligands.

X-ray crystallography has been extremely successful as an approach to solve the structure of large individual proteins, but this technique can run into several limitations when it comes to large (Megadalton range) multi-component complexes: (a) Those large complexes often resist attempts at crystallization, or they may form crystals only after flexible parts have been removed; (b) conversely, successful crystallization may interfere with the study of macromolecular interactions because crystal packing favors particular modes of interaction while disfavoring or entirely prohibiting others; and (c) the large size of a complex increases the volume of data collection and often poses problems in finding multiple isomorphous derivatives with sufficient phasing power. [The recent achievement by several groups in solving the structure of the ribosome (7, 59, 81, 86) is an exception that rather proves the rule: it has followed decades of unsuccessful attempts at crystallization].

Cryo-electron microscopy (cryo-EM) of molecules in single-particle form does not suffer these restrictions, presenting an approach that does not require crystals. The complex being studied is free to assume all functional states without any steric constraints, allowing, in principle, the visualization of the entire dynamic course of the macromolecular interactions. Time resolution can be achieved by taking "snapshots" of the complex at different points in time that are experimentally "trapped" by chemical or physical means. The current drawback of this approach, which might be gradually overcome with time, is that its spatial resolution is limited. However, fortuitously the new methodology has come along at a time when the X-ray structures of many of the players in the interactions are known or have at least become inferable by homology modeling based on sequence comparisons. When all the components of a macromolecular complex are known to atomic resolution, then the low-resolution map of the complex will allow the components to be placed and their atomic interactions to be inferred. Thus, to fully exploit the potential of cryo-EM, it is necessary to find tools that allow the fitting and docking of X-ray coordinates into the lower-resolution cryo-EM maps.

To be sure, the approach of cryo-EM to look at isolated in vitro systems is still a big step away from the solution to the real challenge posed by the need to study macromolecular interactions under conditions closely approaching those in vivo inside the cell [see (38)]. However, there is no doubt that in the long run, three-dimensional (3D) descriptions of the system in isolation will greatly facilitate the task of locating its manifestations in the cellular context [see for instance (8)].

CRYO-EM OF ORDERED ARRAYS VERSUS SINGLE MOLECULES

As a technique of specimen preparation and visualization, cryo-EM has been in existence for almost 20 years (16, 34), not counting the decade before, during which the technique was basically dormant following Taylor & Glaeser's (69) initial invention of the method. The basic technique involves an apparatus that plunges the grid into liquid ethane (Figure 1): the EM grid, on which the specimen is suspended within a thin water layer, is held at the tip of tweezers, which are in turn mounted on a rod that is held in a position to fall under gravity. (The thickness of the water layer is controlled by blotting.) As the rod is released, the grid is rapidly plunged into a bath of liquid ethane at liquid-nitrogen temperature. Owing to the rapid decrease in temperature, the water turns into vitreous ice, which has properties akin to those of liquid water. Most importantly, no crystals are formed and a disruption of the molecule is avoided.

Initially, cryo-EM was exclusively applied to highly ordered specimens: helical fibers, "two-dimensional" crystals (i.e., crystals only one or two unit cells thick),

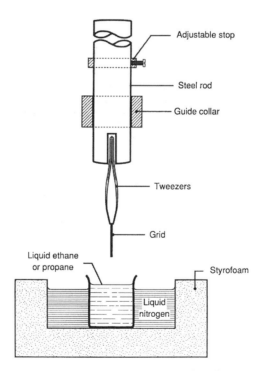

Figure 1 Schematic diagram of a freeze-plunge apparatus. [From Stewart (66), reproduced with permission].

and viruses with high symmetry. In the then-prevailing view, only such specimens could yield quantitative information. Although significant progress was achieved in these applications, relatively few highly visible results were obtained. For proteins of normal sizes, X-ray crystallography is a formidable competitor, as cryo-EM data collection for two-dimensional (2D) crystals at close-to-atomic resolution faces several obstacles: crystal disorder and experimental difficulties (e.g., charging at high tilts and instabilities of the specimen stage). The most promising niche for cryo-EM has been in the area of membrane proteins, but actually only few atomic structures have been solved in this way to date. For large macromolecular complexes, on the other hand, attainment of crystals with good order is often as difficult in two dimensions (suitable for cryo-EM) as it is in three (suitable for X-ray crystallography). As an example, all attempts to solve the ribosome structure using electron microscopy of 2D crystals [e.g., (39, 85)] were eventually abandoned because of poor crystal order.

A potentially much larger field of application was created owing to the development of the single-particle reconstruction method, which requires the molecule to exist on the specimen grid in multiple isolated copies. This method (48–50, 71) and its 2D precursors (18, 22, 25, 73) were developed initially for molecules prepared by negative staining, but their success there was limited by the artifacts introduced by the preparation technique.

In the negative-staining technique, practiced almost exclusively before the invention of cryo-EM, the aqueous specimen is mixed with a 1–2% solution of a heavy metal salt and then air dried. On the grid, molecules so prepared are surrounded by a cast of stain that outlines their shape, leading to a high contrast in the EM image. However, in addition to the fact that no interior density variations of the molecule are visualized, negative staining has the disadvantage that it results in a distortion of the molecule's shape. The breakthrough achieved by the marriage of the two methods, cryo-EM and single-particle reconstruction, can be appreciated by comparing density maps of the 70S ribosome of *Escherichia coli* that were done with negative staining (78) with those by cryo-EM (24). In the first case, the structure appears squashed, without the clearance of the intersubunit space; in the second, the structure is globular, with a clear separation between the 30S and 50S subunits. Another example was provided by comparing density maps of hemocyanin obtained by negative staining with cryo-EM (9) that differ by almost a factor of two in the dimension normal to the electron microscope grid, due to the collapse of the molecule following negative staining and air drying.

PRINCIPLES OF CRYO-EM OF SINGLE PARTICLES

The method of 3D cryo-EM of single particles is currently still evolving. Although the experimental protocol for the EM preparation of such specimens (79) is similar to protocols developed earlier for thin crystals, reflecting on the original work by

Dubochet and coworkers (17), the methods of image processing and reconstruction of molecules in single-particle form are quite different in detail. Many of the algorithms and principles, and the relevant literature, have been described at length [e.g., (19)]. Recent outlines of the methodology in its different versions are found in (23, 43). The subject is also covered by Saibil (56) as part of a more general overview article on molecular structure determination by cryo-EM.

In the single-particle reconstruction approach, the particle (molecule) is thought to occur in multiple copies that have (at least to a first approximation) identical structure. These copies have different orientations within the ice layer, so their spatial relationships can be mathematically described by a series of rigid-body movements of a single object. The transmission electron microscope produces parallel projections of such a set of particles (Figure 2, see color insert). Thus, provided the angular distribution is sufficiently uniform, a series of single micrographs of the untilted specimen (each showing a field with hundreds of particles) will yield all the information necessary to reconstruct the molecule.

A complication arises due to the presence of lens aberrations: The projection images produced in the electron microscope are blurred in a complicated way that depends on the distance ("defocus") of the specimen from the true focus of the objective lens. Removal of the resultant blur, which is described by a "point spread function" [or described alternatively, in Fourier space, by a contrast transfer function (CTF)], necessitates the collection of images with different defocus and the application of CTF correction in the image-processing procedures.

Radiation damage is a major concern, so it is important that data used for the reconstruction originate exclusively from molecules that have "seen" the electron beam only once. Dose levels used are in the range of 10 electrons per A^2. Lower levels pose some problems in locating particles. On the other hand, the classical work by Unwin & Henderson (70) on 2D crystals of bacteriorhodopsin (unstained and embedded in glucose) seemed to indicate that a much lower dose (~ 1 electron/A^2) may be required to preserve features in the range below 10 Å. The subsequent years indicated that the maximum dose sustainable by the specimen depends on a variety of factors, including the type of specimen (e.g., fraction of RNA, and compactness), embedding medium, electron voltage, and specimen temperature. Also, newer microscopes with helium cooling may offer a "radiation protection factor" compared to liquid nitrogen (12a).

The most difficult task in the whole procedure, when the molecule's structure is unknown, is to infer the orientations of the particles from these images. The problem is exacerbated by the great amount of noise in a micrograph, which is a consequence of the low dose needed to minimize radiation damage. This problem of ab initio orientation determination has received a variety of answers: In the "random-conical" data collection method (48), which involves the use of a tilt, geometric relationships are established among a subset of particles that face the grid in the same orientation. In the "method of common lines" (13, 46, 71), particle images are first classified, then class averages presenting different views of the particle are related to one another according to the common lines principle first formulated by Crowther (13). The latter method cannot establish the handedness, however, and requires a tilt for this purpose.

After the initial determination of orientations, the angles are further refined following an iterative cycle (30, 45), in which 3D projection matching alternates with 3D reconstruction. With the angles having been determined (and provided that the angular range is sufficiently covered), the molecule can be reconstructed according to mathematical principles that were formulated by Radon (51), computationally first realized in electron microscopy (14, 32), and subsequently exploited in many applications of medical tomography.

The importance of the geometry of the angular coverage becomes clear from the mathematical formulation of the reconstruction problem as data collection in Fourier space: Here each projection is represented by a central plane (14). The objective is to fill 3D Fourier space with data up to a radius that corresponds to the limiting resolution. As more and more projections having different angles are being added, the manifold of the corresponding central planes starts to cover Fourier space. If an entire range of orientations is not represented in the data set, then a large gap will remain in Fourier space, and the reconstruction (obtained by Fourier synthesis) will show artifacts, such as elongation of features in the direction of the missing angular range. Although large gaps, entirely devoid of projections, are encountered in some studies, as in the case of the calcium release channel (47), it is more common to find regions of relative sparsity. This implies that these regions will be filled eventually, provided that the data set is large enough. An example of this statistical behavior is provided by Figure 3, which shows the observed orientational preferences of the ubiquinone oxireductase molecule that can be explained as the result of the molecule's interaction with the air-water interface (28). Although there are two clear preferences of orientation (related by a flipping of the molecule in the ice), other views also do occur, albeit with lower frequency.

So far, the specimen has been described in terms of a rigid molecule occurring in many identical copies in different orientations. A more realistic model of the experiment must account for the coexistence of different ligand occupancies and conformations of the molecule. These are often linked: The ribosome, for example, undergoes large conformational changes in response to the binding of elongation factor G (EF-G) (1, 20). Conformational changes of a macromolecule are also often associated with the hydrolysis of a nucleotide triphosphate [e.g., ribosome (1); groEL (56); AAA ATPase (55, 87)]. If in such a case only part of a molecule population is bound with the ligand, then the reconstruction from the mixed data set will result in an incorrect density map in which the two states are superposed. Preferably, such mixtures should be sorted out prior to EM imaging by biochemical means, but this is not always possible. Sorting the images in the computer is possible by means of multivariate statistical analysis and classification (10, 19, 72, 73), but the inherently small signal-to-noise (S/N) ratio of the raw images makes it often difficult to detect conformational changes or the presence of small ligands.

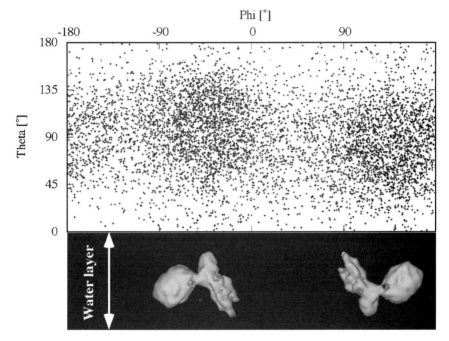

Figure 3   Angular statistics showing the orientational preferences of bovine NADH: ubiquinone oxireductase molecules in the water layer. Each data point on the theta-versus-phi graph represents the orientation of a molecule. In the *lower panel*, the molecule is shown in the two most frequently found orientations within the ice layer. [Reproduced from (28)].

A NOTE ON RESOLUTION

It is unfortunate, and quite confusing to nonspecialists, that two different criteria of resolution are in use. These are both based on the same principle of measurement, introduced for the purpose of characterizing the resolution of molecule images formed by single-particle averaging (25): The data are randomly divided in half, and the procedure leading to the average or reconstruction is applied independently to both data sets. The resulting averages or reconstructions are then compared along rings (in 2D applications) or shells in Fourier space [in 3D applications (74)]. [Recently, the entire approach of using such half-set reconstructions in a resolution assessment has been questioned (29), but no clear alternative has been suggested].

The most popular measure, the Fourier ring or shell correlation (FRC or FSC) (58, 75), measures the degree of correlation between the two reconstructions as a function of radius (i.e., spatial frequency) in Fourier space. The FSC is a curve that starts with a value of 1, indicating excellent agreement at low spatial frequencies, and drops more or less gradually to small values indicating poor agreement (Figure 4). Ideally, this curve, which is easy to reproduce as a figure, should

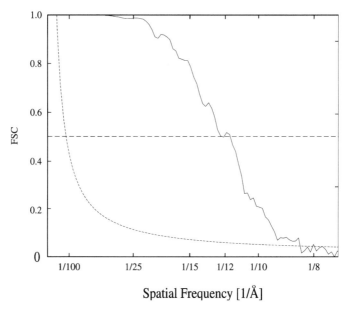

Spatial Frequency [1/Å]

Figure 4 Example for a Fourier shell correlation curve (*solid line*), which expresses the degree of reproducibility of the reconstruction in Fourier space as a function of shell radius. *Dotted line*: so-called 3-σ curve, obtained by multiplying the cross-correlation coefficient expected for pure noise by three. The resolution is quoted either as the Fourier radius where FSC falls below 0.5 (*dashed line*), or as the radius where it falls below the 3-σ curve. It is clear that quotation of a single number (here 11.5 Å for the 0.5 criterion and 8.5 Å for the 3-σ criterion) cannot do justice to the information conveyed by the whole curve. [Adapted from (27)].

accompany every publication of a single-particle reconstruction because it contains all information allowing the resolution behavior to be assessed. Difficulties only arise because of the attempt to summarize the information contained in the curve by a single value. In one method (11, 36), the cutoff is placed at the spatial frequency where the curve drops below the arbitrary but sensible threshold value of 0.5; in the other method (44), the curve is instead compared with the so-called 3-σ curve, indicating three times the correlation expected for pure noise.

The problem is that what one chooses to call resolution is not inconsequential because it determines the presentation and interpretation of the final results. What choice of value makes sense from this point of view can be gauged by looking at the fundamental relationship between cross-correlation coefficient (CCC) and S/N ratio (21): With decreasing CCC, the S/N ratio decreases quite rapidly. A CCC of 0.5 is already equivalent to a S/N ratio of 1, and any values below that lead to even lower S/N ratios. (Note that an S/N ratio of 1 is comparable to the S/N ratio normally found in raw, unprocessed images.) This means that when using the 3-σ resolution value, one is bound to admit Fourier components that are unreliable

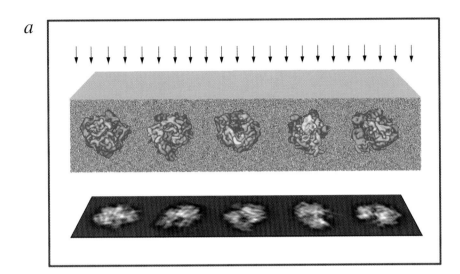

Figure 2 Data collection for single molecule reconstruction in the electron microscope. (*a*) Schematic diagram of data collection. *Arrows* symbolize the impact of the parallel electron beam upon the specimen. Many "copies" of the molecule are lying in random orientations in a thin layer of vitreous ice. In the image plane, parallel projections of the particles are obtained at high magnification. Images of particles lying in the same orientation can be found by employing alignment and classification procedures. (*b*) Example of an actual micrograph, showing 70S ribosomes of *E. coli*. The micrograph was taken on an F30 Tecnai electron microscope (Philips/FEI, Eindhoven) with a helium-cooled specimen stage.

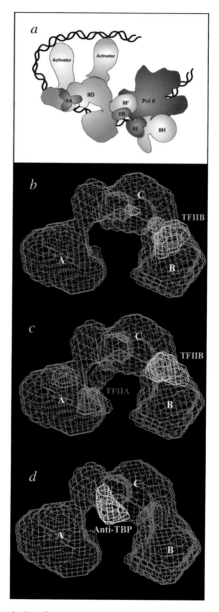

Figure 5 Human transcription factor complex. (*a*) Cartoon representing the spatial relationships and interactions between DNA, activators, transcription factors, and RNA polymerase. The complex shown in (*b–d*) is painted *green* [reproduced from (41)]. (*b–d*) Single-particle reconstruction of the complex formed by TFIID, TFIIA, and TFIIB in a contour representation, and locations of various components as obtained by difference mapping [reproduced from (6)].

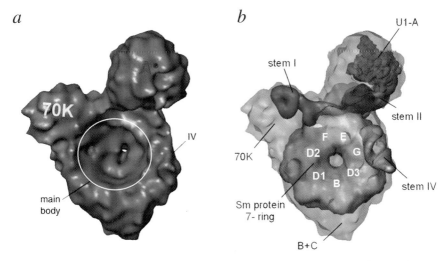

Figure 6 Cryo-EM map of human spliceosomal U1 small nuclear ribonucleoprotein particle at 15 Å resolution (using the 0.5 FSC criterion). (*a*) Density map. Labels: A, protein U1-A; 70S, protein U1-70S; IV, location of 3′-terminal stemloop IV. (*b*) RNA modeled according to known binding interactions between the RNA of U1 and proteins U1-A and U1-70k. Locations of stem loops, heptamer Sm ring (F, E, G, D3, B, D1, D2, based on X-ray structures), U1-70k, U1-A, U1-B, and U1-C are indicated [reproduced from (63)].

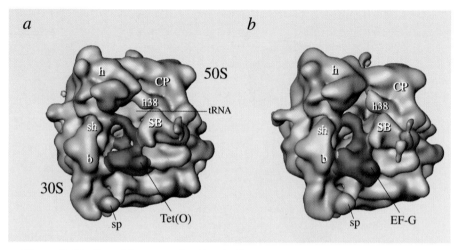

Figure 7 Binding of factors to the *E. coli* ribosome. (*a*) Tetracycline protection protein Tet(O); (*b*) elongation factor G. In both panels, the factor is colored *red*, the ribosome *blue*. In (*a*), P-site tRNA is colored *green*. Tet(O) binds in a very similar position as EF-G, but its domain IV is shaped and positioned differently, such that it forces the release of tetracycline bound to 16S RNA of the small ribosomal subunit. Landmarks: h, sh, sp—head, shoulder, and spur of the 30S subunit; CP, SB, and h38—central protuberance, stalk base, and helix 38 of the 50S subunit [reproduced from (62)].

and polluted by noise [see (36)]. This is not to say that there is no information in this extended range; it is just the fact that the information cannot be reliably distinguished from noise that makes this choice of cutoff questionable.

INTERPRETATION OF CRYO-EM MAPS BY FITTING X-RAY STRUCTURES

Beginning with pioneering work in the virus field (67, 54) and the interpretation of maps showing actin-myosin interaction (52, 60), it has been recognized that cryo-EM and molecular docking can be combined in a powerful way to approach the atomic structure of a large macromolecular complex that cannot be crystallized, provided the X-ray coordinates of the component structures are known. This same approach has proven extremely fruitful in the interpretation of macromolecular complexes visualized by single-particle reconstruction (2, 9, 27, 56, 63).

Docking and fitting of X-ray structures into density maps obtained by cryo-EM [see review provided in (53)] is still done mostly by hand. Criteria for fitting are difficult to rationalize because it often involves compromises between boundary conflicts in different parts of the map. Most seriously, the use of contour-only representations for low-density maps leads to a complete disregard for interior variations of density, and the use of different representations—all-atoms or backbone for the X-ray structure versus contours for the low-resolution density map—requires a great amount of intuition. Despite these shortcomings, coordinates derived by such fittings have been instrumental in the interpretation of molecular interactions in some key biological processes, such as the power stroke in muscle (52), virus-antibody interaction (54), the action of molecular chaperones (57), and translocation in the ribosome (2), and the coordinates have found their way into the protein data bank [see recent tabulation in (37)].

As the foregoing account has shown, there is an urgent need for methods of computational fitting according to quantitative criteria. The approaches currently being pursued fall into three classes: (*a*) those based on cross-correlation [DOCKEM (53), EMFIT (12, 54), COAN (76)], (*b*) those based on a force field derived from the low-resolution map, in a molecular mechanics approach to the modeling of interaction (R. K. Z. Tan, M. S. Van Loock & S. C. Harvey, manuscript submitted), and (*c*) those based on vector quantization [SITUS (82–84)]. Both Rossmann (54) and Roseman (53) base the search on the real-space cross-correlation function between the atomic structure (suitably converted into a density function) and the low-resolution cryo-EM map and use the rotation and translation parameters that maximize the CCC. Roseman's correlation function differs from the standard method in that he uses computation over a local area, along with a local normalization. This method is computationally intensive as it foregoes the computational advantages afforded by the fast Fourier transform algorithm, but it apparently avoids some of the false maxima the global search can run into. Volkmann & Hanein (76) go a step further after the computation of the CCC and define an entire set of possible solutions whose CCC is greater than a certain statistically defined threshold. Next, the atomic structure is placed into all positions of the solution set and checked for compliance with chemical and steric constraints. The scoring of violations then leads to the selection of the final position. The method was recently used in a study of the actin-myosin complex (77).

The force field method by Tan and coworkers (R. K. Z. Tan, M. S. Van Loock & S. C. Harvey, manuscript submitted) represents a further development of a quantitative docking method earlier employed by Malhotra & Harvey (35). Both have as their goal the modeling of RNA structures and their interactions within the constraints of molecular mechanics and the additional constraint of a low-density map. Whereas Malhotra & Harvey (35) devised a penalty only for violation of the boundary of the density map, the new method takes into account the interior densities, as well. A force field is derived from the local gradients of the density map that drives the individual atoms (or pseudo-atoms) of the structure to be fitted into compliance with local density variations.

An entirely different approach to the problem of docking was introduced by Wriggers and coworkers (83). Following this approach borrowed from signal processing, the low- and high-resolution maps to be compared are represented by a finite number of vectors ("code book vectors"). The uniqueness of these representations, achieved by solving an optimization problem using neural networks, makes it possible to match the two maps uniquely. Whereas the initial approach was restricted to rigid body movement of the component structures, the more recent development includes flexible docking, demonstrated on the example of the docking of the EF-G structure into the EF-G difference density map of an EF-G ribosome complex (82).

APPLICATION TO SOME MACROMOLECULAR MACHINES

There has been a recent explosion in the number of applications of cryo-EM single-particle reconstruction. Some of these applications, especially relating to the study of molecular machines, have been recently reviewed by Nogales & Grigorieff (42). In the following, only a few recent areas of application are highlighted, in particular three that are exemplary for the workings of macromolecular machines: transcription, mRNA splicing, and translation. In eukaryotes, these three systems work in tandem, handing products from one to the next. Transcription yields a copy, in the form of mRNA, of the genetic code residing on the DNA. This product is called pre-mRNA because it is not yet in the form where it can be translated. Pre-mRNA leaves the nucleus and enters the cytoplasm, where it is processed by splicing, i.e., excision of untranslatable sequences called introns. The resulting mRNA is ready to be translated by the ribosome. Each of these processes involves a large number of proteins in interaction with RNA, and each works to ensure fidelity in the expression of the genetic intent. (Prokaryotes lack the step of splicing and have no nucleus, thus translation is not physically divided from transcription by a boundary.) To different degrees, cryo-EM has made contributions to these areas, with the ribosome being farthest along and the spliceosome just at the start.

Transcription Complex

The machinery employed for transcription goes through several stages of initiation and assembly, using a number of shared subunits in a modular way (41) (Figure 5*a*, see color insert). Transcription factor TFIID binds to the DNA promoter, triggering the recruitment of the rest of the factors, as well as RNA polymerase II. In the fully assembled machine, RNA polymerase creates a faithful mRNA copy of one of the DNA template strands while the machine ratchets along the DNA. Cryo-EM has been applied to different assembly products: human TFIID-IIA-IIB complex (6) (Figure 5*b*, see color insert), human TFIIH (61), and RNA polymerase (F. Asturias, personal communication). Although the density maps obtained are low resolution, antibody mapping allowed the placement of subunits, and further clues were derived from the position of holes that serve as conduits for the DNA or mRNA.

Spliceosomal snRNP U1

Splicing of pre-mRNA involves the spliceosome, a large complex formed during the interaction of small nuclear ribonucleoproteins (snRNPs) with the mRNA. A major difficulty in imaging the spliceosome in its entirety is that it exists in many different processing states in the cell. Three-dimensional imaging with the technique at hand would require some type of synchronization so that all complexes being imaged would be in the same processing state. Because of this difficulty, a more promising approach is to look at individual snRNPs separately. The result obtained by Stark and coworkers (63) for the component U1 is the first step toward a full characterization of the processing spliceosome (Figure 6, see color insert). As in the case of the transcription complex, the placement of known components into the cryo-EM map amounts to a 3D jigsaw puzzle, which requires clues from immuno-EM and from the topology of the map.

Ribosome

Translation of the genetic message into polypeptide (and from that into protein) is a process that occupies a large fraction of the cell's resources. The ribosome, the site where protein synthesis occurs, is made up of more than 50 proteins and 3 RNAs, which form 2 subunits of unequal size. The ribosome is a macromolecular machine par excellence, in that it employs many movable parts, engages in interactions with a large number of ligands, and achieves high precision in translating the genetic blueprint. X-ray crystallography of ribosomal subunits from thermophilic bacteria (59, 81, 86) and archaebacteria (7) shows that the proteins and rRNA form a meshwork, especially tight in the large subunit.

Cryo-EM was instrumental in producing the first clear 3D images of this complex organelle (24, 26, 64). The best current maps have resolutions in the range of 10 Å (27, 40), which allow proteins to be docked and rRNA helices to be delineated. The positions of tRNA in its various canonical sites were mapped (3, 4, 64a), and the binding positions of the elongation factors were revealed [EF-Tu ternary complex (65), EF-G (1, 2)]. Figure 7 (see color insert) presents a recent example for such localizations: the position of tetracycline protection factor Tet(O) on the 70S *E. coli* ribosome (62).

CURRENT LIMITATIONS AND HOW THEY MIGHT BE OVERCOME

Three-dimensional cryo-EM of single particles, as a method of determining structure and dynamic behavior of macromolecules, is coming of age. Perhaps one of the most telling indications is the title of an article that appeared a few years ago, "Who Needs Crystals Anyway?" (15). One of the most useful features of the technique is the potential for fast turnaround: If everything goes well (high occupancy of binding states; good, random orientational behavior of the particles; flawless electron microscopic data collection), the number of micrographs required to achieve 10–15 Å resolution can be collected within a few days. If a 3D template map exists, a density map for a new data set can be obtained in a matter of days or a couple of weeks.

As more powerful and sophisticated electron microscopes are becoming available and the methods of processing and interpretation are increasingly refined, the question is: Where is the limit? Attainment of close-to-atomic resolution is feasible in principle, provided the particle exceeds a certain size (31). To approach atomic resolution, the number of particles has to be greatly increased. The number should go roughly with the cube of $1/d$ if d is the resolution in Å. For the ribosome, resolutions in the range of $\sim$10 Å can be currently achieved with $\sim$30,000 particles; therefore attainment of $\sim$3 Å would require $27 \times 30,000$ particles, or close to a million. However, this estimate is optimistic for two reasons: (*a*) It does not make allowance for the fact that the S/N ratio decreases with increasing spatial frequency, and (*b*) it does not account for the conformational variability that comes increasingly into plan as the resolution increases. Thus, development of methods for automated data collection and processing will be the key, along with powerful algorithms for sorting data originating from heterogeneous molecule populations.

The work accomplished to date using 3D cryo-EM of single particles has also taught us that many studies of macromolecular interaction already yield significant results at resolutions of 10–20 Å. One of the aims of the development of technology should be to reach the range of resolution routinely, allowing protein subdomain structure and alpha-helical elements to be recognized, i.e., 6–8 Å.

SUMMARY

Understanding molecular interactions is key to understanding the workings of the cell. Molecules engage in dynamic associations ("molecular machines"), forming complexes in this process that are often too large and too flexible for structural studies by X-ray crystallography. As we have seen, cryo-EM is a new, powerful tool that enables us to visualize these complexes despite their unwieldy properties.

Although the resolution is limited, crucial information about the interaction of molecules and their ligands can be gained by fitting atomic structures into the cryo-EM density maps. Each of the examples given, the ribosome, spliceosome, and transcription complex, illustrates the power of this combined approach.

ACKNOWLEDGMENTS

This work was supported by grants from NIH R37GM29169, R01GM55440, P41RR01219, and NSF DBI9871347. I thank Yu Chen for assistance with the preparation of the figures.

Visit the Annual Reviews home page at www.annualreviews.org

LITERATURE CITED

1. Agrawal RK, Heagle AB, Penczek P, Grassucci RA, Frank J. 1999. EF-G-dependent GTP hydrolysis induces translocation accompanied by large conformational changes in the 70S ribosome. *Nat. Struct. Biol.* 6:643–47

2. Agrawal RK, Penczek P, Grassucci RA, Frank J. 1998. Visualization of elongation factor G on the *Escherichia coli* 70S ribosome: the mechanism of translocation. *Proc. Natl. Acad. Sci. USA* 95:6134–38

3. Agrawal RK, Penczek P, Grassucci RA, Li Y, Leith A, et al. 1996. Direct visualization of A-, P-, and E-site transfer RNAs in the *Escherichia coli* ribosome. *Science* 271:1000–2

4. Agrawal RK, Spahn CMT, Penczek P, Grassucci RA, Nierhaus KH, Frank J. 2000. Visualization of tRNA movements on the *Escherichia coli* 70S ribosome during the elongation cycle. *J. Cell Biol.* 150: 447–59

5. Alberts B. 1998. The cell as a collection of protein machines: preparing the next generation of molecular biologists. *Cell* 92:291–94

6. Andel F, Ladurner AG, Inouye C, Tjian R, Nogales E. 1999. Three-dimensional structure of the human TFIID-IIA-IIB complex. *Science* 286:2153–56

7. Ban N, Nissen P, Hansen J, Moore PB, Steitz TA. 2000. The complete atomic structure of the large ribosomal subunit at 2.4 Å resolution. *Science* 289:905–20

8. Böhm J, Frangakis AS, Hergel R, Nickell S, Typke D, Baumeister W. 2000. Toward detecting and identifying macromolecules in a cellular context: template matching applied to electron tomograms. *Proc. Natl. Acad. Sci. USA* 97:14245–50

9. Boisset N, Penczek P, Taveau JC, Frank J. 1995. Three-dimensional reconstruction in vitreous ice of *Androctonus australis* hemocyanin labeled with a monoclonal Fab fragment. *J. Struct. Biol.* 115:16–29

10. Borland L, van Heel M. 1990. Classification of image data in conjugate representation spaces. *J. Opt. Soc. Am.* A7:601–10

11. Böttcher B, Wynne SA, Crowther RA. 1997. Determination of the fold of the core protein of hepatitis B virus by electron cryomicroscopy. *Nature* 386:88–91

12. Cheng RH, Kuhn RJ, Olson NH, Rossmann MG, Choi H-K, et al. 1995. Nucleocapsid and glycoprotein organization in an enveloped virus. *Cell* 80:621–30

12a. Chiu W, Downing KH, Dubochet J, Glaeser RM, Heide HG, et al. 1986. Cryoprotection in electron microscopy. *J. Microsc.* 141:385–91

13. Crowther RA. 1971. Procedures for three-dimensional reconstruction of spherical viruses by Fourier synthesis from electron

micrographs. *Proc. R. Soc. London. Ser. B* 261:221–30

14. DeRosier D, Klug A. 1968. Reconstruction of 3-dimensional structures from electron micrographs. *Nature* 217:130–34

15. DeRosier DJ. 1997. Who needs crystals anyway? *Nature* 386:26–27

16. Dubochet J, Adrian M, Lepault J, McDowall AW. 1985. Cryo-electron microscopy of vitrified biological specimens. *Trends Biochem. Sci.* 10:143–46

17. Dubochet J, Lepault J, Freeman R, Berriman JA, Homo JC. 1982. Electron microscopy of frozen water and aqueous solutions. *J. Microsc.* 128:219–37

18. Frank J. 1975. Averaging of low exposure electron micrographs of non-periodic objects. *Ultramicroscopy* 1:159–62

19. Frank J. 1996. *Three-Dimensional Electron Microscopy of Macromolecular Assemblies*. New York: Academic

20. Frank J, Agrawal RK. 2000. A ratchet-like inter-subunit reorganization of the ribosome during translocation. *Nature* 406: 318–22

21. Frank J, Al-Ali L. 1975. Signal-to-noise ratio of electron micrographs obtained by cross correlation. *Nature* 256:376–79

22. Frank J, Goldfarb W, Eisenberg D, Baker TS. 1978. Reconstruction of glutamine synthetase using computer averaging. *Ultramicroscopy* 3:283–90

23. Frank J, Penczek P, Agrawal RK, Grassucci RA, Heagle AB. 1999. Three-dimensional cryo-electron microscopy of ribosomes. *Methods Enzymol.* 317:276–91

24. Frank J, Penczek P, Grassucci R, Srivastava S. 1991. Three-dimensional reconstruction of the 70S *Escherichia coli* ribosome in ice: the distribution of ribosomal RNA. *J. Cell Biol.* 115:597–605

25. Frank J, Verschoor A, Boublik M. 1981. Computer averaging of electron micrographs of 40S ribosomal subunits. *Science* 214:1353–55

26. Frank J, Zhu J, Penczek P, Li Y, Srivastava S, et al. 1995. A model of protein synthesis based on cryo-electron microscopy

of the *E. coli* ribosome. *Nature* 376:441–44

27. Gabashvili IS, Agrawal RK, Spahn CMT, Grassucci RA, Frank J, Penczek P. 2000. Solution structure of the *E. coli* 70S ribosome at 11.5 Å resolution. *Cell* 100:537–49

28. Grigorieff N. 1998. Three-dimensional structure of bovine NADH: ubiquinone oxidoreductase (complex I) at 22 Å in ice. *J. Mol. Biol.* 277:1033–46

29. Grigorieff N. 2000. Resolution measurement in structures derived from single particles. *Acta Crystallogr. D* 56:1270–77

30. Harauz G, Ottensmeyer FP. 1984. Direct three-dimensional reconstruction for macromolecular complexes from electron micrographs. *Ultramicroscopy* 12:309–20

31. Henderson R. 1995. The potential and limitations of neutrons, electrons and X-rays for atomic resolution microscopy of unstained biological molecules. *Q. Rev. Biophys.* 28:171–93

32. Hoppe W, Schramm HJ, Sturm M, Hunsmann N, Gassmann J. 1976. Three-dimensional electron microscopy of individual biological objects. I. Methods. *Z. Naturforsch A* 31:645–55

33. Jones TA, Zhou JY, Cowan SW, Kjeldgaard M. 1991. Improved methods for building protein models in electron density maps and the location of errors in these models. *Acta Crystallogr. A* 47:110–19

34. Lepault J, Booy FP, Dubochet J. 1983. Electron microscopy of frozen biological suspensions. *J. Microsc.* 129(Pt 1):89–102

35. Malhotra A, Harvey SC. 1994. A quantitative model of the *Escherichia coli* 16 S RNA in the 30 S ribosomal subunit. *J. Mol. Biol.* 240:308–40

36. Malhotra A, Penczek P, Agrawal RK, Gabashvili IS, Grassucci RA, et al. 1998. *Escherichia coli* 70 S ribosome at 15 Å resolution by cryo-electron microscopy: localization of fMet-tRNA$_f^{Met}$ and fitting of L1 protein. *J. Mol. Biol.* 280:103–16

37. Mancini EJ, Fuller SD. 2000. Supplanting crystallography or supplementing microscopy? A combined approach to the study of an enveloped virus. *Acta Crystallogr. D* 56:1278–87

38. McEwen B, Frank J. 2001. Electron tomographic (and other approaches) for imaging molecular machines. *Curr. Opin. Neurobiol.* 11:594–600

39. Milligan RA, Unwin PN. 1986. Location of exit channel for nascent protein in 80S ribosome. *Nature* 319:693–95

40. Müller F, Sommer I, Baranov P, Matadeen R, Stoldt M, et al. 2000. The 3D arrangement of the 23S and 5S rRNA in the *E. coli* ribosomal subunit based on a cryo-electron microscopic reconstruction at 7.5 Å resolution. *J. Mol. Biol.* 298:35–59

41. Nogales E. 2000. Recent structural insights into transcription preinitiation complexes. *J. Cell Sci.* 113:4391–97

42. Nogales E, Grigorieff N. 2001. Molecular machines: putting the pieces together. *J. Cell Biol.* 152:F1–10

43. Orlova EV. 2000. Structural analysis of non-crystalline macromolecules: the ribosome. *Acta Crystallogr. D* 56:1253–58

44. Orlova EV, Dube P, Harris JR, Beckman E, Zemlin F, et al. 1997. Structure of keyhole limpet hemocyanin type 1 (KLH1) at 15 Å resolution by electron cryomicroscopy and angular reconstitution. *J. Mol. Biol.* 271:417–37

45. Penczek PA, Grassucci RA, Frank J. 1994. The ribosome at improved resolution: new techniques for merging and orientation refinement in 3D cryo-electron microscopy of biological particles. *Ultramicroscopy* 53:251–70

46. Penczek PA, Zhu J, Frank J. 1996. A common-lines based method for determining orientations for N > 3 particle projections simultaneously. *Ultramicroscopy* 63:205–18

47. Radermacher M, Rao V, Grassucci R, Frank J, Timerman AP, et al. 1994. Cryo-electron microscopy and three-dimensional reconstruction of the calcium release channel/ryanodine receptor from skeletal muscle. *J. Cell Biol.* 127:411–23

48. Radermacher M, Wagenknecht T, Verschoor A, Frank J. 1986. A new 3-D reconstruction scheme applied to the 50S ribosomal subunit of *E. coli*. *J. Microsc.* 141:RP1–2

49. Radermacher M, Wagenknecht T, Verschoor A, Frank J. 1987. Three-dimensional reconstruction from a single-exposure, random conical tilt series applied to the 50S ribosomal subunit of *Escherichia coli*. *J. Microsc.* 146:113–36

50. Radermacher M, Wagenknecht T, Verschoor A, Frank J. 1987. Three-dimensional structure of the large ribosomal subunit from *Escherichia coli*. *EMBO J.* 6:1107–14

51. Radon J. 1917. Über die Bestimmung von Funktionen durch ihre Integralwerte längs gewisser Mannigfaltigkeiten. Berichte über die Verhandlungen der königlich sächsischen Gesellschaft der Wissenschaften zu Leipzig. *Math. Phys. Klasse* 69:262–77

52. Rayment I, Holden HM, Whittaker M, Yohn CB, Lorenz M, et al. 1993. Structure of the actin-myosin complex and its implications for muscle contraction. *Science* 261:58–65

53. Roseman AM. 2000. Docking structures of domains into maps from cryo-electron microscopy using local correlation. *Acta Crystallogr. D* 56:1332–40

54. Rossmann MG. 2000. Fitting atomic models into electron-microscopy maps. *Acta Crystallogr. D* 56:1341–49

55. Rouiller I, Butel VM, Latterich M, Milligan R, Wilson-Kubalek EM. 2000. A major conformational change in p97 AAA ATPase upon ATP binding. *Mol. Cell* 6:1485–90

56. Saibil HR. 2000. Macromolecular structure determination by cryo-electron microscopy. *Acta Crystallogr. D* 56:1215–22

57. Saibil HR. 2000. Molecular chaperones: containers and surfaces for folding,

stabilising or unfolding proteins. *Curr. Opin. Struct. Biol.* 10:251–58

58. Saxton WO, Baumeister W. 1982. The correlation averaging of a regularly arranged bacterial envelope protein. *J. Microsc.* 127:127–38

59. Schlünzen F, Tocilj A, Zarivach R, Harms J, Glühmann M, et al. 2000. Structure of functionally activated small ribosomal subunit at 3.3 Å resolution. *Cell* 102:615–23

60. Schröder RR, Manstein DJ, Jahn W, Holden H, Rayment I, et al. 1993. Three-dimensional atomic model of F-actin decorated with *Dictyostelium* myosin S1. *Nature* 364:171–74

61. Schultz P, Fribourg S, Poterszman A, Chipoulet M, Mallouh V, et al. 2000. Molecular architecture of human TFIIH. *Cell* 102:599–607

62. Spahn CMT, Blaha G, Agrawal RK, Penczek P, Grassucci RA, et al. 2001. Localization of the tetracycline resistance protein Tet(O) on the ribosome and the inhibition mechanism of tetracycline. *Mol. Cell* 7:1037–45

63. Stark H, Dube P, Lührmann R, Kastner B. 2001. Arrangement of RNA and proteins in the spliceosomal U1 small nuclear ribonucleoprotein particle. *Nature* 409:539–42

64. Stark H, Müller F, Orlova EV, Schatz M, Dube P, et al. 1995. The 70S *Escherichia coli* ribosome at 23 Å resolution: fitting the ribosomal RNA. *Structure* 3:815–21

64a. Stark H, Orlova EV, Rinke-Appel J, Junke N, Müller F, et al. 1997. Arrangement of tRNAs in pre- and post-translational ribosomes revealed by electron cryomicroscopy. *Cell* 88:19–28

65. Stark H, Rodnina MV, Rinke-Appel J, Brimacombe R, Wintermeyer W, van Heel M. 1997. Visualization of elongation factor Tu on the *Escherichia coli* ribosome. *Nature* 389:403–6

66. Stewart M. 1991. Transmission electron microscopy of vitrified biological macromolecular assemblies. In *Electron Microscopy in Biology—A Practical Approach*, ed. JR Harris, pp. 229–42. Oxford, UK: IRL

67. Stewart PL, Fuller SD, Burnett RM. 1993. Difference imaging of adenovirus: bridging the resolution gap between X-ray crystallography and electron microscopy. *EMBO J.* 12:2589–99

68. Deleted in proof

69. Taylor K, Glaeser RM. 1974. Electron diffraction of frozen, hydrated protein crystals. *Science* 186:1036–37

70. Unwin PN, Henderson R. 1975. Molecular structure determination by electron microscopy of unstained crystalline specimens. *J. Mol. Biol.* 94:425–40

71. van Heel M. 1987. Angular reconstitution: a posteriori assignment of projection directions for 3D reconstruction. *Ultramicroscopy* 21:111–24

72. van Heel M. 1989. Classification of very large electron microscopial image data sets. *Optik* 82:114–26

73. van Heel M, Frank J. 1981. Use of multivariate statistics in analysing the images of biological macromolecules. *Ultramicroscopy* 6:187–94

74. van Heel M, Harauz G. 1986. Resolution criteria for three-dimensional reconstruction. *Optik* 73:119–22

75. van Heel M, Keegstra W, Schutter W, van Bruggen EJF. 1982. Arthropod hemocyanin structures studied by image analysis. In *Life Chemistry Reports, The Structure and Function of Invertebrate Respiratory Proteins (Suppl. 1)*, ed. EJ Wood, pp. 69–73. London: Harwood Acad.

76. Volkmann N, Hanein D. 1999. Quantitative fitting of atomic models into observed densities derived by electron microscopy. *J. Struct. Biol* 125:176–84

77. Volkman N, Hanein D, Ouyang G, Trybus KM, DeRosier DJ, Lowey S. 2000. Evidence for cleft closure in actomyosin upon ADP release. *Nat. Struct. Biol.* 7:1147–55

78. Wagenknecht T, Carazo JM, Radermacher M, Frank J. 1989. Three-dimensional reconstruction of the ribosome from

Escherichia coli ribosome in the range of overlap views. *Biophys. J.* 55:465–77

79. Wagenknecht T, Grassucci R, Frank J. 1988. Electron microscopy and computer image averaging of ice-embedded large ribosomal subunits from *Escherichia coli. J. Mol. Biol.* 199:137–47

80. Deleted in proof

81. Wimberly BT, Brodersen DE, Clemons WM Jr, Morgan-Warren RJ, Carter AP, et al. 2000. Structure of the 30S ribosomal subunit. *Nature* 407:327–39

82. Wriggers W, Agrawal RK, Drew DL, McCammon A, Frank J. 2000. Domain motions of EF-G bound to the 70S ribosome: insights from a hand-shaking between multi-resolution structures. *Biophys. Chem.* 79:1670–78

83. Wriggers W, Milligan RA, McCammon JA. 1999. Situs: a package for docking crystal structures into low-resolution maps from electron microscopy. *J. Struct. Biol.* 125:185–95

84. Wriggers W, Milligan RA, Schulten K, McCammon JA. 1998. Self-organizing neural networks bridge the biomolecular resolution gap. *J. Mol. Biol.* 284:1247–54

85. Yonath A, Leonard KR, Wittmann HG. 1987. A tunnel in the large ribosomal subunit revealed by three-dimensional image reconstruction. *Science* 236:813–16

86. Yusupov MM, Yusupova GZ, Baucom A, Lieberman K, Earnest TN, et al. 2001. Crystal structure of the ribosome at 5.5 Å resolution. *Science* 292:883–96

87. Zhang X, Shaw A, Bates PA, Newman RH, Gowen B, et al. 2000. Structure of the AAA ATPase p97. *Mol. Cell* 6:1473–84

Annu. Rev. Biophys. Biomol. Struct. 2002. 31:321–41
DOI: 10.1146/annurev.biophys.31.091701.170951

FORCE EXERTION IN FUNGAL INFECTION

Martin Bastmeyer,[1] Holger B. Deising,[2] and
Clemens Bechinger[3]

[1]*Department of Biology, University of Konstanz, Fach M626, Universitätsstrasse 10,
D-77457 Konstanz Germany; e-mail: martin.bastmeyer@uni-konstanz.de*
[2]*Institut für Pflanzenzüchtung und Pflanzenschutz, Martin-Luther-University
Halle-Wittenberg, Ludwig-Wucherer-Str. 2, D-06099 Halle (Saale) Germany;
e-mail: deising@landw.uni-halle.de*
[3]*Department of Physics, University of Konstanz, Fach M676, Universitätsstrasse 10,
D-77457 Konstanz Germany; e-mail: clemens.bechinger@uni-konstanz.de*

Key Words appressoria, turgor pressure, waveguide microscopy, osmometry,
strain gauge

■ **Abstract** Fungal pathogens of plants or animals invade their hosts either by
secretion of lytic enzymes, exerting force, or by a combination of both. Although many
fungi are thought to rely mostly on lysis of the host tissue, some plant pathogenic fungi
differentiate complex infection cells that develop enormous turgor pressure, which
in turn is translated into force used for invasion. In order to understand mechanisms
of fungal infection in detail, methods have been developed that indirectly or directly
measure turgor pressure and force. In this article, these methods are described and
critically discussed, and their importance in analysis of fungal infection are outlined.

CONTENTS

INTRODUCTION

The capability of invasive growth is a prerequisite for acquiring nutrients from solid
substrata and has been considered essential for pathogenicity of filamentous fungi
(9, 19, 66, 76). Tissue invasion is mediated by apical growth, which is a hallmark of

filamentous fungi (76). The driving force for continuous apical growth and, in the case of pathogenic fungi, invasion is hydrostatic pressure (turgor pressure) within the fungal cells. Generation of significant turgor pressure and its translation into force was observed by Buller (5) more than 40 years ago. In a simple experiment, he showed that an individual basidiocarp, i.e., a fruiting body, of *Coprinus sterquilinus* with a stipe diameter of 6 mm, can raise a weight of 200 g (5). This is a pressure of at least 0.07 MPa (0.7 bar) (41). The ability of mushrooms to lift overlying obstructions and to crack asphalt paving clearly further emphasizes the power of turgor pressure of fungal hyphae.

The question of whether pathogenic fungi penetrate their plant or animal host by mechanical force, after enzymatic dissolution, or by a combination of both, has been controversial for decades (31, 37, 38, 59, 75). The finding that the rice blast fungus *Magnaporthe grisea* generates enough pressure to mechanically breach rice epidermal cells (25) stimulated research to measure fungal force or turgor pressure. In this review, we briefly describe the biology and mode of penetration of different fungal systems. In addition, we discuss various techniques used to evaluate turgor pressure and/or resulting force. In particular, we concentrate on the recently published techniques of strain gauge measurements and waveguide microscopy. Finally, we outline further developments of techniques and applications of force measurement in fungal and other systems.

BIOLOGY OF INVASIVE HYPHAL GROWTH

Fungal hyphae are tube-like structures with a hemispherical or hemiellipsoidal apical region. Hyphal tip growth was described by Reinhardt in 1892 (60). The most accepted model describing hyphal growth, known as the steady-state model of apical wall growth, was developed by Wessels (76). At the extending apex, vesicles carrying enzymes that synthesize the cell wall occur in large numbers and fuse with the plasma membrane at the apical tip. In a laboratory strain of *Neurospora crassa*, close to 40,000 vesicles have been estimated to fuse with the apical plasma membrane per minute, and vesicles occupy approximately 80% of the volume within 1 μm of the hyphal tip (8). As a consequence of massive incorporation of cell wall–biogenic enzymes, fibrillar carbohydrate chains consisting mostly of water-insoluble chitin and β-1,3-glucans are synthesized and an initially flexible cell wall forms. With time, as these polymers fall behind the apex, they interact to form chitin microfibrils and β-glucan triple helices. Covalent links are formed between chitin and β-glucan molecules, and the rigidity of the cell wall increases (76) (Figure 1*a*). Hyphal morphology thus basically depends on the rate of release of wall-destined vesicles and the linear displacement of the vesicle supply center, which is also known as the Spitzenkörper (61, 62).

The driving force of hyphal invasive growth is turgor pressure. This has been demonstrated with oomycetes that do not show regulation of turgor in hyper- or hypo-osmotic solutions (43). Hyphae of the oomycetes *Saprolegnia ferax, Achlya*

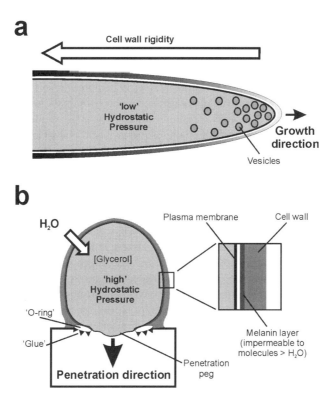

Figure 1 Biology of invasive fungal growth. (*a*) The steady-state model of apical wall growth explains tip growth of filamentous fungi. At the extending apical tip, vesicles carrying enzymes that synthesize the cell wall fuse with the plasma membrane. As a consequence, fibrillar carbohydrate chains are synthesized and an initially flexible cell wall forms. As these polymers fall behind the apex, the fibrillar chains interact to form chitin microfibrils and β-glucan triple helices. Covalent links are formed between chitin and β-glucan molecules, and the rigidity of the cell wall increases. Force is therefore directed toward the growing apex [modified after (76)]. (*b*) Some plant pathogenic fungi form distinct infection cells. These appressoria adhere to the plant surface by secreting a glue and develop a penetration peg at their base. The incorporation of melanin into the cell wall and synthesis of intracellular osmotically active material (glycerol) allow the build up of hydrostatic pressure. Force is then exerted vertically and can be efficiently directed to the cuticle [modified after (24)].

bisexualis, and *A. ambisexualis* respond to osmotic stress caused by elevated concentrations of different osmolytes, such as sorbitol, sucrose, or polyethyleneglycol (PEG-400), by secreting enzymes capable of modifying their cell walls. *Endo*-glucanase activity, but not the activity of other extracellular enzymes such as amylase and protease, increases with increasing osmolyte concentrations in the growth medium and is correlated with reduced tensile strength of the apical cell wall (51). Modification of the mechanical properties of the cell wall thus may also be involved in regulation of force exertion (45). In invasive hyphae of pathogenic fungi exposed to high mechanical resistance, regulation of cell wall strength and turgor could allow focused force exertion and result in more efficient invasive growth (49).

Several pathogenic fungi, parasitic on plants or animals, invade their hosts without major morphogenetic alteration of their hyphae. Examples of plant pathogens belonging to this group are various *Fusarium* species, which often are polyphagous pathogens, or the tomato pathogen *Cladosporium fulvum*. However, minor changes such as increased hyphal diameter within the host tissue may indicate functional differences between vegetative hyphae and infection hyphae (38). Most fungal pathogens of mammals, e.g., *Aspergillus* species, *Cryptococcus neoformans*, zygomycetes such as *Mucor* and *Rhizopus* species, and several dimorphic fungi, are inhaled by their host, and it is assumed that enzymes rather than force play a role in the infection process (55). This view is supported by recent experiments with the oomycete *Pythium insidiosum*, a pathogen of mammals. Measurements with a strain gauge suggest that the force exerted by a hypha would not be sufficient to penetrate human skin and invade underlying tissue (see below), so that high-level synthesis of proteinases may be necessary to support infection (59). Accordingly, plant pathogenic fungi such as *Fusarium* species that lack elaborate infection structures secrete large amounts of cell wall–degrading enzymes (7, 11, 12). Taken together, available data suggest that fungi that do not undergo substantial morphogenesis may rely largely on lytic enzymes rather than force when invading the host (18).

As early as 1883, Frank (17) described germination of conidia of *Fusicladium* sp. and *Gloeosporium* (i.e., *Colletotrichum*) *lindemuthianum* on the plant cuticle and subsequently the swelling of the apex of the germ tube and the formation of a cell or, as he called it, organ. He coined the term appressorium (adhesion organ). Appressoria have different forms. In *Botrytis* species or basidiospore germlings of rust fungi, they are inconspicuous swellings of the germ tubes. In *M. grisea*, *Colletotrichum* species, and many other plant pathogens, they are visible as discrete, swollen, lobed or dome-shaped cells separated from the germ tube by a septum (Figure 2). Frank (17) also identified the penetration pore at the appressorial base as the point of fungal invasion into the host tissue, and he concluded that appressoria are specific organs formed to prepare for invasion of the plant. Appressoria adhere to the plant surface by secreting a potent glue (14, 67) and develop a penetration peg at their base (Figure 1*b*). Force is then exerted vertically and can be efficiently directed to the cuticle (9, 15). The fact that appressorial cell walls consist of different layers (37) indicates elevated levels of turgor pressure in these cells. However, while appressoria are essential for infection by many pathogens (22, 63), the significance of a specific appressorial design remains to be elucidated (18).

Botrytis cinerea is a polyphagous pathogen that causes gray mold on various ornamental and crop plants. *Cochliobolus carbonum* is the causal agent of northern corn blight. Both are well-investigated examples of fungi that infect their host plants after differentiation of nonmelanized appressoria. Whereas the appressoria

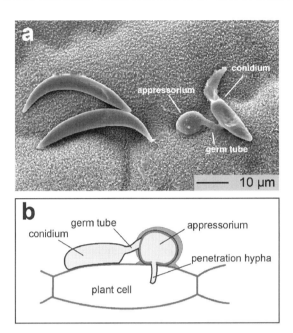

Figure 2   Plant cell infection by *Colletotrichum graminicola*. (*a*) Low-temperature scanning electron micrograph of three conidia on a rice leaf. The conidium to the right has formed an appressorium that is connected to the conidium by the germ tube (courtesy of R. Guggenheim). (*b*) Schematic drawing of a cross section through a conidium, a germ tube, and an appressorium infecting a plant cell.

of *B. cinerea* are rather inconspicuous, *C. carbonum* forms distinct infection cells. Both pathogens synthesize and secrete a vast array of plant cell wall–degrading enzymes during the infection process. Because the appressoria are not melanized, it has been assumed that enzymes rather than force allow penetration. The most significant impediment in clearly defining the importance of enzymatic softening of the substratum is the redundancy of the genes and enzymes involved in plant cell wall degradation. Because many enzymes with different and similar specificities orchestrate the degradation of complex cell wall polymers, targeted inactivation of single genes usually did not significantly alter fungal virulence (1, 53, 64, 70, 71). A breakthrough in evaluating the significance of cell wall–degrading enzymes came with the inactivation of *SNF1* of *C. carbonum*, a gene required for activation of catabolite-repressed genes. In *snf1* mutants, mRNA expression of several genes encoding cell wall–degrading enzymes was downregulated and enzyme activities were drastically reduced. As a result, successful penetration was reduced, indicating that enzymatic lysis of cell wall polymers is important in this fungus, and force alone is not sufficient for penetration of the host cell wall (73).

Some fungi form distinct melanized infection cells. These may be appressoria as in the case of *M. grisea* or *Colletotrichum* species (Figure 2), or hyphopodia as in the case of *Gaeumannomyces graminis*, an economically important pathogen of cereals. Hyphopodia develop from mature hyphae. Appressoria develop from swellings at the tips of conidial germ tubes (23). Melanization leads to reduction of the cell wall pore diameter to values of less than 1 nm, which allows molecules only the size of water to pass through the appressorial wall (Figure 1*b*). As the appressoria mature and melanize, synthesis of osmotically active molecules takes place. Talbot and coworkers have estimated that in appressoria of *M. grisea*, glycerol concentrations of 3.22 mol l^{-1} occur; the osmotic potential generated by such a solution would correspond to 8.7 MPa at 20°C, assuming that this is an ideal solute (10). Extrapolation from psychrometric assays suggest that the turgor pressure is at least 5.8 MPa. Because glycerol can permeate plasma membranes, the only diffusion barrier maintaining high concentrations of this solute is a distinct layer of cell wall–localized melanin. The glycerol concentration in nonmelanized tricyclazole-treated appressoria or appressoria differentiated by mutants with defects in the melanin biosynthesis pathway is significantly lower than that of the wild type (10). Different lines of evidence show that melanin and force exertion are necessary for successful penetration. Targeted inactivation of genes involved in melanin biosynthesis results in nonpathogenic mutants (6, 20, 28, 29, 56). Specific inhibitors of enzymes of the melanin biosynthetic pathway block penetration and are used as fungicides to control fungi that use melanized appressoria for forceful invasion (30, 78, 80). In hyphopodia of *G. graminis*, melanization is associated with reduced cell wall permeability and increased turgor and wall rigidity (48).

In the human pathogenic black yeast *Wangiella dermatitidis* and the neuropathogen *C. neoformans*, melanin localizes to the outer cell wall. In these fungi, melanin has been related to protection from ultraviolet light and oxidizing agents generated during the immune response and from antibody-mediated phagocytosis (4, 54, 77). In the human pathogen *W. dermatitidis*, melanin synthesis changes the biomechanical characteristics of invasive hyphae and has a profound effect upon virulence and disease progression (4).

SYSTEMS AND METHODS FOR MEASURING PRESSURE AND FORCE

Techniques for Indirect Measurement of Turgor Pressure

Indirect methods used to determine turgor pressure of different fungal species include incipient plasmolysis, incipient cytorrhisis, freezing and melting point osmometry, and vapor pressure deficit osmometry. Because these methods have been described and critically discussed in detail (26, 42, 47), we concentrate on techniques used for turgor measurement of pathogenic fungi.

TURGOR MEASUREMENT BY PLASMOLYSIS   If a fungal cell is exposed to high concentrations of osmolytes, water diffuses out of the cell. The accompanying loss of turgor causes different morphological changes depending on the rigidity of the cell wall and the size of the osmotically active molecules (Figure 3*a*). Plasmolysis, the

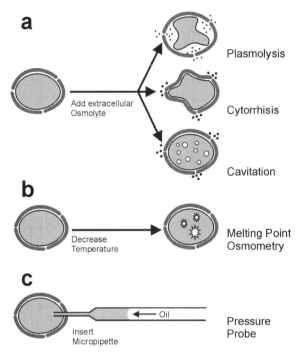

Figure 3 Techniques for measurements of turgor pressure. (*a*) Plasmolysis. (*b*) Melting point osmometry. (*c*) Pressure probe. For further explanation see text.

separation of the plasma membrane from the cell wall, occurs when an extracellular osmolyte diffuses through the cell wall but is excluded by the plasma membrane. Incipient plasmolysis is achieved when the water potential of the intracellular and extracellular solutions are identical. If the size of the osmotically active extracellular molecules is larger than the diameter of the pores of the hyphal cell wall, water follows the potential gradient and diffuses out of the cell. In consequence, the fungal cell collapses, a phenomenon referred to as cytorrhisis (48). However, if the cell wall is rigid so that cytorrhisis cannot occur, osmotic stress may induce formation of gas bubbles in the cytoplasm, a phenomenon known as cavitation (39).

Cytorrhisis experiments with polyethyleneglycol (PEG) molecules of various sizes indicate that melanization of the appressorial wall results in reduction of cell wall pore diameter to less than 1 nm (25), which allows uptake or loss of water, but not of larger molecules, e.g., glycerol. Induction of incipient plasmolysis or cytorrhisis has been used to determine turgor pressure and size of cell wall pores. Based on the value of osmotic pressure, estimates of cellular turgor pressure can be made.

Glycerol has been identified as the solute giving rise to appressorial turgor and can be used to determine the concentration that induces incipient cytorrhisis. In *M. grisea* a glycerol concentration of 3.2 mol l^{-1} was sufficient to induce collapse of 50% of the appressoria (13). This is in good agreement with the glycerol concentration estimated for mature appressoria of this fungus (10). The osmotic potential generated by such a solution would correspond to 8.7 MPa at 20°C, assuming that this is an ideal solute (10). Extrapolation from psychrometrical assays suggests that the turgor produced in the infection droplet is at least 5.8 MPa. Incipient plasmolysis or cytorrhisis experiments with *C. graminicola* indicated a sharp reduction of cell wall pore size as the appressorium matures and melanizes, coinciding with high osmolyte concentrations (J. A. Sugui & H. B. Deising, unpublished data).

In the biotrophic powdery mildew of barley, *Blumeria graminis* f. sp. *hordei*, significant turgor pressure has been demonstrated by incipient plasmolysis and cytorrhisis experiments (57). Turgor in nonmelanized appressoria of this fungus reached a maximum of 2 MPa (incipient cytorrhisis) or 4 MPa (incipient plasmolysis) 12 h post inoculation, which is exactly the time of emergence and extension of the penetration peg. In this fungus the enzyme cellulase is associated with the penetration peg, and it is thought that a combination of enzymatic activity and mechanical force is employed for penetration of the host cell wall (57).

Money and coworkers (48) measured turgor in hyphopodia of the highly destructive ascomycete, *G. graminis*. *G. graminis* causes take-all disease of different cereal grasses, including wheat, rice, and oats (74). Cytoplasmic cavitation experiments performed with PEGs of various sizes indicate a turgor of 1.8 MPa for melanized wild-type hyphopodia and 0.9 MPa for hyphopodia of a dark mutant that synthesizes melanin constitutively (48).

MELTING POINT OSMOMETRY   The melting point of cytoplasmic ice crystals is indicative of the cellular osmolyte concentration (Figure 3*b*). This method, which was first described by Money & Howard (52), involves a cold stage to measure melting points with an accuracy of 0.01–0.02°C, corresponding to an osmolality of 5–10 mmol kg^{-1}. The melting point depression correlates with the intracellular solute concentration; whereas distilled water melts at 0°C, a KCl solution with an osmolality of 1000 mmol kg^{-1} melts at a temperature of -1.86°C (48). Using this technique, the highest reliable measurement from a single melanized appressorium of *M. grisea* was 3.38 MPa, which is less than half the maximum pressure measured by incipient cytorrhisis (25). Although melting of ice crystals could be easily observed in nonmelanized cells, pigmentation interferes with precise determination of the melting point (52). However, although the absolute values may not be reliable, clear differences between melanized wild-type and nonmelanized mutant appressoria were seen, confirming the link between melanization and turgor pressure (52).

Techniques for Direct Measurement of Turgor Pressure

PRESSURE PROBE   Pressure probe micropipettes can be used to gain quantitative data on turgor pressure of cells, as well as on rigidity of the cell wall. When the tip of an oil-filled micropipette is inserted into the fungal cytoplasm, the turgor pressure drives some of the cytosol into the pipette (Figure 3*c*). The pressure required to push the cytosol back so that the oil reaches the pipette tip is taken as the turgor pressure of the cell (42). As only relatively large cells or hyphae can be impaled, the number of species that can be analyzed by this technique is limited. Another disadvantage is that cells with high turgor pressure and rigid cell walls, e.g., the melanized appressoria of *M. grisea* or the hyphopodia of *G. graminis*, may burst when penetrated by the tip of the micropipette (48). When successful, however, this method provides much more accurate data than indirect techniques. Most experiments that utilize this technique involve oomycetes because they have large hyphae. Money & Harold reported a hyphal turgor pressure of 0.4 MPa for *S. ferax* (49) and 0.7 MPa for *A. bisexualis* (50). For an extensive review on this technique the reader is referred to (42).

Techniques for Indirect Measurement of Force

Although invasive force is derived from turgor, its magnitude is dependent on the looseness of the apical cell wall (41). The actual force depends on the interplay of turgor pressure and cell wall characteristics, the latter being controlled by multi-factorial cell wall biogenesis (65, 76).

Methods for indirect force measurements utilize the ability of hyphal growth into substrates of variable known hardness. Since the contribution of substrate-degrading enzymes cannot be ruled out, these methods can only estimate the forces applied by the fungi.

AGAR PENETRATION EXPERIMENTS   Using *S. ferax* as a model fungus that does not vary turgor to compensate for changes of the extracellular osmoticum concentration, Money demonstrated that turgor pressure is the driving force for invasive hyphal growth (41, 42, 47). Increasing concentrations of sucrose (decreasing water potentials) significantly reduced the ability of hyphae to penetrate growth media solidified with agar (Figure 4*a*). Thus, agar penetration tests are useful for estimating the importance of various factors such as cell wall rigidity or turgor, both of which are important for invasive growth. As the strength of agar gels can be measured, e.g., by penetrometers, the pressure and force exerted by invasive hyphae can be estimated. Agar penetration assays have demonstrated that efficient invasive growth of the human pathogen *W. dermatitidis* depends on incorporation of melanin into the fungal cell wall (4). However, as 8% (w/v) agar has a strength of only approximately 0.1 MPa, corresponding to a penetration pressure of 0.1 μN μm^{-2} (4, 47), this technique is not useful for measurements of pressure or force exerted by appressoria of plant pathogenic fungi.

PENETRATION EXPERIMENTS WITH MEMBRANES   In 1895, soon after the classical experiments on fungal tip growth by Reinhardt (60), Miyoshi (40) was the first to attempt force measurements in plant pathogenic fungi. To exclude enzymatic softening of the substratum, he used inert gold membranes (Figure 4*b*). Hyphae of *B. cinerea* and *Penicillium glaucum* were able to penetrate the gold membrane,

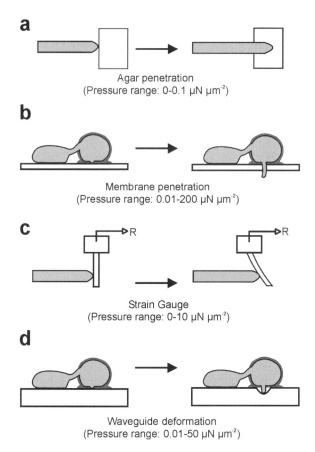

a

Agar penetration
(Pressure range: 0-0.1 µN µm⁻²)

b

Membrane penetration
(Pressure range: 0.01-200 µN µm⁻²)

c

Strain Gauge
(Pressure range: 0-10 µN µm⁻²)

d

Waveguide deformation
(Pressure range: 0.01-50 µN µm⁻²)

Figure 4 Techniques for measurements of force. The corresponding sensitivities are given for each method. (*a*) Agar penetration. (*b*) Membrane penetration. (*c*) Strain gauge. (*d*) Waveguide microscopy. For further explanation see text.

pollen germ tubes were not. A hyphal-shaped cylindrical glass needle was used to determine that a pressure of 0.014 μN μm^{-2}, corresponding to 0.014 MPa, was sufficient to breach the gold membrane. As the diameter of the hypha of *B. cinerea* is only 33 μm^2, a force of 0.46 μN could breach the gold membrane. Miyoshi's experiments also indicated that a pressure of 0.35 and 0.5 MPa would be sufficient to breach onion and epidermal cell walls of *Tradescantia* (40). Howard and coworkers (25) were the first to demonstrate that melanized appressoria employ enormous turgor pressure to penetrate hard surfaces. They showed that appressoria of *M. grisea* could penetrate nonbiodegradable mylar (poly(ethylene terephthalate)) and kevlar (p-phenyleneterephtalamide) films with hardness values up to 250 MPa (or 250 $\times$ 10^6 N m^{-2}). Because the penetration peg of *M. grisea* has a diameter of 1 μm^2, this would predict an appressorial pressure of more than 200 MPa or an invasive force of 200 μN. These values exceed turgor measurements of *M. grisea* (see above) or force measurements of *C. graminicola* (see following section) at least 10-fold. These discrepancies are difficult to explain. However, the macroscopic method used to measure the hardness of mylar films may have overestimated the forces necessary to penetrate the films on a microscopic scale. Although mylar is resistant to microbial degradation and mylar-degrading enzymes are not known, the fungus could use a hitherto unknown mechanism to soften this compound.

Techniques for Direct Measurement of Force

In contrast to the indirect force measurements described above, recent methods have been developed that allow direct determination of force exertion by fungal hyphae and infection cells.

FORCE MEASUREMENT BY STRAIN GAUGE   Force exertion of vegetative hyphae has been directly measured with an ultra-sensitive strain gauge composed of a silicon beam with an evaporated electrical-resistive element (26, 47) (Figure 4c). Hyphae of *A. bisexualis* were allowed to grow from an agar shelf into a well in a culture plate filled with distilled water. When the miniaturized strain gauge (Figure 5a) is positioned in the liquid so that the growing hypha can press against the silicon beam, the latter (together with the resistor) is slightly deformed. As a result, the electrical resistance of the device is changed in proportion to the applied force (Figure 5b). The resolution of this method is better than 1 μN, equivalent to the gravitational force of 10^{-4} g (47). Strain gauge measurements with *A. bisexualis* revealed discontinuous forces (and turgor), corresponding to pulses in hyphal extension rates (26). This confirms earlier results obtained with hyphae of several fungi of different taxa (36). The above strain gauge measurements indicated a total force of 107 μN exerted by large vegetative hyphae of *A. bisexualis* (26), whereas more typical hyphae with diameters of 15 to 25 μm exert a mean force of 12 μN (47). Accordingly, the pressure exertion for hyphae of *A. bisexualis* has been estimated between 0.02 and 0.07 MPa (47). These studies also suggest that 10% or less of the force available from turgor is applied by the hyphal apex against its surroundings, which is consistent with the idea that both turgor and the mechanical strength of the fungal cell wall govern the magnitude of invasive force (47).

In both plant and human pathogenic fungi, the question remains whether force alone or a combination of force and enzymatic dissolution of host tissue is needed for invasive growth. Strain gauge experiments on hyphae of the mammalian pathogen *P. insidiosum*, an oomycete causing rare but potentially lethal infections, indicated that forces of up to 5.0 μN are exerted by hyphal apices, corresponding to a pressure of 0.3 μN μm^{-2} (MPa). As the mechanical resistance of cutaneous and subcutaneous tissue is between 10 and 47 μN μm^{-2} (MPa), extracellular proteases are assumed to reduce tissue resistance 10- to 100-fold (59).

WAVEGUIDE MICROSCOPY   Bechinger et al. used an optical method based on waveguide microscopy to measure forces being exerted by a plant pathogenic fungus

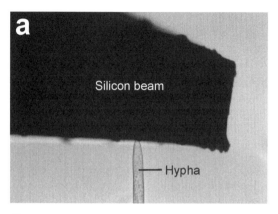

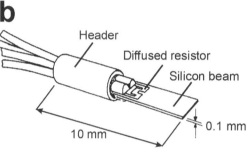

Figure 5   Force measurements with a strain gauge. (*a*) Hyphal apex of *Achlya bisexualis* making contact with silicon beam of strain gauge (picture provided by N. Money). (*b*) Schematic drawing of the strain gauge composed of a silicon beam with a diffused electrical resistor. When the silicon beam together with the resistor is deformed, the electrical resistance of the device is changed in proportion to the applied force (from technical note, A. S. Capto, Horten, Norway).

onto a flexible substrate (2) (Figure 4*d*). The basic idea of the technique relies on total internal reflection, which is the main principle for light propagation in glass fibers as employed for telecommunication purposes (3). When a light beam propagating in a medium with low index of refraction is reflected above a critical angle Θ_c at an interface toward a medium with a higher refraction index, the light beam is totally reflected and thus can propagate along inside the medium. Due to the confinement of the electromagnetic field, only well-defined modes similar to those in a Fabry-Perot interferometer can propagate within a waveguide. The modes are characterized by a resonance condition (72)

$$\cos \Theta_R = m\pi/dk, (m = 1, 2, 3, \ldots), \tag{1}$$

with d being the waveguide thickness, k the wave vector inside the core, Θ_R the angle of incidence at the cladding material, and m the mode index (Figure 6*a*).

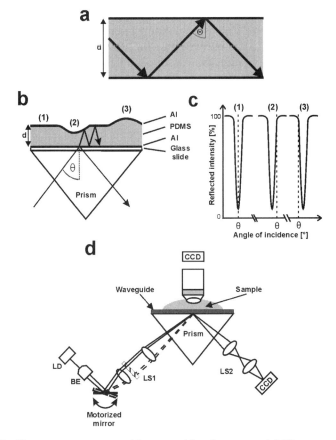

Figure 6 Force measurements with waveguide microscopy. (*a*) Zig-zag mode in an optical waveguide with thickness d. (*b*) The flexible waveguide consists of a silicone layer (PDMS) of thickness d sandwiched between two aluminum layers (Al). (*c*) R(Θ)-curves show strong dips when a waveguide is excited with the angle of resonance strongly depending on the local thickness. Therefore, if the reflected light is imaged at a fixed Θ (*dashed lines*), only those parts of the waveguide that have the proper thickness (1) appear black, while parts that are thinner (2) or thicker (3) appear bright. (*d*) Schematic view of the experimental setup to visualize and measure locally applied forces. The beam diameter of a polarized laser diode (LD) is increased by a beam expander (BE), strikes a mirror, and is guided to the prism through a lens system (LS1). This allows illumination of the same location of the prism base at defined angles of incidence when the mirror is rotated. The reflected light is projected through another lens system (LS2) onto a camera chip (CCD). The setup is attached to the stage of an upright microscope equipped with epi-illuminating optics. The image of the surface of the waveguide is focused onto a second CCD camera.

As can be seen in Equation 1, Θ_R depends strongly on the thickness of the waveguide. This allows determination of the thickness of the waveguide with nanometer precision if Θ_R is accurately measured (32, 34). Accordingly, if laterally resolved measurements of Θ_R are performed (as described below), the principle can be extended to study the two-dimensional topography of a waveguide with a precision in the nanometer range. If the surface of the waveguide is deformed, one obtains an image of the corresponding indentation. Provided that the elastic constants of the waveguide are known, the local force inducing the deformation can be calculated (2).

In order to obtain a high-force resolution, the key challenge is to fabricate waveguides with a high mechanical susceptibility, i.e., a high mechanical response to external forces. Typically, the waveguide consists of a thin, highly elastic polymer film sandwiched between two metal layers as confinements for the electromagnetic wave. Whereas the polymer layer is deposited by spin casting, the metallic films are deposited by thermal evaporation in a high-vacuum chamber. The optical absorption of the polymer in the optical spectrum used should be small to allow undisturbed propagation of the waveguide modes. The metal layers (in particular the top layer, which is exposed to the organism being investigated) should have a high-optical density to make this film as thin as possible. Otherwise the elasticity of the top metal layer might increase the elasticity of the waveguide. In principle, any metal with high-optical density can be used as a top layer. However, from several metals tested, aluminum showed a particularly good biocompatibility. Several polymers, e.g., polydimethylsiloxane (PDMS) or Sylgard 184, can be used as polymer material (2, 21). After deposition of the polymer onto the bottom metal film, it must be cross-linked. This can be achieved by illumination with a ultraviolet light source (light-induced cross-linking) or by adding a cross-linker to the polymer prior to the spin-casting process (chemical cross-linking). Afterward, a second evaporated Al layer of about 50-nm thickness was deposited (Figure 6b). This second metal layer was necessary to prevent any part of the evanescent field of the waveguide from leaking out. Accordingly, the optical waveguide is not sensitive to any dielectric changes on top of the second Al film but is responsive only to changes in its thickness.

In order to couple light into the optical waveguides, a prism-coupling technique was used. This technique has been described by several other groups (33, 58). The waveguide on the supporting glass slide was optically matched onto a glass prism (Figure 6b). When this prism is illuminated from below with an expanded parallel laser beam, an optical waveguide mode is excited whenever the incident angle matches the resonance condition. In this situation, the reflected light intensity $R(\Theta)$ is largely reduced or shows a strong dip. Accordingly, if a waveguide with inhomogeneous thickness or local deformations is illuminated under an incident angle Θ, those regions having the appropriate thickness to support a waveguide mode appear dark in the reflected light field while others appear bright (Figure 6c).

The experimental setup used in the experiments is schematically shown in Figure 6d (2). It consists of a microscope with the waveguide microscope attached to the sample stage. The waveguide microscope is composed of two adjustable arms carrying the optical components for illuminating and imaging the base of the glass prism with the optical waveguide. The reflected light is imaged and stored on a computer. Within 60 s, the mirror is adjusted stepwise to about 200 different Θ-values within a range of about $3°$. From such image sequences for each pixel, a $R(\Theta)$ curve is obtained that finally allows the angle of resonance to be calculated for each pixel (see Equation 1). This procedure yields a reconstruction of the surface topography of the waveguide with vertical resolution of about 1 nm (2). In contrast, the lateral resolution in horizontal direction is in the range of 1 to 2 μm. This is due to the propagating nature of waveguides and therefore is a limitation of the technique. It should be emphasized that the deformation of the waveguide is reversible if the vertical deformations do not exceed $\sim$10%. Accordingly, the technique allows time-dependent measurements.

This method was used to visualize and measure the force that appressoria of *C. graminicola* can exert on an artificial surface. Appressoria formed on the surface of a waveguide (Figure 7a) are indistinguishable from infection structures differentiated on the surface of a plant (Figure 2). The reflected light-intensity image (Figure 7b) shows bright foci correlating spatially with the location of the appressoria. Obviously, the thickness of the waveguide is changed at these sites, indicating exertion of vertical external force. From angle-resolved measurements, the cross section of a typical imprinted region under an appressorium, representing the shape of the penetration hypha forced into the waveguide, can be obtained (Figure 7c). The typical vertical deformation observed in the experiments is about 10 nm, whereas the diameter of the penetration hypha at the appressorial base is about 2 μm. The inset of Figure 7c shows that the area of the waveguide surrounding the penetration hypha is raised, indicating tight adhesion of the appressorial base to the surface of the waveguide. As the waveguide is flexible, detachment of the appressorium owing to insufficient adhesion would result in immediate extinction of the optical signal. This never occurred, indicating that the appressoria adhere as tightly to the waveguides as they would on leaf surfaces.

In order to relate the waveguide deformation to mechanical forces, its mechanical elasticity must be determined. This was done by calibrating the optical response of the waveguide to well-defined external forces exerted by a thin tapered glass capillary with a known spring constant. The spring constant of the waveguide can now be determined by plotting the depth of the indentation as a function of the applied force. With this information one can calculate the force exerted by *C. graminicola* during the formation of the penetration hypha underneath the appressorium to be 16.8 μN (2). Time-resolved force measurements revealed that force exertion typically sets in 100–120 min the after formation of mature (i.e., melanized) appressoria. The latter was monitored by visual inspection with the light microscope. After about 300 min, a steady-state level was reached, which did not change for several hours (2). The method was the first to allow measurement of invasive forces exerted by penetration hyphae and has been considered useful in biophysical investigations of forceful infection (44, 46, 69).

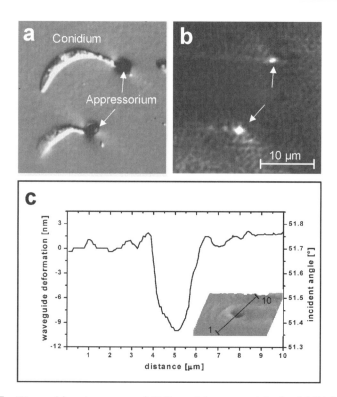

Figure 7 Waveguide microscopy of *Colletotrichum graminicola*. (*a*) Light microscopic image of two conidia from *C. graminicola* forming appressoria on the aluminum surface of a waveguide. (*b*) Reflected light-intensity image of the same area of the waveguide. Two bright foci (*arrows*) correlate spatially with the location of the two appressoria, indicating vertical external pressure. (*c*) Angle-resolved measurements reveal the waveguide topography (*insert in the lower right*). A plot of the cross section of the imprinting region under the appressorium represents the shape of the penetration hypha forced into the waveguide. The typical vertical deformation is ~10 nm. The diameter of the penetration hypha at the appressorial base is ~2 μm.

Waveguide microscopy has recently shown that appressoria of *C. graminicola* exposed to osmotic stress, e.g., by incubation in low concentrations of aequeous PEG-3350, exert increased force, which may be due to synthesis of sugar alcohols in addition to glycerol (J. A. Sugui, K.-F. Giebel, M. Bastmeyer, C. Bechinger & H. B. Deising, unpublished data), as has been reported for osmotically stressed hyphae of *M. grisea* (13). As extracellular osmolyte concentration increased to values exceeding 30% PEG-3350, force exertion decreased drastically. These data show that force exertion is required to successfully breach the cuticle and cell wall of host plant cells. In progress are similar experiments that analyze the importance of different chitin synthase genes of this fungus in appressorial force exertion (S. Werner, K.-F. Giebel, M. Bastmeyer, C. Bechinger & H. B. Deising, unpublished data).

OUTLOOK

During the past decade, different fungal systems, mostly belonging to the ascomycetes, have been recognized as ideal model systems for genetic analyses because they are accessible to methods used in molecular and classical genetics and because they have a haploid genome structure that allows simple analysis of mutants. Several groups have contributed to the understanding of fungal morphogenesis and differentiation of infection structures, and appressoria have received particular attention. In this review, we have emphasized the importance of force in fungal infection, and we are confident that factors contributing to forceful invasion will be genetically dissected, e.g., by site-directed, random or REMI (restriction enzyme-mediated DNA integration) mutagenesis (16, 27, 35, 68).

Factors putatively contributing to either turgor generation or cell wall structure and rigidity have been identified in pathogenic and nonpathogenic fungi; mutants deficient in such factors can be generated without major problems. For example, in *N. crassa* (81) and in other fungi, chitin synthase genes have been cloned and inactivated. Based on accessible gene bank information, genes can be cloned by PCR strategies. Such approaches have demonstrated that some cell wall biosynthesis genes are essential for vitality or pathogenicity of certain fungi. Following such a strategy, four chitin synthase and two β-glucan synthase genes have been cloned from *Colletotrichum graminicola* (H. B. Deising, S. Werner & M. Wernitz, unpublished data), and for some of these genes mutants are available. Inactivation of a single chitin synthase gene of this fungus allows growth only in osmotically stabilized media, and mutants are not able to cause disease (S. Werner & H. B. Deising, unpublished data). While general pathogenicity is easily assessed macroscopically and microscopically, it is difficult to relate mutation to functions such as force generation. As new techniques allowing turgor and force measurement emerge, mutants of fungi that forcefully invade the host can now be evaluated with respect to force generation (69). These techniques, of course, would also allow the analysis of signal transduction mutants, such as the mitogen-activated protein kinase (Mps1) mutant of *M. grisea*, which stops development after mature appressoria have formed, but before invasion (79). Thus, techniques that allow measurement of turgor and force will be indispensable for analyzing and characterizing fungal mutants, especially those parasitic on humans, animals, and plants.

ACKNOWLEDGMENTS

We thank Mary Anne Cahill and Nicholas P. Money for critically reading the manuscript and for many helpful comments. The authors acknowledge financial support by Deutsche Forschungsgemeinschaft: DE 403/5-1, /5-2 and DE 403/7-1 (H. B. Deising) and Forschergruppe 216/3 (M. Bastmeyer and C. Bechinger).

M. Bastmeyer is a Heisenberg Fellow of the DFG and supported by the Fonds der Chemischen Industrie.

Visit the Annual Reviews home page at www.annualreviews.org

LITERATURE CITED

1. Apel-Birkhold PC, Walton JD. 1996. Cloning, disruption, and expression of two endo-β1,4-xylanase genes, *XYL2* and *XYL3*, from *Cochliobolus carbonum*. *Appl. Environ. Microbiol.* 62:4129–35
2. Bechinger C, Giebel K-F, Schnell M, Leiderer P, Deising HB, Bastmeyer M. 1999. Optical measurements of invasive forces exerted by appressoria of a plant pathogenic fungus. *Science* 285:1896–99
3. Born M, Wolf E. 1999. *Principles of Optics.* Cambridge, UK: Cambridge Univ. Press
4. Brush L, Money NP. 1999. Invasive hyphal growth in *Wangiella dermatitidis* is induced by stab inoculation and shows dependence upon melanin biosynthesis. *Fungal Genet. Biol.* 28:190–200
5. Buller AHR. 1931. *Research on Fungi.* Vol. 4. London: Green
6. Butler MJ, Day AW. 1999. Fungal melanins: a review. *Can. J. Microbiol.* 44:1115–36
7. Caprari C, Bergmann C, Migheli Q, Salvi G, Albersheim P, et al. 1993. *Fusarium moniliforme* secretes four *endo*-polygalacturonases derived from a single gene product. *Physiol. Mol. Plant Pathol.* 43:453–62
8. Collinge AJ, Trinci APJ. 1974. Hyphal tips of wild-type and spreading colonial mutants of *Neurospora crassa*. *Arch. Microbiol.* 99:353–68
9. Deising HB, Werner S, Wernitz M. 2000. The role of fungal appressoria in plant infection. *Microbes Infect.* 2:1631–41
10. De Jong JC, McCormack BJ, Smirnoff N, Talbot NJ. 1997. Glycerol generates turgor in rice blast. *Nature* 389:244–45
11. Di Pietro A, Roncero MIG. 1996. Endopolygalacturonase from *Fusarium oxysporum* f. sp. *lycopersici*: purification, characterization, and production during infection of tomato plants. *Phytopathology* 86:1324–30
12. Di Pietro A, Roncero MIG. 1998. Cloning, expression, and role in pathogenicity of *pg1* encoding the major extracellular endopolygalacturonase of the vascular wilt pathogen *Fusarium oxysporum*. *Mol. Plant-Microbe Interact.* 11:91–98
13. Dixon KP, Xu J-R, Smirnoff N, Talbot NJ. 1999. Independent signaling pathways regulate cellular turgor during hyperosmotic stress in appressorium-mediated plant infection by *Magnaporthe grisea*. *Plant Cell* 11:2045–58
14. Ebata Y, Yamamoto H, Uchiyama T. 1998. Chemical composition of the glue from appressoria of *Magnaporthe grisea*. *Biosci. Biotechnol. Biochem.* 62:672–74
15. Emmett RW, Parbery DG. 1975. Appressoria. *Annu. Rev. Phytopathol.* 13:147–67
16. Fang EG, Dean RA. 2000. Site-directed mutagenesis of the *magB* gene affects growth and development in *Magnaporthe grisea*. *Mol. Plant-Microbe Interact.* 13:1214–27
17. Frank B. 1883. Ueber einige neue und weniger bekannte Pflanzenkrankheiten. *Ber. Dtsch. Bot. Ges.* 1:29–34
18. Hahn M, Deising H, Struck C, Mendgen K. 1997. Specificity and recognition phenomena during infection. In *Resistance of Crop Plants Against Fungi*, ed. H Hartleb, R Heitefuss, H-H Hoppe, pp. 33–57. Jena, Ger.: Fischer
19. Hartmann HA, Kahmann R, Bölker M. 1996. The pheromone response factor coordinates filamentous growth and pathogenic development in *Ustilago maydis*. *EMBO J.* 15:1632–41

20. Henson JM, Butler MJ, Day AW. 1999. The dark side of the mycelium: melanins of phytopathogenic fungi. *Annu. Rev. Phytopathol.* 37:447–71

21. Herminghaus S, Riedel M, Leiderer P, Bastmeyer M, Stürmer C. 1997. Optical force microscopy with silicone rubber waveguides. *Appl. Phys. Lett.* 70:22–24

22. Horwitz BA, Sharon A, Lu S-W, Ritter V, Sandrock TM, et al. 1999. A G protein alpha subunit from *Cochliobolus heterostrophus* involved in mating and appressorium formation. *Fungal Genet. Biol.* 26:19–32

23. Howard RJ. 1997. Breaching the outer barriers—cuticle and cell wall penetration. In *The Mycota V. Plant Relationships Part A*, ed. GC Carrol, P Tudzynski, pp. 43–60. Berlin/Heidelberg/New York: Springer

24. Howard RJ, Bourette TM, Ferrari MA. 1991. Infection by *Magnaporthe*: an in vitro analysis. In *Electron Microscopy of Plant Pathogens*, ed. K Mendgen, D-E Lesemann, pp. 251–64. Berlin: Springer

25. Howard RJ, Ferrari MA, Roach DH, Money NP. 1991. Penetration of hard substances by a fungus employing enormous turgor pressures. *Proc. Natl. Acad. Sci. USA* 88:11281–84

26. Johns S, Davis CM, Money NP. 1999. Pulses in turgor pressure and water potential: resolving the mechanics of hyphal growth. *Microbiol. Res.* 154:225–31

27. Kahmann R, Basse C. 1999. REMI (restriction enzyme mediated integration) and its impact on the isolation of pathogenicity genes in fungi attacking plants. *Eur. J. Plant Pathol.* 105:221–29

28. Kawamura C, Moriwaki J, Kimura N, Fujita Y, Fuji S-I, et al. 1997. The melanin biosynthesis genes of *Alternaria alternata* can restore pathogenicity of the melanin-deficient mutants of *Magnaporthe grisea*. *Mol. Plant-Microbe Interact.* 10:446–53

29. Kubo Y, Takano Y, Tsuji G, Horino O, Furusawa I. 2000. Regulation of melanin biosynthesis genes during appressorium formation by *Colletotrichum lagenarium*.

In *Colletotrichum: Host Specificity, Pathology, and Host-Pathogen Interaction*, ed. D Prusky, S Freeman, MB Dickman, pp. 99–113. St. Paul, MN: APS

30. Kurahashi Y, Pontzen R. 1998. Carpropamid: a new melanin biosynthesis inhibitor. *Pflanzenschutz-Nachr. Bayer* 51:247–58

31. Latunde-Dada AO. 2001. Colletotrichum: tales of forcible entry, stealth, transient confinement and breakout. *Mol. Plant Pathol.* 2:187–98

32. Lavers CR. 1992. Optical probing of thin liquid crystal layers using the prism-coupling technique. *Liq. Cryst.* 11:819–32

33. Lavers CR. 1996. Determination of the optical dielectric constants and deformational effects after surface treatment of a polyimide alignment layer used within a ferroelectric liquid crystal device system. *Thin Solid Films* 289:133–39

34. Lavers CR. 1997. The fabrication of optoelectronics integrated planar glass waveguide sensors. *Electron. Beyond* March: 55–57

35. Liu S, Wei R, Arie T, Yamaguchi I. 1998. REMI mutagenesis and identification of pathogenic mutants in blast fungus (*Magnaporthe grisea*). *Chin. J. Biotechnol.* 14: 133–39

36. López-Franco R, Bartnicki-Garcia S, Bracker CE. 1994. Pulsed growth of fungal hyphal tips. *Proc. Natl. Acad. Sci. USA* 91: 12228–32

37. Mendgen K, Deising H. 1993. Infection structures of fungal plant pathogens—a cytological and physiological evaluation. *New Phytol.* 124:193–213

38. Mendgen K, Hahn M, Deising H. 1996. Mechanisms and morphogenesis of penetration by plant pathogenic fungi. *Annu. Rev. Phytopathol.* 34:367–86

39. Milburn JA. 1970. Cavitation and osmotic potentials of *Sordaria* ascospores. *New Phytol.* 69:133–41

40. Miyoshi M. 1895. Die Durchbohrung von Membranen durch Pilzfäden. *Jahrb. Wiss. Bot.* 28:269–89

41. Money NP. 1995. Turgor pressure and the

mechanics of fungal penetration. *Can. J. Bot.* 73:S96–S102

42. Money NP. 1997. Wishful thinking of turgor revisited: the mechanics of fungal growth. *Fungal Genet. Biol.* 21:173–87

43. Money NP. 1998. Mechanics of invasive fungal growth and the significance of turgor in plant infection. In *Molecular Genetics of Host-Specific Toxins in Plant Disease*, ed. K Kohmoto, OC Yoder, pp. 261–71. Dordrecht: Kluwer

44. Money NP. 1999. Fungus punches its way in. *Nature* 401:332–33

45. Money NP. 1999. On the origin and functions of hyphal walls and turgor pressure. *Mycol. Res.* 103:1360

46. Money NP. 1999. To perforate a leaf of grass. *Fungal Genet. Biol.* 28:146–47

47. Money NP. 2001. Biomechanics of invasive hyphal growth. In *The Mycota VIII. Biology of the Fungal Cell*, ed. RJ Howard, NAR Gow, pp. 3–17. Berlin: Springer

48. Money NP, Caesar-TonThat T-C, Frederick B, Henson JM. 1998. Melanin synthesis is associated with changes in hyphopodial turgor, permeability, and wall rigidity in *Gaeumannomyces graminis* var. *graminis*. *Fungal Genet. Biol.* 24:240–51

49. Money NP, Harold FM. 1992. Extension growth of the water mold *Achlya*: interplay of turgor and wall strength. *Proc. Natl. Acad. Sci. USA* 89:4245–49

50. Money NP, Harold FM. 1993. Two water molds can grow without measurable turgor pressure. *Planta* 190:426–30

51. Money NP, Hill T. 1997. Correlation between endoglucanase secretion and cell wall strength in oomycete fungi: implications for growth and morphogenesis. *Mycologia* 89:777–85

52. Money NP, Howard RJ. 1996. Confirmation of a link between fungal pigmentation, turgor pressure, and pathogenicity using a new method of turgor measurement. *Fungal Genet. Biol.* 20:217–27

53. Murphy JM, Walton JD. 1996. Three extracellular proteases from *Cochliobolus carbonum*: cloning and targeted disruption of *ALP1*. *Mol. Plant-Microbe Interact.* 9:290–97

54. Nosanchuk JD, Valadon P, Feldmesser M, Casadevall A. 1999. Melanization of *Cryptococcus neoformans* in murine infection. *Mol. Cell. Biol.* 19:745–50

55. Odds FC. 1991. Potential for penetration of passive barriers to fungal invasion in humans. In *The Fungal Spore and Disease Initiation in Plants and Animals*, ed. GT Cole, HC Hoch, pp. 287–95. New York: Plenum

56. Perpetua NS, Kubo Y, Yasuda N, Takano Y, Furusawa I. 1996. Cloning and characterization of a melanin biosynthetic *THR1* reductase gene essential for appressorial penetration of *Colletotrichum lagenarium*. *Mol. Plant-Microbe Interact.* 9:323–29

57. Pryce-Jones E, Carver T, Gurr SJ. 1999. The roles of cellulase enzymes and mechanical force in host penetration by *Erysiphe graminis* f. sp. *hordei*. *Physiol. Mol. Plant Pathol.* 55:175–82

58. Raether H. 1988. *Surface Plasmons.* Berlin: Springer

59. Ravishankar JP, Davis CM, Davis DJ, MacDonald E, Makselan SD, et al. 2001. Mechanics of solid tissue invasion by the mammalian pathogen *Pythium insidiosum*. *Fung. Genet. Biol.* 34:167–75

60. Reinhardt MO. 1892. Das Wachstum der Pilzhyphen. *Jahrb. Wiss. Bot.* 23:479–565

61. Reynaga-Peña CG, Gierz G, Bartnicki-García S. 1997. Analysis of the role of the Spitzenkörper in fungal morphogenesis by computer simulation of apical branching in *Aspergillus niger*. *Proc. Natl. Acad. Sci. USA* 94:9096–101

62. Riquelme M, Reynaga-Peña CG, Gierz G, Bartnicki-García S. 1998. What determines growth direction in fungal hyphae? *Fungal Genet. Biol.* 24:101–09

63. Ruiz-Roldán MC, Maier FJ, Schäfer W. 2001. *PTK1*, a mitogen-activated-protein kinase gene, is required for conidiation, appressorium formation, and pathogenicity of *Pyrenophora teres* on barley. *Mol. Plant-Microbe Interact.* 14:116–25

64. Scott-Craig JS, Panaccione DG, Cervone F, Walton JD. 1990. Endopolygalacturonase is not required for pathogenicity of *Cochliobolus carbonum* on maize. *Plant Cell* 2:1191–200

65. Sietsma JH, Wessels JGH. 1994. Apical wall biogenesis. In *Growth, Differentiation and Sexuality*, ed. JGH Wessels, F Meinhardt, pp. 125–41. Berlin/Heidelberg: Springer

66. Stoldt VR, Sonneborn A, Leuker CE, Ernst JF. 1997. Efg1p, an essential regulator of morphogenesis of the human pathogen *Candida albicans*, is a member of a conserved class of bHLH proteins regulating morphogenetic processes in fungi. *EMBO J.* 16:1982–91

67. Sugui JA, Leite B, Nicholson RL. 1998. Partial characterization of the extracellular matrix released onto hydrophobic surfaces by conidia and conidial germlings of *Colletotrichum graminicola*. *Physiol. Mol. Plant Pathol.* 52:411–25

68. Sweigard JA, Carroll AM, Farrall L, Chumley FG, Valent B. 1998. *Magnaporthe grisea* pathogenicity genes obtained through insertional mutagenesis. *Mol. Plant-Microbe Interact.* 11:404–12

69. Talbot NJ. 1999. Forcible entry. *Science* 285:1860–61

70. ten Have A, Breuil WO, Wubben JP, Visser J, van Kan JAL. 2001. *Botrytis cinerea* endopolygalacturonase genes are differentially expressed in various plant tissues. *Fungal Genet. Biol.* 33:97–105

71. ten Have A, Mulder W, Visser J, van Kan JAL. 1998. The endopolygalacturonase gene *Bcpg1* is required for full virulence

of *Botrytis cinerea*. *Mol. Plant-Microbe Interact.* 11:1009–16

72. Tien PK. 1977. Integrated optics and new wave phenomena. *Rev. Mod. Phys.* 49:361

73. Tonukari NJ, Scott-Craig JS, Walton JD. 2000. The *Cochliobolus carbonum* SNF1 gene is required for cell wall-degrading enzyme expression and virulence on maize. *Plant Cell* 12:237–48

74. Walker J. 1972. Type studies on *Gaeumannomyces graminis* and related fungi. *Trans. Br. Mycol. Soc.* 58:427–57

75. Walton JD. 1994. Deconstructing the cell wall. *Plant Physiol.* 104:1113–18

76. Wessels JGH. 1993. Wall growth, protein excretion and morphogenesis in fungi. *New Phytol.* 123:397–413

77. Williamson PR. 1997. Laccase and melanin in the pathogenesis of *Cryptococcus neoformans*. *Front. Biosci.* 2:E99–E107

78. Woloshuk CP, Sisler HD, Vigil EL. 1983. Action of the antipenetrant, tricyclazole, on appressoria of *Pyricularia oryzae*. *Physiol. Plant Pathol.* 22:245–59

79. Xu JR, Staiger CJ, Hamer JE. 1998. Inactivation of the mitogen-activated protein kinase Mps1 from the rice blast fungus prevents penetration of host cells but allows activation of plant defense responses. *Proc. Natl. Acad. Sci. USA* 95:12713–18

80. Yamaguchi I, Sekido S, Misato T. 1983. Inhibition of appressorial melanization in *Pyricularia oryzae* by non-fungicidal antiblast chemicals. *J. Pestic. Sci.* 8:229–32

81. Yarden O, Yanofsky C. 1991. Chitin synthase 1 plays a major role in cell wall biogenesis in *Neurospora crassa*. *Genes Dev.* 5:2420–30

Annu. Rev. Biophys. Biomol. Struct. 2002. 31:343–60
DOI: 10.1146/annurev.biophys.31.100901.142129

THE PAPILLOMAVIRUS E2 PROTEINS:
Structure, Function, and Biology

Rashmi S. Hegde
*Division of Developmental Biology, Childrens Hospital Research Foundation, 3333
Burnet Avenue, Cincinnati, Ohio 45229-3039; e-mail: rashmi.hegde@chmcc.org*

Key Words DNA bending, DNA flexibility, electrostatics, protein-DNA interactions, viral carcinogenesis

■ **Abstract** Nearly twenty years after the first high-resolution crystal structures of specific protein-DNA complexes were determined, the stereo-chemical basis for protein-DNA recognition remains an active area of investigation. One outstanding question is, how are proteins able to detect noncontacted sequences in their binding sites? The papillomavirus E2 proteins represent a particularly suitable group of proteins in which to examine the mechanisms of "indirect readout." Coordinated structural and thermodynamic studies of the E2-DNA interaction conducted over the past five years are summarized in this review. The data support a model in which the electrostatic properties of the individual E2 proteins correlate with their affinities for intrinsically flexible or rigidly prebent DNA targets.

CONTENTS

INTRODUCTION

The mechanisms by which DNA sequences are recognized by proteins have been intensely investigated in the past few decades. Although these studies describe intricate hydrogen-bonding networks between amino acid side chains and DNA bases, a simple code for protein-DNA recognition based on noncovalent chemistry has failed to emerge. Instead, it appears that the specificity of protein-DNA reactions derives from a balance of several factors (12, 63). In addition to base–amino acid contacts, these include contacts between the protein and the phospho-diester backbone of the DNA, solvent-mediated interactions, the context of the reactive groups as specified by the protein fold/DNA conformation, and the structural adaptability of the reactants. An added layer of complexity is evident in physiological environments where proteins have to select from among multiple, similar binding-site sequences and interact with these short DNA sequences amid a vast excess of nonspecific DNA. In such situations, it is likely that small differences in reaction affinity or kinetics can profoundly influence regulatory decisions. The evolution of protein-DNA interactions could be viewed as an ongoing process of tailoring the balance between the stereo-chemical constraints outlined above to the desired biological outcomes. The papillomaviruses represent a good model system for the investigation of such issues because there are a large number of viral strains that have coevolved with their vertebrate hosts for over a 100 million years, providing a database for the study of molecular, structural, and functional coevolution. This review describes the relationships between structure and function that have emerged from studies on the E2 proteins of the cancer-associated papillomaviruses.

THE PAPILLOMAVIRUSES

The papillomaviruses are DNA tumor viruses that infect a variety of hosts including several mammalian species. Well over a 100 strains are known to infect humans (17, 86). Infection by the low-risk HPV strains-11 and -6 is commonly associated with benign epithelial warts. Infection by the high-risk strains HPV-16, -18, -31 and -33 is strongly associated with various cancers of the ano-genital tract, most notably cervical carcinomas (87). Although early detection of HPV infection has reduced the mortality associated with these cancers in the Western world, cervical cancer remains a leading cause of death in women in developing countries. Recent epidemiological evidence also points to a relationship between HPV infection and squamous cell carcinomas of the head and neck (55, 60, 74). There is no virus-specific treatment currently available.

The viral genome is a 7.9-kb circular DNA that codes for at least eight early and two late (capsid) proteins [see Figure 2 and (71) for a review of the structure of the genome and the characteristics of individual proteins]. The expression of viral genes is modulated by an 800–base pair long-control region (LCR) that is epithelial tissue specific and regulated by physiological signals. The products of the early genes *E6* and *E7* are oncoproteins that destabilize the cellular tumor suppressors

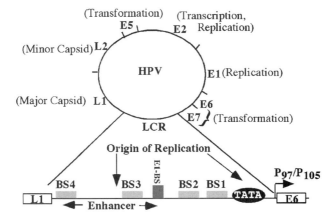

Figure 2   A schematic representation of the HPV genome. The eight early and two late genes are indicated. Below is a schematic of the HPV long-control region. E2-BS 1–4 are represented by *gray boxes*. The binding site for the helicase E1 at the origin of replication is shown as a *black box*. The TATA box and the early promoter P_{97}/P_{105} are also indicated.

p53 and pRB (22, 31, 38, 56, 57). The product of the *E1* gene is a helicase necessary for viral DNA replication. The products of the *E2* gene play key roles in the regulation of viral gene transcription and DNA replication (2, 11, 14, 68, 83). During early stages of viral infection, the E2 protein represses the transcription of the oncogenes *E6* and *E7*. Carcinogenic progression is accompanied by integration of the viral genome, which disrupts the *E2* and *E1* open reading frames. As a result, the expression of *E6* and *E7* is upregulated in cancers. Underscoring the importance of E2 in the infection cycle, reintroduction of E2 into cervical cancer cell-lines leads to repression of *E6/E7* transcription, stabilization of the tumor suppressor p53, and cell-cycle arrest at the G1 phase of the cell cycle (20, 27, 46). E2 can also induce apoptosis by a p53-independent mechanism (16).

STRUCTURES OF THE E2 PROTEINS

The E2 protein, like many families of DNA-binding regulatory proteins, is modular. It is composed of a C-terminal DNA-binding domain and an N-terminal trans-activation domain. E2 exists in solution and binds to DNA as a dimer (19). The approximately 80–amino acid DNA-binding domain does not bear a sequence signature that would place it among any of the established classes of DNA-binding structural motifs.

The E2 DNA-Binding Domain

The structures of the E2 DNA-binding domains (DBD) from several viral strains have been reported. These include the crystal structures of the E2-DBD from the high-risk human cancer–associated strains HPV-16 (32), HPV-18 (43), and HPV-31 (10), and the cow wart–causing strain BPV-1 (34). NMR structures have also been reported for the BPV-1 (84) and HPV-31 (49) E2-DBD.

The E2-DBD is the prototype for a novel structural class of DNA-binding proteins. It forms a dimeric β-barrel, with each subunit contributing an antiparallel 4-stranded β-sheet "half-barrel" (Figure 1a, see color insert). The topology of each subunit is β_1-α_1-β_2-β_3-α_2-β_4. Helix α_1 is the recognition helix housing all of the amino acid residues involved in direct DNA sequence specification. Upon dimerization, strands β_2 and β_4 at the edges of each subunit participate in a continuous hydrogen-bonding network, which results in an 8-stranded β-barrel (Figure 1b, see color insert). The dimer interface is extensive, made up of hydrogen bonds between subunits and a substantial hydrophobic β-barrel core. Oligomerization buries between 1500 Å^2 and 2500 Å^2 in the various structures. The core of the barrel is occupied by large, intricately packed side chains that must contribute significantly to the stability of the dimer (10^{-13} M) (54). Another consequence of this extensive dimer interface is that any rearrangement of the subunits upon interaction with DNA must be subject to a large energetic penalty. In the NMR structures of the free proteins, the recognition helices in each subunit appear relatively mobile as judged by amide exchange rates. In all of the reported structures, the loop connecting β-strands 2 and 3 is disordered. This poorly conserved loop varies in length from six to ten residues in the various E2 proteins. On the whole, sequence conservation among the various E2-DBD ranges from 54% identity (77% similarity) among the closely related strains, HPV-16 and HPV-18, to 33% sequence identity (51% similarity) between distant strains HPV-16 and BPV-1. Greatest conservation is seen in the recognition helix and at the residues of the dimer interface.

The only other DNA-binding protein known to have a dimeric β-barrel structure is the Epstein-Barr virus replication protein EBNA-1 (9). However, in a surprising deviation from the general observation that members of DNA-binding structural families utilize the same secondary structural features for interaction with DNA, in the crystal structure of the EBNA-1/DNA complex, helix α_1 does not directly participate in DNA binding. Instead, all the sequence-specifying contacts with DNA are made by a helix from a flanking domain that reaches into the major groove and an extended chain that is inserted into the minor groove (8). More recently, it has been suggested that EBNA-1 may have two modes of DNA interaction, one of which is similar to that seen in the E2-DNA complex, whereas the other resembles the reported EBNA-1/DNA complex structure. This model remains under investigation (13).

Although the tertiary structure of all characterized E2-DBDs is similar, there is an interesting variation in the relative orientations of the two subunits. This variation is most clearly seen when one subunit of each E2 dimer is superimposed and the orientations of the nonsuperimposed subunits are compared (Figure 1c, see color insert). In this manner, the E2 proteins can be divided into two classes: (a) HPV-16 and HPV-31 fall into one group and (b) HPV-18 and BPV-1 fall into another. The recognition helix of the nonsuperimposed subunit of HPV-16 E2 is displaced by approximately 4.0 Å and tilted by 25° relative to the corresponding recognition helix of BPV-1 and HPV-18 E2. These differences in quaternary structure are likely to impact upon the DNA deformation induced by E2 binding. Intriguingly, this structural classification of the E2 dimers separates the closely related HPV-16 and HPV-18 E2 proteins, while classifying the more divergent BPV-1 and HPV-18 E2 proteins together. This observation is relevant in light of the proposal that small domains of viral proteins may hold a record of a common evolutionary history that can be detected by similarities in three-dimensional structure (7).

The E2 Activation Domain

High-resolution crystal structures of the E2 activation domains from strains HPV-16 (3) and HPV-18 (30) have been reported, showing that not all activation domains are disordered in the free state (25, 72). The E2 activation domain consists of two domains, a curved anti-parallel β-sheet domain and a helical domain containing three anti-parallel helices. The HPV-16 E2 activation domain is dimeric in the crystal structure with conserved, mutationally sensitive residues occupying the dimer interface. It has been suggested that activation domain–mediated oligomerization could play a role in interaction between E2 molecules bound at distant E2-binding sites on the viral genomes, mediating DNA looping and other higher-order DNA structures (3). However, it is not yet clear whether dimerization via the activation domains is seen in intact E2 proteins.

Little structural information is available for the linker region (40–200 amino acids) that connects the DBD and the activation domains in the various E2 proteins. Although this region is poorly conserved, there is evidence suggesting that it is important for E2 function. For example, phosphorylation of Ser residues in the BPV-1 E2 linker is necessary for the regulation of viral DNA replication (51, 52), the linker is critical for the regulatory functions of HPV-11 E2 during mRNA transcription and viral DNA replication (85), and it has been proposed that a second trans-activation domain in the linker region of BPV-1 E2 might function by altering the kinetics of TATA-binding protein (TBP)-DNA interaction (73). Additionally, E2-DBD constructs that include segments of the linker have greater stability and DNA-binding affinity than the minimal DBD, whereas DNA-binding specificity remains unaltered (66).

THE E2-DNA INTERACTION

E2 proteins from all papillomavirus strains bind a consensus palindromic sequence ACCgNNNNcGGT (referred to here as the "E2-binding site" or E2-BS). The nucleotides indicated by lowercase letters are preferred but not required for specific recognition of the site by E2. The central NNNN region is referred to as the "spacer," and its length is absolutely conserved in all papillomaviruses, although the sequence composition varies with strain. Multiple occurrences of this binding site are found on the papillomavirus genomes. In BPV-1 there are 12 E2-binding palindromic sequences and an additional 5 sites that differ at a single nucleotide position but are protected in footprinting assays (48). In the high-risk HPV genomes, there are four E2-BS arranged in a conserved fashion (Figure 2). They are found immediately upstream of the early promoter (P_{97} in HPV-16, P_{105} in HPV-18) that regulates expression of the viral oncogenes *E6* and *E7*, as well as the gene for the replication protein E1, and the *E2* gene. The biological consequences of E2-E2-BS interactions vary with the context of the E2-BS and can include repression of transcription, activation of transcription, and viral DNA replication. As a result, the order of E2-BS occupancy is likely to play a critical role in the papillomavirus life and infection cycles.

Although there is no consensus sequence for the E2-BS spacer, in the HPV genomes this spacer tends to be rich in A:T base-pairs when compared to the E2-BS on the BPV-1 genome. Several years ago Bedrosian & Bastia demonstrated that HPV-16 E2 binds with increased affinity to E2-BS that contain A:T-rich spacers (4). Hines et al. (36) showed that HPV-16 E2 has a clear preference for spacers containing AA[A/T]N sequences and that the preference was not simply for an A:T-rich sequence, e.g., an E2-BS bearing the spacer sequence TTAA was bound with lower affinity compared to the AATT spacer (some of this data is summarized in Figure 4*a*). A similar spacer sequence preference was observed for HPV-18 E2 (43) and HPV-11 E2 (1). In contrast, BPV-1 E2 does not display any significant ability to discriminate between E2-BS with different spacer sequences (36). In order to examine the structural basis for the unique DNA-binding properties of the BPV and HPV E2 proteins crystallographic studies of the HPV-18 E2-DBD bound to a high-affinity DNA target [E2-BS with an AATT spacer, henceforth referred to as E2-BS (AATT)] were compared to the HPV-18 E2-DBD complex with an E2-BS containing a non-A:T-rich spacer (E2-BS (ACGT)) (43). These structures were compared to structures of BPV-1 E2-DBD bound to the same two E2-BS sequences. In addition, the structures of the free proteins (32, 34) and free DNA oligonucleotides (37, 69) have also been determined. These data provide us with an opportunity to rigorously examine direct protein-DNA interactions, sequence-dependent DNA conformation, structural changes upon protein-DNA interaction, and solvent-mediated contacts.

Structures of E2-DNA Complexes

In all E2-DNA complexes, the recognition helices are inserted into successive major grooves of the DNA (Figure 3*a*, see color insert), making direct contact with the consensus half-sites of the E2-BS (33, 34, 43). The protein undergoes only minor adjustments upon DNA binding in order to achieve symmetrical contact with the DNA major grooves. The most notable change in protein structure is seen in the BPV-1 E2-DNA complex, where the 10–amino acid loop between strands $\beta 2$ and $\beta 3$ assumes an ordered conformation. It is anchored to the DNA by contacts between Arg side chains (R370) and phosphates at positions $+/-4$ and $+/-3$ from

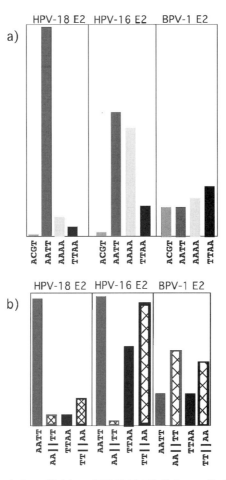

Figure 4   (*a*) The relative affinities of HPV-18 E2 (*left panel*), HPV-16 E2 (*middle panel*), and BPV-1 E2 (*right panel*) for E2-BS containing spacer sequences ACGT, AATT, AAAA, and TTAA are indicated by the relative heights of the bars. (*b*) The relative affinities of HPV-18 E2 (*left panel*), HPV-16 E2 (*middle panel*), and BPV-1 E2 (*right panel*) for E2-BS containing intact and nicked spacer sequences are indicated by the relative heights of the bars. Nicks are indicated by *parallel lines* (‖).

the dyad axis. Interestingly, a similar disorder-to-order transition is not seen upon HPV-18 E2-DNA interaction.

DNA wraps around the E2 β-barrel enclosing both recognition helices in successive major grooves. The DNA is bent by 43°–51° toward the central minor groove (in the spacer region) and the flanking major grooves (in the region of the consensus half-sites of the E2-BS). There is no kinking at any particular base-step. The helix axis is relatively straight at the half-sites, with most of the deformation being absorbed by the central spacer. Both major and minor grooves facing the protein are compressed. BPV-1 and HPV-18 E2 proteins induce the same global DNA deformation, but the mechanisms of deformation are different. The central minor groove is narrowed to 8.5 Å in HPV-18 E2-DNA complexes as compared with a less-significant narrowing to 9.8 Å in the BPV-1 E2 complexes (Figure 3*b*, see color insert). Thus E2 proteins impose unique groove widths on the E2-BS DNA regardless of the intrinsic conformational propensities of the DNA sequences.

In comparing the structures of BPV-1 E2 and HPV-18 E2 bound to two different binding sites (with spacer AATT versus ACGT), the trajectory of the DNA is similar. The propeller twisting and roll angles of the central noncontacted base pairs were also comparable, indicating that despite their conformational preferences while free in solution, protein binding imposes the same conformational restrictions on all sequences. In particular, A:T-rich sequences, which in solution are known to have high propeller twists and interbase pair hydrogen bonds (58), are constrained in the E2-DNA complexes to a less propeller-twisted conformation with negative roll angles bending the DNA toward the minor groove.

No structural data are yet available on DNA complexes of HPV-16 E2 and HPV-31 E2. Because these proteins differ from HPV-18 E2 and BPV-1 E2 in the relative orientations of their subunits (Figure 1*c*), the amino acids that make sequence-specifying DNA contacts are displayed differently. It has been proposed that the deformation of DNA necessary for the E2-BS to make symmetrical contact with the recognition helices of HPV-16/31 E2 could be different from that seen in the available HPV E2-DNA co-crystal structures (32, 43). Recent spectroscopic evidence supporting this prediction was presented by Ferreiro et al. (24). They used near-UV circular dichroism (CD) to show partial unwinding and base unstacking of the E2-BS when bound to HPV-16 E2, as distinct from the change in winding angle and base pair twist seen in the CD spectrum of a BPV-1 E2/E2-BS complex.

Direct Readout

Amino acid residues from the recognition helices participate in a hydrogen-bonding network with the identity elements of the E2-BS (Figure 3*c*, see color insert). The interactions are inter-digitated; two of the four amino acid side chains contact more than one base-pair, and two of the three base pairs that form each half-site are contacted by more than one amino acid. Interactions are symmetric across the dyad axis of the palindromic binding site. These structural models provide a straightforward rationale for the half-site specificity of E2-DNA interactions. In crystal structures of high- and low-affinity HPV-18 E2/DNA complexes, the same direct hydrogen bonds are seen between protein and DNA; thus direct protein-DNA contacts are not the likely mediators of the differences in binding affinity.

In all reported E2/DNA structures there are no visible contacts, either direct or solvent-mediated, with the nucleotides that comprise the minor groove of the DNA facing the protein (the central NNNN spacer). This lack of base-specific interaction is in keeping with the absence of any clear consensus for this spacer region in the E2-BS found on the various viral genomes.

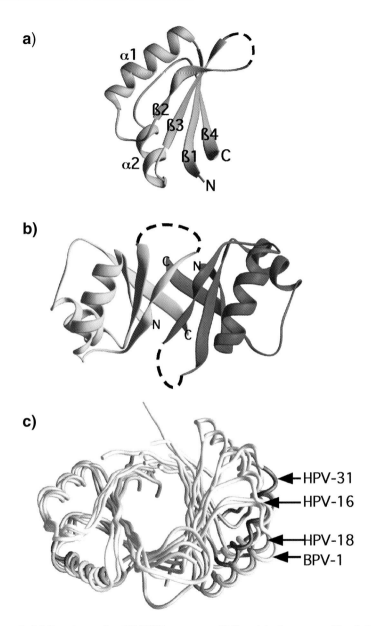

Figure 1 (*a*) Topology of an E2-DBD monomer. Helix α1 is the recognition helix. The disordered segment between strands β2 and β3 is indicated by a *dashed line*. (*b*) The E2-DBD dimer. The subunits are indicated in *blue* and *cyan*. (*c*) Comparison of the E2-DBD from BPV-1, HPV-18, HPV-16, and HPV-31. The left subunit of each protein is superimposed. The recognition helices are highlighted in different colors. The proteins fall into two groups based on the location of the nonsuperimposed recognition helices; BPV-1 and HPV-18 fall into one class, while HPV-16 and HPV-31 fall into another class.

a)

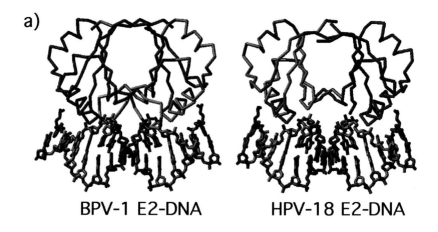

BPV-1 E2-DNA   HPV-18 E2-DNA

b)

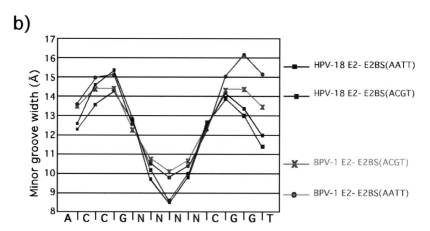

Figure 3 (*a*) The BPV-1 E2-DNA complex (*left*) and the HPV-18 E2-DNA complex (*right*). The subunits of both proteins are indicated in *blue* and *yellow*. The conserved half-sites of the E2-BS are indicated in *pink*. Note the *green loops* connecting β2 and β3 in each subunit of BPV-1 E2 that reach across the molecular dyad to make phosphate contacts. The corresponding loop in HPV-18 E2 remains disordered upon DNA binding and is not shown in this diagram. (*b*) Plot of the minor groove widths in the complexes of HPV-18 E2 and BPV-1 E2 with E2-BS(AATT) and E2-BS(ACGT) as calculated by X3DNA (50). The notable feature is that in both complexes the HPV-18 E2 protein causes a more-significant minor groove compression than does BPV-1 E2. (*c*) (page C-3) Schematic drawings of the protein-DNA contacts seen in crystal structures of HPV-18 E2-DBD bound to E2-BS(AATT) and E2-BS(ACGT), and of BPV-1 E2-DBD bound to E2-BS(AATT) and E2-BS(ACGT). Base pairs in the conserved identity elements are depicted by *filled rectangles* and, preferred base pairs are shown as *gray rectangles*. Phosphates contacted by the proteins are *gray circles*. *Red circles* represent water molecules. The *hatched lines* represent van der Waal s contact. For simplicity, phosphate interactions are shown in the top half of each panel, and base contacts are shown in the bottom half. However, all contacts are dyad symmetric. These figures have been adapted from (34) and (43).

c)

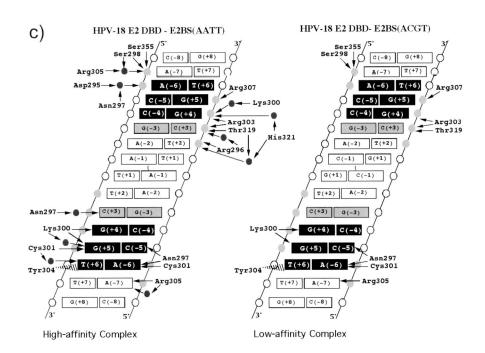

HPV-18 E2 DBD - E2BS(AATT)

HPV-18 E2 DBD- E2BS(ACGT)

High-affinity Complex

Low-affinity Complex

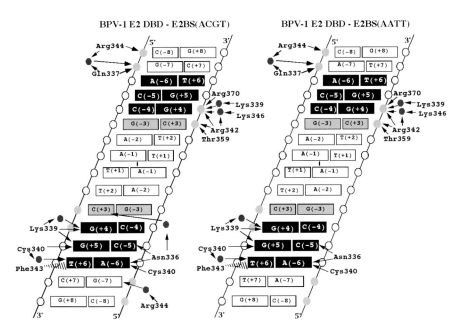

BPV-1 E2 DBD - E2BS(ACGT)

BPV-1 E2 DBD - E2BS(AATT)

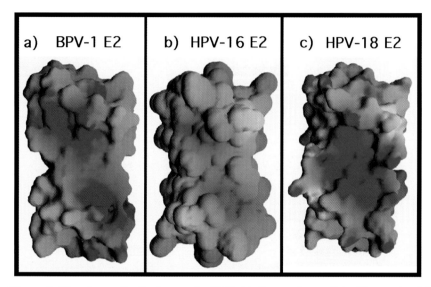

Figure 5 The charge distribution on the DNA-binding surfaces of the E2 proteins (*a*) BPV-1 E2, (*b*) HPV-16 E2, and (*c*) HPV-18 E2. The potential energy surfaces were calculated by GRASP (59). Positive potentials are *blue* and negative potentials are *red*. Water probe radius of 1.4 , potential displayed on a —15 k$_b$T to +15 k$_b$T scale.

Mechanism of Noncontacted Sequence Recognition by E2

Both crystallographic and solution (4, 48) evidence indicate that direct protein-DNA contacts do not contribute to the ability of the HPV E2 proteins to select for E2-BS containing A:T-rich spacer sequences. Furthermore, the high- and low-affinity complexes of HPV-18 E2 with DNA were comparable in terms of buried surface area at the protein-DNA interface, global DNA deformation, and protein structural changes upon complex formation. Although HPV-18 E2 and BPV-1 E2 deform DNA in a similar manner upon interaction, BPV-1 E2 does not have the same spacer sequence discrimination capabilities as HPV-18 E2. These observations strongly imply that an "indirect readout" (62) mechanism is responsible for the varied abilities of the E2 proteins to discriminate among binding sites that differ only in the noncontacted spacer sequence. These observations are important in establishing both the chemistry of E2-DNA interactions and papillomavirus biology because the spacer sequences found in the viral genomes parallel the trends noted above, i.e., the E2-BS in the HPV genomes have A:T-rich spacers, whereas the BPV-1 E2-BS do not.

Is the E2-BS DNA Predisposed to Adopt the Conformation Found in the E2-DNA Complexes?

Despite the global stiffness suggested by the ∼150–base pair persistence length of B-form DNA (40), local base-sequence-dependent variations in conformational properties exist. These result in polymorphisms at a macroscopic level (e.g., B- and A-DNA) as well as microstructural features such as curvature and flexibility. Many DNA-binding proteins are sensitive to DNA microstructure. In particular, it has been established that a protein that bends DNA will bind better to an appropriately phased prebent DNA molecule (39) and that A:T-rich DNA sequences have characteristic conformational properties that can be detected by DNA-binding proteins. Is the spacer sequence preference of the HPV E2 proteins a reflection of the intrinsic conformational complementarity between the protein's DNA-binding surface and the A:T-rich spacer-containing E2-BS?

Shakked and colleagues have determined the crystal structures of E2-BS used in the co-crystal structures described in the previous section, i.e., E2-BS with spacer sequences ACGT (69) and AATT (37). In E2-BS (ACGT) the free DNA is straight with a gentle roll-induced positive writhe. The helices are continuously bent toward the major groove in a manner qualitatively similar to A-DNA, but with a helical repeat of 10.5 base pairs/turn as in B-DNA. When compared to the structure of the DNA in complex with BPV-1 E2, the half-sites have a root mean square deviation (r.m.s.d.) of only 0.6 Å. Thus, they are essentially identical. However, the conformation of the central spacer is substantially different between the free and protein-bound DNA (r.m.s.d. is 1.8 Å). Bending of the central region in the complexes is directed toward the minor groove, the opposite direction to that of the free target. In contrast, the bending of the flanking ACCG/CGGT half-sites is toward the major groove paralleling that of the same segments in free DNA. Thus, the major deformation imposed on the DNA target upon protein binding is in the noncontacted central sequence. Energy calculations using the free and protein-bound DNA structures suggest that the central ACGT sequence is particularly deformable (69).

In contrast to what was seen in the E2-BS (ACGT) structure, the E2-BS with an AATT spacer was bent toward the central minor groove by 9°. This deformation was accompanied by a reduction of minor groove width to 9.3 Å in the region of the AATT spacer. As a result, E2-BS (AATT) is predeformed in a manner similar to that seen in E2-DNA complexes. This favorable prebending of E2-BS (AATT) might well constitute a "structural code" for protein recognition embedded in the DNA sequence (37). Although the more pronounced narrowing of the minor groove in the HPV-18 E2-DNA complexes when compared to the BPV-1 E2-DNA complexes correlates with the preference of HPV-18 E2 for A:T-rich spacer-containing binding sites, it is surprising that BPV-1 E2, which also narrows the central minor groove upon interaction, does not have a similar spacer sequence preference.

A RELATIONSHIP BETWEEN DNA FLEXIBILITY AND E2-BINDING AFFINITY

At any given locus the DNA helix axis is preferentially deformable toward either the major or the minor grooves. In-phase deformability of successive nucleotide steps can result in net curvature comparable to static axial bending. Positive correlations between DNA conformational flexibility and protein-binding affinity have been established in several protein-DNA systems where complex formation is accompanied by DNA deformation, e.g., 434 and P22 repressors, cAMP receptor protein (CRP or CAP) and the TATA-binding protein (TBP) (26, 35, 44, 45, 65). In these cases, a positive correlation has also been found between protein-DNA-binding affinity and favorable prebending of the DNA target.

A probe into the contribution of spacer flexibility to the DNA-binding affinities of HPV-16 E2, HPV-18 E2, and BPV-1 E2 showed that the proteins are differentially sensitive to DNA flexibility (36, 43). BPV-1 E2 was less sensitive to DNA flexibility than were HPV-16 and HPV-18 E2 (Figure 4b). The introduction of flexibility in the E2-BS (via either a nick or a gap in the spacer region) decreased the affinity of a binding site for HPV-16/18 E2. This effect was most striking for sequences (AA[A/T]N spacers) for which HPV E2 displays the greatest affinity. The TTAA spacer contains a flexible TpA step (61), and introducing a nick into such a sequence did not result in the same dramatic drop in affinity seen with the other A-tract spacer-containing sites.

In contrast, BPV-1 E2-DNA binding is moderately favored by DNA flexibility. This observation is in keeping with structural evidence regarding the distortion of the DNA upon BPV-1 E2 binding and the lack of direct protein-spacer interactions (33). These results on BPV-1 E2 also concur with conclusions drawn from the bacteriophage 434 studies of the correlation between protein-binding affinity and DNA flexibility. The 434 repressor/operator interaction has a hierarchy of spacer sequence preference in its operator sites (AAAA > ATAT ≫ ACGT) analogous to that seen for HPV-16/18 E2. However, when a backbone nick was introduced at the central phosphodiester bond, 434 binding affinity increased approximately fivefold (44, 45). This result was attributed to the increased flexibility of the nicked target. The results with BPV-1 E2, although not conclusive, are also consistent with increased affinity toward more flexible DNA targets, e.g., TTAA and nicked and gapped spacer-containing binding sites. However, the fact that the DNA-binding affinity of HPV E2 is significantly reduced by DNA torsional flexibility suggests that spacer recognition is mediated by a mechanism distinct from that seen for the 434 repressor or BPV-1 E2.

Flexibility introduces two additional terms to the free-energy change upon binding: (*a*) the difference in energy of the free and bound states of the flexible ligand and (*b*) the loss of entropy accompanying immobilization by the protein. Increased stability of a complex with an oligonucleotide that is flexible in the free state, as in the BPV-1 E2-DNA complexes, implies that the interactions formed upon protein binding are able to overcome the entropic penalty resulting from constraining the conformation.

Electrostatics and DNA Deformation

Several DNA-bending mechanisms involving electrostatic forces have been proposed. Maher and colleagues suggest that the ability to bend is latent in DNA by virtue of the balanced negative charges on the phosphates that maintain it as a stiff rod (75–80, 82). When charges on one face of the DNA cylinder are neutralized by a ligand, a net force bending the DNA toward the neutralized surface is exerted. Using chemical means of achieving asymmetric charge neutralization, such as replacement of phosphate groups by methyl phosphonates and the tethering of ammonium groups on appropriately placed bases, they have demonstrated significant DNA bending. By this "phantom protein" approach, these investigators suggest that asymmetric charge neutralization is sufficient to induce DNA bending.

Kerppola and coworkers have proposed an alternative model in which the electrostatic force exerted by the protein actively initiates DNA bending toward the positive surface (41, 42, 47, 67). The response of DNA is then a passive deformation. These models need not be mutually exclusive because long-range electrostatic forces could initiate the process of DNA bending, and when the phosphates are within range of the positively charged side chains of the protein, asymmetric charge neutralization could occur. In some cases, bending away from a neutral surface is thought to be the driving force of DNA deformation. Predominantly hydrophobic protein-DNA interfaces, as observed in complexes of DNA with TBP and the SRY and LEF proteins, are thought to increase the repulsion between negatively charged DNA backbone phosphates, causing them to bend away from the protein surface (23). It has also been proposed that the neutralization of selected phosphates in protein-DNA complexes reduces flexibility and increases DNA curvature (28, 29).

An Electrostatic Model for E2-DNA-Binding Specificity

Significant differences exist in the electrostatic potential energy surfaces of BPV-1, HPV-18 E2, and HPV-16 E2 (Figure 5, see color insert). Overall, HPV-16 E2 is less charged all along the DNA-interaction surface compared with BPV-1 E2. Consistent with these observations, HPV-16 E2 makes fewer contacts with the DNA phosphate backbone than BPV-1 E2 (4). Positive charge localized near the C termini of the recognition helices of BPV-1 E2 is notably absent on the HPV-16 E2 surface.

As in the case of the bZIP peptides (53, 64, 75, 78–80), BPV-1 E2 has a basic amino acid cluster positioned such that electrostatic forces can be exerted upon the phosphate backbone of DNA to facilitate bending. This phenomenon may contribute to the ability of BPV-1 E2 to bind DNA sites that are not predeformed, resulting in less stringent requirements regarding the sequence of the noncontacted spacer nucleotides (4, 36, 48). Because HPV-16 E2 lacks this accumulation of positive charge, it is reasonable to hypothesize that it would have greater affinity toward prebent DNA molecules that are predisposed to be sterically complementary to the protein surface, such as E2-BS with A-tract-containing spacers.

HPV-18 E2 has an accumulation of positive charge in the center of its DNA-interaction surface. This positive charge would be juxtaposed against the minor groove of the E2-BS upon DNA interaction. The minor grooves of A:T-rich sequences are more negative than those of G:C-rich sequences because of the more negative electrostatic potentials of T (O_2) and A (N_3) compared with C (O_2) and G (N_3). Electrostatic complementarity between the positive HPV-18 E2 surface and the negative minor groove of E2BS with A:T-rich spacer sequences might contribute to the noncontacted spacer sequence preferences of HPV-18 E2. This model is similar to one proposed for the interaction with DNA of the 434 and 434 Cro proteins (21) wherein the presence of an Arg side chain (Arg43 in 434) that interacts with the minor-groove of DNA is responsible for the ability of these proteins to discriminate between TpA and CpG as the central base pair. In support of this model, the R43A mutation decreases the affinity of 434 repressor for its binding site 500-fold (44). This electrostatic model is also supported by the different salt dependencies of the DNA-binding reaction as a function of the central base pairs (5, 6).

In summary the ability of the various E2 proteins to detect noncontacted DNA sequences may involve electrostatic mechanisms. The BPV-1 E2 protein induces DNA to collapse toward the cationic charges on its interaction surface. Hence it actively bends DNA. HPV-16 E2 lacks similarly positioned positive patches; hence it prefers appropriately prebent DNA, such as A-tract–containing sequences. HPV-18 E2 has a cationic surface that is juxtaposed against the central minor groove of the E2-BS. This property may well result in the observed preference for the more electronegative minor groove of A:T-rich spacer-containing E2-BS. Confirmation of these models awaits more rigorous examination of the E2-DNA interaction and its relationship with DNA conformational flexibility.

BINDING SITE SELECTION BY E2
AND PAPILLOMAVIRUS BIOLOGY

Papillomaviruses replicate in terminally differentiated cells that have exited the cell cycle. Because viral DNA replication is dependent on host cell factors, they need to activate the oncogenes *E6* and *E7*. The expressed E6 and E7 proteins can then bind and inactivate two negative regulators of cell proliferation, p53 and Rb. However elevated E6 and E7 protein levels are associated with malignant progression, and hence their production needs to be controlled for a productive viral life cycle. Thus, a fine balance between activation and repression of the early E6/E7 promoter is necessary.

Transcriptional modulation of early viral gene expression is a central regulatory event. In the absence of viral gene products, HPV early gene transcription is activated by host cell transcription factors, which interact with the LCR upstream of the major early promoter of high-risk HPVs. The basal activity of these promoters can be further modulated by viral E2 proteins. Four E2-BS are located in highly conserved positions in the LCR of all high-risk HPVs. At least three of these sites are essential for a productive viral life cycle. The specific arrangement of E2-BS within the LCR appears to be more important for viral replication than merely the number of sites (81). Viral DNA replication and gene expression patterns reflect the relative occupancy of E2-BS as the concentration of the E2 protein varies. Hence, the ability of E2 to select among the available binding sites is relevant to the regulation of the viral life and infection cycles.

Binding of E2 to promoter-proximal BS1 interferes with the recognition of the neighboring TATA box by TBP (18). E2 may also affect the stability of the preassembled preinitiation complex after binding of TBP to DNA has occurred. Furthermore, binding of E2 to BS2 and BS3 may contribute to promoter repression by competition with cellular transcription factors such as SP1 (15). E2 binding at BS4 can specifically upregulate viral early gene expression. E2 binding at BS3 is necessary for viral DNA replication. The HPV-18 E2 protein binds with the highest affinity to BS4 and with reduced affinity to sites BS1 and BS2 (15, 70). Thus at low concentrations of E2, when the E6/E7 promoter is activated, BS4 is occupied. As E2 concentrations rise, the E6 promoter is repressed, concomitant with E2 occupation of BS1 and BS2. This sequence of E2-DNA-binding events correlates with an initial increase in early gene expression, increasing the concentration of E2. Subsequent binding of E2 to sites BS1, BS2, and BS3 would lead to repression of transcription and the initiation of viral gene replication. E2 bound to BS4 could counteract total repression of transcription, ensuring that the E6 and E7 proteins are expressed at a level necessary to maintain a cellular environment that permits viral replication. The evidence strongly suggests that recognition of DNA sequence-dependent conformational propensities contributes to the ability of the E2 proteins to discriminate between consensus E2-BS present on the viral genomes. Thus the physicochemical properties of the E2 proteins are uniquely tailored for optimal temporal regulation of gene expression and replication.

The results of investigations on the E2-DNA interaction described here show that the E2 proteins differ in the distribution of charge on their DNA-interaction surface and that this property correlates with their abilities to detect conformational flexibility in their DNA targets. A better, more quantitative understanding of the mechanisms of indirect readout suggested by these studies awaits further experimentation. It will also be interesting to examine whether the abilities of other proteins to induce DNA bending via electrostatic forces can be correlated to the intrinsic deformability of DNA.

ACKNOWLEDGMENTS

This review is dedicated to the memory of Paul B. Sigler. I gratefully acknowledge numerous helpful discussions with collaborators Michael Brenowitz and Zippora Shakked, members of my laboratory who participated in some of the projects described here, and the NIH for financial support.

Visit the Annual Reviews home page at www.annualreviews.org

LITERATURE CITED

1. Alexander KA, Phelps WC. 1996. A fluorescence anisotropy study of DNA binding by HPV-11 E2C protein: a hierarchy of of E2-binding sites. *Biochemistry* 35:9864–72

2. Androphy EJ, Lowy DR, Schiller JT. 1987. Bovine papillomavirus E2 trans-acting gene product binds to specific sites in papillomavirus DNA. *Nature* 325:70–73

3. Antson AA, Burns JE, Moroz OV, Scott DJ, Sanders CM, et al. 2000. Structure of the intact transactivation domain of the human papillomavirus E2 protein. *Nature* 403:805–9

4. Bedrosian CL, Bastia D. 1990. The DNA-binding domain of HPV-16 E2 protein interaction with the viral enhancer: protein-induced DNA bending and role of the non-conserved core sequence in binding site affinity. *Virology* 174:557–75

5. Bell AC, Koudelka GB. 1993. Operator sequence context influences amino acid-base-pair interactions in 434 repressor-operator complexes. *J. Mol. Biol.* 234:542–53

6. Bell AC, Koudelka GB. 1995. How 434 repressor discriminates between OR1 and OR3: the influence of contacted and noncontacted base pairs. *J. Biol. Chem.* 270:1205–12

7. Bernard HU, Chan SY, Delius H. 1994. Evolution of papillomaviruses. *Curr. Top. Microbiol. Immunol.* 186:33–54

8. Bochkarev A, Barwell JA, Pfuetzner RA, Bochkareva E, Frappier L, Edwards AM. 1996. Crystal structure of the DNA-binding domain of the Epstein-Barr virus origin-binding protein, EBNA1, bound to DNA. *Cell* 84:791–800

9. Bochkarev A, Barwell JA, Pfuetzner R, Furey WJ, Edwards AM, Frappier LD. 1995. Crystal structure of the DNA-binding and dimerization domain of the Epstein-Barr origin-binding protein EBNA1. *Cell* 83:39–46

10. Bussiere DE, Kong X, Egan DA, Walter K, Holzman TF, et al. 1998. Structure of the E2 DNA-binding domain from human papillomavirus serotype 31 at 2.4 Å. *Acta Crystallogr. D* 54:1367–76

11. Chiang C-M, Ustav M, Stenlund A, Ho TF, Broker TR, Chow LT. 1992. Viral E1 and E2 proteins support replication of homologous and heterologous papillomavirus origins. *Proc. Natl. Acad. Sci. USA* 89:5799–803

12. Choo Y, Klug A. 1994. Toward a code for the interactions of zinc fingers with DNA: selection of randomized fingers displayed on phage. *Proc. Natl. Acad. Sci. USA* 91:11163–67

13. Cruickshank J, Shire K, Davidson AR, Edwards AM, Frappier L. 2000. Two domains of the Epstein-Barr virus origin DNA-binding protein, EBNA1, orchestrate sequence-specific DNA binding. *J. Biol. Chem.* 275:22273–77

14. Del Vecchio AM, Romaczuk H, Howley PM, Baker CC. 1992. Transient replication of human papillomavirus DNAs. *J. Virol.* 66:5949–58

15. Demeret C, Desaintes CMY, Thierry F. 1997. Different mechanisms contribute to the E2-mediated transcriptional repression of human papillomavirus type 18 viral oncogenes. *J. Virol.* 71:9343–49

16. Desaintes C, Goyat S, Garbay S, Yaniv M, Thierry F. 1999. Papillomavirus E2 induces p53-independent apoptosis in HeLa cells. *Oncogene* 18:4538–45

17. de Villiers EM. 1994. Human pathogenic papillomavirus types: an update. *Curr. Top. Microbiol. Immunol.* 186:1–12

18. Dostatni N, Lambert PF, Sousa R, Ham J, Howley PM, Yaniv M. 1991. The functional BPV-1 E2 trans-activating protein can act as a repressor by preventing formation of the initiation complex. *Genes Dev.* 5:1657–71

19. Dostatni N, Thierry F, Yaniv M. 1988. A dimer of BPV-1 E2 containing a protease resistant core interacts with its DNA target. *EMBO J.* 7:3807–16

20. Dowhanick JJ, McBride AA, Howley PM. 1995. Suppression of cellular proliferation by the papillomavirus E2 protein. *J. Virol.* 69:7791–99

21. Duong TH, Zakrzewska K. 1998. Se-quence specificty of bacteriophage 434 repressor-operator complexation. *J. Mol. Biol.* 280:31–39

22. Dyson N, Howley PM, Munger K, Harlow E. 1989. The human papilloma virus-16 E7 oncoprotein is able to bind to the retinoblastoma gene product. *Science* 243:934–37

23. Elcock AH, McCammon JA. 1996. The low dielectric interior of proteins is sufficient to cause major structural changes in DNA on association. *J. Am. Chem. Soc.* 118:3787–88

24. Ferreiro DU, Lima LM, Nadra AD, Alonso LG, Goldbaum FA, de Prat-Gay G. 2000. Distinctive cognate sequence discrimination, bound DNA conformation, and binding modes in the E2 C-terminal domains from prototype human and bovine papillomaviruses. *Biochemistry* 39:14692–701

25. Frankel AD, Kim PS. 1991. Modular structure of transcription factors: implications for gene regulation. *Cell* 65:717–19

26. Gartenberg MR, Crothers DM. 1988. DNA sequence determinants of CAP-induced bending and protein binding affinity. *Nature* 333:824–29

27. Goodwin EC, Yang E, Lee CJ, Lee HW, DiMaio D, Hwang ES. 2000. Rapid induction of senescence in human cervical carcinoma cells. *Proc. Natl. Acad. Sci. USA* 97:10978–83

28. Gurlie R, Zakrzewska K. 1998. DNA curvature and phosphate neutralization: an important aspect of specific protein binding. *J. Biomol. Struct. Dyn.* 16:605–18

29. Harrington RE, Winicov H. 1994. New concepts in protein-DNA recognition: sequence-directed DNA bending and flexibility. *Prog. Nucleic Acid Res. Mol. Biol.* 47:195–270

30. Harris SF, Botchan MR. 1999. Crystal structure of the human papillomavirus type 18 E2 activation domain. *Science* 284:1673–77

31. Hawley-Nelson P, Vousden KH, Hubbert NL, Lowy DR, Schiller JT. 1989. HPV16

E6 and E7 proteins cooperate to immortalize human foreskin keratinocytes. *EMBO J.* 8:3905–10

32. Hegde RS, Androphy EJ. 1998. Crystal structure of the E2 DNA-binding domain from human papillomavirus type 16: implications for its DNA binding-site selection mechanism. *J. Mol. Biol.* 284:1479–89

33. Hegde RS, Grossman SR, Laimins LA, Sigler PB. 1992. Crystal structure at 1.7 Å of the bovine papillomavirus-1 E2 DNA-binding domain bound to its DNA target. *Nature* 359:505–12

34. Hegde RS, Wang A-F, Kim S-S, Schapira M. 1998. Subunit rearrangement accompanies sequence-specific DNA-binding by the bovine papillomavirus-1 E2 protein. *J. Mol. Biol.* 276:797–808

35. Hilchey SP, Koudelka GB. 1997. DNA-based loss of specificity mutations. Effects of DNA sequence on the contacted and noncontacted base preferences of bacteriophage P22 repressor. *J. Biol. Chem.* 272:1646–53

36. Hines CS, Meghoo C, Shetty S, Biburger M, Brenowitz M, Hegde RS. 1998. DNA structure and flexibility in the sequence-specific binding of papillomavirus E2 proteins. *J. Mol. Biol.* 276:809–18

37. Hizver J, Rozenberg H, Frolow F, Rabinovich D, Shakked Z. 2001. DNA bending by an adenine-thymine tract and its role in gene regulation. *Proc. Natl. Acad. Sci. USA* 98:8490–95

38. Howley PM, Munger K, Werness BA, Phelps WC, Schlegel R. 1989. Molecular mechanisms of transformation by the human papillomaviruses. *Princess Takamatsu Symp.* 20:199–206

39. Kahn JD, Crothers DM. 1992. Protein-induced bending and DNA cyclization. *Proc. Natl. Acad. Sci. USA* 89:6343–47

40. Kahn JD, Crothers DM. 1993. DNA bending in transcription initiation. *Cold Spring Harbor Symp. Quant. Biol.* 58:115–22

41. Kerppola TK. 1996. Fos and Jun bend the AP-1 site: effects of probe geometry on the detection of protein-induced DNA bending. *PNAS* 93:10117–22

42. Kerppola TK, Curran T. 1997. The transcription activation domains of Fos and Jun induce DNA bending through electrostatic interactions. *EMBO J.* 16:2907–16

43. Kim SS, Tam JK, Wang AF, Hegde RS. 2000. The structural basis of DNA target discrimination by papillomavirus E2 proteins. *J. Biol. Chem.* 275:31245–54

44. Koudelka CB, Harrison SC, Ptashne M. 1987. Effect of non-contacted bases on the affinity of 434 operator for 434 repressor and *cro*. *Nature* 326:886–89

45. Koudelka GB, Carlson P. 1992. DNA twisting and the effects of non-contacted bases on the affinity of 434 repressor for 434 operator. *Nature* 355:89–91

46. Lechner MS, Mack DH, Finicle AB, Crook T, Vousden KH, Laimins LA. 1992. Human papillomavirus E6 proteins bind p53 in vivo and abrogate p53-mediated repression of transcription. *EMBO J.* 11:3045–52. Erratum. 1992. *EMBO J.* 11(11):4248

47. Leonard DA, Rajaram N, Kerppola TK. 1997. Structural basis of DNA bending and oriented heterodimer binding by the basic leucine zipper domains of Fos and Jun. *PNAS* 94:4913–18

48. Li R, Knight J, Bream G, Stenlund A, Botchan M. 1989. Specific recognition nucleotides and their DNA context determine the affinity of E2 protein for 17 binding sites in the BPV-1 genome. *Genes Dev.* 3:510–26

49. Liang H, Petros AM, Meadows RP, Yoon HS, Egan DA, et al. 1996. Solution structure of the DNA-binding domain of a human papillomavirus E2 protein: evidence for flexible DNA-binding regions. *Biochemistry* 35:2095–103

50. Lu XJ, Shakked Z, Olson WK. 2000. Λ-DNA conformational motifs in ligand-bound double helices. *J. Mol. Biol.* 300(4):819–40

51. Lusky M, Fontane E. 1991. Formation of the complex of bovine papillomavirus E1 and E2 proteins is modulated by E2 phosphorylation and depends upon sequences

within the carboxyl terminus of E1. *Proc. Natl. Acad. Sci. USA* 88:6363–67

52. McBride AA, Howley PM. 1991. Bovine papillomavirus with a mutation in the E2 serine 301 phosphorylation site replicates at a high copy number. *J. Virol.* 65:6528–34

53. Metallo SJ, Paolella DN, Schepartz A. 1997. The role of a basic amino acid cluster in target site selection and non-specific binding of bZIP peptides to DNA. *Nucleic Acids Res.* 25:2967–72

54. Mok Y-K, de Prat-Gay G, Jonathan BP, Bycroft M. 1996. Equilibrium dissociation and unfolding of the dimeric human papillomavirus strain-16 E2 DNA-binding domain. *Protein Sci.* 5:310–19

55. Mork J, Lie AK, Glattre E, Hallmans G, Jellum E, et al. 2001. Human papillomavirus infection as a risk factor for squamous-cell carcinoma of the head and neck. *N. Engl. J. Med.* 344:1125–31

56. Munger K, Phelps WC, Bubb V, Howley PM, Schlegel R. 1989. The E6 and E7 genes of the human papillomavirus type 16 together are necessary and sufficient for transformation of primary human keratinocytes. *J. Virol.* 63:4417–21

57. Munger K, Werness BA, Dyson N, Phelps WC, Harlow E, Howley PM. 1989. Complex formation of human papillomavirus E7 proteins with the retinoblastoma tumor suppressor gene product. *EMBO J.* 8:4099–105

58. Nelson HCM, Finch JT, Luisi BF, Klug A. 1987. The structure of an oligo(dA)-oligo(dT) tract and its biological implications. *Nature* 330:221–26

59. Nicholls A, Sharp KA, Honig B. 1991. Protein folding and association: insights from the interfacial and thermodynamic properties of hydrocarbons. *Proteins Struct. Funct. Genet.* 11:281–96

60. Nishioka S, Fukushima K, Nishizaki K, Gunduz M, Tominaga S, et al. 1999. Human papillomavirus as a risk factor for head and neck cancers—a case-control study. *Acta Otolaryngol. Suppl.* 540:77–80

61. Olson WK, Gorin AA, Lu XJ, Hock LM, Zhurkin VB. 1998. DNA sequence-dependent deformability deduced from protein-DNA crystal complexes. *Proc. Natl. Acad. Sci. USA* 95:11163–68

62. Otwinowski Z, Schevitz RW, Zhang R-G, Lawson CL, Joachimiak A, et al. 1988. Crystal structure of the trp repressor/operator complex at atomic resolution. *Nature* 335:321–29

63. Pabo CO, Nekludova L. 2000. Geometric analysis and comparison of protein-DNA interfaces: Why is there no simple code for recognition? *J. Mol. Biol.* 301:597–624

64. Paolella DN, Liu Y, Fabian MA, Schepartz A. 1997. Electrostatic mechanism for DNA bending by bZIP proteins. *Biochemistry* 36:10033–38

65. Parvin JD, McCormick RJ, Sharp PA, Fisher DA. 1995. Pre-bending of a promoter sequence enhances affinity for the TATA-binding factor. *Nature* 373:724–27

66. Pepinsky RB, Prakash SS, Corina K, Grossel MJ, Barsoum J, Androphy EJ. 1997. Sequences flanking the core DNA-binding domain of bovine papillomavirus type 1 E2 contribute to DNA-binding function. *J. Virol.* 71:828–31

67. Rajaram N, Kerppola TK. 1997. DNA bending by Fos-Jun and the orientation of heterodimer binding depend on the sequence of the AP-1 site. *EMBO J.* 16:2917–25

68. Romanczuk H, Thierry F, Howley PM. 1990. Mutational analysis of *cis*-elements involved in E2 modulation of human papillomavirus type 16 P97 and type 18 P105 promoters. *J. Virol.* 64:2849–59

69. Rozenberg H, Rabinovich D, Frolow F, Hegde RS, Shakked Z. 1998. Structural code for DNA recognition revealed in crystal structures of papillomavirus E2-DNA targets. *Proc. Natl. Acad. Sci. USA* 95:15194–99

70. Sanders CM, Maitland NJ. 1994. Kinetic and equilibrium studies of the human papillomavirus type-16 transcription regulatory protein E2 interacting with core enhancer elements. *Nucleic Acids Res.* 22:4890–97

71. Scheffner M, Romanczuk H, Munger K, Huibregtse JM, Mietz JA, Howley PM. 1994. Functions of human papillomavirus proteins. *Curr. Top. Microbiol. Immunol.* 186:83–99

72. Sigler PB. 1988. Acid blobs and negative noodles. *Nature* 333:210–12

73. Steger G, Ham J, Lefebvre O, Yaniv M. 1995. The bovine papillomavirus I E2 protein contains two activation domains: one that interacts with TBP and another that functions after TBP binding. *EMBO J.* 14:329–40

74. Steinberg BM, DiLorenzo TP. 1996. A possible role for human papillomaviruses in head and neck cancer. *Cancer Metastasis Rev.* 15:91–112

75. Strauss JK, Maher LJ. 1994. DNA bending by asymmetric phosphate neutralization. *Science* 266:1829–34

76. Strauss JK, Roberts C, Nelson MG, Switzer C, Maher LJ. 1996. DNA bending by hexamethylene-tethered ammonium ions. *PNAS* 93:9515–20

77. Strauss-Soukup JK, Maher LJ. 1997. DNA bending by GCN4 mutants bearing cationic residues. *Biochemistry* 36:10026–32

78. Strauss-Soukup JK, Maher LJ. 1997. Role of asymmetric phosphate neutralization in DNA bending by PU.1. *J. Biol. Chem.* 272:31570–75

79. Strauss-Soukup JK, Maher LJ. 1998. Electrostatic effects in DNA bending by GCN4 mutants. *Biochemistry* 37:1060–66

80. Strauss-Soukup JK, Vaghefi MM, Hogrefe RI, Maher LJ. 1997. Effects of neutralization pattern and stereochemistry on DNA bending by methylphosphonate substitutions. *Biochemistry* 36:8692–98

81. Stubenrauch F, Lim HB, Laimins LA. 1998. Differential requirements for conserved E2 binding sites in the life cycle of oncogenic human papillomavirus type 31. *J. Virol.* 72:1071–77

82. Tomky LA, Strauss-Soukup KK, Maher LJ. 1998. Effects of phosphate neutralization on the shape of the AP-1 transcription factor binding site in duplex DNA. *Nucleic Acids Res.* 26:2298–305

83. Ustav M, Stenlund A. 1991. Transient replication of BPV-1 requires two viral polypeptides encoded by the E1 and E2 open reading frames. *EMBO J.* 10:449–57

84. Veeraraghavan S, Mello CC, Androphy EJ, Baleja JD. 1999. Structural correlates for enhanced stability in the E2 DNA-binding domain from bovine papillomavirus. *Biochemistry* 38:16115–24

85. Zou N, Lin BY, Duan F, Lee KY, Jin G, et al. 2000. The hinge of the human papillomavirus type 11 E2 protein contains major determinants for nuclear localization and nuclear matrix association. *J. Virol.* 74:3761–70

86. Zur Hausen H, de Villiers EM. 1994. Human papillomaviruses. *Annu. Rev. Microbiol.* 48:427–47

87. Zur Hausen H, Schneider A, eds. 1987. *The Role of Papillomaviruses in Human Anogenital Cancer*, pp. 245–63. New York: Plenum

Annu. Rev. Biophys. Biomol. Struct. 2002. 31:361–92
DOI: 10.1146/annurev.biophys.31.101101.140858

CONFORMATIONAL DYNAMICS OF THE CHROMATIN FIBER IN SOLUTION: Determinants, Mechanisms, and Functions

Jeffrey C. Hansen

Department of Biochemistry, The University of Texas Health Science Center at San Antonio, 7703 Floyd Curl Drive, Mail Code 7760, San Antonio, Texas 78229-3900; e-mail: hansen@uthscsa.edu

Key Words histone, nucleosome, DNA, macromolecular interactions, nucleus, transcription, replication

■ **Abstract** Chromatin fibers are dynamic macromolecular assemblages that are intimately involved in nuclear function. This review focuses on recent advances centered on the molecular mechanisms and determinants of chromatin fiber dynamics in solution. Major points of emphasis are the functions of the core histone tail domains, linker histones, and a new class of proteins that assemble supramolecular chromatin structures. The discussion of important structural issues is set against a background of possible functional significance.

CONTENTS

1056-8700/02/0609-0361$14.00

INTRODUCTION AND TERMINOLOGY

Dating to the mid-1970s, thousands of papers have examined the structural properties of the chromatin fiber, or its subunit, the nucleosome (47, 135, 147, 150). Despite this intense effort, and the availability of atomic-level structures of both the histone octamer (7) and nucleosome core particles (88, 124), many aspects of chromatin structure remain poorly understood. One such area is the conformational dynamics of the chromatin fiber. A chromatin fiber can exist in many different locally folded structures in solution in vitro and also is packaged into higher-order chromosomal-level domains in vivo (16, 135, 150, 155) (Figure 1). Most previous reviews in this area have focused on questions relating to chromatin fiber structures per se, e.g., is the maximally folded "30-nm fiber" an irregular helix or regular solenoid (138, 145, 156). The precise structures adopted by chromatin in solution are the subject of continued debate (138, 145, 156), and there is no indication that these questions will be answered definitively in the near future.

This article addresses the molecular determinants and mechanisms responsible for chromatin fiber dynamics in solution. There are several reasons why a critical discussion of these topics is timely. A great deal has been learned recently

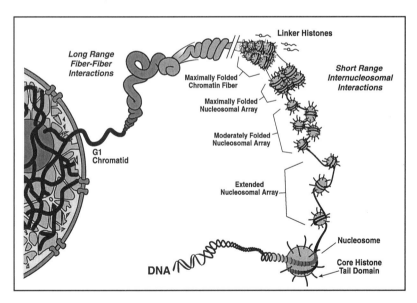

Figure 1 Schematic illustration of chromatin fiber condensation. Shown are the steps involved in the folding of extended nucleosomal arrays into maximally folded chromatin fibers. Each step is discussed in detail in the text, as are the functional roles of the core histone tail domains and linker histones. The break in the fiber illustrates that the maintenance of chromosomal level domain structure does not appear to be obligatorily linked to the extent of local chromatin fiber folding.

about how the condensation process occurs and is regulated. Multiple, independent mechanisms are involved in the control of chromatin fiber dynamics, although the mechanistic details remain elusive. Important insights have been gained into the relationship between the formation and stability of the condensed chromatin structures. Intriguingly, the primary macromolecular determinants of chromatin fiber dynamics, the core histone N-terminal tail domains, also interact with functionally important chromosomal proteins and are the site of numerous posttranslational modifications that influence transcription, replication, recombination, and repair (47, 135, 147, 150). Thus, the tail domains appear to provide a direct connection between chromatin fiber dynamics and regulation of nuclear functions. Finally, it recently has been documented that there is a class of chromatin-associated proteins capable of causing global rearrangement of the chromatin fiber into unique higher-order suprastructures.

While there no longer is any question that the chromatin fiber is intimately involved in the regulation of nuclear functions (6, 150, 151, 157), most studies have focused on individual nucleosomes in specific regions of the genome rather than on the global functional properties of the surrounding chromatin fiber. Further, it is common for functional models to depict the chromatin fiber as a completely extended array of nucleosomes, even though the chromatin fiber is condensed under "physiological" ionic conditions in vitro. Moreover, at least in some cases chromatin fiber dynamics are modulated by posttranslational modifications and core histone variants known to influence genomic functions (e.g., tail domain acetylation). Because structure and function inevitably are linked during regulation of biological processes, potential in vivo functional consequences of chromatin fiber dynamics must be carefully considered.

The primary chromatin literature is filled with terms, such as nucleosome, which often have different meanings in different contexts. Throughout this article the following definitions are used: A *histone octamer* is composed of two each of the *core histones* H2A, H2B, H3, and H4 and is assembled in vitro and in vivo from one H3/H4 tetramer and two H2A/H2B dimers (6). Each of the core histones consists of a uniquely structured C-terminal *histone fold domain* and an N-terminal *tail domain*. H2A is the only core histone that also possesses a canonical C-terminal tail domain. *Nucleosomal arrays* are composed of long DNA bound to multiple core histone octamers at $\sim$160–210-bp intervals. A *nucleosome* consists of $\sim$146–165 bp of DNA wrapped around each histone octamer in a nucleosomal array. To maintain consistency with the primary literature, a *nucleosome* also will be used to describe isolated particles in which $\sim$145–200 bp of DNA are bound to a single histone octamer. Isolated nucleosomes that contain 147 $\pm$ 2–3 bp of DNA are *nucleosome core particles*, while particles containing > 150 bp of DNA are referred to as *mononucleosomes*. The DNA wrapped around a histone octamer is called *nucleosomal DNA*, while the DNA that separates adjacent histone octamers in nucleosomal arrays and chromatin fibers is called *linker DNA*. The terms *chromatin* and *chromatin fiber* are used interchangeably and refer to nucleosomal arrays complexed with one or more *chromatin-associated proteins*.

Chromatin samples traditionally have been isolated from endogenous sources (47, 135, 150). However, it now is possible to assemble nucleosomes, nucleosomal arrays, and chromatin fibers in vitro entirely from pure components (26, 89). Much of the progress discussed in this article has come from the characterization of these defined model systems, which because of their compositional homogeneity and structural monodispersity have allowed new insights into the molecular basis of nucleosome and chromatin fiber dynamics in solution.

STRUCTURAL DYNAMICS OF THE NUCLEOSOME

Nucleosomes are not static protein-DNA complexes but rather intrinsically dynamic macromolecular assemblages (135, 147, 150). In this section I begin with a brief overview of the histone octamer and nucleosome core particle structures. Key points relating to nucleosome conformational changes and structural instability are highlighted, as well as the structural and functional ramifications of core histone tail domain mobility and rearrangement.

X-Ray Crystallography of the Histone Octamer and Nucleosome Core Particle

X-ray crystal structures of both the histone octamer (7) and the nucleosome core particle (88) have been obtained at high resolution. During the past several years these structures have served as the primary basis for interpreting nucleosome function in chromatin fibers. The details of the crystallography studies have been reviewed extensively (90, 98, 110). In the global context of the chromatin fiber, the crystal structures of the histone octamer and nucleosome core particle have proved useful in certain specific areas. The histone octamer structure (7) provided novel information about the unique molecular structures of individual H2A/H2B dimers and H3/H4 tetramers and the H2A/H2B dimer-H3/H4 tetramer interfaces in the histone octamer (8, 9). These studies also led to a detailed prediction for the pathway of nucleosomal DNA wrapping around the histone octamer (8) and to the discovery of the "histone fold" as a unique evolutionarily conserved dimerization motif (9, 14). The nucleosome core particle structure (91) revealed the actual path of nucleosomal DNA around the histone octamer and showed that it was remarkably similar to the predicted path. This work also demonstrated that both the histone fold domains within each core histone and the various interaction interfaces observed in the histone octamer remained largely unchanged in the nucleosome. Taken together, these results indicate that the secondary and tertiary structures of the core histones in the histone octamer and nucleosome core particle are virtually identical. An important ramification of these and other related findings is that determinants for wrapping nucleosomal DNA reside mainly in the core histone octamer, as was first suggested by the observation that the intrinsic structure present in naked DNAs in solution is no longer detectable after assembly of the same DNAs into a mononucleosome (68).

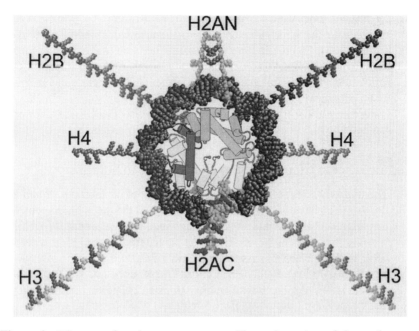

Figure 2 Diagram of nucleosome structure. Shown is a view of the nucleosome along the DNA superhelical axis. The nucleosomal DNA and protein interior are drawn according to the crystal structure of the nucleosome core particle (88). The internal histone fold domains of H2A, H2B, H3, and H4 are shaded black, dark gray, light gray, and medium gray. For conceptual purposes, each of the core histone N-terminal tail domains and the H2A C-termini (H2AC) are projected as linear polypeptide chains corresponding in close scale to the rest of the nucleosome. However, as discussed in the text, each tail domain is highly mobile, is likely to contain secondary structure, and is located differently in nucleosome core particles, mononucleosomes, and chromatin fibers. The figure was provided courtesy of Dr. J. J. Hayes. Adapted from (153).

In contrast to the protein interior of the nucleosome core particle, the externally located core histone tails were not observed in the crystal structures of either the nucleosome core particle or histone octamer (7, 88, 124) (Figure 2). As will be discussed in detail below, the core histone tail domains are primary determinants of chromatin fiber dynamics. Hence, crystallographic studies unfortunately have provided no clues regarding the protein chemistry that underlies the complex functions of the tail domains in chromatin. Somewhat surprisingly, the nucleosome core particle crystal structure yielded no evidence for tail domain interactions with nucleosomal DNA. A large number of solution studies have demonstrated that the core histone tail domains bind to the nucleosomal DNA of nucleosome core particles under low salt conditions and at physiological ionic strengths (11, 13, 69, 79, 100, 135, 150). Presumably, tail domain–nucleosomal

DNA interactions were not observed in the nucleosome core particle crystal structure due to the high, nonphysiological concentrations of divalent metal ions ($\sim$50 mM $MnCl_2$) present in the crystals. The issue of tail domain mobility and rearrangement in nucleosomes and in the chromatin fiber is a major focus of this article. Finally, as highlighted in the next section, the nucleosome in solution can assume multiple conformational states. Thus, the core histone octamer and nucleosome core particle crystal structures provide a view of just one of many potentially biologically important conformations of the nucleosome.

Conformational Changes of the Nucleosome in Solution

The mostly widely studied in vitro determinant of nucleosome structure in solution is salt concentration (12, 38, 39, 43, 160). As the salt is raised above 600 mM NaCl, the nucleosome dissociates through sequential release of H2A/H2B dimers, followed by dissociation of H3/H4 tetramers from DNA (159). This is the reverse of the nucleosome assembly pathway that occurs both in vitro and in vivo (6, 47, 150). At lower salt concentrations the conformation of the nucleosome core particle varies significantly, changing from an oblate to a prolate shape as the NaCl concentration is raised from 5–200 mM NaCl [(38) and references therein]. In 100–200 mM NaCl, the nucleosome core particle appears to have the same general hydrodynamic shape expected from the crystal structure (38). In addition to solution parameters, conformational changes in the nucleosome also can be caused by drug binding (29) and can occur in response to binding of chromatin-associated proteins such as linker histones (60, 80). Thus, in contrast to the extremely stable molecular interfaces within H2A/H2B dimers and H3/H4 tetramers (9, 98), the interfaces between the H2A/H2B dimers and H3/H4 tetramers in the nucleosome are considerably more pliant.

Interaction of DNA with the histone octamer surface is relatively unstable. In 100–300 mM NaCl, $\sim$5%–20% of the nucleosome core particles in a sample spontaneously dissociate into free DNA (12, 160). The released histone octamers do not further dissociate into H2A/H2B dimers and H3/H4 tetramers, but instead they bind as intact histone octamers to other nucleosome core particles (12, 43, 120, 160). This same dissociation behavior also is observed for linear nucleosomal arrays in moderate NaCl concentrations (65). Further evidence for nucleosome dynamics comes from kinetic studies of restriction enzyme access to nucleosomal DNA-binding sites, as determined by a quantitative site exposure assay (104, 105, 148). At the molecular level, site exposure is thought to involve localized transient dissociation and rebinding of nucleosomal DNA to the histone octamer (104, 105, 148). The equilibrium constant, K_{conf}, describing the local nucleosomal DNA unwrapping transition varies from 10^{-5} near the nucleosome psuedo-dyad axis to 10^{-3} near the nucleosome periphery, reflecting a probability of site exposure that varies from about 1 in 10,000 near the dyad to 1 in 1000 for sites located near the nucleosome edge (3). K_{conf} is reasonably dependent on DNA sequence but does not strongly depend on either the core histone tail domains (103) or the presence of additional linker DNA in a mononucleosome (28). Transient site exposure of nucleosomal DNA also has been observed in the nucleosomes within a linear nucleosomal array (86, 87). These studies show that nucleosomal DNA in effect breathes on the surface of the histone octamer in real time. As a consequence, even DNA elements seemingly buried within nucleosomes are exposed at biologically significant levels provided that the affinity and local concentration of the DNA-binding protein are sufficiently high.

The site exposure studies strongly suggest that local nucleosomal DNA dissociation/rebinding allows proteins to bind to their cognate sites in nucleosomal DNA with physiologically relevant rates and extents. In addition, ATP-dependent chromatin remodeling complexes (e.g., SWI/SNF) may exploit the intrinsic instability of nucleosomal DNA to dramatically enhance the rate of site exposure (1, 50, 86, 87). Nucleosome conformational changes also appear to be associated with gene activation (30, 37, 48, 76, 101). It is unclear whether these functionally altered nucleosome conformations are related to one or more of the different structures observed in solution in vitro. Finally, it is worth noting that nucleosome conformational changes in principle can have profound effects on tail domain function in the chromatin fiber. That is, as the shape of the nucleosome changes the orientation of the tail domains of any given nucleosome relative to surrounding nucleosomes will change as well. Because tail domain–mediated internucleosomal interactions are required for chromatin condensation (see below), it is possible that modulation of internucleosomal tail domain interactions through alteration of nucleosome conformation may be one mechanism for influencing the higher-order structure of the chromatin fiber.

Core Histone Tail Domain Mobility and Rearrangement

The most dynamic and mobile domains of the nucleosome are the core histone N- and C-terminal tails (69, 135, 150). One critical consequence of core histone tail mobility is that these domains are located differently in nucleosome core particles, mononucleosomes, and chromatin fibers, i.e., they rearrange to different locations depending on the context in which they are isolated or assembled. Understanding tail domain rearrangement is essential for grasping the complexity of tail domain function in nucleosomes and the chromatin fiber.

As mentioned above, the core histone tail domains of a nucleosome core particle loosely interact with the nucleosomal DNA under low and moderate salt conditions (11, 13, 79, 100, 135, 150). Specifically, the H3 and H4 tails interact with the central 70–80 base pairs of nucleosomal DNA, while the H2A and H2B tails interact with the more peripheral nucleosomal DNA (11, 41). Consequently, selective proteolytic removal of the core histone tail domains (20) leads to no significant difference in hydrodynamic shape or salt-dependent stability of "tailless" nucleosome core particles, but it does result in somewhat altered DNase I cleavage patterns and differences in the thermal melting of nucleosomal DNA (11, 85, 143). Functional models showing tail domains bound to nucleosomal DNA are based on such results and as such assume that the tail domains of nucleosomal arrays bind to nucleosomal DNA under physiological conditions. Evidence that this assumption may be incorrect first came from cross-linking experiments showing that residues in the H2A and H2B tail domains were bound to the histone-free, extranucleosomal "linker" DNA of an $\sim$210-bp nucleosome rather than to nucleosomal DNA (108). Studies of the C-terminal tail domain of H2A showed that although this tail could be cross-linked to sites near the dyad of nucleosome core particles (134), the H2A C-terminal tail did not occupy the dyad location in either nucleosomal arrays (134) or intact nuclei (107). These results directly demonstrated rearrangement of a specific histone tail domain from a non-nucleosomal position to nucleosomal DNA, concomitant with digestion of nuclei and chromatin fibers into nucleosome core particles. Importantly, the "rearrangement" phenomenon is general. The majority of the contacts made by all the tail domains in a 210-bp mononucleosome are altered by the presence of extranucleosomal linker DNA (4). Moreover, the tail domains are not bound to nucleosomal DNA while mediating salt-dependent chromatin folding (46).

These results lead to several important conclusions. First, digestion of native chromatin fibers into nucleosome core particles, or assembly of nucleosome core particles in vitro from pure components, leaves the tail domains literally no choice but to interact with nucleosomal DNA. However, there is no experimental data indicating that the tail domains of nucleosomal arrays or chromatin fibers are bound to nucleosomal DNA under physiologically relevant conditions. Second, studies utilizing native and tailless nucleosome core particles in retrospect must be carefully (re)evaluated given that tail domain function in nucleosome core particles does not recapitulate tail domain function in the chromatin fiber. As will be discussed in the next sections, the tail domains specifically mediate all stages of chromatin fiber condensation and bind to specific chromatin-associated proteins. All available in vitro data support the conclusion that most, if not all, of the functions of the tail domains in the chromatin fiber are mediated by protein-protein interactions and tail domain–linker DNA interactions. Conclusions to the contrary generally can be explained by the tail domain rearrangement that occurs upon isolation or assembly of nucleosome core particles in vitro.

STRUCTURAL DYNAMICS OF THE CHROMATIN FIBER

The molecular basis of chromatin condensation has intrigued scientists for three decades. Once thought of solely in terms of chromosomal DNA packaging in the nucleus, chromatin fiber condensation is now recognized as having widespread biological functions (6, 47, 150). The past five years have seen significant advances toward elucidating the determinants and mechanisms that control chromatin fiber condensation. Multiple essential functions of the core histone tail domains have been identified. The mechanistic interplay between the tail domains and linker histones during formation of stably folded chromatin fibers is much better understood. The extent to which posttranslational modifications of the tail domains and core histone sequence variants influence fiber dynamics is becoming clearer. The mechanisms that underlie chromatin condensation are surprisingly complex and cannot be explained purely by electrostatic-based phenomena. Accurate solution structures have been obtained for moderately folded chromatin fibers, although the structure of the maximally folded "30-nm fiber" remains unknown. Finally, there is recent evidence that certain chromatin-associated proteins can reconfigure the canonical chromatin fiber into higher-order "suprastructures."

In Vitro Conformational States

Most solution structural studies have focused on characterization of linker histone–containing chromatin fibers, with relatively little attention paid to nucleosomal arrays (47, 135, 150). This stems partly from the widely held view that a linker histone–nucleosome complex (i.e., "chromatosome") is the fundamental structural subunit of the chromatin fiber (47, 135, 150). In addition, the dynamic behavior of nucleosomal arrays identified in early in vitro studies was not considered to be biologically relevant (126). It is now known that the conformational dynamics of nucleosomal arrays in solution result from specific actions of the core histone tail domains (47, 61, 66, 69). Very importantly, the tails perform the same functions in both nucleosomal arrays and linker histone–containing chromatin fibers (25). Furthermore, nucleosomal arrays and linker histone–containing chromatin fibers both fold through the same intrinsic pathway outlined in Figure 3 (24). As a result, recent studies of nucleosomal arrays have yielded much insight into chromatin fiber dynamics. Throughout this article I primarily emphasize results obtained with defined nucleosomal array and chromatin model systems assembled in vitro from pure components (26). The significant increase in homogeneity of the reconstituted systems relative to samples obtained from endogenous sources, together with advanced solution analysis methods, have yielded many key results. In this regard, the solution structures of endogenous arrays and reconstituted model systems are identical as visualized by electron cryo-microscopy (ECM), both in the absence and presence of linker histones (24). Furthermore, reconstituted and native 12-mer nucleosomal arrays fold identically in NaCl (52). Thus, the defined model systems exhibit the same structural behavior in solution as endogenous nucleosomal arrays.

Figure 3 summarizes the structural states of chromatin in solution as defined by analytical hydrodynamic studies. Nucleosomal arrays and chromatin fibers are in equilibrium between extended, moderately folded, maximally folded, and oligomeric conformational states. Panel A describes the specific results obtained with length- and compositionally defined 12-mer nucleosomal array and chromatin model systems having an average nucleosome repeat length of 208 bp (119), while panel B shows the generalized scheme that applies to nucleosomal arrays and chromatin fibers of any length. Note that analysis by hydrodynamic methods yields an unparalleled assay for the extent of folding in solution (i.e., how compact the array is relative to the minimally and maximally folded states), but it does not directly address structures per se. Defined 12-mer nucleosomal arrays under low salt conditions (e.g., 10 mM Tris buffer) sediment at 29S, which is near the

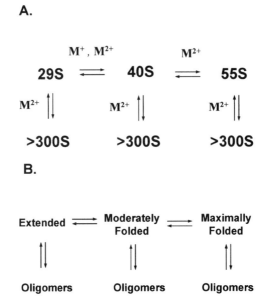

Figure 3 Structural states of nucleosomal arrays in solution. (*A*) Summary of analytical hydrodynamic analyses of salt-dependent folding and oligomerization of defined 12-mer nucleosomal array model systems. M^+ and M^{2+} represent monovalent and divalent cations. (*B*) Generalized description of the solution dynamics of nucleosomal arrays. Linker histone–containing chromatin fibers exhibit the same condensation pathways (25), although the equilibrium is shifted in favor of the maximally folded and oligomerized conformational states (24). See text for details.

predicted sedimentation coefficient for a fully extended beads-on-a-string conformation (62). Such highly extended nucleosomal arrays traditionally are referred to as "10-nm-diameter filaments" (135, 150) and have been observed since the earliest in vitro characterizations of chromatin fiber dynamics (135, 150). Fully extended arrays provide a useful reference point for interpreting studies of salt-dependent condensation. However, the 10-nm beads-on-a-string conformation in essence is an artifact resulting from exposure of nucleosomal arrays to a low salt environment in vitro. In the physiological range of ionic conditions, nucleosomal arrays never adopt such a fully extended conformation (see below).

Defined nucleosomal arrays exhibit continuous increases in their average sedimentation coefficient ($s_{20,w}$) with increasing monovalent salt concentrations, as observed in previous sedimentation analyses of heterogeneous populations of endogenous nucleosomal arrays (23, 51, 140). The average $s_{20,w}$ of the 12-mer nucleosomal arrays increased from ~29S in low salt TE buffer to near 40S in >150 mM NaCl (52, 62). The same extent of folding is observed in ~1 mM $MgCl_2$ (116). A 40S array is predicted to have the same extent of folding as a contacting zig-zag or open helical structure (62). In contrast, a maximally folded "30-nm-diameter" structure modeled as a contacting helix is predicted to sediment at $\sim$55S (62). Importantly, when the sedimentation of defined 12-mer nucleosomal arrays was analyzed by a method that removes diffusion from sedimentation velocity boundaries to yield the $s_{20,w}$ distribution of the entire sample (136), a heterogeneous population of structures ranging from 29S to $\sim$40S was observed in $\sim$100–250 mM NaCl (52, 62). Increases in the NaCl concentration led to increases across the entire $s_{20,w}$ distribution (including the average $s_{20,w}$ measured at the boundary midpoint), indicating that the overall equilibrium was shifted toward the 40S structure. However, a heterogeneous population of partially folded species was observed in all NaCl concentrations studied (52, 62). Removal of salt led to reestablishment of a single 29S species, indicating that transition is reversible. These data demonstrated that 12-mer nucleosomal arrays in NaCl are in equilibrium between 29S and 40S structural states (Figure 3*A*), which correspond to fully extended and moderately folded extents of compaction, respectively (Figure 3*B*). However, the extensive heterogeneity revealed that the moderately folded conformation of nucleosomal arrays is inherently unstable. Several studies suggest that the moderately folded conformation is formed by interaction of adjacent nucleosomes in the array (i.e., nucleosome n with nucleosomes $n + 1$ and $n - 1$). For example, defined nucleosomal arrays containing only 6–7 nucleosomes per 12-mer DNA template possess few adjacent nucleosomes (63, 161) and are unable to fold in $MgCl_2$, whereas templates containing 8–9 nucleosomes have several runs of adjacent nucleosomes and exhibit modest $s_{20,w}$ increases relative to 12-mer nucleosomal arrays under the same conditions (49). Electron microscopy (EM) studies have visualized a close approach of adjacent nucleosomes in a moderately folded 12-mer nucleosomal array in NaCl (52). Additionally, the simultaneous existence of closely packed and extended stretches of nucleosomes in the same array were observed in EM studies of both native (126) and reconstituted 12-mer nucleosomal arrays (52) in NaCl. Taken together, these results provide a plausible explanation for the conformational heterogeneity of nucleosomal arrays in salt solutions. Given that formation of the moderately folded conformation requires neighboring nucleosome-nucleosome interactions, all of the array-bound nucleosomes will be in equilibrium between non-interacting and interacting states. If the equilibrium constant for the nucleosome-nucleosome interactions is small (i.e., the interactions are weak), a mixture of the two states will be present in any given individual nucleosomal array. When extrapolated to an entire population of nucleosomal arrays, such behavior would produce the types of partially folded/partially extended array structures seen in the EM studies and would lead to the $s_{20,w}$ heterogeneity observed in sedimentation experiments.

Nucleosomal arrays achieve considerably greater levels of intramolecular folding in the presence of divalent salts, e.g., 1–2 mM $MgCl_2$ (Figure 3*A*). The maximally folded state of a chromatin fiber has been modeled as a simple contacting helix. As mentioned above, for a 12-mer nucleosomal array this corresponds to an $\sim$55S species (Figure 3*A*). The extent of compaction of the maximally folded conformation (62) is equivalent to the classically defined "30-nm-diameter fiber"

(135, 150). The demonstration that nucleosomal arrays can form the maximally folded conformational state in the absence of linker histones came from sedimentation analysis of defined 12-mer nucleosomal arrays in $MgCl_2$. These experiments showed that a small fraction ($\sim$5%–10%) of the arrays sedimented at $\sim$55S in 2 mM $MgCl_2$ (116, 132), whereas the distribution of the entire sample ranged from $\sim$40S to 55S. Thus, the maximally folded conformation can be formed by nucleosomal arrays in $MgCl_2$, but this structure also is not intrinsically stable in solution. Twelve-mer nucleosomal arrays containing only 1–2 nucleosome-free "gaps" (i.e., 10–11 nucleosomes per DNA template) were unable to form the 55S structure in 2 mM $MgCl_2$ (116), strongly suggesting that a stretch of six consecutive nucleosomes is required to achieve the maximally folded state. Weak internucleosomal interactions also can explain the $s_{20,w}$ heterogeneity present in $MgCl_2$, except that in this case formation of the maximally folded state is presumed to require interaction of nucleosome n with $n \pm 6$. The importance of six consecutive nucleosomes for forming most of the different models of the 30-nm fiber (e.g., irregular helix, regular solenoid) has been recognized for some time (135, 150).

In addition to the two intramolecular folding transitions, nucleosomal arrays also self-associate to form large oligomeric structures (Figure 3). Oligomerization of nucleosomal arrays is induced at higher $MgCl_2$ concentrations than in folding (115, 116) and does not occur in monovalent salts (115, 135, 150). The mechanism of Mg^{2+}-dependent oligomerization of 12-mer nucleosomal arrays has been rigorously characterized by low-speed sedimentation velocity experiments (115). The oligomerization transition is highly cooperative and involves at least two distinct steps. Individual 12-mer arrays initially self-associate to form soluble intermediates that sediment at several hundred S, followed by further oligomerization with increasing salt to form increasingly large polymers that sediment in the thousands of S (115). Salt-dependent oligomerization is freely reversible. Extensively oligomerized 12-mer nucleosomal arrays completely dissociate into fully extended 29S "monomeric" arrays upon return to Mg^{2+}-free buffer (115). Importantly, oligomerization occurs independently of whether the individual nucleosomal arrays are extended, moderately folded, or maximally folded. Both arrays of H3/H4 tetramers and 12-mer nucleosomal arrays containing <6–7 nucleosomes are able to oligomerize, although neither can fold (115). Thus, oligomerization is not obligatorily coupled to intramolecular folding in vitro, i.e., nucleosomal arrays and chromatin fibers do not need to first form the maximally folded conformation in order to oligomerize. This finding has important ramifications for properly interpreting in vitro folding data (discussed below). There is considerable circumstantial evidence suggesting that in vitro oligomerization is related to long-range transitions that participate in global compaction of interphase chromosomal fibers (6, 18, 115, 117, 144), including the observation that many of the in vitro properties of nucleosomal array oligomers and "chromonema" fibers (18, 19) are virtually identical (6, 115). Note that in vitro folding and oligomerization collectively will be referred to as condensation. Finally, one should be aware that oligomerization of nucleosomal arrays and chromatin fibers historically has been referred to as "precipitation" or "salt-insolubility" (135, 150). It is now evident that such terms do not accurately describe the self-association transition, which is reversible, cooperative, and produces large, soluble oligomeric species.

Functional Complexity of the Core Histone Tail Domains

The core histone tail domains are essential determinants of chromatin fiber dynamics. However, from a structural biology perspective these domains are enigmas. This section describes the extensive involvement of the core histone tail domains in mediating chromatin fiber condensation and addresses key unanswered issues involving tail domain function in chromatin. Lysine or arginine residue account for approximately one third of each core histone N-terminal tail domain sequence (135, 150). The large concentration of positively charged residues ($\sim$100/nucleosome), together with the absence of observable tail domain secondary structure in NMR studies of free histones or isolated tail domain peptides (21, 22), suggests a simple functional model in which the tail domains mediate chromatin fiber dynamics by binding to DNA as unstructured coils and neutralizing negative charge (61, 64). Recent studies, however, have documented an unexpected degree of complexity of tail domain function during chromatin fiber condensation (46, 61, 64). It now appears that the tail domains mediate chromatin condensation through multiple molecular mechanisms, only one of which may involve simple DNA charge neutralization.

Much of the insight into the roles of the core histone tail domains in chromatin condensation has come from analysis of "tailless" nucleosomal arrays and chromatin fibers (25, 46, 52, 97, 132). Tailless arrays are assembled from core histone octamers that have had major portions of their tail domains selectively removed by trypsin. The sites of tail domain proteolysis have been well mapped and characterized for each core histone (20). Tailless nucleosomal arrays are unable to form the maximally folded conformation (132) or oligomerize (115), even in several hundred millimolar $MgCl_2$. However, at these high salt concentrations tailless arrays are able to form the moderately folded conformation (132). The inability of high levels of Mg^{2+} to substitute for the missing tail domains in the latter stages of chromatin condensation provided the first suggestion that the tails may function in part through nonelectrostatic mechanisms. Additional evidence for the complexity of tail domain involvement in chromatin fiber condensation came from studies of "hybrid" nucleosomal arrays lacking either their H3/H4 or H2A/H2B N-termini (97, 132). Neither of these two hybrid tailless arrays could form the maximally folded conformation in high $MgCl_2$ (132). In contrast, both of the hybrid nucleosomal arrays were able to oligomerize, albeit at higher $MgCl_2$, than were required for intact arrays (97, 132). To summarize, selective proteolysis studies have demonstrated that in the absence of the tail domains only the moderately folded conformation can be formed at high Mg^{2+} concentrations, that the H2A/H2B and H3/H4 N-tail domains are required to form the maximally folded conformation, and that only the H3/H4 or H2A/H2B tail domains are required for oligomerization.

These empirical observations establish that the core histone tail domains mediate each of the different steps in chromatin condensation (Figure 3) through distinct mechanisms (61, 64). Given that there are 10 tail domains per nucleosome, further studies will be required to elucidate the functions of the individual tails during chromatin condensation.

What molecular mechanisms are involved in tail domain–mediated fiber dynamics? The fact that high Mg^{2+} concentrations induce formation of moderately folded tailless chromatin fibers suggests a general electrostatic function for one or more of the tail domains in the initial folding transition. The H3 tail domains likely perform this function by binding linker DNA (82), and the H4 tails may be involved as well (97, 132). However, the inability of high divalent cation concentration to induce either maximal array folding or oligomerization in the absence of the tail domains strongly suggests that the tails modulate these transitions through mechanisms that are not entirely electrostatic (64, 132). This conclusion is supported by studies showing that neutralization of only ~10% of the total positive charges in the N-termini of each nucleosome by acetylation inhibited formation of the maximally folded nucleosomal array conformation to the same extent as complete removal of all the tail domains (133). Given the well-documented ability of the tail domains to specifically bind certain chromatin-associated proteins (42, 70, 95, 130), the most straightforward explanation for the nonelectrostatic component of tail domain function in chromatin fiber dynamics is that they act through protein-protein interactions, e.g., internucleosomal tail-tail interactions (61, 64) and/or binding of the tail domains to exposed protein domains on the surface of other nearby nucleosomes (91). One cannot completely rule out additional interactions with DNA, but they would have to involve salt-independent binding modes.

Do the tails possess secondary structure while mediating chromatin fiber dynamics, or do these domains function as random coils? As mentioned previously, short tail domain peptides are completely unstructured in solution (22). However, it is quite feasible that the tail domains of nucleosomal arrays and chromatin fibers adopt secondary structure as a consequence of macromolecular interactions (see 64). For example, although tail domain interaction with nucleosomal DNA is purely an in vitro phenomenon (see above), the H3 and H4 N-termini nevertheless are ~50% α-helical when bound to the nucleosomal DNA of nucleosome core particles (13). Furthermore, acetylation of lysine residues increases the α-helical content of the tail domains when bound to nucleosomal DNA in a nucleosome core particle (142). Circumstantial evidence in favor of structured tail domains includes predictions that each of the tail domains can form one or more stretches of secondary structure (64). Also, specific interactions of the tail domains with chromatin-associated proteins presumably involve structured tail domains. Importantly in this regard, amino acids 21–28 of the H3 tail N terminus are predicted to form an α-helix and are required for H3 tail domain–TUP1 interactions in vitro (70). Similarly, amino acids 1–20 of the H4 N terminus are predicted to have strong α-helical character and are required for Sir3p and Sir4p to bind the H4 N terminus in vitro (42). In summary, it is likely that the core histone N-termini contain α-helices and perhaps other structural motifs when functioning in their natural chromatin context (64). This idea dates back to the speculations of Mann & Grunstein (93) and was predicted by even the earliest secondary structure algorithms (135).

While the past several years have seen significant advances in the understanding of tail domain function in chromatin, many questions remain. For example, does each tail domain perform a single dedicated function during chromatin condensation, or is the same tail domain capable of performing different functions at each stage of the condensation process? What are the tail domain interaction partners during chromatin condensation? Are the tail domains structurally malleable in order to participate in multiple types of macromolecular interactions, and what are the strengths of these tail domain interactions? These questions must be answered in order to better understand the structure/function relationships of the unmodified core histone tail domains, as well as the effects of tail domain posttranslational modifications on these relationships.

Linker Histones and Fiber Stability

Linker histones (e.g., H1, H5) comprise a large family (135, 150) of chromatin-associated proteins that bind to nucleosomes and influence chromatin fiber dynamics (109, 145, 149, 154, 163). Linker histones are nonessential in lower organisms but essential in vertebrates (10, 54). For many years linker histones were considered to be necessary to induce folding of the chromatin fiber, although this is now known to be incorrect. Members of the canonical linker histone family possess a long, basic C terminus, a structured central globular domain, and a short N-terminal sequence (135, 150). Crystallographic studies of the chicken erythrocyte H5 globular domain (111) revealed a structure that is closely related to other winged helix DNA-binding proteins, including prokaryotic cAMP receptor protein and the eukaryotic transcription factor, HNF-3 (9, 14). However, linker histones have no structural homology to the core histone fold domains (9, 14). In retrospect, linker histones historically bear the name histones because they are present in ~1:1 stoichiometry with nucleosomes in bulk chromatin in vivo (135, 150). The linker histone globular domain can bind to several different sites on the nucleosome (34, 128, 129), although it is unclear whether only one or all of these sites are occupied in the nucleosomes of a chromatin fiber. Linker histones stabilize interaction of an additional 20 bp of DNA with the nucleosome periphery (118), which significantly reduces in vitro nucleosome sliding and mobility (102, 137, 139). The 165-bp particle containing two full turns of DNA and one bound linker histone per nucleosome often is referred to as a chromatosome (135, 150).

Linker histones stabilize the folded and oligomeric states of chromatin fibers in vitro. The stabilizing effect of linker histones was first documented by early EM studies, which showed that nucleosomal arrays in NaCl and MgCl$_2$ adopted a wide range of partially folded and extended structures (see above), while linker histone–containing nucleosomal arrays condensed into more uniform, maximally folded structures under the same conditions (125–127). More recently, sedimentation studies have shown that a heterogeneous population of partially folded 12-mer nucleosomal arrays in ~0.7 mM $MgCl_2$ can be converted into a homogeneous, maximally folded ~55S species upon binding 1 H5 per nucleosome (24). However, even these linker histone–containing chromatin fibers sedimented as a heterogeneous population of 40–55S species at lower salt (e.g., $\leq$0.5 mM $MgCl_2$ or $\leq$80 mM NaCl). Thus, sufficient salt concentrations are required to form a stable maximally folded conformation, even when linker histones are components of the chromatin fiber. In addition, 12-mer chromatin model systems containing less than 1 bound H5 per nucleosome also sedimented as a distribution of ~40–55S species, indicating that a continuous stretch of bound linker histones are required for maximum stabilization of folded chromatin fibers. Oligomerization also is stabilized by linker histones in the sense that less $MgCl_2$ is required to induce oligomerization of chromatin fibers than nucleosomal arrays (24). Similarly, linker histone–containing chromatin fibers, but not nucleosomal arrays, oligomerize in monovalent salts (24, 135, 150).

Studies of endogenous nucleosomal array preparations reassembled with selectively proteolyzed chicken erythrocyte H5 have shown that the H5 globular domain alone cannot stabilize chromatin folding when bound at physiological stoichiometries (2). In contrast, a fragment containing the H5 globular domain and C-terminal tail yielded identical results as intact H5 (2). This indicates that the highly basic linker histone C terminus is responsible for stabilization of folded chromatin fibers, presumably by binding to linker DNA (see below). To date, no specific function has been attributed to the linker histone N terminus. The globular domain most likely helps stabilize wrapping of peripheral nucleosomal DNA (135, 150), and because of its ability to self-associate (27, 92), it may mediate certain types of fiber-fiber interactions. It is commonly perceived that the globular domain also is responsible for directing the proper location of the linker histone C terminus in the chromatin fiber. However, given that the globular domain appears to occupy multiple sites on a nucleosome (34, 128, 129), together with the potentially energetically dominant effect of C-terminal domain-linker DNA interactions, it is possible that the C-terminal domain may actually influence the nucleosomal location of the globular domain in chromatin. There is some experimental evidence for this notion (2). Clearly, a systematic dissection of the functions of the individual linker histone domains using a combination of engineered mutants and reconstituted model systems will be needed to better understand linker histone domain function in chromatin fiber dynamics. Also, it is important to note that the results described in this section were obtained with the chicken erythrocyte linker histone variant H5, the homolog of mammalian $H1^\circ$ (135, 150). These linker histones may have specialized functions relating to chromatin fiber dynamics. Whether other linker histone variants have equivalent effects on chromatin fiber folding and oligomerization remains to be determined. Finally, there is considerable evidence indicating that at least some of the functions of linker histones in chromatin in vivo occur at the level of the nucleosome, rather than by influencing the stability of condensed chromatin fibers (35, 54, 146).

Condensation Mechanisms: The Electrostatic Conundrum

There is no question that DNA charge neutralization plays a major role in chromatin condensation. Folding and oligomerization occur only in the presence of inorganic or organic cations, even when linker histones are components of the chromatin fiber. Stabilization of the maximally folded chromatin conformation requires the $\sim$110–amino acid linker histone C-terminal tail, which contains $\sim$70% positively charged residues (135, 150). Theoretical analyses conclude that DNA charge neutralization by ionic and macromolecular factors can account for all the folding free energy necessary to form stable 30-nm fibers (32). Nevertheless, even under high Mg^{2+} conditions, tailless linker histone–containing chromatin fibers cannot condense (25). Given that many of the functions of the tail domains in chromatin do not appear to involve simple DNA charge neutralization (see above), how does one reconcile these seemingly disparate observations?

A great deal of partially contorted genomic DNA must occupy a small volume in any given region of an extensively folded chromatin fiber. This constitutes a severe energetic penalty that only can be overcome with the help of extensive DNA charge neutralization. Inorganic and organic (e.g., polyamines) cations neutralize DNA charge according to the tenets of polyelectrolyte theory (15, 32, 123). Monovalent cations are less effective than polyvalent cations because only the latter site bind to DNA. However, while salt is absolutely necessary for chromatin condensation, salt alone cannot induce chromatin condensation in the absence of the core histone tail domains. The simplest explanation for these results is that the core histone tail domains specify the concerted series of internucleosomal interactions required to form the moderately folded and maximally folded chromatin fiber conformations. These internucleosomal interactions collectively must be weak, given the conformational heterogeneity observed in the sedimentation and EM studies. Complete stabilization of maximally folded chromatin fibers thus requires additional macromolecular input in the form of linker histones. As a consequence of the interaction of their extremely basic C-terminal tail domain with linker DNA, linker histones provide the additional localized charge neutralization necessary to shift the equilibrium completely to the maximally folded state. Thus, for any given stretch of chromatin fiber, the extent of folding will be dependent on the local ionic environment, the functional status of the core histone tail domains, and the presence of linker histones. Interestingly, these same three determinants also mediate oligomerization, even though folding and oligomerization are not mechanistically coupled.

Recent single molecule studies also support a folding mechanism that is dependent on weak nucleosome-nucleosome interactions. In these experiments the force required to stretch a single chromatin fiber at different ionic strengths, and hence at different states of compaction, was measured directly by attaching laser "tweezers" to each end of the fiber and applying extension forces from 0–20 pN (36). The primary empirical observations from these studies were that a reversible decondensation transition occurred at an applied force of 5–6 pN, while at $\geq$20 pN the chromatin transitions were irreversible (most likely due to dissociation of histones from the DNA). Accompanying theoretical studies of the reversible de-condensation transition (75) yielded several extremely important results. Specifically, accurate modeling of stretching data obtained under salt conditions that induce chromatin fiber folding required the introduction of a parameter describing attractive interactions between closely spaced nucleosomes. Additionally, these internucleosomal interactions required only weak attractive forces. While tail domain–linker DNA interactions are often cited as the mechanistic basis for weak internucleosomal interactions, model studies have shown that interaction of the H4 tail domain peptide with DNA is quite strong in vitro, with an apparent K_d of $\sim 10^{-9}$ M in physiological salts (72). As outlined above, protein-protein interactions involving the tail domains currently are the best candidates for mediating weak nucleosome-nucleosome interactions. An interesting aspect of the fiber stretching studies is that at ~ 150 mM NaCl a linker histone–containing chromatin fiber in solution normally would be oligomerized (24, 141). Because folding and oligomerization are not coupled, the stretching experiments performed in 150 mM NaCl undoubtedly characterized chromatin fibers that were significantly more folded than those imaged at lower salt in microscopy studies. Unfortunately, however, it is not technically possible to use solution methods to determine precisely how folded the structures were in 150 mM NaCl and, in particular, whether the fibers were completely stabilized in the maximally folded state prior to stretching.

On the Structures of Condensed Chromatin Fibers in Solution

The pros and cons of the many different proposed models of 30-nm fiber structure have been recounted in detail elsewhere (135, 138, 145, 150, 156). The primary reason for the continued lack of progress in this area is that individual nucleosomes and linker DNA cannot be directly visualized in the maximally folded state. In recent years, results of ECM and atomic force microscopy (AFM) studies of linker histone–containing chromatin fibers have argued for a structure of the 30-nm fiber that consists of an irregular open helix with straight linker DNA segments (16, 17, 81, 83, 162). A similar structure is consistent with recent modeling studies (15, 75). Although the evidence for such structures is quite convincing, there has been no reference point in these studies for the overall extent of compaction of the structure being imaged, i.e., at the salt concentrations studied, is the fiber in a moderately or maximally folded conformation, or somewhere in between? To address this issue, sedimentation and ECM analyses of defined 12-mer chromatin model systems were performed under identical ionic conditions (17). The sedimentation studies indicated that the fibers had condensed only into the moderately folded state under the conditions of the ECM imaging studies. In retrospect, both the ECM and AFM results support a mechanism in which extended linker histone–containing chromatin fibers "flip" into an open irregular 30-nm-diameter helix with straight linker DNA segments at rather low NaCl concentrations (5–10 mM). This partially folded structure further compacts at higher salt due to close approach of adjacent nucleosomes, thereby forming the moderately folded conformation. Importantly, the microscopy studies have provided no evidence for the structure of the maximally folded 30-nm fiber because salt-induced fiber oligomerization occurs prior to formation of the maximally folded conformation in solution. In summary, virtually all ECM and AFM studies have characterized moderately folded structures at the relatively low salt concentrations studied. That the moderately folded conformation has a diameter of ∼30 nm is coincidental and has led to much confusion in the literature. To this day no studies have visualized the nucleosomes and linker DNA in the maximally folded 30-nm-diameter state. Nevertheless, whatever the actual structure of the maximally folded 30-nm conformation may be, there are strong indications that it is formed from an intermediate that has an irregular open-helical structure with straight elastic linker DNA segments.

Core Histone Posttranslational Modifications and Sequence Variants

Most core histone posttranslational modifications occur on specific residues in the various core histone tail domains (135, 150). These modifications include acetylation, phosphorylation, methylation, ubiquitination, ADP-ribosylation, and biotinylation (135, 150). Because of the extensive involvement of the core histone tail domains in chromatin fiber condensation, it seems likely that at least some core histone posttranslational modifications will have significant effects on chromatin fiber dynamics. Although the relationships between core histone posttranslational modifications and chromatin function presently are being studied intently (31, 112, 114, 153, 158), there is a relative paucity of data regarding posttranslational modification effects on chromatin fiber structural dynamics. The same is true for core histone sequence variants. To date, only the influence of acetylation has been characterized in detail. The effects of ubiquitination, and the essential sequence variant, H2A.Z, have been studied to a lesser extent.

Early studies of acetylated 12-mer nucleosomal arrays demonstrated that acetylation disrupted formation of the moderately folded state in 50–200 mM NaCl (53). A detailed examination of the Mg^{2+}-dependent condensation of differentially acetylated 12-mer nucleosomal arrays (133) yielded several key findings. In these studies, nucleosomal arrays were reconstituted from histone octamers containing a weight average of 2, 6, or 12 acetates per octamer, representing 8%, 23%, and 46% of the total possible acetylatable sites. For nucleosomal assays containing an average of two and six acetates per histone octamer, Mg^{2+}-dependent formation of the moderately and maximally folded conformations was indistinguishable. In distinct contrast, nucleosomal arrays containing an average of 12 acetates per histone octamer were unable to form the maximally folded conformation (133). Thus, essentially complete loss of tail domain function occurred under conditions where only 12 out of ∼100 total tail domain positive charges were neutralized by acetates, further suggesting that charge neutralization is not a primary mechanism through which the tail domains mediate higher-order folding (see above). Regardless of the mechanistic details, acetylation clearly is a potent regulator of nucleosomal array folding in vitro. Acetylation partially disrupts oligomerization of nucleosomal arrays (106, 133), as indicated by the requirement for increased amounts of $MgCl_2$ to induce 50% oligomerization as the acetylation content is increased. There is some in vivo evidence that acetylation may antagonize polyamine-induced chromatin condensation in yeast (133). As noted above, there is a large body of older data involving effects of acetylation on chromatin "solubility" that is directly relevant to oligomerization, including the observation that chromatin samples enriched in active genes have increased levels of acetylation and oligomerize at higher salt concentrations than bulk chromatin (113).

Acetylation appears to be less effective at causing unfolding of linker histone–containing chromatin fibers than nucleosomal arrays, as judged by several solution (94, 141) and EM (5) analyses. In addition, while acetylated chromatin fibers exhibit only a reduced ability to fold and oligomerize, tailless chromatin fibers can do neither. Thus, linker histones in some way prevent acetylation from effectively disrupting tail domain function during chromatin condensation. These results suggest that acetylation may be intended to regulate the structural dynamics and biological function of nucleosomal arrays more so than chromatin fibers, i.e., acetylation normally may function at some point after linker histone dissociation has occurred. In this regard, the P/CAF histone acetyltransferase exhibits a reduced ability to acetylate linker histone–containing chromatin fibers compared with nucleosomal arrays (71).

Although there is older evidence suggesting that many posttranslational modifications may influence chromatin fiber dynamics (135, 150), the only other modification that has been examined by in vitro model system studies is ubiquitination of the H2A C terminus (73). This study found that nucleosomal arrays containing two ubiquitin groups per nucleosome formed the moderately and maximally folded nucleosomal array conformations equally as well as unmodified arrays, suggesting that the H2A C-terminal tail domain has little role in chromatin fiber folding. However, like acetylation, ubiquitinated nucleosomal arrays required more salt to oligomerize (73). Because of the current intense interest in the biological functions of tail domain posttranslational modifications (31, 112, 114, 153, 158), it will be important in the future to characterize how each posttranslational modification, alone and together, influences the different steps in chromatin fiber condensation. Toward this end, it also will be important to determine whether the mechanistic basis of the proposed "histone code" (74, 122) is actually a structure-based code in which posttranslational modifications function by altering the protein chemistry of the tail domains (64, 142). It should be noted that a major barrier to understanding the mechanistic basis of posttranslational modifications is the present lack of knowledge of the actions of the unmodified tail domains.

The core histone sequence variant, H2A.Z, is an essential protein in several organisms (33, 44). The crystal structure of an H2A.Z-containing nucleosome core particle revealed little difference from the canonical nucleosome core particle structure (124). However, 12-mer nucleosomal arrays assembled with this variant showed an increased propensity to fold and a decreased ability to oligomerize relative to native nucleosomal arrays (45). While the functional significance of these findings remains to be established in vivo, they indicate that stretches of chromatin fibers enriched in H2A.Z exhibit completely unique in vitro condensation properties relative to any other type of chromatin fiber studied to date. As such, this variant (and perhaps certain posttranslational modifications as well) in principle will be able to globally "mark" chromosomal domains in vivo. A chromosome-wide function for H2A.Z has been suggested by molecular cytology studies, which show nonrandom but widespread distribution of this variant in *Drosophila* chromosomes (78). As with posttranslational modifications, detailed structural analyses of core histone variants on chromatin fiber dynamics undoubtedly will prove to be a fruitful area of future research.

Protein-Mediated Assembly of Higher-Order Structural States

To this point the discussion has centered on the intrinsic structural dynamics of nucleosomal arrays and how linker histones function to stabilize the intrinsic condensation pathway of the chromatin fiber. During the past several years, an entirely different area of chromatin fiber dynamics has emerged. Specifically, in vitro and in vivo studies have documented protein-mediated assembly of the canonical chromatin fiber into well-defined supramolecular structures. The proteins studied to date fall into two distinct classes, depending on whether they bind to the chromatin fiber through core histone tail domain interactions. Examples of the latter are the yeast-silencing proteins Sir3p and Tup1p, which interact with the H3 and H4 N-terminal tail domains (42, 70). Recently, Sir3p has been purified to near homogeneity and its binding to naked DNA and nucleosomal substrates characterized (55). At stoichiometries of approximately one Sir3p per nucleosome, large defined supramolecular structures comprised of many individual Sir3p proteins and nucleosomal arrays were formed. Assembly of these structures was dependent on Sir3p binding to both the core histone tail domains and DNA (55). Sir3p is known to self-associate (121) and may form multiple oligomeric species (e.g., dimers, tetramers) under the conditions studied in vitro (J. C. Hansen and C. A. Fox, unpublished data). A model depicting the proposed molecular basis for the in vitro results is shown in Figure 4A. The same type of protein-mediated fiber-fiber "bridging" or cross-linking has been proposed to explain the unusual chromatin domain mediated by Tup1p interactions with a yeast minichromosome in vivo (40). Of note, there appear to be two molecules of Tup1p per nucleosome in this chromatin domain, again suggesting a role for protein oligomerization. A different mechanism is used by the avian blood cell heterochromatin protein, MENT (57–59), which induces interfiber cross-linking by binding to linker DNA rather than the core histone tail domains (Figure 4B). While the specific biological actions of each of these proteins differ, all three appear to possess one or more chromatin fiber–binding domains and are capable of self-association. Proteins with such properties inevitably will possess the ability to bridge nucleosomes together over long distances, in the process creating higher-order domains that are likely

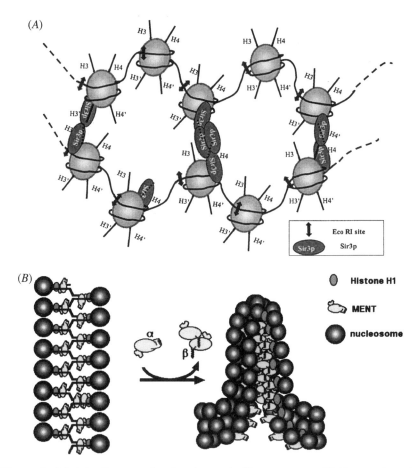

Figure 4   Models of supramolecular chromatin fiber structures. (*A*) Proposed mechanism for Sir3p-dependent cross-linking of nucleosomal arrays. Shown is only a small portion of the defined supramolecular nucleoprotein species formed upon mixing Sir3p and 12-mer nucleosomal arrays in vitro. Reproduced from reference (55) with permission. Copyright 2001 National Academy of Sciences, U.S.A. (*B*) MENT-dependent establishment of a supramolecular "fold-back" domain. MENT is a serpin-like protein that appears to bind to the linker DNA of linker histone–containing chromatin fibers. Subsequent self-association of MENT is proposed to cause to fiber-fiber bridging. Reproduced from reference (57) with permission.

to be functionally repressive. The degree of bridging will be dependent on the oligomeric state of the protein and on its concentration in the vicinity of the chromatin domain. Note that the specific structural and functional characteristics of such chromosomal domains will almost certainly be influenced by other proteins besides those responsible for bridging, e.g., certain silenced yeast domains contain not only Sir3p, but also Sir4p, Rap1p, and the Sir2p histone deacetylase (56, 121).

FUTURE PERSPECTIVES: TOWARD LINKING STRUCTURE AND FUNCTION

Characterization of the structural basis of chromatin fiber dynamics has proven to be a difficult task, befitting the enormous complexity of the chromatin fiber and its many components. Equally daunting have been the attempts to understand how functions such as transcription, replication, recombination, and repair occur in the context of chromatin rather than naked DNA. Perhaps not surprisingly, the tendency in the past has been to study structure and function separately. In the future, one of the greatest challenges will be deciphering how chromatin fiber dynamics influences, and is influenced by, nuclear functions. A comprehensive speculative discussion of chromatin structure/function relationships exceeds the scope of this review and has been discussed to varying degrees elsewhere (6, 47, 150). Consequently, I conclude by briefly highlighting several ways in which chromatin fiber dynamics may be biologically relevant, with the intent of illustrating general principles likely to be applicable to numerous specific functional processes.

Perhaps the most obvious question when considering functional ramifications of chromatin fiber dynamics is whether the solution behavior of chromatin fibers in vitro is relevant in vivo. Toward this end, short stretches of 10-nm and 30-nm chromatin fibers can exist in extensively coiled 100–200-nm-diameter chromonema chromosomal domains without causing widespread chromosomal fiber decondensation (18). This suggests that local chromatin fiber dynamics and long-range chromosomal domain structures are uncoupled in vivo, a conclusion that also is consistent with the physical uncoupling of folding and oligomerization of nucleosomal arrays and chromatin fibers in vitro (115). Thus, the mechanisms and determinants of chromatin fiber dynamics characterized in vitro should have direct relevance to those regions of the genome that are not otherwise assembled into some type of stable, higher-order supramolecular domain (see previous section). At any given chromosomal locus, the effects of chromatin fiber dynamics in principle can range from almost none to completely repressive depending on the configuration, extent of posttranslational modifications, and linker histone content in that region of the fiber. As discussed above, linker histone dissociation yields stretches of unstably folded nucleosomal arrays. In this regard, two extremely important papers measuring fluorescence recovery after photobleaching have documented rapid linker histone exchange in vivo (84, 96). Linker histone–green fluorescent protein constructs were expressed in cultured cells followed by photobleaching of selected regions of the nucleus. Linker histone fluorescence was recovered in several minutes, whereas no appreciable recovery of H2B fluorescence occurred during the same time period. The mechanism of exchange between different chromosomal regions appears to involve linker histone dissociation, followed by diffusion through the nucleus and chromatin rebinding (84). Consequently, in the kinetic period of H1 exchange, the regions of the genome transiently devoid of H1 adopt the structural properties of nucleosomal arrays. Nucleosomal arrays also can be generated in a more specific manner by directed mechanisms that cause linker histone dissociation, e.g., phosphorylation. Importantly, even a heterogeneous population of folded nucleosomal arrays can be repressive to a eukaryotic RNA polymerase in vitro, depending on whether the overall extent of compaction favors the maximally folded state (64, 67, 133). The in vitro transcriptional repression can be overcome by core histone acetylation (133), selective histone octamer depletion (66), and H2A/H2B dimer removal (67), each of which significantly reduces the extent of folding in vitro and is associated with transcriptional activation in vivo (150). Just as the site exposure mechanism allows kinetic access to nucleosomal DNA, rapid linker histone exchange in vivo guarantees that nuclear machinery will have kinetic access to nucleosomal arrays (152). Note that not all functions of folding need be repressive. SWI/SNF (77), the glucocorticoid receptor (99), and the transcription factor, HNF3 (K. Zaret, personal communication), each can bind to extensively condensed chromatin. This is significant because DNA sequences separated by up to ∼1200 bp are brought in close spatial proximity by one turn of the maximally folded conformation. Because the extent of chromatin fiber condensation itself can be regulated by many different functionally relevant parameters, chromatin fiber dynamics ultimately possesses the ability to function as a macromolecular rheostat that imparts fine control over processes that otherwise would either simply be on or off, e.g., factor-dependent transcription initiation from a given promoter.

Chromatin fiber dynamics also appears to regulate genome accessibility in conjunction with replication-coupled chromatin assembly (6, 47), albeit for a different specific purpose. In this case, the dispersive segregation of parental nucleosomes (which contain linker histones and other chromatin-associated proteins) onto nascent DNA will ensure that these regions of newly replicated chromatin will be extensively folded and the DNA largely inaccessible to other macromolecules. In contrast, the nascent DNA present between the regions of parental nucleosomes is complexed with H3/H4 tetramers (6). Arrays of H3/H4 tetramers are unfolded under physiological salt conditions (67, 131), and the DNA readily accessible to transcription factors in vitro (131). Thus, the unique configuration and composition of newly replicated chromatin appears to exploit chromatin fiber dynamics to help facilitate competition between nucleosome assembly and transcription factor binding at the time of DNA replication (150).

These brief scenarios represent the tip of the iceberg when considering all the possible functional effects of chromatin fiber dynamics. Although the specific details will vary on a case-by-case basis, the general structural principles outlined in this article should be generally applicable to regulation of numerous nuclear processes that occur in a chromatin environment. By combining continued investigations of the mechanisms and determinants of chromatin fiber dynamics in solution, with experiments specifically designed to investigate the structural status of the chromatin fiber during functional processes, in the future it will be possible to decipher the many likely linkages between chromatin fiber dynamics and modulation of specific nuclear functions.

ACKNOWLEDGMENTS

I am grateful to Drs. J. Hayes, C. Peterson, A. Wolffe, and P. Georgel for helpful discussions. Work in the author's laboratory is supported by NIH grant GM45916. This review is dedicated to the memory of Alan P. Wolffe (follow the Supplemental Material link on the Annual Reviews homepage at http://www.annualreviews.org/).

Visit the Annual Reviews home page at www.annualreviews.org

LITERATURE CITED

1. Aalfs JD, Kingston RE. 2000. What does "chromatin remodeling" mean? *Trends Biochem. Sci.* 25:548–55
2. Allan J, Mitchell T, Harborne N, Bohm L, Crane-Robinson C. 1986. Roles of H1 domains in determining higher order chromatin structure and H1 location. *J. Mol. Biol.* 187:591–601
3. Anderson JD, Widom J. 2000. Sequence and position-dependence of the equilibrium accessibility of nucleosomal DNA target sites. *J. Mol. Biol.* 296:979–87
4. Angelov D, Vitolo JM, Mutskov V, Dimitrov S, Hayes JJ. 2001. Preferential interaction of the core histone tail domains with linker DNA. *Proc. Natl. Acad. Sci. USA* 98:6599–604
5. Annunziato AT, Frado L-LY, Seale RL, Woodcock CLF. 1988. Treatment with sodium butyrate inhibits the complete condensation of interphase chromatin. *Chromosoma* 96:132–38
6. Annunziato TA, Hansen JC. 2000. Role of histone acetylation in the assembly, maintenance, and modulation of chromatin structures. *Gene Exp.* 9:37–61
7. Arents G, Burlingame RW, Wang BW, Love WE, Moudrianakis EN. 1991. The nucleosomal core histone octamer at 3.1 Å resolution: a tripartite protein assembly and a left-handed superhelix. *Proc. Natl. Acad. Sci. USA* 88:10148–52
8. Arents G, Moudrianakis EN. 1993. Topography of the histone octamer surface: repeating structural motifs utilized in the docking of nucleosomal DNA. *Proc. Natl. Acad. Sci. USA* 90:10489–93
9. Arents G, Moudrianakis EN. 1995. The histone fold: a ubiquitous architectural motif utilized in DNA compaction and protein dimerization. *Proc. Natl. Acad. Sci. USA* 92:11170–74
10. Ausio J. 2000. Are linker histones (histone H1) dispensable for survival? *Bioessays* 22:873–77
11. Ausio J, Dong F, van Holde KE. 1989. Use of selectively trypsinized nucleosome core particles to analyze the role of the histone "tails" in the stabilization of the nucleosome. *J. Mol. Biol.* 206:451–63
12. Ausio J, Seger D, Eisenberg H. 1984. Nucleosome core particle stability and conformational change. *J. Mol. Biol.* 176:77–104
13. Baneres JL, Martin A, Parello J. 1997. The N tails of histones H3 and H4 adopt a highly structured conformation in the nucleosome. *J. Mol. Biol.* 273:503–8
14. Baxevanis AD, Arents G, Moudrianakis EN, Landsman D. 1995. A variety of DNA-binding and multimeric proteins contain the histone fold motif. *Nucleic Acids Res.* 23:2685–91
15. Beard DA, Schlick T. 2001. Computational modeling predicts the structure and dynamics of chromatin fiber. *Structure* 9:105–14
16. Bednar J, Horowitz RA, Dubochet J, Woodcock CL. 1995. Chromatin conformation and salt-induced compaction: three-dimensional structural information

from cryoelectron microscopy. *J. Cell Biol.* 131:1365–76

17. Bednar J, Horowitz RA, Grigoryev SA, Carruthers LM, Hansen JC, et al. 1998. Nucleosomes, linker DNA, and linker histone form a unique structural motif that directs the higher-order folding and compaction of chromatin. *Proc. Natl. Acad. Sci. USA* 95:14173–78

18. Belmont AS, Bruce K. 1994. Visualization of G1 chromosomes: a folded, twisted, supercoiled chromonema model of interphase chromatid structure. *J. Cell Biol.* 127:287–302

19. Belmont AS, Dietzel S, Nye AC, Strukov YG, Tumbar T. 1999. Large-scale chromatin structure and function. *Curr. Opin. Cell Biol.* 11:307–11

20. Bohm L, Crane-Robinson C. 1984. Proteases as structural probes for chromatin: the domain structure of histones. *Biosci. Rep.* 4:365–86

21. Bradbury EM, Carpenter BG, Rattle HWE. 1973. Magnetic resonance studies of deoxyribonucleoprotein. *Nature* 247:257–61

22. Bradbury EM, Cary PD, Crane-Robinson C, Riches PL, Johns EW. 1972. Nuclear-magnetic resonance and optical-spectrosopic studies of conformation and interactions in the cleaved halves of histone F2B. *Eur. J. Biochem.* 26:482–89

23. Butler PJG, Thomas JO. 1980. Changes in chromatin folding in solution. *J. Mol. Biol.* 140:505–29

24. Carruthers LM, Bednar J, Woodcock CL, Hansen JC. 1998. Linker histones stabilize the intrinsic salt-dependent folding of nucleosomal arrays: mechanistic ramifications for higher-order chromatin folding. *Biochemistry* 37:14776–87

25. Carruthers LM, Hansen JC. 2000. The core histone N-termini and linker histones function independently during chromatin folding. *J. Biol. Chem.* 275:37285–90

26. Carruthers LM, Tse C, Walker K III, Hansen JC. 1999. Assembly of defined nucleosomal array and chromatin model systems from pure components. *Methods Enzymol.* 304:19–35

27. Carter GJ, van Holde K. 1998. Self-association of linker histone H5 and of its globular domain: evidence for specific self-contacts. *Biochemistry* 37:12477–88

28. Chafin DR, Vitolo JM, Henricksen LA, Bambara BA, Hayes JJ. 2000. Human DNA ligase I efficiently seals nicks in nucleosomes. *EMBO J.* 19:5492–501

29. Chaires JB, Dattagupta N, Crothers DM. 1983. Binding of daunomycin to calf thymus nucleosomes. *Biochemistry* 22:284–92

30. Chen TA, Sterner R, Cozzolino A, Allfrey VG. 1990. Reversible and irreversible changes in nucleosome structure along the c-fos and c-myc oncogenes following inhibition of transcription. *J. Mol. Biol.* 212:481–93

31. Cheung P, Allis CD, Sassone-Corsi P. 2000. Signaling to chromatin through histone modifications. *Cell* 103:263–67

32. Clark DJ, Kimura T. 1990. Electrostatic mechanism of chromatin folding. *J. Mol. Biol.* 211:883–96

33. Clarkson MJ, Wells JR, Gibson F, Saint R, Tremethick DJ. 1999. Regions of variant histone His2AvD required for *Drosophila* development. *Nature* 399:694–97

34. Crane-Robinson C. 1997. Where is the globular domain of linker histone located on the nucleosome? *Trends Biochem. Sci.* 22:75–77

35. Crane-Robinson C. 1999. How do linker histones mediate differential gene expression? *Bioessays* 21:367–71

36. Cui Y, Bustamante C. 2000. Pulling a single chromatin fiber reveals the forces that maintain its higher-order structure. *Proc. Natl. Acad. Sci. USA* 97:127–32

37. Czarnota GJ, Bazett-Jones DP, Mendez E, Allfrey VG, Ottensmeyer FP. 1997. High resolution microanalysis and three-dimensional nucleosome structure associated with transcribing chromatin. *Micron* 28:419–31

38. Czarnota GJ, Ottensmeyer FP. 1996.

Structural states of the nucleosome. *J. Biol. Chem.* 271:3677–83

39. Dong F, Nelson C, Ausio J. 1990. Analysis of the changes in the structure and hydration of the nucleosome core particle at moderate ionic strengths. *Biochemistry* 29:10710–16

40. Ducker CE, Simpson RT. 2000. The organized chromatin domain of the repressed yeast, a cell-specific gene STE6 contains two molecules of the corepressor Tup1p per nucleosome. *EMBO J.* 19:400–9

41. Ebralidse KK, Brachev SA, Mirzabekov AD. 1988. A highly basic histone H4 domain bound to the sharply bent region of nucleosomal DNA. *Nature* 331:365–67

42. Edmondson DG, Smith M, Roth SY. 1996. Repression domain of the yeast global repressor Tup1 interacts directly with histones H3 and H4. *Genes Dev.* 10:1247–59

43. Eisenberg H, Felsenfeld G. 1981. Hydrodynamic studies of the interaction between nucleosome core particles and core histones. *J. Mol. Biol.* 150:537–55

44. Faast R, Thonglairoam V, Schulz TC, Beall J, Wells JR, et al. 2001. Histone variant H2A.Z is required for early mammalian development. *Curr. Biol.* 11:1183–87

45. Fan JY, Gordon F, Luger K, Hansen JC, Tremethick DJ. 2002. The essential histone variant H2A.Z regulates the equilibrium between different chromatin conformational states. *Nat. Struct. Biol.* 9:172–76

46. Fletcher TM, Hansen JC. 1995. Core histone tail domains mediate oligonucleosome folding and nucleosomal DNA organization through distinct molecular mechanisms. *J. Biol. Chem.* 270:25359–62

47. Fletcher TM, Hansen JC. 1996. The nucleosomal array: structure/function relationships. *Crit. Rev. Eukaryot. Gene Exp.* 6:149–88

48. Fletcher TM, Ryu BW, Baumann CT, Warren BS, Fragoso G, et al. 2000. Structure and dynamic properties of a glucocorticoid receptor-induced chromatin transition. *Mol. Cell. Biol.* 20:6466–75

49. Fletcher TM, Serwer P, Hansen JC. 1994. Quantitative analysis of macromolecular conformational changes using agarose gel electrophoresis: application to chromatin folding. *Biochemistry* 33:10859–63

50. Fry CJ, Peterson CL. 2001. Chromatin remodeling enzymes: Who's on first? *Curr. Biol.* 11:R185–97

51. Gale JM, Smerdon MJ. 1988. Photofootprint of nucleosome core DNA in intact chromatin having different structural states. *J. Mol. Biol.* 204:949–58

52. Garcia-Ramirez M, Dong F, Ausio J. 1992. Role of the histone "tails" in the folding of oligonucleosomes depleted of histone H1. *J. Biol. Chem.* 267:19587–95

53. Garcia-Ramirez M, Rocchini C, Ausio J. 1995. Modulation of chromatin folding by histone acetylation. *J. Biol. Chem.* 270: 17923–28

54. Georgel PT, Hansen JC. 2001. Linker histone function in chromatin: dual mechanisms of action. *Biochem. Cell Biol.* 79: 313–16

55. Georgel PT, Palacios DeBeer MA, Pietz G, Fox CA, Hansen JC. 2001. Sir3-dependent assembly of supramolecular chromatin structures *in vitro*. *Proc. Natl. Acad. Sci. USA* 98:8584–89

56. Gottschling DE. 2000. Gene silencing: two faces of SIR2. *Curr. Biol.* 10:R708–11

57. Grigoryev SA. 2001. Higher-order folding of heterochromatin: protein bridges span the nucleosome arrays. *Biochem. Cell Biol.* 79:227–41

58. Grigoryev SA, Bednar J, Woodcock CL. 1999. MENT, a heterochromatin protein that mediates higher order chromatin folding, is a new serpin family member. *J. Biol. Chem.* 274:5626–36

59. Grigoryev SA, Woodcock CL. 1998. Chromatin structure in granulocytes. A link between tight compaction and accumulation of a heterochromatin-associated protein (MENT). *J. Biol. Chem.* 273: 3082–89

60. Guschin D, Chandler S, Wolffe AP. 1998.

Asymmetric linker histone association directs the asymmetric rearrangement of core histone interactions in a positioned nucleosome containing a thyroid hormone response element. *Biochemistry* 37:8629–36

61. Hansen JC. 1997. The core histone N-termini: combinatorial interaction domains that link chromatin structure with function. *Chemtracts Biochem. Mol. Biol.* 10:56–69

62. Hansen JC, Ausio J, Stanik VH, van Holde KE. 1989. Homogenous reconstituted oligonucleosomes, evidence for salt-dependent folding in the absence of histone H1. *Biochemistry* 28:9129–36

63. Hansen JC, Lohr D. 1993. Assembly and structural properties of subsaturated chromatin arrays. *J. Biol. Chem.* 268:5840–48

64. Hansen JC, Tse C, Wolffe AP. 1998. Structure and function of the core histone N-termini: more than meets the eye. *Biochemistry* 37:17637–41

65. Hansen JC, van Holde KE, Lohr D. 1991. The mechanism of nucleosome assembly onto oligomers of the sea urchin 5S DNA positioning sequence. *J. Biol. Chem.* 266:4276–82

66. Hansen JC, Wolffe AP. 1992. The influence of chromatin folding on transcription initiation and elongation by RNA polymerase III. *Biochemistry* 31:7977–88

67. Hansen JC, Wolffe AP. 1994. A role for histones H2A/H2B in chromatin folding and transcriptional repression. *Proc. Natl. Acad. Sci. USA* 91:2339–43

68. Hayes JJ, Bashkin J, Tullius TD, Wolffe AP. 1991. The histone core exerts a dominant constraint on the strucutre of DNA in a nucleosome. *Biochemistry* 30:8434–40

69. Hayes JJ, Hansen JC. 2001. Nucleosomes and the chromatin fiber. *Curr. Opin. Genet. Dev.* 11:124–29

70. Hecht A, Laroche T, Strahl-Bolsinger S, Gasser SM, Grunstein M. 1995. Histone H3 and H4 N-termini interact with SIR3 and SIR4 proteins: a molecular model for the formation of heterochromatin in yeast. *Cell* 80:583–92

71. Herrera JE, West KL, Schiltz RL, Nakatani Y, Bustin M. 2000. Histone H1 is a specific repressor of core histone acetylation in chromatin. *Mol. Cell. Biol.* 20:523–29

72. Hong L, Schroth GP, Matthews HR, Yau P, Bradbury EM. 1993. Studies of the DNA binding properties of histone H4 amino terminus. Thermal denaturation studies reveal that acetylation markedly reduces the binding constant of the H4 "tail" to DNA. *J. Biol. Chem.* 268:305–14

73. Jason LJ, Moore SC, Ausio J, Lindsey G. 2001. Magnesium-dependent association and folding of oligonucleosomes reconstituted with ubiquitinated H2A. *J. Biol. Chem.* 276:14597–601

74. Jenuwein T, Allis CD. 2001. Translating the histone code. *Science* 293:1074–80

75. Katritch V, Bustamante C, Olson WK. 2000. Pulling chromatin fibers: computer simulations of direct physical micromanipulations. *J. Mol. Biol.* 295:29–40

76. Kinyamu HK, Fryer CJ, Horwitz KB, Archer TK. 2000. The mouse mammary tumor virus promoter adopts distinct chromatin structures in human breast cancer cells with and without glucocorticoid receptor. *J. Biol. Chem.* 275:20061–68

77. Krebs JE, Fry CJ, Samuels ML, Peterson CL. 2000. Global role for chromatin remodeling enzymes in mitotic gene expression. *Cell* 102:587–98

78. Leach TJ, Mazzeo M, Chotkowski HL, Madigan JP, Wotring MG, Glaser RL. 2000. Histone H2A.Z is widely but nonrandomly distributed in chromosomes of *Drosophila melanogaster. J. Biol. Chem.* 275:23267–72

79. Lee KM, Hayes JJ. 1997. The N-terminal tail of histone H2A binds to two distinct sites within the nucleosome core. *Proc. Natl. Acad. Sci. USA* 94:8959–64

80. Lee KM, Hayes JJ. 1998. Linker DNA and

H1-dependent reorganization of histone-DNA interactions within the nucleosome. *Biochemistry* 37:8622–28

81. Leuba SH, Bustamante C. 1999. Analysis of chromatin by scanning force microscopy. *Methods Mol. Biol.* 119:143–60

82. Leuba SH, Bustamante C, van Holde K, Zlatanova J. 1998. Linker histone tails and N-tails of histone H3 are redundant: scanning force microscopy studies of reconstituted fibers. *Biophys. J.* 74:2830–39

83. Leuba SH, Yang G, Robert C, Samori B, van Holde K, et al. 1994. Three-dimensional structure of extended chromatin fibers as revealed by tapping-mode scanning force microscopy. *Proc. Natl. Acad. Sci. USA* 91:11621–25

84. Lever MA, Th'ng JP, Sun X, Hendzel MJ. 2000. Rapid exchange of histone H1.1 on chromatin in living human cells. *Nature* 408:873–76

85. Lilley DM, Tatchell K. 1977. Chromatin core particle unfolding induced by tryptic cleavage of histones. *Nucleic Acids Res.* 4:2039–55

86. Logie C, Peterson CL. 1997. Catalytic activity of the yeast SWI/SNF complex on reconstituted nucleosome arrays. *EMBO J.* 16:6772–82

87. Logie C, Tse C, Hansen JC, Peterson CL. 1999. The core histone N-terminal domains are required for multiple rounds of catalytic remodeling by the SWI/SNF and RSC complexes. *Biochemistry* 38:2514–22

88. Luger K, Mader AW, Richmond RK, Sargent D, Richmond TJ. 1997. Crystal structure of the nucleosome core particle at 2.8 angstrom resolution. *Nature* 389:251–60

89. Luger K, Rechsteiner TJ, Richmond TJ. 1999. Preparation of nucleosome core particles from recombinant histones. *Methods Enzymol.* 304:3–19

90. Luger K, Richmond TJ. 1998. DNA binding within the nucleosome core. *Curr. Opin. Struct. Biol.* 8:33–40

91. Luger K, Richmond TJ. 1998. The his-tone tails of the nucleosome. *Curr. Opin. Genet. Dev.* 8:140–46

92. Maman JD, Yager TD, Allan J. 1994. Self-association of the globular domain of histone H5. *Biochemistry* 33:1300–10

93. Mann RK, Grunstein M. 1992. Histone H3 N-terminal mutations allow hyperactivation of the yeast GAL1 gene in vivo. *EMBO J.* 11:3297–306

94. McGhee JD, Nickol JM, Felsenfeld G, Rau DC. 1983. Histone acetylation has little effect on the higher order following of chromatin. *Nucleic Acids Res.* 11:4065–75

95. McQuibban GA, Commisso-Cappelli CN, Lewis PN. 1998. Assembly, remodeling, and histone binding capabilities of yeast nucleosome assembly protein 1. *J. Biol. Chem.* 273:6582–90

96. Misteli T, Gunjan A, Hock R, Bustin M, Brown DT. 2000. Dynamic binding of histone H1 to chromatin in living cells. *Nature* 408:877–81

97. Moore SC, Ausio J. 1997. Major role of the histones H3-H4 in the folding of the chromatin fiber. *Biochem. Biophys. Res. Commun.* 230:136–39

98. Moudrianakis EN, Arents G. 1993. Structure of the histone octamer core of the nucleosome and its potential interactions with DNA. *Cold Spring Harbor Symp. Quant. Biol.* 58:273–79

99. Muller WG, Walker D, Hager GL, McNally JG. 2001. Large-scale chromatin decondensation and recondensation regulated by transcription from a natural promoter. *J. Cell Biol.* 154:33–48

100. Mutskov V, Gerber D, Angelov D, Ausio J, Workman J, Dimitrov S. 1998. Persistent interactions of core histone tails with nucleosomal DNA following acetylation and transcription factor binding. *Mol. Cell. Biol.* 18:6293–304

101. Nacheeva GA, Guschin DY, Preobrazhenskaya OV, Karpov VL, Elbradise KK, Mirzabekov AD. 1989. Change in the pattern of histone binding to DNA upon transcriptional activation. *Cell* 58:27–36

102. Pennings S, Meeserman G, Bradbury EM. 1994. Linker histones H1 and H5 prevent the mobility of positioned nucleosomes. *Proc. Natl. Acad. Sci. USA* 91:10275–79

103. Polach KJ, Lowary PT, Widom J. 2000. Effects of core histone tail domains on the equilibrium constants for dynamic DNA site accessibility in nucleosomes. *J. Mol. Biol.* 298:211–23

104. Polach KJ, Widom J. 1995. Mechanism of protein access to specific DNA sequences in chromatin: a dynamic equilibrium model for gene regulation. *J. Mol. Biol.* 254:130–49

105. Polach KJ, Widom J. 1996. A model for the cooperative binding of eukaryotic regulatory proteins to nucleosomal target sites. *J. Mol. Biol.* 258:800–12

106. Pollard K, Samuels ML, Crowley KA, Hansen JC, Peterson CP. 1999. Functional interaction between GCN5 and polyamines: a new role for core histone acetylation. *EMBO J.* 18:5622–33

107. Postnikov Y, Shick V, Belyavsky A, Khrapko KR, Brodolin KL, et al. 1991. Distribution of high mobility group proteins 1/2, E and 14/17 and linker histones H1 and H5 on transcribed and nontranscribed regions of chicken erythrocyte chromatin. *Nucleic Acids Res.* 19:717–25

108. Pruss D, Wolffe AP. 1993. Histone-DNA contacts in a nucleosome core containing a *Xenopus* 5S rRNA gene. *Biochemistry* 32:6810–14

109. Ramakrishnan V. 1997. Histone H1 and chromatin higher-order structure. *Crit. Rev. Eukaryot. Gene Exp.* 7:215–30

110. Ramakrishnan V. 1997. Histone structure and the organization of the nucleosome. *Annu. Rev. Biophys. Biomol. Struct.* 26:83–112

111. Ramakrishnan V, Finch JT, Graziano V, Lee PL, Sweet RM. 1993. Crystal structure of globular domain of histone H5 and its implications for nucleosome binding. *Nature* 362:219–23

112. Rice JC, Allis CD. 2001. Histone methylation versus histone acetylation: new insights into epigenetic regulation. *Curr. Opin. Cell Biol.* 13:263–73

113. Ridsdale JA, Henzdel MF, Decluve GP, Davie JR. 1990. Histone acetylation alters the capacity of the H1 histones to condense transcriptionally active/competent chromatin. *J. Biol. Chem.* 265:5150–56

114. Roth SY, Denu JM, Allis CD. 2001. Histone acetyltransferases. *Annu. Rev. Biochem.* 70:81–120

115. Schwarz PM, Felthauser A, Fletcher TM, Hansen JC. 1996. Reversible oligonucleosome self association: dependence on divalent cations and core histone tail domains. *Biochemistry* 35:4009–15

116. Schwarz PM, Hansen JC. 1994. Formation and stability of higher order chromatin structures. Contributions of the histone octamer. *J. Biol. Chem.* 269:16284–88

117. Sen D, Crothers DM. 1986. Condensation of chromatin: role of multivalent cations. *Biochemistry* 25:1495–503

118. Simpson RT. 1978. Structure of the chromatosome, a chromatin core particle containing 160 base pairs of DNA and all the histones. *Biochemistry* 17:5524–31

119. Simpson RT, Thoma F, Brubaker JM. 1985. Chromatin reconstituted from tandemly repeated cloned DNA fragments and core histones: a model system for study of higher order structure. *Cell* 42:799–808

120. Stein A. 1979. DNA folding by histones: the kinetics of chromatin core particle reassembly and the interaction of nucleosomes with histones. *J. Mol. Biol.* 130:103–34

121. Stone EM, Pillus L. 1998. Silent chromatin in yeast: an orchestrated medley featuring Sir3p. *Bioessays* 20:30–40

122. Strahl BD, Allis CD. 2000. The language of covalent histone modifications. *Nature* 403:41–45

123. Subirana JA. 1992. Order and disorder in 30 nm chromatin fibers. *FEBS Lett.* 302:105–7

124. Suto RK, Clarkson MJ, Tremethick DJ,

Luger K. 2000. Crystal structure of a nucleosome core particle containing the variant histone H2A.Z. *Nat. Struct. Biol.* 7:1121 24

125. Thoma F, Koller T. 1977. Influence of histone H1 on chromatin structure. *Cell* 12: 101–7

126. Thoma F, Koller T, Klug A. 1979. Involvement of histone H1 in the organization of the nucleosome and the salt-dependent superstructures of chromatin. *J. Cell Biol.* 83:402–27

127. Thoma F, Losa R, Koller T. 1983. Involvement of domains of histones H1 and H5 in the structural organization of the soluble chromatin fiber. *J. Mol. Biol.* 167:619–40

128. Thomas JO. 1999. Histone H1: location and role. *Curr. Opin. Cell Biol.* 11:312–17

129. Travers A. 1999. The location of the linker histone on the nucleosome. *Trends Biochem. Sci.* 24:4–7

130. Treischmann L, Martin B, Bustin M. 1998. The chromatin unfolding domain of chromosomal protein HMG-14 targets the N-terminal tail of histone H3 in nucleosomes. *Proc. Natl. Acad. Sci. USA* 95: 5468–73

131. Tse C, Fletcher TM, Hansen JC. 1998. Enhanced transcription factor access to arrays of H3/H4 tetramer-DNA complexes: implications for replication and transcription. *Proc. Natl. Acad. Sci. USA* 95:12169–73

132. Tse C, Hansen JC. 1997. Hybrid trypsinized nucleosomal arrays: identification of multiple functional roles of the H2A/H2B and H3/H4 N-termini in chromatin fiber compaction. *Biochemistry* 36:11381–88

133. Tse C, Sera T, Wolffe AP, Hansen JC. 1998. Disruption of higher-order folding by core histone acetylation dramatically enhances transcription of nucleosomal arrays by RNA polymerase III. *Mol. Cell. Biol.* 18:4629–38

134. Usachenko SI, Bavykin SG, Gavin IM, Bradbury EM. 1994. Rearrangement of

the histone H2A C-terminal domain in the nucleosome. *Proc. Natl. Acad. Sci. USA* 91:6845–49

135. van Holde KE. 1988. *Chromatin.* New York: Springer-Verlag

136. van Holde KE, Weischet WO. 1978. Boundary analysis of sedimentation-velocity experiments with monodisperse and paucidisperse solutes. *Biopolymers* 17:1387–403

137. van Holde KE, Yager TD. 1985. Nucleosome motion: evidence and models. In *Structure and Function of the Genetic Apparatus*, ed. C Niccolini, POP Ts'o, pp. 35–53. New York: Plenum

138. van Holde KE, Zlatanova J. 1995. Chromatin higher order structure: chasing a mirage? *J. Biol. Chem.* 270:8373–76

139. Varga-Weisz PD, Blanks TA, Becker PB. 1995. Energy-dependent chromatin accessibility and nucleosome mobility in a cell-free system. *EMBO J.* 14:2209–16

140. Walker IO. 1984. Differential dissociation of histone tails from core chromatin. *Biochemistry* 23:5622–28

141. Wang X, He C, Moore SC, Ausio J. 2001. Effects of histone acetylation on the solubility and folding of the chromatin fiber. *J. Biol. Chem.* 276:12764–68

142. Wang X, Moore SC, Laszckzak M, Ausio J. 2000. Acetylation increases the alpha-helical content of the histone tails of the nucleosome. *J. Biol. Chem.* 275:35013–20

143. Whitlock JP, Simpson RT. 1977. Histone-DNA interations in chromatin core particles. *J. Biol. Chem.* 252:6516–20

144. Widom J. 1986. Physicochemical studies of the folding of the 100 Å nucleosome filament into the 300 Å filament. *J. Mol. Biol.* 190:411–24

145. Widom J. 1989. Toward a unified model of chromatin folding. *Annu. Rev. Biophys. Biophys. Chem.* 18:365–95

146. Widom J. 1998. Chromatin structure: linking structure to function with histone H1. *Curr. Biol.* 8:R788–91

147. Widom J. 1998. Structure, dynamics, and

function of chromatin in vitro. *Annu. Rev. Biophys. Biomol. Struct.* 27:285–327

148. Widom J. 1999. Equilibrium and dynamic nucleosome stability. *Methods Mol. Biol.* 119:61–77

149. Wolffe AP. 1997. Histone H1. *Int. J. Biochem. Cell Biol.* 29:1463–66

150. Wolffe AP. 1998. *Chromatin: Structure and Function.* New York: Academic. 3rd ed.

151. Wolffe AP, Guschin D. 2000. Chromatin structural features and targets that regulate transcription. *J. Struct. Biol.* 129:102–22

152. Wolffe AP, Hansen JC. 2001. Nuclear visions: functional versatility from structural instability. *Cell* 104:631–34

153. Wolffe AP, Hayes JJ. 1999. Chromatin disruption and modification. *Nucleic Acids. Res.* 27:711–20

154. Wolffe AP, Khochbin S, Dimitrov S. 1997. What do linker histones do in chromatin? *Bioessays* 19:249–55

155. Woodcock CL, Dimitrov S. 2001. Higher-order structure of chromatin and chromosomes. *Curr. Opin. Genet. Dev.* 11:130–35

156. Woodcock CL, Horowitz RA. 1995. Chromatin organization reviewed. *Trends Cell Biol.* 5:272–77

157. Workman JL, Kingston RE. 1998. Alteration of nucleosome structure as a mechanism of transcriptional regulation. *Annu. Rev. Biochem.* 67:545–79

158. Wu J, Grunstein M. 2000. 25 years after the nucleosome model: chromatin modifications. *Trends Biochem. Sci.* 25:619–23

159. Yager TD, McMurray CT, van Holde KE. 1989. Salt-induced release of DNA from nucleosome core particles. *Biochemistry* 28:2271–81

160. Yager TD, van Holde KE. 1984. Dynamics and equilibrium of nucleosomes at elevated ionic strength. *J. Biol. Chem.* 259: 4212–22

161. Yodh JG, Lyubchenko YL, Shlyakhtenko LS, Woodbury N, Lohr D. 1999. Evidence for nonrandom behavior in 208-12 subsaturated nucleosomal array populations analyzed by AFM. *Biochemistry* 38:15756–63

162. Zlatanova J, Leuba SH, van Holde K. 1998. Chromatin fiber structure: morphology, molecular determinants, structural transitions. *Biophys. J.* 74:2554–66

163. Zlatanova J, Leuba SH, van Holde K. 1999. Chromatin structure revisited. *Crit. Rev. Eukaryot. Gene Exp.* 9:245–55

Annu. Rev. Biophys. Biomol. Struct. 2002. 31:393–422
DOI: 10.1146/annurev.biophys.31.091701.171000

PARAMAGNETIC RESONANCE OF BIOLOGICAL METAL CENTERS

M. Ubbink,[1] J. A. R. Worrall,[1] G. W. Canters,[1] E. J. J. Groenen,[2] and M. Huber[2]

[1]Leiden Institute of Chemistry, Leiden University, P.O. Box 9502, 2300 RA Leiden, The Netherlands, e-mail: canters@chem.leidenuniv.nl
[2]Department of Molecular Physics, Huygens Laboratory, Leiden University, P.O. Box 9504, 2300 RA Leiden, The Netherlands; e-mail: mat@molphys.leidenuniv.nl

Key Words hf EPR, NMR, proteins, relaxation, g-tensor

■ **Abstract** The review deals with recent advances in magnetic resonance spectroscopy (hf EPR and NMR) of paramagnetic metal centers in biological macromolecules. In the first half of our chapter, we present an overview of recent technical developments in the NMR of paramagnetic bio-macromolecules. These are illustrated by a variety of examples deriving mainly from the spectroscopy of metalloproteins and their complexes. The second half focuses on recent developments in high-frequency EPR spectroscopy and the application of the technique to copper, iron, and manganese proteins. Special attention is given to the work on single crystals of copper proteins.

CONTENTS

INTRODUCTION

For the study of the magnetic properties of paramagnetic proteins, EPR seems to be the method of choice. Recent instrumental and methodological developments have significantly enlarged the scope of the technique. High-field/high-frequency spectrometers have become available, as have pulsed methods, which are based on electron-spin-echo (ESE) detection. The pulsed excitation enables the manipulation of the spin system, thereby considerably increasing spectral resolution, and allows more-dimensional spectroscopy, in analogy to modern nuclear magnetic resonance (NMR) methodology. The use of higher microwave frequencies and higher magnetic fields implies an enhanced spectral resolution, an improved sensitivity for small samples, and the possibility to study paramagnetic centers with a large zero-field splitting. In particular, protein crystals of submillimeter size may be investigated, which opens up the possibility to unravel the magnetic anisotropies in great detail.

On the other hand, for a long time the application of NMR techniques to the study of paramagnetic proteins was considered somewhat of an oddity because the presence of paramagnetic centers or impurities in an NMR sample destroys the resolution of the spectrum. This loss of resolution, however, is less severe when the paramagnetic center exhibits fast electronic relaxation, and by the application of advanced pulse techniques and data handling methods it has become possible to overcome the limitations that the paramagnetism previously posed. The presence of paramagnetism in a protein now offers opportunities for obtaining structural and mechanistic information by means of NMR that have no counterpart in the NMR study of diamagnetic proteins. Paramagnetic probes such as spin labels or lanthanide ions are deliberately introduced to provide structural and mechanistic information not obtainable otherwise. The observed shifts and line broadenings can be important sources of information regarding spin density distribution in the active center as well as the dynamic behavior of the site. A paramagnetic probe may provide unique information about the structure of protein/protein encounter complexes. The anisotropic part of the electronic paramagnetism can be used to partially align the protein molecules with respect to the external magnetic field. The resulting spectral effects in the NMR spectrum may give additional clues as to the three-dimensional structure of the protein. As both techniques in principle can address the same set of problems, it seemed worthwhile to see how far they have developed and whether they are covering common ground.

The first half of this chapter reviews high-frequency NMR of paramagnetic proteins, presenting an overview of the possibilities and limitations of the technique at its present state of development. The various points are illustrated with examples from the recent literature. The second half deals with high-frequency EPR of proteins. The high-frequency instrumental developments are reviewed in the first section while the next section focuses on individual examples of proteins that have been studied in some depth by high-frequency EPR. Both halves close with a brief outlook for the near future.

BACKGROUND

The Paramagnetic Shift

A paramagnetic center affects the magnetic properties of surrounding nuclei in both a time-dependent and time-averaged manner. Time-dependent fluctuations of the magnetic field resulting from the unpaired electron at the metal center provide relaxation mechanisms that give rise to shorter T_1 (longitudinal) and T_2 (transverse) relaxation times and, in the case of T_2, line broadening. The time-averaged magnetic field severely affects the resonance frequencies of nuclei close to the paramagnetic center, which leads to many signals being shifted outside the classical diamagnetic window.

In the NMR spectrum of a paramagnetic protein, the total observed chemical shift is described by

$$\delta_{obs} = \delta_{dm} + \delta_{pm}, \tag{1}$$

where δ_{obs}, δ_{dm}, and δ_{pm} are the observed, diamagnetic, and paramagnetic shifts. The paramagnetic shift is caused by the hyperfine interaction of the unpaired electron(s) with the nucleus. The hyperfine interaction comprises two contributions. The Fermi contact term (A_{iso}), which is isotropic, results from spin density in the s-orbitals of the nucleus. It is caused by delocalization of spin density from the metal orbitals onto the (ligand) orbitals (25, 82). The shift due to the Fermi contact term, δ_{Fc}, is given by (81)

$$\delta_{Fc}^{j} = \frac{A_{iso}^{j}/h}{3\beta\gamma_j/2\pi} \left(\frac{\chi_{xx}}{g_{xx}} + \frac{\chi_{yy}}{g_{yy}} + \frac{\chi_{zz}}{g_{zz}} \right), \tag{2}$$

where χ_{ii} and g_{ii} ($ii = xx, yy, zz$) are the principal components of the paramagnetic susceptibility tensor χ and the g-tensor; β is the Bohr magneton; γ_j is the gyromagnetic ratio of the nucleus j; and A_{iso}^{j} measures the Fermi contact interaction between the nucleus j and the unpaired electron spin.

The second contribution to the hyperfine interaction is the dipolar part, which can cause an additional paramagnetic shift at the nucleus. This shift has an isotropic component, which causes the pseudocontact shift δ_{ps} in liquid solution NMR if the magnetic susceptibility tensor χ of the paramagnetic center (metal ion) is anisotropic or if the metal ion has a spin $S > {}^1\!/_2$ and possesses a significant zero-field splitting. The shift influences the chemical shifts of both ligated and nonligated nuclei, and it can be calculated using dipolar formulae. Applying the metal-centered dipole approximation, the relationship between δ_{ps} and the χ tensor for $S = {}^1\!/_2$ systems is given by

$$\delta_{ps}^{j} = \frac{1}{12\pi N} \left[\Delta\chi_{ax}(3\cos^2\theta - 1)R^{-3} + 1.5\Delta\chi_{rh}(\sin^2\theta\cos2\phi)R^{-3} \right]$$

$$\Delta\chi_{ax} = \chi_{zz} - 0.5(\chi_{xx} + \chi_{yy}) \quad \text{and} \quad \Delta\chi_{rh} = \chi_{xx} - \chi_{yy}, \tag{3}$$

where N is Avogadro's number; $\Delta\chi_{ax}$ and $\Delta\chi_{rh}$ are the axial and rhombic magnetic susceptibilities; and R, θ, and ϕ are the spherical polar coordinates of the nucleus j relative to the principal axes of the χ tensor.

The Fermi contact and dipolar terms vary in their relative and absolute contributions to the paramagnetic shift of protons on the periphery of the active-site ligands. The contributions from both terms depend on the spin state and magnetic anisotropy of the metal ion at the active site. By obtaining the temperature dependence of the hyperfine signals over a wide temperature range, the sign, the slope, and the sign of the intercept of the resultant Curie plots unequivocally identify a Curie-, hypo-Curie-, hyper-Curie-, and non-Curie-type temperature dependence of the respective signals (12, 72). For Curie behavior, the straight line intercepts $(T^{-1} = 0)$ at the corresponding diamagnetic position. Moreover, Curie-type plots show whether unusual magnetic behavior, such as nonzero intercepts, for the system is being observed owing to excited-state contributions to the dipolar term and curvature due to hindered rotation of substituent groups or zero-field splitting contributions to the dipolar shift (84).

Relation of NMR and EPR Approaches

EPR is complementary to NMR, as the same interactions are measured in both cases, in NMR from the point of view of the nucleus and in EPR from the point of view of the electronic spin(s). Due to their different historical developments, the two techniques are described within different theoretical frameworks, which has led to differences in nomenclature. We outline briefly the connection between the terms relevant in the present context.

The hyperfine interaction tensor, A, can be measured directly by EPR, electron-spin echo envelope modulation (ESEEM), or electron-nuclear double resonance (ENDOR) techniques, as described below. With respect to the equations given above, it has to be kept in mind that EPR measures the magnetic effect of the nucleus on the electron spin, whereas NMR measures the opposite. In NMR, large hyperfine couplings are difficult to measure because they cause large line broadenings. In EPR, the resolution for small hyperfine interactions is limited, therefore hyperfine couplings of nuclei close to the metal center are observed.

For structure determination in NMR, the χ-tensor is used, which is related to the g-tensor. The g-tensor is one of the main observables of the EPR experiment, and both the magnitude of the anisotropy and the directions of the principal axes can be obtained (see below). If the electronic ground state of the paramagnetic center is energetically far below the excited states, the magnetic anisotropy tensor can be obtained from the g-tensor

$$\chi_{ii} = \frac{N\beta^2 S(S+1)}{3kT} g_{ii}^2. \tag{4}$$

For Cu^{2+}, this equation should be valid. For other metal systems, this condition is not necessarily fulfilled, and in such cases the correlation between the g-tensor and the χ-tensor needs to include the excited states of the paramagnetic centers. The difference in measurement temperature (EPR at temperatures below 10 K, NMR at ambient temperature) needs to be taken into account and may make it difficult to correlate EPR and NMR results.

Relaxation in Paramagnetic NMR

Both the Fermi contact and dipolar coupling contribute to the relaxation of the nuclear spin (32, 110, 111). For nuclei with large gyromagnetic ratios, such as protons, large-molecular-weight metalloproteins, and metal ions with high S values (i.e., a large number of unpaired electrons), a third relaxation mechanism is significant. This type of relaxation, called Curie relaxation, is a consequence of the interaction between nuclear spin and the time-averaged (static) electron magnetic moment (67, 127). As the magnitude of the induced magnetic moment is proportional to the external magnetic field, this contribution is field dependent. It is only relevant for T_2 relaxation and thus leads to line broadening.

A mathematical description of relaxation mechanisms is not given here and the reader is referred to a number of excellent texts on this subject (7, 11, 26). However, in brief, for paramagnetic systems, the contact relaxation rate is proportional to $A_{iso,j}^2$, and the dipolar and Curie relaxation to first approximation can be considered isotropic and to fall off with R^6 (metal nucleus distance). For each relaxation mechanism the time dependence of the electron-nucleus interaction at the nucleus is characterized by a correlation time. Apart from possible chemical exchange, this correlation time is influenced by the electronic relaxation time, τ_s (for contact and dipolar relaxation), and the molecular tumbling time, τ_r (for dipolar and Curie relaxation). For dipolar relaxation, either τ_s or τ_r can dominate depending on the size of τ_s, which may vary over several orders of magnitude for different metals, spin states, and ligations.

PARAMAGNETIC NMR

Spin Density Distribution in and Around Paramagnetic Active Sites

Paramagnetic NMR of redox proteins is a powerful technique to gain knowledge of the electronic structure of the active site and thus give an insight into possible mechanisms of electron transfer. The intrinsic information contained in the hyperfine shifted signals and relaxation data has proven crucial for a detailed understanding of the electronic structure not easily obtained by other spectroscopic techniques.

To obtain information regarding the electronic structure of the metalloprotein in question first requires a sufficient number of specific assignments around the active (metal) site. Over the past fifteen years significant progress has been achieved in appropriately designed NMR experiments to combat the rapid relaxation of active-site residues due to the presence of the unpaired electron(s). Techniques such as saturation transfer (78), 1D/2D nuclear Overhauser enhancement (NOE) measurements, and T_1 relaxation measurements (57, 95, 112, 113) have allowed in many cases complete proton resonance assignments of active-site residues in low-spin ferric peroxidases and globins (38, 57, 83, 107), iron-sulfur proteins (28), and metal-substituted blue-copper proteins (96, 97, 105). These methods have been further extended to tackle strongly paramagnetic environments such as in *Rhodobacter capsulatus* cytochrome *c'* (11, 117), high-spin ferric heme proteins such as peroxidases and globins (6, 34, 50), *Clostridium pasteurianum* rubredoxins (28, 131), and also for blue-copper proteins with Cu(II) as the paramagnetic center (19, 21).

An example of the use of paramagnetic NMR in context of the above has been reported for the type-3 binuclear copper protein tyrosinase (36). In the oxidized [Cu(II)-Cu(II)] form, the ground state is diamagnetic due to an antiferromagnetic coupling between the spins on the two copper centers. From Figure 1, however, the downfield part of the NMR spectrum (15–55 ppm) exhibits a number of paramagnetically shifted signals that are observed due to the presence of a paramagnetic (S = 1) excited triplet state, accessible at room temperature. By using a combination of T_1 relaxation data, D_2O exchange, 1D NOE experiments, and Curie temperature dependence of the paramagnetic signals, information regarding the active-site structure has been obtained.

Once the assignments for proton resonances in the paramagnetic and diamagnetic reference state of the metalloprotein in question are known, the pseudocontact shift can be extracted for nuclei of noncoordinated residues by subtracting the diamagnetic chemical shift from the paramagnetic chemical shift. Providing a structural model of the protein by either X-ray or NMR is available, the χ-tensor can be determined. To do this the size of the magnetic susceptibility components

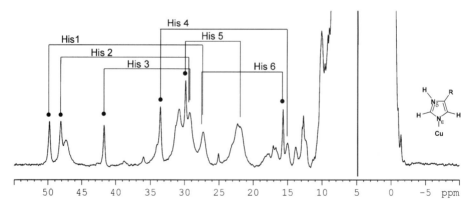

Figure 1   600-MHz ^{1}H NMR spectrum of the chloride-bound *Streptomyces antibioticus* met-tyrosinase. The six sharp lines (•) have been assigned to the His Nδ protons based on H/D exchange experiments. By one-dimensional NOE experiments all sharp signals could be correlated with broader signals originating from the His Cε protons, as indicated. The observed NOE patterns show that all His are coordinated through the Nε atoms (36).

Figure 3 Stereorepresentation of the solution structure of *Synechocystis* PCC6803 Cu(II) plastocyanin, shown as an ensemble of 35 C$^{\alpha}$ traces [PDB entry 1i0w, (18)] overlaid with the crystal structure of a triple mutant (A42D, D47P, A63L) of same protein [PDB entry 1pcs, (104)] shown as a *red* C$^{\alpha}$ coil. The coppers of the solution structure models are shown as *blue spheres*. Note that the solution structure is best defined in areas far away from the metal and poorer toward the metal due to the paramagnetic nature of the Cu(II).

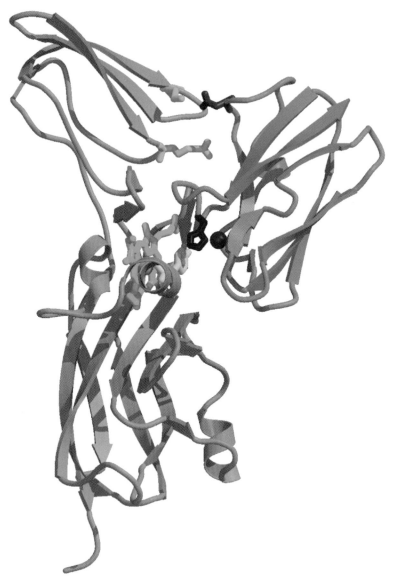

Figure 4 The complex of plastocyanin (*blue*) and cytochrome *f* (*brown*) from plants, as determined on the basis of intermolecular pseudocontact shifts [PDB entry 2pcf, (121)], with the heme in *green* and the copper depicted as a *blue sphere*.

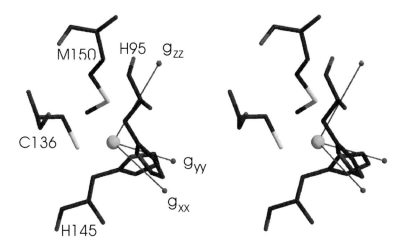

Figure 6 Stereorepresentation showing the orientation of the principal axes system of the g-tensor for the type-1 copper site of nitrite reductase from *Alcaligenes faecalis* (125).

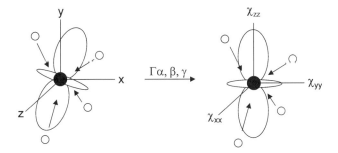

Figure 2 Schematic representation of the conversion of the molecular reference coordinate system (x, y, z) into the χ-tensor. A five-parameter fit is performed to determine the Euler angles α, β, and γ and $\Delta\chi_{ax}$ and $\Delta\chi_{rh}$ (Equation 3) by using experimentally obtained pseudocontact shifts from surrounding nuclei (*open circles*).

$\Delta\chi_{ax}$ and $\Delta\chi_{rh}$ (Equation 3) need to be obtained as well as the three Euler rotation angles that transform the molecular reference coordinate system into the coordinate system defined by the principal axes of the χ-tensor (Figure 2). On the basis of a set of observed pseudocontact shifts, a five-parameter fit is performed to determine the χ-tensor angles and components (56, 132).

Such a determination using proton δ_{ps} as input is now routine for low-spin ferric heme proteins such as c- and b-type cytochromes (4, 59, 132, 133), and the determination of the χ-tensor for high-spin ferric heme proteins (6, 34, 116) along with Co^{II}- and Ni^{II}-substituted blue-copper proteins (53, 54) and rubredoxins (129) has also been achieved. Knowledge of the angles and anisotropies of the χ-tensor reveals valuable information on the active-site structure, which has elegantly been demonstrated in numerous studies with peroxidases and globins by LaMar and coworkers. Furthermore, the R^{-3} distance dependence of the δ_{ps} (as compared to the R^{-6} for the NOE) allows for the use of δ_{ps} as powerful long-range structural constraints. This first demands determining the orientation of the χ-tensor, and such a determination is a prerequisite to the use of δ_{ps} to generate or refine a solution NMR structure (9, 13) or determine a protein-protein (68, 121) or protein-drug complex (118), as discussed in the next sections.

Once the χ-tensor is known, the δ_{Fc} contribution to the chemical shifts of protons belonging to residues coordinated to the metal ion can be obtained:

$$\delta_{pm} = \delta_{ps} + \delta_{Fc}. \tag{5}$$

The contact contribution to the chemical shift depends on the unpaired spin density in the s-orbital of a given nucleus and is given in Equation 2. Two mechanisms have been proposed to account for this spin delocalization (26). The first, direct unpaired spin density transfer, transmits unpaired spin density of the same sign, whereas the second, termed spin-polarization, involves a mechanism through which the sign of the spin density can change between consecutive nuclei.

In a system of the type $M-S-CH_2$, where M is a paramagnetic metal ion coordinated to a cysteine or methionine sulfur, the spin density experienced by the protons depends on the spin density on the S donor atom (ρ_s) and the $M-S-C-H^i$ dihedral angle, ϕ_i. Thus the contact couplings generally obey a Karplus-type relationship (76), which in EPR is known as the Heller-McConnell relation:

$$(A_i/h) = b \cos^2 \phi_i + c, \qquad (6)$$

where $i = 1, 2$; $b = B\rho_s$; and $c = C\rho_s$, with B and C constants and ϕ_i measured with respect to the sulfur orbital carrying the unpaired spin density, thus allowing information about both the geometric and the electronic structures of the system to be obtained.

Application of Equation 6 to metal-substituted blue-copper proteins has shown that the contact shift for the two S-coordinating ligands (Met and Cys) depends simply on the square cosine, indicating that only σ bonds are involved in the spin delocalization (54). In other cases, such as in the mixed valence binuclear Cu_A site (49, 106), ferredoxins, and HIPIPs (28), the relationship depends on the square sine of the dihedral angle, and thus a π-type spin delocalization is dominant. Thus, by careful analysis of the contact shift, knowledge of the mechanism of spin delocalization onto the ligands and its influence on the interaction with the metal ion can be obtained. This allows the study of the relationship between the electronic structure and the redox properties of the protein.

For low-spin heme proteins, a similar Karplus-style relationship has been formulated (27, 76). This describes the relationship between the contact and pseudocontact shifts and the orientation of the axial ligands for bis-histidine and cyanide-histidine heme proteins using the ^1H paramagnetic shifts of the four heme methyl groups at 298 K. In a similar manner Turner and colleagues (85) have shown that the ^{13}C shifts of all eight porphyrin substituents and their temperature dependencies can be related to the orientation of the ligands in bis-histidine heme proteins. More recently a modification of the original equation to account for ligands other than histidine and to include temperatures other than 298 K has been put forward (119).

Structure Determination of Paramagnetic Macromolecules

Structure determination of nonparamagnetic proteins is based on distance information derived from the NOE, dihedral angles based on the three-bond scalar coupling between nuclei (^3J) couplings, and from angular information obtained with residual dipolar couplings. The NOE is caused by cross-relaxation of two spins and depends on the distance between these nuclei to the sixth power. Thus, the observation of a cross-peak in a NOESY spectrum implies a close distance between the two nuclei (<5 Å). When most protons of a protein and all their NOE cross-peaks have been assigned, a large set of distance restraints has been obtained that can be used to calculate the three-dimensional structure of the protein. The ^3J depends in a predictable way on the dihedral angle between the nuclei. Therefore, the measurement of the coupling provides additional restraints for the structure calculation. In the past few years, residual dipolar couplings obtained by partial alignment of proteins have also been implemented in protein structure calculations (98).

The properties of paramagnetic proteins limit the use of the methods described above. Large chemical shift changes due to contact and pseudocontact contributions make the assignment of the nuclei and protons in particular less obvious. The main problem is, however, the paramagnetic contribution to both T_1 and T_2 relaxation. Fast T_2 relaxation results in large linewidths, making the detection of resonances difficult. It also obscures ^3J couplings because these are generally below 10 Hz. Fast T_1 relaxation affects the cross-relaxation and thus the NOE. Given the distance dependencies of the paramagnetism, it is obvious that these effects are most severe for nuclei close to the metal. While regions far away from the metal can be analyzed as in nonparamagnetic proteins, the active site and its immediate environment remain invisible when the above-mentioned general methods are applied.

Yet, the paramagnetic effects can also be used to our advantage. The pseudo-contact contribution depends on both the distance from metal to nucleus and the orientation of the nucleus relative to the paramagnetic susceptibility tensor. Thus, it contains structural information about the protein. This is a long-range effect because it falls off with the distance to the third power (Equation 3) rather than the sixth power such as the NOE. In the context of structure determination, contact contributions to the chemical shift could be considered a paramagnetic analog of the ^3J coupling and can be applied similarly to obtain structural restraints of metal ligand residues (see the previous section). Dipolar paramagnetic T_1 relaxation is also distance dependent and can be used to obtain additional restaints for nuclei close to the metal.

Naturally, the paramagnetic effects can only be measured provided the resonances can be detected and assigned. Paramagnetic metals with fast electronic relaxation cause only limited broadening of the resonances of the surrounding residues. For this reason, in heme proteins even the signals close to the iron can be observed, and a considerable number of structures has been solved. Because several recent reviews dealing with heme proteins are available (8, 14, 30, 86, 120), these will not be discussed here. It has been possible to solve several solution structures even for proteins with metals that cause more significant broadening, such as FeS proteins (28). Recently Bertini and coworkers determined the first the structure of a paramagnetic copper protein, plastocyanin (18). Cu(II) has a long electronic relaxation time, resulting in the loss of all proton signals within ~8 Å of the copper, when using standard methods (122). This problem was solved by using standard NMR experiments in which various delay times are shortened to give optimal performance on the broadened signals. Protons of some ligands too broad to be detected directly could be assigned by one-dimensional saturation transfer to the reduced form in a mixture of oxidized and reduced plastocyanin. By determining the intensity of the saturation transfer effect as a function of the decoupler offset frequency, the resonance position in the paramagnetic state can be determined (21). In addition to NOE restraints, T_1-based distance restraints were used for the structure calculation. Pseudocontact effects are small in Cu(II) proteins because of the low anisotropy of the magnetic susceptibility, and they were not applied. Although the area around the copper site is not as well defined as the remainder of the protein (Figure 3, see color insert), the structure in general is in good agreement with the crystal structure of the protein, illustrating that even paramagnetic proteins with difficult metals are amenable to structure determination.

Tu and Gochin have used a similar approach to solve the structure of a DNA duplex, d(TTGGCCAA)$_2$, in tight association with chromomycin-A$_3$ and cobalt (64, 118). In DNA molecules, a lack of long-range NOEs usually results in well-defined local structure but poorly defined overall structure. The pseudocontact effects caused by the Co provide restraints over relatively long distances and are thus valuable.

Protein Complexes: Structures and Electron Transfer Characteristics

Contact-shifted resonances are often shifted outside the diamagnetic region. Many studies have taken advantage of the extra resolution provided by the paramagnetism to analyze the effects of complex formation between proteins. Because the applied methods, such as chemical shift perturbation analysis, are otherwise standard, they are not discussed here.

Paramagnetic line broadening can be used to determine electron transfer rates between proteins. The most well-known application is the so-called electron self-exchange reaction, in which an electron is exchanged between the oxidized and reduced states of a protein. Under certain conditions, the linewidth increase of a resonance of a nucleus close to the metal in the diamagnetic state is proportional to the rate of electron self-exchange and the concentration of the paramagnetic form of the protein. Ma et al. reported on a new method to measure electron self-exhange (90) using the so-called super-WEFT (74) method. Super-WEFT is similar to an inversion recovery experiment. The delay time after the first 180° inversion pulse is optimized such that signals with short T_1 values due to the paramagnetic effect relax to (near) equilibrium, while resonances with diamagnetic T_1 values relax just to zero intensity (saturation). The following 90° pulse thus produces selectively a signal for the paramagnetic resonances, even in the diamagnetic region of the spectrum.

A recent application of self-exchange was also described by Ma et al. (89). They determined the T_1 values of nuclei in paramagnetic plastocyanin indirectly by measuring the T_1 values of the diamagnetic state in a mixture of oxidized and reduced protein. The work demonstrates that the predicted distance dependence of the paramagnetic broadening holds well for protons but, unexpectedly, not for ^{15}N and ^{13}C nuclei.

Another application of self-exchange is the determination of electron transfer rates within and between azurin molecules that have been cross-linked to dimers (123). Intramolecular and intermolecular electron transfer rates in a mixture of oxidized and reduced proteins could be determined by NMR, demonstrating that a short cross-link inhibits electron transfer within an azurin dimer, while a long linker provides sufficient flexibility to enable the formation of a complex in which electron transfer is highly efficient (123a).

Pseudocontact effects result in chemical shift changes of any nucleus close to the metal. The nucleus does not need to be part of the same molecule as the metal because the effect is through-space. The intermolecular effect can be used to determine the relative orientation of two proteins in a transient complex, as has been shown for two complexes of plastocyanin and cytochrome f (46, 121). When plastocyanin binds to the cytochrome f in its paramagnetic state, pseudocontact shifts caused by the heme are observed for nuclei in the so-called hydrophobic patch of plastocyanin. In combination with other restraints, these shifts can be used to determine how plastocyanin is oriented relative to the heme and thus to cytochrome f (Figure 4, see color insert). This study provided strong evidence for an electron transfer pathway from the heme to the copper via its exposed ligand histidine. Similar intermolecular pseudocontact effects have been demonstrated in the complex of cytochrome b_5 and cytochrome c (68).

Recent Developments

Several new applications of paramagnetic NMR have been reported, some of which provide additional aids in the structural analysis of paramagnetic proteins.

1. With the availability of proteins that are uniformly enriched in ^{15}N or ^{13}C, it has become feasible to determine pseudocontact shifts for large sets of heteroatoms and to calculate the magnetic susceptibility tensor. It was found for both ^{15}N (35, 116, 133) and ^{13}C (J. A. R. Worrall, unpublished results) nuclei that the correlation of observed versus calculated pseudocontact shifts is much poorer than for protons. Because the pseudocontact shift is defined as the difference between the chemical shift in the paramagnetic and diamagnetic states, small structural changes between the two states might be responsible for the poor correlation. However, for ^{15}N nuclei, which are the most sensitive for structural changes because of their involvement in hydrogen bonding, it was demonstrated that this is not the case. Even in partly unfolded protein, the correlation remains poor (29). The reason for this is unclear.

2. In protein NMR, there is a renewed interest in the application of lanthanides. They have been used to reduce spectral overlap in crowded protein spectra (108), and they have recently been incorporated in Ca-binding sites of proteins. Diamagnetic and weakly paramagnetic lanthanides make it possible to get structural restraints around the binding site, and the strongly paramagnetic ones, such as Dy, make it possible to obtain pseudocontact shifts up to 40 Å away from the binding site (2). A systematic analysis of the magnetic properties of the range of lanthanides bound to calmodulin was recently reported [(23); See also point 5].

3. Spin labels have been used for a long time in EPR, but recently their relaxation effects have also been employed to obtain the overall fold of proteins. For

this purpose, a nitroxide spin label is attached to an engineered Cys residue at the surface of the protein. It was demonstrated that dipolar paramagnetic relaxation effects on both T_1 (62) and T_2 (15) can be used to obtain reliable distance restraints for structure determination. By making several mutants with the Cys residue at different positions, a set of distance restraints is produced that covers most of the protein backbone. Spin labels have also been used to improve the structure of a DNA duplex with a Pt-adduct (55).

4. As indicated previously, the static, averaged field of the unpaired electron is a significant cause of nuclear relaxation, particularly for large molecules at high magnetic fields. This Curie spin relaxation (CSR) also shows cross-correlation with dipole-dipole (DD) relaxation, similar to DD/CSA (CSA, chemical shift anisotropy) cross-correlation [(91) and references therein]. Because the DD/CSR cross-correlated relaxation rate depends on the third power of the distance between the nucleus and the electron (assumed to be located on the metal), long-range structural restraints can be obtained, as has been demonstrated for ^{15}N-labeled cytochrome c' in the reduced high-spin state (33).

5. At very strong magnetic fields, the tumbling of molecules is not completely isotropic due to weak alignent of the magnetic susceptibility tensor with the external magnetic field. In that case, the dipolar coupling between spins is no longer averaged to zero. For diamagnetic macromolecules, the residual dipolar coupling for a pair of coupled ^{1}H-^{15}N spins is generally small, even at the highest field currently achievable (21.1 T), but for paramagnetic macro-molecules the alignment can result in significant residual dipolar couplings, which can be used for structural characterization (5, 10, 16, 73, 114, 115) similar to residual dipolar couplings obtained from induced alignment, such as in solutions containing dilute liquid crystals. The alignment is determined by both paramagnetic and diamagnetic susceptibility tensors, which need not be oriented along the same principal axis, but methods have been described to separate both contributions (5, 10, 48). The degree of aligment depends on the size and the anisotropy of the paramagnetic susceptibility. Lanthanides are thus excellent candidates for alignment studies (20, 24, 31, 39, 88, 128) but iron (5, 10, 114, 115, 129) and cobalt (88) can also be used. To obtain alignment of proteins that do not bind these metals, a small extentsion, an EF hand (88) or Zn finger (61), can be fused to the N- or C-termini of the protein to bind a lanthanide EF hand or cobalt Zn finger.

HIGH-FREQUENCY EPR

Background

In recent years, the study of metalloproteins has benefited from a renewal in EPR methodology and instrumentation. High-field/high-frequency spectrometers have become available as well as pulsed methods. Applications of pulsed EPR spectroscopy to metal centers in proteins have been summarized in two recent reviews (47, 99). The impact of the application of higher magnetic fields and higher microwave frequencies for the study of metalloproteins is the subject of our review. An overview of high frequency EPR investigations in the context of coordination chemistry has been presented recently (70).

For many years, experiments in EPR were performed around 9 GHz (X-band) with excursions to lower (2 GHz, L-band; 4 GHz, S-band) and higher (24 GHz, K-band; 35 GHz, Q-band) frequencies. An "avant la lettre" multi-frequency (70 to 400 GHz) EPR experiment, albeit at low sensitivity, was performed on met-hemoglobin by Alpert et al. as early as 1973 (3). Following the pioneering work of Lebedev and his coworkers (65), several groups built high-field spectrometers (87, 100, 101, 130) and used these in studies on biological samples. Until now most high-field/high-frequency studies on metalloproteins have been performed at 95 GHz (W-band). The first spectrometers at this frequency were developed in the early 1990s, both in the continuous-wave (100) and pulsed (130) mode, and recently a W-band spectrometer has become commercially available (71a). The home-built 95-GHz spectrometer of the Leiden group is equipped with a single-mode cylindrical cavity and allows magnetic fields up to 5.5 T and temperatures as low as 1.2 K. It has provisions for pulsed ENDOR and ESEEM experiments, and it is specially designed for studies on single crystals (51).

In order to appreciate the developments toward higher magnetic fields and microwaves, consider the spin Hamiltionian:

$$H = \beta_e \, \vec{B}_0 \cdot \vec{\vec{g}} \cdot \vec{S} - \sum_i g_i \, \beta_n \, \vec{B}_0 \cdot \vec{I}_i + \vec{S} \cdot \vec{\vec{D}} \cdot \vec{S}$$

$$+ \sum_i \vec{S} \cdot \vec{\vec{A}}_i \cdot \vec{I}_i + \sum_i \vec{I}_i \cdot \vec{\vec{Q}}_i \cdot \vec{I}_i. \tag{7}$$

Here the first two terms represent the field-dependent electron and nuclear Zeeman interactions (β_e Bohr magneton, β_n nuclear magneton, g_i the g factor of nucleus i). The next terms in the spin Hamiltonian are field independent. The third term represents the fine-structure interaction, which leads to the so-called zero-field splitting for electron-spin quantum numbers $S > \frac{1}{2}$. The g-tensor, through its deviation from the free-electron g value, and the fine-structure D tensor globally probe the electronic structure of the paramagnetic site of the protein. Both last terms in the spin Hamiltonian provide local probes of the electronic structure at the metal and ligand nuclei. The fourth term represents the interaction of the electron and the nuclear magnetic moments as described by the hyperfine A tensor. The fifth term, which only occurs for nuclear spin quantum numbers $I > \frac{1}{2}$, represents the interaction of the nuclear quadrupole moment with the electric-field gradient at the nucleus.

An EPR experiment is commonly labeled high-frequency when microwave radiation of frequencies ≥ 95 GHz is being applied. A true high-field/high-frequency experiment requires resolution of the anisotropy of the g-tensor, which makes the lower limit to the frequency dependent on the sample (94). For metalloproteins, the upper limit to the field seems to be set by g-strain broadening, which increases with field. This broadening is the result of the distribution of g values derived from the (induced) micro-heterogeneity of the protein sample (69). As long as the Zeeman interaction dominates, high field and high frequency go hand in hand. For high-spin systems, high frequencies may be needed even at low fields because the microwave quantum should be of the order of the zero-field splitting.

Before reviewing the achievements of high-frequency EPR in the study of metalloproteins, the goals and advantages of this approach are listed. First, as indicated above, high-field/high-frequency aims at enhanced g resolution. Accurate values of the principal components g_{xx}, g_{yy}, and g_{zz} may be obtained, whereas the anisotropy of the g-tensor is often (partly) hidden under the EPR line at standard X-band frequencies. The deviation Δg of the tensor components from the free-electron g value is derived from spin-orbit coupling, which increases with atomic number. Consequently, the largest contribution to Δg results from the spin density in the atomic orbitals at the metal ion and thus provides information on the metal orbitals that participate in the molecular orbitals that describe the unpaired electron(s). As seen in Equation 2, the g-tensor is also required in order to interpret the paramagnetic shift of the NMR transitions. Besides the determination of accurate g values, the enhanced resolution for high-frequency EPR enables the recognition of conformational heterogeneity at the metal site of the protein and of contributions from different paramagnetic species to the EPR spectrum.

A second advantage of EPR at higher microwave frequencies concerns sensitivity. Although the minimum number of detectable spins remains roughly the same, the absolute sensitivity increases with frequency. At liquid-helium temperatures, the Boltzmann spin polarization becomes significant, thus increasing the signal. More important is the smaller wavelength that translates into a reduced volume of the resonator, which corresponds to a high-filling factor for small samples. In combination with the performance of the microwave components, an overall increase of the EPR sensitivity results. For example, an increase by about three orders of magnitude has been observed for sample volumes of the order of 0.1 μl at 95 GHz compared to 9 GHz. For metalloprotein samples, the increased absolute sensitivity is particularly relevant in two respects. First, the number of spins per molecular mass is low compared to small-molecule samples, and the amount of sample available is often limited. Second, the high sensitivity for small samples makes high-frequency EPR cut out for protein single-crystal studies. Commonly, single crystals of proteins are of submillimeter size, which results in a low-filling factor at X-band. For these crystal sizes, an EPR frequency of 95 GHz may be ideal because the sample volume within the single-mode cavity and the dimension of the crystal nicely match while the protein crystal is still large enough to be manipulated. Evidently, the study of single crystals bears a great advantage. An investigation of the EPR spectrum as a function of the orientation of the magnetic field with respect to the crystal allows the determination of the complete interaction tensors, the principal values and the directions of the principal axes.

With regard to the direction of the principal axes, notice that the EPR experiment provides such directions for the various molecules in the unit cell in a laboratory axes system with an accuracy that, depending on the line width, may well reach $\pm 1°$. In order to translate this knowledge into an orientation of the g-tensor within the metalloprotein molecule, the EPR data have to be connected to X-ray diffraction data. This may, but need not, imply a separate X-ray experiment on the sample mounted for EPR depending on the space group. Once the directions derived from EPR are fixed with respect to the crystallographic axes and the latter have been assigned, the problem is solved for cases where one molecule occupies the unit cell. When more molecules are present in the crystallographic unit cell, the analysis may not be trivial and need not necessarily lead to a unique solution. Whether the orientation of the g-tensor principal axes in the paramagnetic center can be obtained depends on the accuracy of the EPR data (determined by the linewidth), the number of centers in the asymmetric unit of the crystallographic unit cell, and the symmetry relation between the centers within each asymmetric unit.

High-field EPR might also be beneficial for high-spin systems $(S > \frac{1}{2})$, which is evident when the zero-field splitting is so large that they are EPR-silent at low magnetic fields. In addition, if an EPR signal is detected at low frequencies and fields, the interpretation is often hampered by the fact that only one transition is observed. For half-integer high-spin systems, the hyperfine lines corresponding to the central EPR transition $(m_s = +\frac{1}{2} \leftrightarrow -\frac{1}{2})$ get narrower at higher magnetic fields. The linewidth is commonly determined by second- and higher-order fine-structure broadening, which is inversely proportional to the magnetic-field strength. Moreover, spectral resolution increases because forbidden transitions between nuclear sublevels are suppressed at higher field values.

The transitions that result from hyperfine interactions are commonly, at most, partly resolved in an EPR spectrum. Much information is hidden under the inhomogeneously broadened EPR line, and a number of methods have been devised to increase the spectral resolution. As yet, two of these have been exploited at higher frequencies, ENDOR and ESEEM. In ENDOR, besides the microwave field that drives the EPR $(\Delta m_S = \pm 1)$ transitions, a radio-frequency field that drives the NMR $(\Delta m_I = \pm 1)$ transitions is applied. The ENDOR signal concerns the change of the amplitude of the EPR signal when sweeping the radio-frequency field through the nuclear transition. A considerable increase in spectral resolution results for ENDOR compared with EPR, particularly when the electron spin is coupled to many equivalent nuclei and when nuclei with different magnetic moments are involved. In the latter case, high fields significantly contribute to the effectiveness of ENDOR because the hyperfine transitions related to different nuclei become further separated owing to the increased difference of their nuclear Zeeman frequencies. For metalloproteins, experiments have been demonstrated for microwave frequencies up to 95 GHz and radio frequencies up to 150 MHz.

While ENDOR is being performed both in continuous wave and pulsed mode, the ESEEM technique essentially concerns the time domain. Owing to the coupling of the electron spin to the nuclear spins, the electron-spin-echo intensity becomes modulated as a function of the separation time between the exciting microwave pulses. The modulation frequencies correspond to the energy differences between the nuclear sublevels of the electron-spin eigenstates, and Fourier transformation of the time-domain signal leads to a spectrum that reveals the nuclear frequencies, similar to the ENDOR spectrum. The modulation depth depends on the simultaneous excitation of allowed and forbidden transitions, i.e., on the mixing of the nuclear Zeeman states, which seems to argue against the application of high magnetic fields. In fact, this condition makes ESEEM at low and high EPR frequencies complementary. At each EPR frequency, those nuclei show up for which the hyperfine interaction (which should be anisotropic) is significant compared to the Zeeman interaction. A particularly advantageous situation occurs when the hyperfine and Zeeman interaction (nearly) cancel in one of the electron-spin manifolds, which may be achieved by proper tuning of the external magnetic field. For metalloproteins, ESEEM experiments at low EPR frequencies have been informative with respect to weakly coupled nuclei. This may equally well apply at high EPR frequencies for strongly coupled, e.g., metal-coordinated, nuclei, but this area is largely unexplored.

A further advantage of the increased spectral resolution at high frequency as far as ENDOR and ESEEM are concerned is the possibility to achieve single-crystal-like orientation selection for randomly oriented samples with relatively small g anisotropy. Tuning to the canonical magnetic fields, corresponding to g_{xx}, g_{yy}, and g_{zz}, provides tensorial information about the hyperfine interaction, albeit in the g-tensor axes system.

Copper Proteins

In 1993, a systematic and quantitative high-frequency EPR study of the metal site of the blue-copper protein azurin started when it was realized that the submillimeter single crystals available for this protein could be investigated by 95-GHz ESE-detected EPR (41). In the oxidized form, the copper ion has formally a charge of 2+, which corresponds to a $(3d)^9$-electron configuration and $S = {}^1\!/_2$. The typical ligation of copper in the type 1 site, two histidines and one cysteine strongly bound to the copper ion that is close to the NNS plane spanned by the coordinating nitrogens and sulphur atoms, gives rise to a nearly axial g-tensor. The g_{xx} and g_{yy} components are not resolved at X-band frequency. During past years, wild-type azurin from *Pseudomonas aeruginosa*, for which the sulphur of a methionine provides a fourth and weak ligand to the copper, and some of its mutants have been studied by 95-GHz pulsed EPR (41, 44, 126), ENDOR (42, 45), and ESEEM (43) spectroscopy. Similarly, the type-1 copper site of the enzyme nitrite reductase from *Alcaligenes faecalis* has been investigated recently (125).

The EPR experiments at 95 GHz clearly revealed the nonaxiality of the g-tensor (Figure 5). Accurate values of g_{xx}, g_{yy}, and g_{zz} were obtained for wild-type azurin (41), for its mutants M121Q (44) and M121H (126), in which the weak axial copper ligand methionine has been replaced, and for nitrite reductase (125). For these systems, the value of g_{zz} deviates +0.19 to +0.29 from the free-electron g value, which reveals the dominant d_{xy} character of the singly occupied molecular

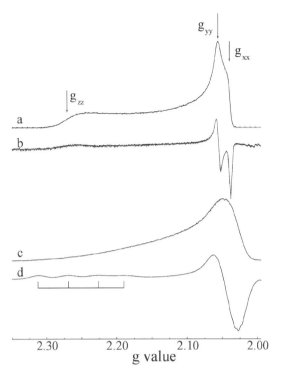

Figure 5   ESE-detected and continuous-wave EPR spectra at W-band (*a, b*) and at X-band (*c, d*) of *Pseudomonas aeruginosa* azurin. Copper hyperfine interaction is visible in the low-field part of spectrum (*d*) (124).

orbital (SOMO). Interestingly, the rhombicity ($g_{yy} - g_{xx}$) varies remarkably when the methionine ligand is replaced by a stronger ligand, glutamine for M121Q and histidine for M121H. The rhombicity of the g-tensor triples for M121Q compared to that for wild-type azurin, whereas it gets negligibly small for M121H. Analysis of the spin-orbit coupling reveals that the SOMO contains, besides the d_{xy} orbital, appreciable contributions of the d_{z^2} for M121Q and of the d_{yz} (d_{xz}) orbital for M121H (126).

In the study of single crystals at 95 GHz, EPR lines in the ESE-detected EPR spectra for various orientations of the magnetic field with respect to the crystal could be assigned to the respective protein molecules in the unit cell, e.g., 16 for wild-type azurin (41). For the azurin mutants M121Q and M121H, the high resolution at 95 GHz revealed an interesting conformational bi-stability of the copper site. More lines than compatible with the space group were observed in the EPR spectra. The resonance fields revealed the presence of a second paramagnetic center with a distinct g-tensor, which was interpreted to derive from a different conformation of the metal site (126).

In addition to the principal values, the experiments on the single crystals of the type-1 copper proteins have provided the direction of the principal axes of the g-tensors. The direction of the g_z axis, related to the largest principal g component, represents a sensitive probe of the SOMO. For wild-type azurin, the g_z axis is perpendicular to the CuNN plane (N referring to the nitrogens of the equatorial histidine ligands), and the direction is conserved for mutants M121Q and M121H. This direction of g_z is closely parallel to the direction of the bond between copper and the axial ligand for wild-type azurin and M121Q ($15°$ and $10°$), but for M121H the g_z axis makes an angle of $41°$ with the direction of the copper-axial nitrogen bond. This further indicates that in the latter case the d_{yz} (d_{xz}) orbital is involved in the binding with the nitrogen lone pair orbital of the axial histidine. For nitrite reductase, an angle of $60°$ is found (Figure 6, see color insert). For a detailed description of the analysis of the observed direction of g_z, we refer to the original papers (41, 44, 125, 126).

Hyperfine interactions have been investigated at high frequencies for type-1 copper proteins. The copper hyperfine interaction, which is resolved in the $g_{\parallel}$ region of the spectrum at X-band, is no longer resolved at W-band due to g-strain broadening (Figure 5). Ligand hyperfine interactions have successfully been studied by pulsed ENDOR and ESEEM at W-band. At low fields, the signals of protons and nitrogens severely overlap, but at 3.3 T the Zeeman frequencies are about 140 MHz and 10 MHz for ^{1}H and ^{14}N, respectively, and the ranges of the ENDOR lines become fully separated. Pulsed ENDOR signals of ^{1}H (40), ^{14}N (42, 45), and ^{15}N (42) were detected for azurin at 95 GHz. The nitrogen signals were found to derive from weakly coupled nuclei, the two remote nitrogens of the copper-coordinated histidines and three backbone nitrogens. An orientational study was performed for single crystals of ^{14}N azurin and ^{15}N azurin. Due to the resolution achieved for the crystals and the combination of ^{14}N and ^{15}N data, complete hyperfine tensors were obtained for all five nitrogens and complete quadrupole tensors for the histidine nitrogens and one of the backbone nitrogens (42). The hyperfine tensors for the remote nitrogens of the two histidines are considerably different, whereas the quadrupole tensors are similar. The principal axes of the quadrupole tensors follow the symmetry of the local bonds, which underscores the assignment of the tensors, and the principal values reflect the relatively strong hydrogen bonds in which the amide hydrogens of histidine-117 (to a water oxygen) and histidine-46 (to a carbonyl oxygen) are involved. The hyperfine tensors reflect the unequivalence with regard to the delocalization of the SOMO over the two copper-coordinated histidines. The isotropic hyperfine coupling amounts to 1.30 MHz and 0.87 MHz for the Nεs of histidine-117 and histidine-46. The anisotropic components of the hyperfine interaction are substantial and informative with regard to the delocalization of the SOMO. Simplified orbital models have been used to translate the hyperfine data into a spin-densitiy distribution, which shows that the anisotropic hyperfine interaction of the remote nitrogens contains roughly equal contributions from the spin densities on Nε, Nδ, and Cu. Recent quantum-chemical studies indicate that an ab initio calculation of ligand hyperfine tensors comes within reach for type-1 copper proteins (75, 124).

ESEEM studies for azurin have illustrated the possibilities of this time-domain technique when applied at different microwave frequencies. The sensitivity of ESEEM at X-band for the study of the remote nitrogens of imidazoles bound to copper, known since the pioneering studies of Mims & Peisach (93), were extensively exploited in the study of proteins. At 95 GHz, ESEEM is ideally suited to investigate the copper-coordinated nitrogens. With hyperfine interactions in the order of 20 MHz, about twice the nuclear Zeeman interaction, these interactions are close to cancellation in one of the electron-spin manifolds, and deep modulations of the echo signal are expected. This has been observed for azurin, and in combination with the use of single crystals, a high resolution has been achieved. An ESEEM study, as a function of the orientation of the magnetic field with respect to the crystal, has provided hyperfine and quadrupole tensors for both nitrogens coordinated to the copper ion. The anisotropic hyperfine interaction reveals the σ-character of the coordination of the histidine imidazoles, which should be taken into account when interpreting proton NMR data. The isotropic hyperfine coupling of the nitrogen is 1.4 times larger for histidine-117 than for histidine-46, which shows the difference in the delocalization of the SOMO over the histidines. For both histidines, a ratio of close to 20 was found for the isotropic hyperfine coupling of the coordinated and remote nitrogen.

Recently, paramagnetic proton NMR data for blue-copper proteins have been discussed in relation to the distribution of the spin density over the metal site. The hyperfine couplings of the β-CH_2 protons of the copper-coordinated cysteine from such studies have been compared with those obtained from Q-band ENDOR (21). In principle, data from both methods should be complementary, but the required accuracy has not yet been reached. Pulsed ^1H (^2H) ENDOR studies on single crystals of (isotopically labeled) blue-copper proteins at 95 GHz may well provide the hyperfine data necessary to calculate the pseudocontact shift for the β-CH_2 protons.

The bi-nuclear Cu_A site in the recombinant water-soluble fragment of subunit II of *Thermus thermophilus* cytochrome c oxidase ba3 has been investigated by combining X- and W-band–pulsed EPR spectroscopy (66, 109). The high-frequency data provide the resolution to distinguish the Cu_A signals from those of an additional type-2 Cu site and to separate the ^1H from the ^{14}N ENDOR spectrum. The latter spectra reveal the hyperfine interactions of the cysteine β-protons and the strongly coupled histidine nitrogens.

For copper proteins, g-strain broadening does not seem to limit the application of high-field EPR. Gaffney et al. discuss this for dicupric lactoferrin (60). Using a model to describe the anisotropy of the linewidths along the different orientations, g-strain parameters were determined from EPR at 2 GHz and 9 GHz. The linewidths obtained by W-band EPR were in agreement with the predictions from lower frequency EPR, suggesting that no additional strain mechanisms become operative for Cu (II) at 95 GHz. Incidentally, the W-band experiments showed that splittings in the g_{xx}, g_{yy} region of the X-band EPR spectra, which were attributed to a superhyperfine interaction of nitrogens with the copper center in a previous X-band EPR study, are due to a Mn(II) impurity. At X-band, the manganese signals overlap with the g_{xx} and g_{yy} features of Cu (II), but at W-band they are well separated from the copper resonances and thus can be identified as Mn(II).

High-Field EPR on Systems Other Than Copper

MANGANESE-IONS IN PROTEINS   Significant progress has been made in the understanding of the ligand and electronic structure of Mn(II) sites in proteins by high-field EPR including multi-frequency approaches. In proteins, Mn(II) is able to replace Ca(II), an ion that often has a structural function and is not redox active. The advantages of high-field EPR for high-spin systems (Mn(II) with $S = \frac{5}{2}$) are that the linewidth becomes narrower at higher frequencies, because the zero-field splitting becomes less important, and the simplification of the spectra due to the suppression of forbidden transitions. For Mn(II), most studies focus on the $M_s = -\frac{1}{2}$ to $+\frac{1}{2}$ transition, which occurs around $g = 2$ and consists of 6 lines owing to the hyperfine interaction with the manganese nucleus ($I = \frac{5}{2}$). The reduced linewidth essentially increases the sensitivity of high-field EPR for Mn(II), which as an undesired side effect causes Mn(II) impurities in biological preparations to become more obvious at higher fields.

Cytochrome c oxidase contains a manganese-binding site at a distance of approximately 10 Å from the redox active Cu_A site discussed above. It is found at the interface of two domains in the protein, where Mn(II) replaces the native Ca(II). The EPR spectra at X-, Q-, and W-band are presented in (77), and simulations were performed to determine the parameters D, E, and A_{Mn} that fit spectra at all three EPR frequencies. Spectra at different frequencies are sensitive to different parameters. For example, the hyperfine interaction is best obtained from W-band EPR, whereas D and E are determined from the data at lower frequency. By comparing manganese signals from samples where the Cu_A center is reduced (diamagnetic) and oxidized (paramagnetic, total spin $S = \frac{1}{2}$), the dipolar interaction of Mn(II) and Cu_A is determined. The distance corresponding to the dipolar interaction between these centers agrees well with the distance obtained from X-ray crystallography.

The G protein ras p21 has been investigated by 95- and 139-GHz EPR. ras p21 is involved in signal transduction and regulation of cell differentiation. It contains a nonredox-active metal ion, which in the native protein is a Ca(II) ion. This ion is involved in binding GDP and GTP and therefore is part of the functionality of this protein. For EPR studies, Ca(II) has been replaced by Mn(II). One of the controversial issues was the nature and number of ligands around the Ca(II), especially the number of water ligands, which could not be unambiguously determined by X-ray crystallography and previous X-band EPR experiments. High-field EPR at 139 GHz (17) was performed on frozen solutions of this protein, and the number of water ligands was deduced from the line-shape changes upon exchanging water with $H_2{}^{17}O$. Protein with isotopically labeled Thr was used to determine the role of Thr35 coordination (71). Later studies showed that in liquid solution narrower linewidths allow one to directly observe the ^{17}O hfc (63, 103), and line-shape simulations lead to a reinterpretation of the number of water ligands as compared to

(17). The data in (103) reveal that a narrowing of the EPR lines by about a factor of 2 going from Q-band to W-band EPR sufficiently improves the resolution to determine that 3 rather than 4 water ligands are present in the native GDP-bound form of the enzyme.

The manganese-binding site in concanavalin A, a saccharide-binding protein whose function is yet unknown, has been investigated by Goldfarb and coworkers (58). The protein was investigated by pulsed ENDOR at 95 GHz in frozen solution and in single crystals (92). From ^{1}H and ^{2}H ENDOR the hyperfine parameters of the protons of coordinated H_2O molecules and imidazole protons of the His ligands were determined, yielding information about the electronic structure in addition to structural information. Distances between the paramagnetic center and protons of histidines were obtained from the measured hyperfine couplings using a point dipole model. For the protons of two H_2O molecules, four pairs of $A_\parallel$ and $A_\perp$ were found, but they could not be assigned to the respective H_2O molecules. It was also demonstrated that the larger difference in Boltzmann population at high magnetic fields and low temperatures can be used to assign transitions to the respective M_S quantum numbers and thus determine the sign of the hyperfine coupling constant. Recently, single-crystal ENDOR at 95 GHz on concanavalin A was performed by the same group, showing the advantages of single-crystal EPR also for that system. The angular dependence of the ENDOR spectra of all four protons were analyzed (37), and from the hyperfine tensors the directions and distances of the protons were derived. In the EPR spectra of this site, along specific directions a splitting of the signals is observed that is not in agreement with the space group of the crystal. This splitting is attributed to manganese centers with different zero-field splitting parameters. It is interesting that a similar behavior was found for the g-tensor of the copper in mutants of azurin (M121H and M121Q) described above. Whether these inhomogeneities could be a more general feature and a result of manipulating the protein by mutagenesis in the azurin mutants or by chemical means by exchanging the native metal ion by manganese can only be speculated at present.

In view of the difficulties of determining proton locations or even the nature of a ligand around a metal site by X-ray crystallography, e.g., whether OH^- or H_2O is bound, studies of the hyperfine interaction of metal ligands have significant potential for the understanding of metal protein function.

IRON PROTEINS   High-spin Fe(III) centers in proteins are difficult to study by X-band EPR because usually the zero-field splitting is larger than the microwave quantum ($\sim$0.3 cm^{-1}), which results in incomplete spectra that are difficult to interpret. The zero-field splitting of the high-spin ferric iron of met-hemoglobin was determined from spectra at microwave frequencies between 70 and 400 GHz (3). In order to demonstrate the usefulness of high-field EPR, a study by Doctor & Gaffney (52) presents line-shape simulations for the high-spin Fe(III) in lipoxygenase to determine what can be expected in high-field EPR. No high-field EPR spectra were measured, which precludes comparison with experiments. A detailed study of the line-shape of the signal of high-spin ferric ion (Fe(III)) in diferric transferrin including experimental data and their simulation is given in (60). Diferric transferrin is an example for which D > hv at X-band, making the spectra difficult to interpret, whereas D < hv at W-band, a zero-field splitting parameter D of 0.28 cm^{-1} is found. Furthermore, a given disorder, i.e., a distribution of D and/or E values, contributes less to the linewidth at W-band than at X-band frequency, resulting in better-resolved W-band EPR spectra. For catalase, on the other hand, W-band is not a sufficiently high frequency to reach the condition D < hv. Therefore, only a lower limit of 7 cm^{-1} for D could be determined. The effects of disorder on the EPR spectra are discussed in detail and simulations are shown in order to demonstrate the spectral changes expected in the presence of distributions of D and E values. From these studies a picture emerges of the spectroscopic properties of high-spin ferric iron. The results illustrate the need for a multi-frequency approach, with emphasis on high-frequency EPR. Measurements of the linewidth of the g = 5.85 line of met-myoglobin by Reijerse et al. (102) showed a linear increase of the linewidth from X-band to D-band (130 GHz).

In some cases high-field EPR helps to distinguish the origin of paramagnetic centers in proteins. One such example served to disprove an iron center as the locus of paramagnetism. In a ribonucleotide reductase mutant Y122H a paramagnetic state can be created, which was analyzed using W-band EPR and X-band ENDOR by Kolberg et al. (79). Initial suggestions of an iron center as being the origin of the paramagnetism were in disagreement with the small g-anisotropy observed in W-band EPR. On the basis of the W-band EPR results, the center was identified as an amino acid–based radical center, which has a strong interaction with two Fe ions. A coupling scheme for the radical state involving all three centers is proposed based on the size of the magnitude of the ^{57}Fe hyperfine coupling.

Future Aspects of High-Field EPR

It is expected that integer spin systems with large zero-field interactions, which are EPR silent at lower fields, will be investigated by high-field EPR. Examples of where such an approach would be useful are Mn(III) in manganese enzymes, Fe(II) in hemoglobin, Fe(IV), Co(I) in vitamin B12-binding enzymes, Ni(II), Mo(IV) in oxidases, and W(IV) in dehydrogenases [list compiled in (70, 102)]. So far, the corresponding metal centers have been investigated in inorganic complexes [see for example the study by Krzystek et al. (80)], but one can expect that the corresponding proteins will come under investigation. So far the biggest obstacle is the relatively high sample concentration required for the high-frequency transmission spectrometers available to date, a limitation that will become less severe with increased spectrometer sensitivity.

During recent years, EPR has witnessed a true revival, not the least driven by the developments toward higher frequencies. The ideal EPR frequency does not exist, the most appropriate frequency varies with the system and problem under study. The most important aspect of the development of EPR toward higher frequencies may well be that a multi-frequency approach has come within reach. Especially for proteins, for which samples are always complex and sometimes ill-defined while their EPR spectra contain a lot of information that is often largely hidden under inhomogeneously broadened lines, the availability of diverse techniques in a range of frequencies adds considerably to the effectiveness of EPR. Applications to metalloproteins, although limited as yet, promise to be one of the most fruitful areas within EPR for years to come.

ACKNOWLEDGMENTS

This work was performed under the auspices of the BIOMAC graduate school of Leiden and partly supported by TMR hemeworks contract FMRX-CT98-0218. We are grateful to A. W. J. W. Tepper for the preparation of Figure 1.

Visit the Annual Reviews home page at www.annualreviews.org

LITERATURE CITED

1. Deleted in proof
2. Allegrozzi M, Bertini I, Janik MBL, Lee YM, Lin GH, Luchinat C. 2000. Lanthanide-induced pseudocontact shifts for solution structure refinements of macromolecules in shells up to 40 angstrom from the metal ion. *J. Am. Chem. Soc.* 122:4154–61
3. Alpert Y, Couder Y, Tuchendler J, Thomé H. 1973. Determination of the zero-field splitting in human acid methemoglobin by millimeter and submillimeter ESR experiments. *Biochim. Biophys. Acta* 322:34–37
4. Arnesano F, Banci L, Bertini I, Felli IC. 1998. The solution structure of oxidized rat microsomal cytochrome b(5). *Biochemistry* 37:173–84
5. Arnesano F, Banci L, Bertini I, van der Wetering K, Czisch M, Kaptein R. 2000. The auto-orientation in high magnetic fields of oxidized cytochrome b(562) as source of constraints for solution structure determination. *J. Biomol. NMR* 17:295–304
6. Asokan A, deRopp JS, Newmyer SL, Oritz de Montellano P, La Mar GN. 2001. Solution 1H NMR of the molecular and

electronic structure of the heme cavity and substrate binding pocket of high-spin ferric horseradish peroxidase: effect of His42Ala mutation. *J. Am. Chem. Soc.* 123:4243–54
7. Banci L. 1993. NMR relaxation in paramagnetic metalloproteins. In *NMR of Paramagnetic Molecules*, ed. LT Berliner, T Reuben, pp. 79–108. NY/London: Plenum
8. Banci L. 2000. Structure and dynamics of heme proteins. *J. Porphyr. Phthaloc.* 4:390–91
9. Banci L, Bertini I, Bren KL, Cremonini MA, Gray HB, et al. 1996. The use of pseudocontact shifts to refine solution of paramagnetic metalloproteins: Met80Ala cyano-cytochrome c as an example. *J. Biol. Inorg. Chem.* 1:117–26
10. Banci L, Bertini I, Huber JG, Luchinat C, Rosato A. 1998. Partial orientation of oxidized and reduced cytochrome b(5) at high magnetic fields: magnetic susceptibility, anisotropy contributions and consequences for protein solution structure determination. *J. Am. Chem. Soc.* 120:12903–9
11. Banci L, Bertini I, Luchinat C. 1991.

Nuclear and Electron Relaxation. Weinheim: VCH

12. Banci L, Bertini I, Luchinat C, Pierattelli R, Shokhirev NV, Walker FA. 1998. Analysis of the temperature dependence of the H-1 and C-13 isotropic shifts of horse heart ferricytochrome c: explanation of Curie and anti-Curie temperature dependence and nonlinear pseudocontact shifts in a common two-level framework. *J. Am. Chem. Soc.* 120:8472–79

13. Banci L, Bertini I, Savellini GG, Romagnoli A, Turano P, et al. 1997. Pseudocontact shifts as constraints for energy minimization and molecular dynamics calculations on solution structures of paramagnetic metalloproteins. *Protein Struct. Funct. Genet.* 29:68–76

14. Banci L, Presenti C. 2000. Perspectives in inorganic structural biology: solution structures of metalloproteins. *J. Biol. Inorg. Chem.* 5:422–31

15. Battiste JL, Wagner G. 2000. Utilization of site-directed spin labeling and high-resolution heteronuclear nuclear magnetic resonance for global fold determination of large proteins with limited nuclear Overhauser effect data. *Biochemistry* 39:5355–65

16. Beger RD, Marathias VM, Volkman BF, Bolton PH. 1998. Determination of internuclear angles of DNA using paramagnetic assisted magnetic alignment. *J. Magn. Reson.* 135:256–59

17. Bellew BF, Halkides CJ, Gerfen GJ, Griffin RG, Singel DJ. 1996. High-frequency (139.5 GHz) electron paramagnetic resonance characterization of $Mn(II)$-(H_2O)-^{17}O interactions in GDP and GTP forms of p21 ras. *Biochemistry* 35:12186–93

18. Bertini I, Ciurli S, Dikiy A, Fernández CO, Luchinat C, et al. 2001. The first solution structure of a paramagnetic copper(II) protein: the case of oxidized plastocyanin from the cyanobacterium *Synechocystis* PCC6803. *J. Am. Chem. Soc.* 123:2405–13

19. Bertini I, Ciurli S, Dikiy A, Gasanov R, Luchinat C, et al. 1999. High-field NMR studies of oxidized blue copper proteins: the case of spinach plastocyanin. *J. Am. Chem. Soc.* 121:2037–46

20. Bertini I, Felli IC, Luchinat C. 2000. Lanthanide induced residual dipolar couplings for the conformational investigation of peripheral (NH2)-N-15 moieties. *J. Biomol. NMR* 18:347–55

21. Bertini I, Fernández CO, Karlsson BG, Leckner J, Luchinat C, et al. 2000. Structural information through NMR hyperfine shifts in blue copper proteins. *J. Am. Chem. Soc.* 122:3701–7

22. Deleted in proof

23. Bertini I, Janik MBL, Lee YM, Luchinat C, Rosato A. 2001. Magnetic susceptibility tenser anisotropies for a lanthanide ion series in a fixed protein matrix. *J. Am. Chem. Soc.* 123:4181–88

24. Bertini I, Janik MBL, Liu GH, Luchinat C, Rosato A. 2001. Solution structure calculations through self-orientation in a magnetic field of a cerium(III) substituted calcium-binding protein. *J. Magn. Reson.* 148:23–30

25. Bertini I, Luchinat C. 1986. *NMR of Paramagnetic Molecules in Biological Systems.* Menlo Park, CA: Benjamin Cummings

26. Bertini I, Luchinat C, Aime S. 1996. NMR of paramagnetic substances. *Coord. Chem. Rev.* 150:1–293

27. Bertini I, Luchinat C, Parigi G, Walker FA. 1999. Heme methyl H-1 chemical shifts as structural parameters in some low-spin ferriheme proteins. *J. Biol. Inorg. Chem.* 4:515–19

28. Bertini I, Luchinat C, Rosato A. 1999. NMR spectra of iron-sulfur proteins. *Adv. Inorg. Chem.* 47:251–82

29. Bertini I, Luchinat C, Turano P. 2000. N-15 chemical shift changes in cytochrome b(5): redox-dependent vs. guanidinium chloride-induced changes. *J. Biol. Inorg. Chem.* 5:761–64

30. Bertini I, Rosato A, Turano P. 1999.

Solution structure of paramagnetic met-alloproteins. *Pure Appl. Chem.* 71:1717–25

31. Biekofsky RR, Muskett FW, Schmidt JM, Martin SR, Browne JP, et al. 1999. NMR approaches for monitoring domain orientations in calcium-binding proteins in solution using partial replacement of Ca2+ by Tb3+. *FEBS Lett.* 460:519–26

32. Bloembergen N. 1957. Proton relaxation times in paramagnetic solutions. *J. Chem. Phys.* 27:572–73

33. Boisbouvier J, Gans P, Blackledge M, Brutscher B, Marion D. 1999. Long-range structural information in NMR studies of paramagnetic molecules from electron spin-nuclear spin cross-correlated relaxation. *J. Am. Chem. Soc.* 121:7700–1

34. Bougault CM, Dou Y, Ikeda-Saito M, Langry KC, Smith KM, La Mar GN. 1998. Solution H-1 NMR study of the electronic structure and magnetic properties of high-spin ferrous or deoxy myoglobins. *J. Am. Chem. Soc.* 120:2113–23

35. Boyd J, Dobson CM, Morar AS, Williams RJP, Pielak GJ. 1999. H-1 and N-15 hyperfine shifts of cytochrome c. *J. Am. Chem. Soc.* 121:9247–48

36. Bubacco L, Salgado J, Tepper AWJW, Vijgenboom E, Canters GW. 1999. H-1 NMR spectroscopy of the binuclear Cu(II) active site of *Streptomyces antibioticus* tyrosinase. *FEBS Lett.* 442:215–20

37. Carmieli R, Manikandan P, Kalb AJ, Goldfarb D. 2001. Proton postions in the Mn(II) binding site of concanavalin A as determined by single crystal high-field ENDOR spectroscopy. *J. Am. Chem. Soc.* 123:8378–86

38. Chen ZG, deRopp JS, Hernandez G, LaMar GN. 1994. 2D NMR approaches to characterizing the molecular-structure and dynamic stability of the active-site for cyanide-inhibited horseradish-peroxidase. *J. Am. Chem. Soc.* 116:8772–83

39. Contreras MA, Ubach J, Millet O, Rizo J, Pons M. 1999. Measurement of one bond dipolar couplings through lanthanide-induced orientation of a calcium-binding protein. *J. Am. Chem. Soc.* 121:8947–48

40. Coremans JWA. 1996. W-band electron spin echo spectroscopy of azurin. PhD thesis. Univ. Leiden. 157 pp.

41. Coremans JWA, Poluektov OG, Groenen EJJ, Canters GW, Nar H, Messerschmidt A. 1994. A W-band electron-paramagnetic-resonance study of a single crystal of azurin. *J. Am. Chem. Soc.* 116:3097–101

42. Coremans JWA, Poluektov OG, Groenen EJJ, Canters GW, Nar H, Messerschmidt A. 1996. A W-band electron nuclear double resonance study of single crystals of N-14 and N-15 azurin. *J. Am. Chem. Soc.* 118:12141–53

43. Coremans JWA, Poluektov OG, Groenen EJJ, Canters GW, Nar H, Messerschmidt A. 1997. A W-band electron spin echo envelope modulation study of a single crystal of azurin. *J. Am. Chem. Soc.* 119:4726–31

44. Coremans JWA, Poluektov OG, Groenen EJJ, Warmerdam GCM, Canters GW, et al. 1996. The azurin mutant Met-121Gln: a blue-copper protein with a strong axial ligand. *J. Phys. Chem.* 100:19706–13

45. Coremans JWA, van Gastel M, Poluektov OG, Groenen EJJ, den Blaauwen T, et al. 1995. An ENDOR and ESEEM study of the blue-copper protein azurin. *Chem. Phys. Lett.* 235:202–10

46. Crowley P, Otting G, Schlarb-Ridley BG, Canters GW, Ubbink M. 2001. Hydrophobic interactions in a cyanobacterial plastocyanin-cytochrome *f* complex. *J. Am. Chem. Soc.* 123:10444–53

47. Deligiannakis Y, Louloudi M, Hadjiliadis N. 2000. Electron spin echo envelope modulation (ESEEM) spectroscopy as a tool to investigate the coordination environment of metal centers. *Coord. Chem. Rev.* 204:1–112

48. Demene H, Tsan P, Gans P, Marion D. 2000. NMR determination of the magnetic susceptibility anisotropy of cytochrome c' of *Rhodobacter capsulatu*s by (1) J (HN) dipolar coupling constants measurement: characterization of its monomeric state in solution. *J. Phys. Chem. B* 104:2559–69

49. Dennison C, Berg A, deVries S, Canters GW. 1996. H-1 NMR studies of the paramagnetic Cu-A center of cytochrome oxidase. *FEBS Lett.* 394:340–44

50. DeRopp JS, LaMar GN. 1991. 2D NMR assignment of hyperfine-shifted resonances in strongly paramagnetic metalloproteins—resting-state horseradishperoxidase. *J. Am. Chem. Soc.* 113:4348–50

51. Disselhorst JAJM, van der Meer H, Poluektov OG, Schmidt J. 1995. A pulsed EPR and ENDOR spectrometer operating at 95 GHz. *J. Magn. Reson. A* 115:183–88

52. Doctor KS, Gaffney BJ. 1996. High-frequency EPR predictions for the nonheme iron protein lipoxygenase. *Appl. Magn. Reson.* 11:425–35

53. Donaire A, Jimenez B, Moratal JM, Hall JF, Hasnain SS. 2001. Electronic characterization of the oxidized state of the blue copper protein rusticyanin by H-1 NMR: Is the axial methionine the dominant influence for the high redox potential? *Biochemistry* 40:837–46

54. Donaire A, Salgado J, Moratal JM. 1998. Determination of the magnetic axes of cobalt(II) and nickel(II) azurins from H-1 NMR data: influence of the metal and axial ligands on the origin of magnetic anisotropy in blue copper proteins. *Biochemistry* 37:8659–73

55. Dunham SU, Turner CJ, Lippard SJ. 1998. Solution structure of a DNA duplex containing a nitroxide spin-labeled platinum d(GpG) intrastrand cross-link refined with NMR-derived long-range electron-proton distance restraints. *J. Am. Chem. Soc.* 120:5395–406

56. Emerson SD, LaMar GN. 1990. NMR determination of the orientation of the magnetic-susceptibility tensor in cyanometmyoglobin—a new probe of steric tilt of bound ligand. *Biochemistry* 29:1556–66

57. Emerson SD, LaMar GN. 1990. Solution structural characterization of cyanometmyoglobin—resonance assignment of heme cavity residues by 2-dimensional NMR. *Biochemistry* 29:1545–56

58. Epel B, Poppl A, Manikandan P, Vega S, Goldfarb D. 2001. The effect of spin relaxation on ENDOR spectra recorded at high magnetic fields and low temperatures. *J. Magn. Reson.* 148:388–97

59. Feng Y, Roder H, Englander SW. 1990. Redox-dependent structure change and hyperfine nuclear magnetic resonance shifts in cytochrome c. *Biochemistry* 29:3494–504

60. Gaffney BJ, Maguire BC, Weber RT, Maresch GG. 1999. Disorder at metal sites in proteins: a high-frequency-EMR study. *Appl. Magn. Reson.* 16:207–21

61. Gaponenko V, Dvoretsky A, Walsby C, Hoffman BM, Rosevear PR. 2000. Calculation of z-coordinates and orientational restraints using a metal binding tag. *Biochemistry* 39:15217–24

62. Gaponenko V, Howarth JW, Columbus L, Gasmi-Seabrook G, Yuan J, et al. 2000. Protein global fold determination using site-directed spin and isotope labeling. *Protein Sci.* 9:302–9

63. Geyer M, Schweins T, Herrmann C, Prisner T, Wittinghofer A, Kalbitzer HR. 1996. Conformational transitions in p21(ras) and in its complexes with the effector protein Raf-RBD and the GTPase activating protein GAP. *Biochemistry* 35:10308–20

64. Gochin M. 2000. A high-resolution structure of a DNA-chromomycin-Co(II) complex determined from pseudocontact shifts in nuclear magnetic resonance. *Struct. Fold. Design* 8:441–52

65. Grinberg OY, Dubinskii AA, Shuvalov

VF, Oranskii LG, Kurochkin VI, Lebedev YS. 1976. Submillimeter ESR spectroscopy of free radicals. *Dokl. Phys. Chem.* 230:923–30

66. Gromov I, Krymov V, Manikandan P, Arieli D, Goldfarb D. 1999. A W-band pulsed ENDOR spectrometer: setup and application to transition metal centers. *J. Magn. Reson.* 139:8–17

67. Gueron M. 1975. Nuclear relaxation in macromolecules by paramagnetic ions: a novel mechansim. *J. Magn. Reson.* 19:58–66

68. Guiles RD, Sarma S, DiGate RJ, Banville D, Basus VJ, et al. 1996. Pseudocontact shifts used in the restraint of the solution structures of electron transfer complexes. *Nat. Struct. Biol.* 3:333–39

69. Hagen WR. 1989. G-strain: inhomogeneous broadening in metalloprotein EPR. In *Advanced EPR*, ed. AJ Hoff, pp. 785–812. Amsterdam: Elsevier

70. Hagen WR. 1999. High-frequency EPR of transition ion complexes and metalloproteins. *Coord. Chem. Rev.* 192:209–29

71. Halkides CJ, Bellew BF, Gerfen GJ, Farrar CT, Carter PH, et al. 1996. High-frequency (139.5 GHz) electron paramagnetic resonance spectroscopy of the GTP form of p21 ras with selective ^{17}O labeling of threonine. *Biochemistry* 35:12194–200

71a. Höfer P, Maresch GG, Schmalbein D, Holczer K. 1996. *Bruker Rep.* 142:15–21

72. Horrocks WDJ, Greenberg ES. 1974. Isotropic nuclear magnetic resonance shifts in low-spin iron (III) porphyrin and hemin systems. A theoretical interpretation of temperature dependencies. *Mol. Phys.* 27:993–99

73. Hus JC, Marion D, Blackledge M. 2000. De novo determination of protein structure by NMR using orientational and long-range order restraints. *J. Mol. Biol.* 298:927–36

74. Inubushi T, Becker ED. 1983. Efficient detection of paramagnetically shifted

NMR resonances by optimizing the WEFT pulse sequence. *J. Magn. Reson.* 51:128–33

75. Jaszewski AR, Jezierska J. 2001. Hybrid density functional approach to the isotropic and anisotropic hyperfine couplings with N-14 and H-1 nuclei in the blue copper proteins. *Chem. Phys. Lett.* 343:571–80

76. Karplus M. 1963. Vicinal proton coupling in nuclear magnetic resonance. *J. Am. Chem. Soc.* 85:2870–71

77. Käss H, MacMillan F, Ludwig B, Prisner TF. 2000. Investigation of the Mn binding site in cytochrome c oxidase from *Paracoccus denitrificans* by high-frequency EPR. *J. Phys. Chem. B* 104: 5362–71

78. Keller RM, Wuthrich K. 1981. Multiple irradiation ^1H NMR experiments with hemoproteins. In *Biological Magnetic Resonance*, ed. LJ Berliner, J Reuben, 3:1–52. NY: Plenum

79. Kolberg M, Bleifuss G, Potsch S, Graslund A, Lubitz W, et al. 2000. A new stable high-valent diiron center in R2 mutant Y122H of *E. coli* ribonucleotide reductase studied by high-field EPR and Fe-57-ENDOR. *J. Am. Chem. Soc.* 122:9856–57

80. Krzystek J, Telser J, Pardi LA, Goldberg DP, Hoffman BM, Brunel LC. 1999. High-frequency and -field electron paramagnetic resonance of high-spin manganese(III) in porphyrinic complexes. *Inorg. Chem.* 38:6121–29

81. Kurland RJ, McGarvey BR. 1970. Isotropic NMR shifts in transition metal complexes: the calculation of the Fermi contact and pseudocontact terms. *J. Magn. Reson.* 2:286–301

82. LaMar GN. 1973. NMR of paramagnetic porphyrins. In *NMR of Paramagnetic Molecules; Principles and Applications*, ed. GN LaMar, WD Horrocks Jr, RH Holm, pp. 85–126. New York: Academic

83. LaMar GN, Asokan A, Espiritu B, Yeh

DC, Auclair K, Oritz de Montellano P. 2001. Solution 1H NMR of the active site of substrate-bound, cyanide-inhibited human heme oxygenase. *J. Biol. Chem.* 276:15676–87

84. LaMar GN, Walker FA. 1979. NMR of paramagnetic porphyrins. In *The Porhyrins*, ed. D Dolphin, Vol. IV B, pp. 57–161. New York: Academic

85. Louro RO, Correia IJ, Brennan L, Coutinho IB, Xavier AV, Turner DL. 1998. Electronic structure of low-spin ferric porphyrins: C-13 NMR studies of the influence of axial ligand orientation. *J. Am. Chem. Soc.* 120:13240–47

86. Luchinat C. 1999. NMR of paramagnetic proteins. *J. Inorg. Biochem.* 74:38–38

87. Lynch WB, Earle KA, Freed JH. 1988. 1-mm wave ESR spectrometer. *Rev. Sci. Instr.* 59:1345–51

88. Ma C, Opella SJ. 2000. Lanthanide ions bind specifically to an added "EF-hand" and orient a membrane protein in micelles for solution NMR spectroscopy. *J. Magn. Reson.* 146:381–84

89. Ma LX, Jorgensen AMM, Sorensen GO, Ulstrup J, Led JJ. 2000. Elucidation of the paramagnetic R-1 relaxation of heteronuclei and protons in Cu(II) plastocyanin from *Anabaena variabilis*. *J. Am. Chem. Soc.* 122:9473–85

90. Ma LX, Philipp E, Led JJ. 2001. Determination of the electron self-exchange rates of blue copper proteins by super-WEFT NMR spectroscopy. *J. Biomol. NMR* 19:199–208

91. Madhu PK, Grandori R, Hohenthanner K, Mandal PK, Muller N. 2001. Geometry dependent two-dimensional heteronuclear multiplet effects in paramagnetic proteins. *J. Biomol. NMR* 20:31–37

92. Manikandan P, Carmieli R, Shane T, Kalb AJ, Goldfarb D. 2000. W-band ENDOR investigation of the manganese-binding site of concanavalin A: determination of proton hyperfine couplings and their signs. *J. Am. Chem. Soc.* 122:3488–94

93. Mims WB, Peisach J. 1976. Assignment of a ligand in stellacyanin by a pulsd EPR method. *Biochemistry* 15:3863–69

94. Möbius K. 2000. Primary processes in photosynthesis: What do we learn from high-field EPR spectroscopy? *Chem. Soc. Rev.* 29:129–39

95. Moore GR, Williams G. 1984. Assignment of 1H-NMR resonances of the heme and axial histidine ligand of mitochondrial cytochrome c. *Biochim. Biophys. Acta* 788:147–50

96. Moratal JM, Salgado J, Donaire A, Jimenez HR, Castells J. 1993. COSY and NOESY characterization of cobalt(II)-substituted azurin from *Pseudomonas aeruginosa*. *Inorg. Chem.* 32:3587–88

97. Moratal JM, Salgado J, Donaire A, Jimenez HR, Castells J, Martinez-Ferrer MJ. 1993. H-1 2D-NMR characterization of Ni(II)-substituted azurin from *Pseudomonas aeruginosa*. *Magn. Reson. Chem.* 31:S41–46

98. Prestegard JH, Al Hashimi HM, Tolman JR. 2000. NMR structures of biomolecules using field oriented media and residual dipolar couplings. *Q. Rev. Biophys.* 33:371–424

99. Prisner TF, Rohrer M, MacMillan F. 2001. Pulsed EPR spectroscopy: biological applications. *Annu. Rev. Phys. Chem.* 52:279–313

100. Prisner TF, Rohrer M, Möbius K. 1994. Pulsed 95-GHz high-field EPR heterodyne spectrometer with high spectral and time resolution. *Appl. Magn. Reson.* 7:167–83

101. Prisner TF, Un S, Griffin RG. 1992. Pulsed ESR at 140 GHz. *Isr. J. Chem.* 32: 357–63

102. Reijerse EJ, van Dam PJ, Klaassen AK, Hagen WR, van Bentum PM, Smith GM. 1998. Concepts in high-frequency EPR—applications to bio-inorganic systems. *Appl. Magn. Reson.* 14:153–67

103. Rohrer M, Prisner TF, Brugmann O, Käss H, Spoerner M, et al. 2001. Structure of the metal-water complex in Ras

center dot GDP studied by high-field EPR spectroscopy and P-31 NMR spectroscopy. *Biochemistry* 40:1884–89

104. Romero A, De la Cerda B, Varela PF, Navarro JA, Hervas M, De la Rosa MA. 1998. The 2.15 angstrom crystal structure of a triple mutant plastocyanin from the cyanobacterium *Synechocystis* sp. PCC 6803. *J. Mol. Biol.* 275:327–36

105. Salgado J, Kalverda AP, Diederix REM, Canters GW, Moratal JM, et al. 1999. Paramagnetic NMR investigations of Co(II) and Ni(II) amicyanin. *J. Biol. Inorg. Chem.* 4:457–67

106. Salgado J, Warmerdam G, Bubacco L, Canters GW. 1998. Understanding the electronic properties of the Cu-A site from the soluble domain of cytochrome c oxidase through paramagnetic H-1 NMR. *Biochemistry* 37:7378–89

107. SatterLee JD, Erman JE. 1991. Proton NMR assignment of heme contacts and catalytically implicated amino acids in cyanide-ligated cytochrome c peroxidase determined from one- and two-dimensional nuclear Overhauser effects. *Biochemistry* 4398–405

108. Sattler M, Fesik SW. 1997. Resolving resonance overlap in the NMR spectra of proteins from differential lanthanide-induced shifts. *J. Am. Chem. Soc.* 119: 7885–86

109. Slutter CE, Gromov I, Epel B, Pecht I, Richards JH, Goldfarb D. 2001. Pulsed EPR/ENDOR characterization of perturbations of the Cu-A center ground state by axial methionine ligand mutations. *J. Am. Chem. Soc.* 123:5325–36

110. Solomon I. 1955. Relaxation processes in a system of two spins. *Phys. Rev.* 99: 559–65

111. Solomon I, Bloembergen N. 1956. Nuclear magnetic interactions in the HF molecule. *J. Chem. Phys.* 25:261–66

112. Thanabal V, deRopp JS, LaMar GN. 1987. 1H NMR study of the electronic and molecular structure of the heme cavity in horseradish peroxidase. Complete heme resonance assignments based on saturation transfer and nuclear Overhauser effects. *J. Am. Chem. Soc.* 109:265–72

113. Thanabal V, deRopp JS, LaMar GN. 1987. Identification of the catalytically important amino acid residue resonances in ferric low-spin horseradish peroxidase with nuclear Overhauser effect measurements. *J. Am. Chem. Soc.* 109:7516–25

114. Tolman JR, Flanagan JM, Kennedy MA, Prestegard JH. 1995. Nuclear magnetic dipole interactions in field-oriented proteins—information for structure determination in solution. *Proc. Natl. Acad. Sci. USA* 92:9279–83

115. Tolman JR, Flanagan JM, Kennedy MA, Prestegard JH. 1997. NMR evidence for slow collective motions in cyanometmyoglobin. *Nat. Struct. Biol.* 4:292–97

116. Tsan P, Caffrey M, Daku ML, Cusanovich M, Marion D, Gans P. 1999. Unusual contact shifts and magnetic tensor orientation in *Rhodobacter capsulatus* ferrocytochrome c': NMR, magnetic susceptibility, and EPR studies. *J. Am. Chem. Soc.* 121:1795–805

117. Tsan P, Caffrey M, Daku ML, Cusanovich M, Marion D, Gans P. 2001. Magnetic susceptibility tensor and heme contact shifts determinations in the *Rhodobacter capsulatus* ferricytochrome c': NMR and magnetic susceptibility studies. *J. Am. Chem. Soc.* 123:2231–42

118. Tu K, Gochin M. 1999. Structure determination by restrained molecular dynamics using NMR pseudocontact shifts as experimentally determined constraints. *J. Am. Chem. Soc.* 121:9276–85

119. Turner DL. 2000. Obtaining ligand geometries from paramagnetic shifts in low-spin haem proteins. *J. Biol. Inorg. Chem.* 5:328–32

120. Turner DL, Brennan L, Chamberlin SG, Louro RO, Xavier AV. 1998. Determination of solution structures of paramagnetic proteins by NMR. *Eur. Biophys. J. Biophys. Lett.* 27:367–75

121. Ubbink M, Ejdeback M, Karlsson BG, Bendall DS. 1998. The structure of the complex of plastocyanin and cytochrome f, determined by paramagnetic NMR and restrained rigid-body molecular dynamics. *Structure* 6:323–35

122. Ubbink M, Lian LY, Modi S, Evans PA, Bendall DS. 1996. Analysis of the H-1-NMR chemical shifts of Cu(I)-, Cu(II)- and Cd-substituted pea plastocyanin—metal-dependent differences in the hydrogen-bond network around the copper site. *Eur. J. Biochem.* 242:132–47

123. Van Amsterdam IMC, Ubbink M, Jeuken LJC, Verbeet MP, Einsle O, et al. 2001. Effects of dimerization on protein electron transfer. *Chem. Eur. J.* 7:2398–406

123a. Van Amsterdam IMC, Ubbink M, Einsle O, Messerschmidt A, Merli A, et al. 2002. Dramatic modulation of electron transfer in protein complexes by crosslinking. *Nat. Struct. Biol.* 9:48–52

124. Van Gastel M. 2000. *Type 1 copper sites in proteins. Spectroscopy and quantum chemistry.* PhD thesis. Univ. Leiden, Leiden. 147 pp.

125. Van Gastel M, Boulanger MJ, Canters GW, Huber M, Murphy MEP, et al. 2001. A single-crystal electron paramagnetic resonance study at 95 GHz of the type 1 copper site of the green nitrite reductase of *Alcaligenes faecalis. J. Phys. Chem. B* 105:2236–43

126. Van Gastel M, Canters GW, Krupka H, Messerschmidt A, de Waal EC, et al. 2000. Axial ligation in blue-copper proteins. A W-band electron spin echo detected electron paramagnetic resonance study of the azurin mutant M121H. *J. Am. Chem. Soc.* 122:2322–28

127. Vega AJ, Fiat D. 1976. Nuclear relaxation processes of paramagnetic complexes. The slow-motion case. *Mol. Phys.* 31:347–55

128. Veglia G, Opella SJ. 2000. Lanthanide ion binding to adventitious sites aligns membrane proteins in micelles for solution NMR spectroscopy. *J. Am. Chem. Soc.* 122:11733–34

129. Volkman BF, Wilkens SJ, Lee AL, Xia B, Westler WM, et al. 1999. Redox-dependent magnetic alignment of *Clostridium pasteurianum* rubredoxin: measurement of magnetic susceptibility anisotropy and prediction of pseudocontact shift contributions. *J. Am. Chem. Soc.* 121:4677–83

130. Weber RT, Disselhorst JAJM, Prevo LJ, Schmidt J, Wenckebach WTH. 1989. Electron spin echo spectroscopy at 95 GHz. *J. Magn. Reson.* 81:129–44

131. Wilkens SJ, Xia B, Weinhold F, Markley JL, Westler WM. 1998. NMR investigations of *Clostridium pasteurianum* rubredoxin. Origin of hyperfine H-1, H-2, C-13 and N-15 NMR chemical shifts in iron-sulfur proteins as determined by comparison of experimental data with hybrid density functional calculations. *J. Am. Chem. Soc.* 120:4806–14

132. Williams G, Clayden NJ, Moore GR, Williams RJP. 1985. Comparison of the solution and crystal structures of mitochondrial cytochrome c. *J. Mol. Biol.* 183:447–60

133. Worrall JAR, Kolczak U, Canters GW, Ubbink M. 2001. Interaction of yeast iso-1-cytochrome c with cytochrome c peroxidase investigated by [N-15, H-1] heteronuclear NMR spectroscopy. *Biochemistry* 40:7069–76

Annu. Rev. Biophys. Biomol. Struct. 2002. 31:423–41
DOI: 10.1146/annurev.biophys.31.101101.140930

COMPUTATIONAL CELL BIOLOGY:
Spatiotemporal Simulation of Cellular Events

Boris M. Slepchenko, James C. Schaff, John H. Carson, and Leslie M. Loew
*Center for Biomedical Imaging Technology, University of Connecticut Health Center,
Farmington, Connecticut 06117; e-mail: les@volt.uchc.edu*

Key Words model, simulation, kinetics, diffusion, cell physiology

■ **Abstract** The field of computational cell biology has emerged within the past 5 years because of the need to apply disciplined computational approaches to build and test complex hypotheses on the interacting structural, physical, and chemical features that underlie intracellular processes. To meet this need, newly developed software tools allow cell biologists and biophysicists to build models and generate simulations from them. The construction of general-purpose computational approaches is especially challenging if the spatial complexity of cellular systems is to be explicitly treated. This review surveys some of the existing efforts in this field with special emphasis on a system being developed in the authors' laboratory, *Virtual Cell*. The theories behind both stochastic and deterministic simulations are discussed. Examples of respective applications to cell biological problems in RNA trafficking and neuronal calcium dynamics are provided to illustrate these ideas.

CONTENTS

INTRODUCTION

In the past 20 years, the advent and dissemination of revolutionary new technologies have permitted cell biologists to probe the physics and chemistry of living cells in situ. Confocal and two-photon excited fluorescence microscopies permit investigators to study the structure and dynamics of living cells with submicrometer three-dimensional (3D) spatial resolution and with time resolutions as fast as milliseconds. These quantitative microscopies can be combined with fluorescent indicators and fluorescent protein constructs to enable the study of the spatiotemporal behavior of individual molecules in cells. Patch clamp electrophysiological recording can be used to study ion currents through single-channel proteins or across the entire cell membrane. All these techniques can be further combined with methods to impart specific perturbations to cells such as photorelease of caged compounds to deliver controlled doses of second messengers or laser tweezer manipulations to determine the response of cells to mechanical stresses. Thus many of the cellular mechanisms, which in the past could only be studied in reconstituted artificial environments in test tubes, can now be studied in their native milieu and spatial organization.

Matching the advances in microscope-based technologies for studying living cells has been enormous progress in our cumulative knowledge of biomolecular structure and function. Massive structural biology efforts have produced extensive databases of 3D protein structures. High-throughput molecular biology and molecular genetics technologies have led to descriptions of the full genomes of several organisms, including, of course, the human genome. More recently, high-throughput proteomics technologies promise to catalog, for a given state of a given cell, the dynamic levels of and interactions between all proteins and their post-translational modifications. This wealth of molecular data has spawned the field of bioinformatics to provide computational tools for the organization, analysis, and synthesis of all this information. However, there is a critical need for new computational approaches that can link all the molecular-level data to the cellular processes that can be probed with the microscope. The nascent field of computational cell biology is emerging to fill this need and is the subject of this review.

The overall goal of computational cell biology is to enable cell biologists to build and exercise predictive models of cellular processes. An operational definition of the term model is most appropriately formulated in relation to the scientific method. A model, in this language, is simply a collection of hypotheses and facts brought together in an attempt to understand a phenomenon. Indeed, the choice of which hypotheses and facts to collect and the manner in which they are assembled themselves constitute additional hypotheses. For a cell biological model, the facts and hypotheses are composed of the molecular species and the biochemical or electrophysiological transformations that are presumed to underlie the cellular events. A prediction based on the model is in one sense most useful if it does not match the experimental details of the process—it then unequivocally tells us that the elements of the model are inaccurate or incomplete. Although such negative results are not always publishable, they are a tremendous aid in refining our understanding. If the prediction does match the experiment, it can never guarantee the truth of the model but should suggest other experiments that can test the validity of critical elements; ideally, it should also provide new predictions that can, in turn, be verified experimentally.

The very complexity of cell biological processes necessitates the development of new computational approaches to enable the application of the classical scientific method. A pair of separate factors contributes to this problem. First, the large number of interdependent chemical reactions and structural components that combine to affect and regulate a typical cell biological process forces one to seek the help of a computer to build a model and generate quantitative predictions from it. A structured computational framework is required to gather the relevant data about a cellular system and then execute mathematically rigorous simulations to establish whether the elements that were so identified are sufficient to produce an experimentally observed biological endpoint. The second factor recognizes that scientists trained in experimental cell biology are not typically equipped with sufficient mathematical, physical, or computational expertise to generate quantitative predictions from models. Conversely, theoretical biologists are often trained in the physical sciences and have difficulty communicating with experimentalists (bifurcation diagrams, for example, will not serve as a basis for a common language). Appropriate computational tools will therefore provide an interface that enables biologists to easily build models, run simulations, and visualize simulation results in a way that allows direct comparison to experiments. At the same time, these tools should be sufficiently sophisticated that they can facilitate the analysis of models by theorists and thus, ultimately, promote communication and collaboration between these communities.

This review describes current efforts to address this need, especially within the area of spatial modeling. We do not attempt to cover the large body of mathematical modeling studies that have used ad hoc approaches with either analytical solutions or numerical simulations that address only a specific problem. Rather, we focus on the design and application of several new general-purpose software tools for modeling intracellular physiology. The concentrations of reacting molecular species as a function of time in a well-mixed reactor can be obtained by solving ordinary differential equations (ODEs) that specify the rate of change of each species as a function of the concentrations of the molecules in the system. If membrane transport and electrical potential are to be included in the model, the rate expressions can become more complex but can still be formulated in terms of a system of ODEs. However, when diffusion of molecules within the complex geometry of a cell is also considered, the resultant "reaction/diffusion" system requires the solution of partial differential equations (PDEs) that describe variations in concentration over space and time. We discuss the difference between stochastic and deterministic approaches to solving reaction/diffusion systems to develop an understanding of when each is appropriate. We then briefly review existing tools for analyzing biochemical systems at the ODE level. Finally, three software systems for the construction and analysis of spatial models will be described, *StochSim, MCell*, and *Virtual Cell*. *Virtual Cell* was developed in our lab, and we describe it in the most detail including examples of both continuous and stochastic spatial models of cell biological processes that have been studied.

STOCHASTIC AND DETERMINISTIC DESCRIPTIONS OF CELLULAR PROCESSES

A continuous approach to spatially resolved biochemical systems based on reaction-diffusion PDEs provides a deterministic description in terms of average species concentration. This description is accurate and effective so long as the number of molecules in a system is macroscopically large. In this case, thermal stochastic fluctuations around average values are relatively small and can therefore be ignored. The complexity of most realistic models of cellular processes would require that the equations be solved numerically, so both a spatial domain and a time interval have to be sampled, and the equations should be correspondingly discretized. The resultant linear algebraic system is then solved by employing effective linear solvers. The most common approaches in engineering disciplines can be usually categorized as finite difference (37) or finite element methods (44). However, these approaches are difficult to implement within an automated software tool designed to solve problems on cells with arbitrary geometries.

The finite volume method, developed originally for problems in heat transfer (27), is especially well-suited to simulations in cell biological systems (31, 33). It is closely related to finite difference methods but allows for good control of boundary conditions and surface profile assumptions while preserving the conservative nature of the equations. Most importantly, the finite volume formalism accommodates the heterogeneous spatial organization of cellular compartments. As implemented in the *Virtual Cell*, the simulation geometry is composed of uniformly sampled rectangular volume elements. Piecewise linear interpolation functions are used to interpret the values of molecular concentrations and electric potentials between element centers. Within such elements, the rate of change of the concentration of a given molecular species is simply the sum of fluxes entering the volume element from its adjacent neighbors plus the rate of production of the given species via reactions. Appropriate jump boundary conditions are implemented at boundaries between dissimilar compartments (i.e., membrane transport conditions). The numerical formulation involves integrating the equations in time over each volume element using appropriate interpolation profiles and boundary conditions. The solution of each integration relates a small neighborhood of sample values over space and time. In choosing a solution method for the resulting system of algebraic equations, numerical stability, given the physically appropriate constraints associated with physiological models, must be considered. Accordingly, diffusion is treated implicitly, i.e. concentrations satisfy the system of simultaneous linear equations evaluated at the next time point to maintain stability. The iterative method originally chosen for solving the linear algebraic system builds on effective routines used for one-dimensional systems and is relatively easy to implement. However, there are some significant drawbacks, such as the need to solve for all the elements in the rectangular domain even if only some compartments are of interest. Moreover, in order for the method to converge in a reasonably small number of iterations, the ratio $\lambda = D\Delta t/\Delta x^2$, where D is the diffusion coefficient, Δt is the time step, and Δx is the spatial step, must be kept small. This imposes severe restrictions on the time step if high-spatial resolution is required and creates significant problems for running realistic 3D simulations. These issues were resolved, at least partially, by using a different linear solver. Linear solvers based on Krylov space approximations, such as the conjugate gradient method, in conjunction with a preconditioner (an operator that approximates the inverse of the matrix but can be applied at a low computational cost), become powerful and robust. There are commercial packages that implement a range of Krylov space methods, as well as many of the well-known preconditioners (e.g., PCGPAK, Scientific Computing Associates, New Haven, Connecticut). This has produced significant improvements in computational times and enables the practical application of these methods to much larger systems.

If the number of molecules involved in a process is relatively small, the fluctuations can become important. In this case, the continuous description is no longer sufficient and stochastic effects have to be included in a model. Single-channel ionic currents are one such example. While predictions based on the deterministic Hodgkin-Huxley model (20) are usually good for macroscopic phenomena, because of the nonlinearity of the system, stochastic behavior of ion channels proves to be important in some circumstances even when the number of channels is relatively large (35). Similar issues arise in calcium dynamics where the calcium concentration (calcium sparks, calcium waves) (22) can be significantly affected by the stochastic firing of calcium channels. Stochastic fluctuations of macromolecules are crucial for understanding the dynamics of vesicles and granules driven by competing molecular motors. In the case of a relatively small number of participating particles, a system that would be described deterministically by reaction-diffusion PDEs requires fully stochastic treatment. In this approach, diffusion is described as Brownian random walks of individual particles, and chemical kinetics is simulated as stochastic reaction events. Numerical stochastic simulations in this case are based on pseudo-random-number generation (28). They are often called Monte Carlo simulations (the term, originally introduced by Ulam and von Neumann in the days of the Manhattan Project) since throwing a dice is actually a way to generate a random number. Because Monte Carlo methods are general, relatively simple, and straightforward to implement, they can provide a numerical solution of the original reaction-diffusion system even when stochastic fluctuations are not an issue (see the description of *MCell*, below).

In situations where one subsystem requires discrete stochastic formulation, whereas the other can be treated deterministically, the problem can be described in terms of stochastic differential equations (17). As an example, in the Hodgkin-Huxley model, the membrane voltage is treated as a continuous deterministic variable described through a set of differential equations, whereas the single channel behavior is random. A natural way to introduce stochasticity in the model is to replace open probabilities by the actual numbers of open channels (9, 13). In fact, Hodgkin and Huxley introduced variables in their model to represent the proportion of open gates for various ions. The number of open channels is random and is governed by a corresponding Markov kinetic model that explicitly incorporates the internal workings of the ion channels. Mathematically, the membrane potential is now described by a stochastic differential equation with a discrete random process. Effects of stochasticity on nonlinear systems with excitable or bistable behavior and numerical approaches to stochastic differential equations are areas of active ongoing research (17, 41).

Numerical solution of stochastic differential equations includes the combination of numerical techniques commonly applied to regular differential equations and Monte Carlo methods employing random-number generators. But especially relevant for computational cell biology, the pioneering work by Gillespie (14, 15) on stochastic models for chemical reactions utilized an elegantly efficient algorithm in which the probabilities of each reaction are calculated from rate constants and numbers of substrate molecules. A stochastic method is used to determine which reaction will occur based on their relative probabilities. The time step is then adjusted to match the particular reaction that occurs. After the reaction is complete, the numbers of substrate molecules are readjusted prior to the next cycle. The Gillespie algorithm has been used extensively to analyze stochastic events in the field of biochemical kinetics. When combined with stable, accurate numerical schemes developed for the conventional differential equations, they can be applied for numerical solution of stochastic differential equations with discrete random processes. This type of approach has been utilized in the *Virtual Cell* to combine the deterministic description of a continuously distributed species (RNA) with the stochastic treatment of discrete particles (RNA granules) (see below).

MODELING SOFTWARE FOR NONSPATIAL BIOCHEMICAL SYSTEMS

This review does not cover the well-established field of molecular structure and dynamics simulations, as this is outside the problem domain we define as cell biology. However, another well-established target for computational approaches that is worthy of mention is neuroscience, where a number of software tools are available to simulate the electrophysiological behavior of single neurons and neuronal networks. Because these tools can treat membrane transport and electrical potential in cells, they are quite relevant to our problem domain. The two most prevalent programs are NEURON (18) and GENESIS (5). Both use cable theory (21) to treat the dynamics of electrical signals in the complex geometries of neurons. This theory solves the equation for membrane potential in a series of connected segments with the overall topology of the neuron. Ideally, each segment is small enough to be treated as a compartment that establishes electrical equilibrium rapidly on the timescale of the overall dynamics that are being modeled; in this way the problem can be reduced to solving ODEs, even for a geometry as complex as a neuron. Even more pertinent to cell biology are the recent efforts at generalizing these modeling tools to treat intracellular signaling networks. Hines & Carnevale (19) have added a model description language, NMODL, to

NEURON that accommodates this larger problem domain. Bhalla has developed a new interface called KINETIKIT that adapts GENESIS for chemical kinetics (http://www.ncbs.res.in/~bhalla/kkit/index.html); this tool was employed in an insightful analysis of the modularity of subsystems within complex signaling networks (4).

Several software tools have been developed from the ground up specifically to build complex biochemical reaction pathways and numerically simulate the time course of the individual molecular species within them. Each tool can translate reaction schemes into the corresponding system of ODEs and contains embedded numerical methods for their solution. GEPASI (24) (http://www.gepasi.org/) is one of the best established of these systems. It has an extensive list of predefined kinetic types that significantly aid in the construction of models. It also offers access to a number of optimization methods for deducing reasonable values of those parameters that are not well constrained from experimental determinations. Jarnac/Scamp (30) (http://members.tripod.co.uk/sauro/biotech.htm) is a scripting language that allows users to build, manipulate, and analyze metabolic pathway models with a syntax that is familiar to biologists and avoids having to deal with differential equations. DBSolve (16) (http://websites.ntl.com/~igor.goryanin/) is noteworthy because it has been designed to interface readily with pathway databases. It also contains mathematical tools such as bifurcation and metabolic control analysis. Berkeley Madonna was developed by Oster & Macey (http://www.berkeley madonna.com/) as a general purpose modeling and analysis tool that allows both graphical and text-based inputs of reaction kinetics; it contains several efficient solvers and provides capabilities for bifurcation and sensitivity analysis.

A different philosophy drives the ECELL Project (42) (http://www.e-cell.org/). This is a computational system for constructing whole-cell models, and a model of a self-sustaining primitive cell, based on a subset of 127 genes from the genome of a mycoplasma, has been completed. The model simulations are based on a series of reaction rules that are designed to rapidly calculate the effects of perturbations to individual components of the system. Models of red blood cells and mitochondria are currently under development. Ultimately, the aim of the project is to develop accurate computational models of complex cells such as cardiac myocytes.

At an early stage of development is another ambitious project, BioSpice, from the laboratory of Adam Arkin (http://www.lbl.gov/~aparkin/). While this laboratory has focused on analyzing prokaryotic genetic circuits (23), BioSpice is ultimately intended as a general purpose modeling framework for both genetic and biochemical networks. The open architecture of BioSpice is also intended to ease the incorporation of new software modules that can expand the capabilities of the system according to the needs of the modeling community. A similar philosophy is behind the development of a new software architecture, JSIM (http://nsr.bioeng.washington.edu/), for a simulation tool that models solute transport and exchange in the cardiovascular system; the aim here is also to produce a sufficiently open architecture so that the software can be easily enhanced and adapted to meet the needs of other modeling communities, including cell biology.

Although we have given references for all these software tools, the best information about the availability and current status of these packages is found on the developers' websites. Also, it is doubtful that this list is exhaustive; it is clear that the collection of tools for computational approaches to cell biology is rapidly growing.

SOFTWARE FOR SPATIAL MODELS: *StochSim*, *MCell*, and *Virtual Cell*

StochSim

The extraordinary efficiency of the Gillespie stochastic kinetics algorithm (14, 15) is achieved by restricting the decision process to selecting which reaction will occur and adjusting the time step accordingly. Focusing exclusively on the reaction avoids consideration of the properties of individual reactive species as discrete entities, which minimizes processing time when the number of reacting species is large. However, processing time increases in proportion to the number of different reactions. Furthermore, the Gillespie approach does not easily accommodate the existence of multiple states of different substrates, which may affect their reactivities, and since individual reactive species are not identified as discrete elements, their states, positions, and velocities within the reaction volume cannot be followed over time.

The *StochSim* program developed by Morton-Firth and Bray (24a–c) to analyze complex stochastic signaling pathways in bacterial chemotaxis addresses the "multi-state" problem by shifting the focus from the reaction to the individual reactive species. In this program individual molecules or molecular complexes are represented as discrete software objects or intracellular automata. The time step is set to accommodate the most rapid reaction in the system. At each time step two separate molecules are sequentially selected at random from the total population. Dummy "pseudo-molecules" are included in the population to simulate uni-molecular reactions. A random-number generator is used to determine if a reaction will occur between the two selected molecules by comparison to a look up table of probabilities of all possible reactions. When a reaction occurs the system is updated according to the stoichiometry of the reaction. Molecules that exist in more than one state are encoded as "multi-state molecules" using a series of binary flags to represent different states of the molecule such as conformation, ligand binding, or covalent modification. The flags can modify the reactivity of the molecule, and reactions can modify the flags associated with a multi-state molecule. If the number of reactions is small and the number of molecules large, *StochSim* may be less efficient than the Gillespie algorithm. However, in systems where molecules can exist in multiple states, *StochSim* is generally faster, with the added advantage of being able to track individual molecules over multiple time steps.

The initial version of *StochSim* (version 1.0) treated the system as a well-mixed solution, omitting spatial heterogeneity. A more recent version (22a) includes a simple two-dimensional molecular lattice where nearest neighbor interactions

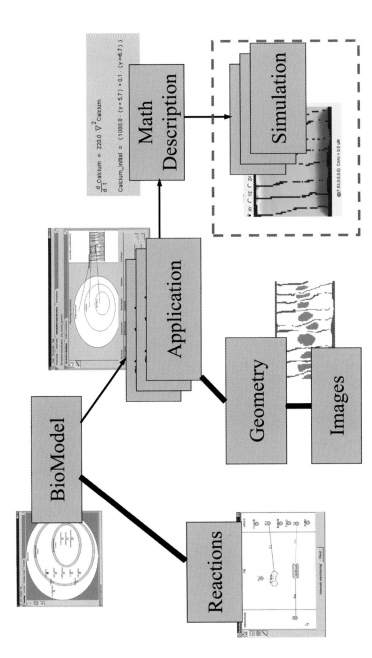

Figure 1 The modeling process within the *Virtual Cell* BioModel workspace. Each component of the overall model is labeled over a screen snapshot of the corresponding section of the user interface. The individual components and the flow of model and simulation specification are described in the text. A model entered through the MathModel workspace would have the geometry directly linked to the Math Description, but could still spawn multiple simulations.

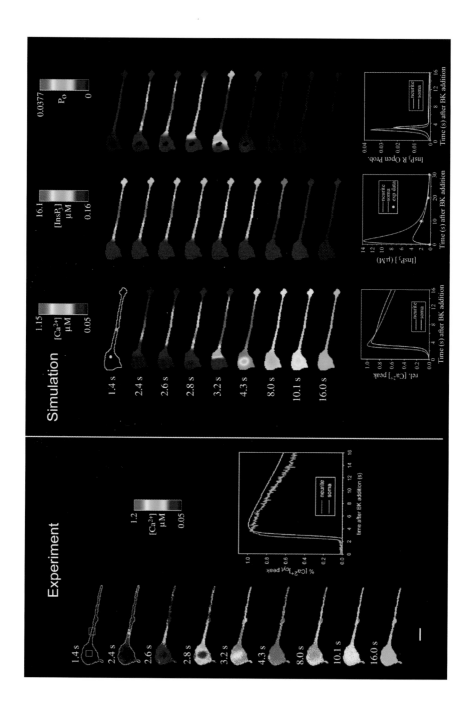

Figure 2 Experiment and simulation of calcium dynamics following BK stimulation of a N1E-115 neuroblastoma cell. A 250 nM solution of BK was applied uniformly to the cell at time 0, and the $[Ca^{2+}]_{cyt}$ is monitored with fura-2 to produce the experimental record shown in the left column. The data were collected through a microscope using a cooled ccd camera at 15 frames/sec. Representative frames are shown, and the change in calcium in the neurite (*green box*) and soma (*yellow box*) are plotted in the inset. The *Virtual Cell* simulation shown in the next column provides a good match to the experiment. The third and fourth columns display the simulation results for $[InsP_3]_{cyt}$ and P_o, the open probability of the $InsP_3$-sensitive calcium channel in the ER membrane. Details on the model components have been published (11, 12), and this figure has been adapted from that work (12).

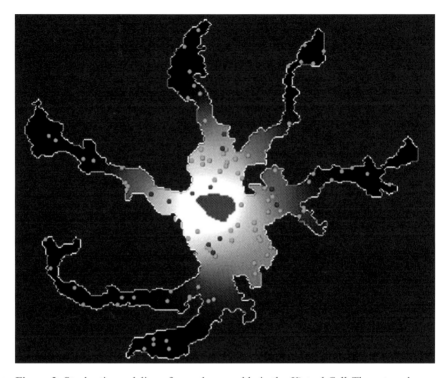

Figure 3 Stochastic modeling of granule assembly in the *Virtual Cell*. The external contour of an oligodendrocyte in culture was extracted from a confocal micrograph of an oligodendrocyte injected with fluorescent dextran to visualize the cytoplasmic volume. Dextran was size-excluded from the interior of the nucleus (shown as *dark gray*). RNA was set at a constant (high) concentration in the nucleus and could diffuse through the nuclear envelope as a disperse species creating a concentration gradient within the cytoplasm (shown in *gray scale*). Individual granules are represented as discrete particles that walk randomly throughout the cytoplasm and undergo elastic collisions at the plasma membrane and nuclear envelope. Core granules (lacking RNA) are shown in *green*. Diffusing RNA molecules are captured to individual granules. When the number of captured RNA molecules reaches a threshold, the granule is shown in *red*. Granules tend to get trapped in varicosities and diverticuli in the distal processes.

can affect the reactivities of molecules in the lattice. Implementation of the lattice was used to test the hypothesis that the remarkable sensitivity and dynamic range of bacterial chemotaxis is achieved through adaptive receptor clustering where ligand-induced changes in the signaling activity of receptors are propa gated throughout the cluster by nearest neighbor interactions (5a, 35a). This is a particularly compelling illustration of the importance of including spatial heterogeneity in stochastic modeling of intracellular reactions.

MCell

Another software package designed for realistic 3D simulations of cellular physiology, *MCell*, is described by its authors as a general Monte Carlo simulator of cellular microphysiology (www.MCell.cnl.salk.edu). It is written by T. M. Bartol Jr. and J. R. Stiles based on their initial code specifically tailored for simulating the generation of postsynaptic miniature endplate currents (1, 40). The user interaction with *MCell* is carried out through input files written in a special model description language (MDL) (38), an approach similar to the one implemented in GENESIS (5). MDL allows a user to create different types of diffusing ligand molecules with various initial distributions, define patterns of ligand release, specify arbitrary locations of surfaces representing membranes and their interaction with ligand molecules, define multiple types of ligand-binding sites and arbitrary chemical reaction mechanisms for different ligands and their binding sites, and select the type and format of output data that can be visualized.

The software then parses the MDL input files, creates the corresponding C++ objects, and executes a simulation according to the user instructions. *MCell* utilizes Monte Carlo random walk and chemical reaction algorithms using pseudo-random-number generation. One of *MCell*'s convenient features is checkpointing, which involves stopping and restarting a simulation as many times as desired. At each checkpoint, one or more modifications to MDL files can be made, including changing surface permeability and location (thus modeling moving surfaces), modifying reactants and reaction mechanisms, and varying the output type and format.

The simulation domain in *MCell* is a rectangular box containing arbitrary surfaces. Because Monte Carlo simulations do not require volume sampling, geometry treatment reduces to surface triangulation, which results in a list of polygons. 3D surface reconstruction is a preprocessing step that is not a part of a *MCell* simulation. Third-party software should be used for this purpose. Once a surface is generated, it is necessary to edit properties of the triangles that comprise the surface, e.g., add particular types of binding sites at different densities, or specify different permeability for different ligands. The automatic tools that would simplify and accelerate this step are under development.

As the number of participating objects grows, the Monte Carlo algorithms become slow. To speed up simulations, *MCell* is optimized by using 3D spatial partitioning that makes computing speed virtually independent of microdomain geometric complexity. Running parallel computations, another way to speed up

Monte Carlo simulations, is also being pursued in *MCell*. Although currently the successful applications of *MCell* are limited to microphysiology of synaptic transmission (39), other areas of possible *MCell* application include statistical chemistry, diffusion theory, single-channel simulation and data analysis, noise analysis, and Markov processes.

Virtual Cell

THE MODELING PROCESS WITHIN THE *VIRTUAL CELL* ENVIRONMENT   The *Virtual Cell* is a software environment that is being specifically developed to enable the use of modeling as an aid to the design and interpretation of experiments in cell biology (31–34). It can be accessed and run over the Internet from within a web browser (www.nrcam.uchc.edu). It is designed for biologists with little training in physics and math, as well as for experienced mathematical modelers. It achieves this by providing two separate workspaces for construction of models that are designed with the needs of each community in mind. The BioModel workspace abstracts the model components through inputs specifying compartmental topologies, molecular species and their location, kinetic expressions for the reactions and membrane fluxes, and the geometry. The Math workspace allows for the input of a model with a mathematics description language (VCMDL). Importantly, models developed through the BioModel workspace are used to generate a VCMDL version of the model that, if desired, may be modified or refined within the Math workspace; this can facilitate collaboration between biologists and modelers.

Simulations are performed and results are analyzed and visualized with tools that are common to both workspaces. Simulations of both nonspatial (i.e., ODEs) and spatial (PDEs) models can be performed. For nonspatial models, compartments are assigned appropriate volume fractions relative to their parents in the model topology and surface-to-volume ratios for the proper treatment of membrane fluxes. In spatial models, the segmented regions within a 1D, 2D, or 3D image are connected to the corresponding compartments in the topology. The geometry is prepared for a model in a separate Geometry workspace and can come from a segmented experimental image or can be defined analytically. Systems of ODEs are solved numerically with a choice of several solvers including variable time step stiff solvers. PDEs are solved via the finite volume method (27, 37) adapted for the inclusion of membrane transport processes as well as automated pseudo-steady-state approximations for fast reactions (31, 36). These are all implemented in an extensive C++ library that also includes software for stochastic simulations of particle motion and the reaction of individual molecules with continuously distributed species. At present, however, only deterministic models are fully treatable through the web-based interface.

Figure 1 (see color insert) schematizes the way in which the modeling process is structured within the *Virtual Cell*. This hierarchical structure emphasizes a general physiology definition, the BioModel, that specifies the topology of the system, the identities and locations of molecular species, and reactions and membrane transport kinetics. The BioModel can then have several Applications that each specify a particular geometry, boundary conditions, default initial concentrations and parameter values, and whether any of the reactions are sufficiently fast to permit a pseudo-steady-state approximation. Also at the Application level, individual reactions can be disabled as an aid in determining the proper initial conditions for a prestimulus stable state. An application of a BioModel is sufficient to completely describe the governing mathematics of the model, and as noted above, a VCMDL file is generated at this point. The *Virtual Cell* is designed to maintain a separation between this mathematical description, generated either via a BioModel or a MathModel, and the details of how the simulations are implemented. As shown in Figure 1, several simulations can be spawned from a given Application. The simulation specifications include the choice of solver, time step, and mesh size for spatial simulations, and overrides of the default initial conditions or parameter values. A local sensitivity analysis service is also available at the simulation level to aid in parameter estimation and to determine which features of the model are most critical in determining its overall behavior.

The *Virtual Cell* software displays spatial and nonspatial simulation solutions for the variables over time. The spatial data viewer displays a single plane section of a 3D data set and can sample the solution along an arbitrary curve (piecewise linear or Bezier spline) or at a set of points. Membranes are displayed as curves superimposed on the volume mesh, and membrane variables are displayed along these curves. The nonspatial data viewer plots any number of variables over time on the same plot. All plot windows support a tabular display that allows the user to copy the data into any spreadsheet program. A completely integrated data export service provides for data retrieval in a number of formats (e.g., comma-separated value, gif images, Apple QuickTime movies, animated gif movies) and data reduction schemes (subset of variables, time, and space including data sampling at selected points and along selected curves). Because the model can be mapped to a geometry acquired directly from the microscope, many of the same image analysis tools used to analyze experiments can be applied directly to simulation results. A poor correspondence between simulation and the experiment indicates that the model must be either incomplete or incorrect; indeed such negative results are highly informative because they can suggest how the hypotheses underlying the model need to be modified to accommodate the experiments. When the simulations are consistent with experiment, the ability to visualize the behavior of experimentally inaccessible molecular species often provides important new insights and suggests new experiments to further test the model validity. To illustrate some of these concepts, we now summarize the results of two studies that utilized the *Virtual Cell* system. The second of these takes advantage of stochastic modeling capabilities included in the *Virtual Cell* C++ library but have not yet been migrated to the web-based user interface.

DETERMINISTIC *VIRTUAL CELL* MODEL OF CALCIUM DYNAMICS IN A NEURONAL CELL   The *Virtual Cell* software is a valuable tool for formulating and testing hypotheses on the behavior of complex intracellular reaction/diffusion systems. A key to the successful application of this kind of modeling is that there be sufficient data to formulate reasonable quantitative hypotheses and that there be appropriate experimental methods available to validate or disprove the predictions of a model. The study of intracellular calcium signals fulfills these requirements exceptionally. This is because of the ready availability of fluorescence microscopy–based methods for following the spatial and temporal patterns of calcium changes in living cells [e.g., (26, 43)]. Arguably, it is the availability of these methods that has led to an explosion of interest in calcium dynamics and that, in turn, has led to further studies of the biochemical and electrophysiological events that lie upstream and downstream from the calcium signal. Ample data are often available to begin the development of a *Virtual Cell* model with few additional experiments. On the other hand, the molecules and mechanisms that can be involved in the control of intracellular calcium are sufficiently numerous and complex so as to make it difficult to understand experimentally observed behavior without the use of modeling.

In particular, inositol-1,4,5-triphosphate (InsP$_3$)-mediated calcium release from the endoplasmic reticulum (ER) is a common mechanism for receptor-mediated signaling in many cell types (2, 3, 29). We have used the *Virtual Cell* to help analyze and interpret experimental data on the details of the calcium release process in differentiated N1E-115 neuroblastoma cells (11, 12). In addition to providing insights on how morphology controls spatiotemporal patterns of InsP3 signaling within the cell, the needs of the calcium modeling have inspired significant improvements to the *Virtual Cell* such as a generalized automated pseudo-steady-state treatment for fast reactions (36) and a flux correction algorithm for the "staircase" membranes in the finite volume method (33).

In our study, the neuromodulator bradykinin (BK) was the external stimulus that set off InsP$_3$ production at the inner surface of the plasma membrane. Combining calcium imaging, quantitative uncaging of microinjected InsP$_3$, and simulations from the *Virtual Cell* led to the conclusion that BK triggers a buildup of InsP$_3$ in the neurite at a rate and to an extent much greater than in the soma (11, 12). The proximal segment of the neurite is the critical region for a response to a BK stimulus and is necessary and sufficient to initiate and propagate the calcium signal to other regions of the cell. The high surface-to-volume ratio in the neurite intensifies the InsP$_3$ signal in this region. A high density of ER calcium stores in the soma (predicted by the simulations and then confirmed by 3D immunofluorescence) balances the rapid rise of [InsP$_3$]$_{cyt}$ in the neurite to explain the contrasting results for both global and focal stimulations of these cells.

Figure 2 (see color insert) shows the results of an experiment and a simulation for the response of a cell to uniform global application of BK. The experimental data were collected on a fast digital-imaging microscope using the fluorescence from the indicator fura-2 to record the spatiotemporal changes in [Ca^{2+}]$_{cyt}$. Because the simulation was based on the cell geometry of the experiment, a direct comparison of the observed and predicted $[Ca^{2+}]_{cyt}$ dynamics can be made (first two columns of Figure 2). It must be emphasized that this close match between experiment and simulation was achieved only after many iterations between modeling and data collection, which helped to uncover previously unknown or misunderstood details of the components of the system (such as the high density of stores in the soma, as mentioned above). Also in Figure 2 are simulation results for the spatiotemporal pattern of $InsP_3$ and the open state of the $InsP_3$ receptor calcium channel in the ER. This ability to visualize molecular species that are inaccessible experimentally is one of the most valuable benefits of computational modeling.

STOCHASTIC MODELS FOR RNA TRAFFICKING IN THE *VIRTUAL CELL*   RNA trafficking targets expression of specific proteins to particular subcellular compartments and minimizes ectopic expression elsewhere in the cell. Studies of RNA trafficking in oligodendrocytes reveal that RNAs are assembled into trafficking intermediates termed granules (8), each containing multiple (approximately 30) RNA molecules (25), associated RNA-binding proteins, components of the translation machinery, and molecular motors (conventional kinesin and cytoplasmic dynein). RNAs with similar trafficking pathways are co-assembled into the same granules, whereas RNAs with different trafficking pathways are segregated into different granules. Conventional kinesin moves granules toward the plus ends of microtubules while cytoplasmic dynein moves granules toward the minus ends. The balance of power between kinesin and dynein activities in individual granules determines their direction and rate of movement along microtubules (6). Time lapse analysis of granule dynamics in living cells reveals rapid back-and-forth vibration along the axis of the microtubule, which is believed to reflect stochastic fluctuations in motor activities in individual granules. Biased activity of kinesin over dynein results in translocation of specific RNA granules to the periphery of the cell.

A stochastic model for granule assembly has been developed in the *Virtual Cell*. RNA is treated as a disperse chemical species that diffuses from a source in the nucleus, through the nuclear envelope into the cytoplasm where RNA molecules are captured, to core granules treated as discrete species moving stochastically throughout the cytoplasmic volume and undergoing elastic interactions with the cell membrane and nuclear envelope. The simulation is constrained within a 2D profile of an actual oligodendrocyte extracted from a confocal microscopic image data. The parameters used in the simulation—RNA concentrations in the nucleus and cytoplasm, number of granules in the cytoplasm, rate of movement of granules, rate of diffusion of RNA, rate of export of RNA from the nucleus, and number of RNA molecules per granule—are either experimentally determined or estimated based on observations in other systems. The simulation integrates chemical reactions and diffusion of a disperse species (RNA) with stochastic properties of mobile discrete species (granules) constrained by elastic interactions with immobile structures (membranes) within the cell. A representative image from the simulation is shown in Figure 3 (see color insert). The entire simulation is available at http://www.nrcam.uchc.edu/rna_traffick_dir/rna_traffick.html. The kinetics of granule assembly in the *Virtual Cell* recapitulate the kinetics observed experimentally in microinjected oligodendrocytes. As the simulation proceeds, granules tend to accumulate in varicosities and diverticuli within the cell in a pattern reminiscent of the distribution of granules observed experimentally in microinjected oligodendrocytes. The unusual fractal geometry of the reaction volume, which is a realistic representation of the intracellular space in an oligodendrocyte, appears to constrain the movement of granules in ways that could not be predicted based on simulations in a symmetric reaction volume. This example illustrates the importance of using actual image data to define the geometry of the reaction volume.

A stochastic model for granule dynamics on microtubules has also been developed using the *Virtual Cell* (7). Microtubules are represented as one-dimensional, oriented contours of arbitrarily defined shapes decomposed into discrete contour elements. Granules are represented as zero-dimensional points, which can be captured to microtubules if one or more contour element is within a specified capture radius, corresponding to the actual size (approximately 0.5 μm) of an RNA granule in a living cell. Each granule contains multiple plus end and minus end motors, each of which can be in one of three states relative to the microtubule (U, unbound; I, bound inactive; and A, bound active). Granule capture is a stochastic event mediated by binding of a specific motor molecule to a specific contour element. The type of motor that binds to the contour at each time step depends on the population of motors of each type associated with the granule and the corresponding motor on-rates multiplied by Δt. Monte Carlo methods are used to determine whether the granule will be captured within each time step, and if captured, which motor will bind to the contour element.

Once captured to a microtubule, granule movement along the axis of the microtubule is determined by stochastic state transitions for each motor associated with the granule. Because there are two types of motors in each granule, there are eight single-motor state transition rates: $k_{ai}^{\pm}, k_{ia}^{\pm}, k_{ui}^{\pm}, k_{iu}^{\pm}$. An important simplifying assumption is that the granule can have no more than one active motor at any time. The instantaneous behavior of the granule then depends on the type of the active motor (if there is one) and the state of the "cloud" of inactive motors. The discrete-valued variable s determines the state of the granule depending on the type of the active motor. This variable can take on one of the three values: $s = 0$, no active motors, the granule does not move; $s = 1$, a minus motor is active, the granule is moving toward the minus end with the velocity v_-; and $s = 2$, a plus motor is active, the granule is moving toward the plus end with the velocity v_+. Because the numbers of plus and minus motors in the cloud, $N_{\pm}$, are large, the state of the cloud can be described by two continuous variables, $P_{\pm}$, representing the probabilities for the plus and minus inactive motors to be in a bound state, so that the instantaneous number of inactive bound plus and minus motors are $N_+ P_+$ and $N_- P_-$. The discrete and continuous variables are separated in the sense that the dynamics of the discrete variable s is determined by the rates of the A $\leftrightarrow$ I transitions, whereas the dynamics of the continuous variables $P_{\pm}$ depend on the rates of the I $\leftrightarrow$ U transitions. However, the variables are also interdependent because the active motor exerts strain on inactive bound motors, making it easier for them to detach from the microtubule, and the inactive bound motors exert drag on the active motor, creating an additional load on it. Granule dynamics in the *Virtual Cell* recapitulate experimentally observed granule dynamics. Moreover, because the positions and the velocities of individual granules and the states of motors within each granule can both be tracked over time, it is possible to correlate particular aspects of granule dynamics with specific state transitions of the motors within the granule leading to experimentally testable predictions concerning the way stochastic interactions of different molecular motors result in directional intracellular trafficking of RNA granules.

The *Virtual Cell* program has several important advantages for stochastic modeling in eukaryotic cells. First, realistic image-based cell geometries are used to define intracellular reaction volumes, which constrain the stochastic behavior of intracellular reactants in unexpected ways. Second, definitions of reactive species can include multiple states described as either discrete parameters or continuous variables, which provide extraordinary contextual richness and behavioral versatility. Third, dynamic transformation and translocation of multiple individual reactive species can be tracked over time, facilitating integration of spatially heterogeneous stochastic models with simultaneous deterministic reaction/diffusion models. A major future challenge for the *Virtual Cell* will be to integrate dynamic shape changes in the reaction volume within the powerful and flexible stochastic modeling platform already developed. If this can be accomplished, the holy grail of stochastic modeling of cell motility may be attainable using the *Virtual Cell*.

FUTURE CHALLENGES AND PROSPECTS

Future development and enhancement of computational tools for cell biology will provide opportunities to develop larger and more realistic models with a wider range of modeling capabilities. One advantage of using computer tools in cell modeling is the potential ability to deal with complex models. The only prudent way to construct complex models is to assemble them from smaller submodels (modeling cassettes) that are well understood and tested. To make sure that the model components are compatible, a careful analysis of assumptions is necessary. Ideally, the results of this analysis should be documented in some formal way so that the compatibility test could be made automatic. The analysis of the most successful mathematical models that are frequently used in cell modeling with respect to all the assumptions, both explicit and implicit, made in constructing those models is a first step in this direction.

As we move toward modeling complex systems on realistic 3D structures, computational efficiency of numerical algorithms becomes a critical issue. Numerical methods should be fully automated, reasonably accurate, stable, and fast. Because of variability in biological systems, it is particularly important in biological applications to be able to rerun simulations a number of times with varying parameters. Therefore, even 3D simulations of complex systems must complete within a relatively short time. The numerical algorithms currently used in the *Virtual Cell* are applicable to a wide range of problems, particularly now that we have developed and implemented the automatic numerical approach to fast reactions in reaction/diffusion systems (36). However, we use a fixed time step spatial solver and leave it to the user to specify the time step. In combination with currently used explicit treatment of reactions and membrane fluxes, this may lead to numerical instability when the chosen time step is larger than characteristic times of explicitly treated processes. Also, it is currently the user's responsibility to distinguish the fast subsystem, although, in principle, it is possible to automatically detect the fast subsystems based on the values of reaction constants, initial concentrations, and other simulation parameters. Usually, the most time-consuming part of a simulation is solving the large linear algebraic system resulting from the discretization of governing PDEs. The optimal choice of a linear solver and the parameters associated with it is therefore critical to the efficiency and robustness of the overall package. To improve stability, accuracy, and overall efficiency of numerical simulations, the issues of reaction stiffness in the PDEs, more accurate representation of irregular boundaries, and choice of effective linear solvers need to be addressed.

Although software systems such as *StochSim, MCell*, and *Virtual Cell* provide modeling capabilities to cell biologists and biophysicists, which would previously have required highly specialized training in numerical methods and mathematical physics, their problem domains do not encompass all the areas of interest in the broad field of cell biology. In particular, the *Virtual Cell* features currently accessible from the user interface are limited to deterministic reaction/diffusion systems mapped to arbitrary, but fixed, geometries including arbitrary fluxes and reactions associated with membranes. Although a wide range of cellular processes falls into this category, additional features are being developed, including modeling membrane potential, stochastic processes, lateral diffusion in membranes, and one-dimensional structures such as microtubules and microfilaments. Currently some of these are only accessible through custom executables that call on these features through the C++ library. It remains to make them accessible through the user interface. Also needed are computational tools to treat cell structural dynamics to enable the construction of models of such processes as cell migration or mitosis. Such tools will be especially challenging because they will require new formulations for the physics underlying cell structural changes; in contrast to the firm theoretical foundation for reaction/diffusion processes, this physics has not yet been firmly established.

ACKNOWLEDGMENTS

The authors thank their colleagues, Ann Cowan, Susan Krueger, Frank Morgan, Ion Moraru, Charles Fink, John Wagner, James Watras, and Daniel Lucio, for their many contributions to this work. The NIH National Center for Research Resources has supported this work through grant RR13186.

Visit the Annual Reviews home page at www.annualreviews.org

LITERATURE CITED

1. Bartol TM Jr, Land BR, Salpeter EE, Salpeter MM. 1991. Monte Carlo simulation of miniature endplate current generation in the vertebrate neuromuscular junction. *Biophys. J.* 59:1290–307
2. Berridge MJ. 1993. Inositol trisphosphate and calcium signalling. *Nature* 361:315–25
3. Berridge MJ. 1998. Neuronal calcium signaling. *Neuron* 21:13–26
4. Bhalla US, Iyengar R. 1999. Emergent properties of networks of biological signaling pathways. *Science* 283:381–87
5. Bower JM, Beeman D. 1998. *The Book of GENESIS: Exploring Realistic Neural Models with the General Neural Simulation System.* New York: Springer. 2nd ed.
5a. Bray D, Levin MD, Morton-Firth CJ. 1998. Receptor clustering as a cellular mechanism to control sensitivity. *Nature* 393:85–88
6. Carson JH, Cui H, Barbarese E. 2001. The balance of power in RNA trafficking. *Curr. Opin. Neurobiol.* 11:558–63
7. Carson JH, Cui H, Krueger W, Slepchenko B, Brumwell B, et al. 2001. RNA trafficking in oligodendrocytes. In *Cell Polarity and Subcellular Localization*, ed. D Richter, pp. 69–81. Berlin: Springer
8. Carson JH, Kwon S, Barbarese E. 1998. RNA trafficking in myelinating cells. *Curr. Opin. Neurobiol.* 8:607–12
9. Clay J, Defelice L. 1983. Relationship between membrane excitability and single channel open-close kinetics. *Biophys. J.* 42:151–57
10. Deleted in proof
11. Fink CC, Slepchenko B, Moraru II, Schaff J, Watras J, et al. 1999. Morphological control of inositol-1,4,5-trisphosphate-dependent signals. *J. Cell Biol.* 147:929–35
12. Fink CC, Slepchenko B, Moraru II, Watras J, Schaff J, et al. 2000. An image-based

model of calcium waves in differentiated neuroblastoma cells. *Biophys. J.* 79:163–83
13. Fitzhugh R. 1965. A kinetic model of the conductance changes in nerve membrane. *J. Cell. Comp. Physiol.* 66:111–18
14. Gillespie DT. 1977. Exact stochastic simulation of coupled chemical reactions. *J. Phys. Chem.* 81:2340–61
15. Gillespie DT. 2001. Approximate accelerated stochastic simulation of chemically reacting systems. *J. Chem. Phys.* 115:1715–33
16. Goryanin I, Hodgman TC, Selkov E. 1999. Mathematical simulation and analysis of cellular metabolism and regulation. *Bioinformatics* 15:749–58
17. Higham DJ. 2001. An algorithmic introduction to numerical simulation of stochastic differential equations. *SIAM Rev.* 43:525–46
18. Hines ML, Carnevale NT. 1997. The NEURON simulation environment. *Neural Comput.* 9:1179–209
19. Hines ML, Carnevale NT. 2000. Expanding NEURON's repertoire of mechanisms with NMODL. *Neural Comput.* 12:995–1007
20. Hodgkin AL, Huxley AF. 1952. A quantitative description of membrane current and its application to conduction and excitation in nerve. *J. Physiol.* 117:500–44
21. Jack JJB, Noble D, Tsien RW. 1975. *Electric Current Flow in Excitable Cells.* Oxford: Clarendon. 502 pp.
22. Keizer J, Smith GD, Ponce-Dawson S, Pearson JE. 1998. Saltatory propagation of Ca^{2+} waves by Ca^{2+} sparks. *Biophys. J.* 75:595–600
22a. Le Novere N, Shimizu TS. 2001. STOCHSIM: modelling of stochastic biomolecular processes. *Bioinformatics* 17:575–76

23. McAdams HH, Arkin A. 1998. Simulation of prokaryotic genetic circuits. *Annu. Rev. Biophys. Biomol. Struct.* 27:199–224

24. Mendes P, Kell D. 1998. Non-linear optimization of biochemical pathways: applications to metabolic engineering and parameter estimation. *Bioinformatics* 14:869–83

24a. Morton-Firth CJ. 1998. *Stochastic simulation of cell signaling pathways.* PhD thesis. Cambridge Univ. 263 pp.

24b. Morton-Firth CJ, Bray D. 1998. Predicting temporal fluctuations in an intracellular signalling pathway. *J. Theor. Biol.* 192:117–28

24c. Morton-Firth CJ, Shimizu TS, Bray D. 1999. A free-energy-based stochastic simulation of the Tar receptor complex. *J. Mol. Biol.* 286:1059–74

25. Mouland AJ, Xu H, Cui H, Krueger W, Munro TP, et al. 2001. RNA trafficking signals in human immunodeficiency virus type 1. *Mol. Cell. Biol.* 21:2133–43

26. Nuccitelli R, ed. 1994. *A Practical Guide to the Study of Calcium in Living Cells,* Vol. 40. *Methods in Cell Biology.* San Diego: Academic Press. 342 pp.

27. Patankar SV. 1980. *Numerical Heat Transfer and Fluid Flow.* Washington, DC: Taylor & Francis. 197 pp.

28. Press WH, Tuekolsky SA, Vetterling WT, Flannery BP. 1999. *Numerical Recipes in C (The Art of Scientific Computing).* Cambridge, UK: Cambridge Univ. Press. 2nd ed.

29. Putney JW Jr, Bird GS. 1993. The inositol phosphate-calcium signaling system in nonexcitable cells. *Endocr. Rev.* 14:610–31

30. Sauro HM. 1993. SCAMP: a general-purpose simulator and metabolic control analysis program. *Comput. Appl. Biosci.* 9:441–50

31. Schaff J, Fink CC, Slepchenko B, Carson JH, Loew LM. 1997. A general computational framework for modeling cellular structure and function. *Biophys. J.* 73:1135–46

32. Schaff J, Loew LM. 1999. The virtual cell. In *Biocomputing: Proceedings of the 1999 Pacific Symposium,* ed. RB Altman, AK Dunker, L Hunter, TE Klein, K Lauderdale, pp. 228–39. Singapore: World Sci.

33. Schaff JC, Slepchenko BM, Choi Y, Wagner JM, Resasco D, et al. 2001. Analysis of non-linear dynamics on arbitrary geometries with the Virtual Cell. *Chaos* 11:115–31

34. Schaff JC, Slepchenko BM, Loew LM. 2000. Physiological modeling with the Virtual Cell framework. *Methods Enzymol.* 321:1–23

35. Schneidman E, Freedman B, Segev I. 1998. Ion channel stochasticity may be critical in determining the reliability and precision of spike timing. *Neural Comput.* 10:1679–703

35a. Shimizu TS, Le Novere N, Levin MD, Beavil AJ, Sutton BJ, et al. 2000. Molecular model of a lattice of signalling proteins involved in bacterial chemotaxis. *Nat. Cell. Biol.* 2:792–96

36. Slepchenko BM, Schaff JC, Choi YS. 2000. Numerical approach to fast reaction-diffusion systems: application to buffered calcium waves in bistable models. *J. Comp. Phys.* 162:186–218

37. Smith GD. 1985. *Numerical Solution of Partial Differential Equations: Finite Difference Methods.* Oxf. Appl. Math. Comput. Sci. Ser. Oxford: Clarendon. 3rd ed.

38. Stiles JR, Bartol TM, Salpeter EE, Salpeter MM. 1998. Monte Carlo simulation of neurotransmitter release using MCell, a general simulator of cellular physiological processes. In *Computational Neuroscience,* ed. J Bower, pp. 279–84. New York: Plenum

39. Stiles JR, Kovyazina IV, Salpeter EE, Salpeter MM. 1999. The temperature sensitivity of miniature endplate currents is mostly governed by channel gating: evidence from optimized recordings and Monte Carlo simulations. *Biophys. J.* 77:1177–87

40. Stiles JR, Van HD, Bartol TM Jr, Salpeter EE, Salpeter MM. 1996. Miniature end-plate current rise times less than 100 microseconds from improved dual record-ings can be modeled with passive acetyl-choline diffusion from a synaptic vesicle. *Proc. Natl. Acad. Sci. USA* 93:5747–52

41. Sulis W, Trofimova I, eds. 2001. *Nonlin-ear Dynamics in the Life and Social Sci-ences*, Vol. 320. NATO Science Series: Life Sciences. Amsterdam: IOS

42. Tomita M, Hashimoto K, Takahashi K, Shimizu TS, Matsuzaki Y, et al. 1999. E-CELL: software environment for whole-cell simulation. *Bioinformatics* 15:72–84

43. Williams DA, Bowser DN, Petrou S. 1999. Confocal Ca^{2+} imaging of organelles, cells, tissues, and organs. *Methods Enzy-mol.* 307:441–69

44. Zienkiewicz OC, Taylor RL. 2000. *Finite Element Method: Vol. 1, The Basis.* Lon-don: Butterworth-Heinemann. 712 pp. 5th ed.

Annu. Rev. Biophys. Biomol. Struct. 2002. 31:443–84
DOI: 10.1146/annurev.biophys.31.082901.134348

RHODOPSIN: Insights from Recent Structural Studies

Thomas P. Sakmar, Santosh T. Menon, Ethan P. Marin, and Elias S. Awad

Howard Hughes Medical Institute, Laboratory of Molecular Biology and Biochemistry, The Rockefeller University, New York, New York, 10021; e-mail: sakmar@mail.rockefeller.edu

Key Words G protein–coupled receptor, vision, chromophore, retinal, signal transduction

■ **Abstract** The recent report of the crystal structure of rhodopsin provides insights concerning structure-activity relationships in visual pigments and related G protein–coupled receptors (GPCRs). The seven transmembrane helices of rhodopsin are interrupted or kinked at multiple sites. An extensive network of interhelical interactions stabilizes the ground state of the receptor. The ligand-binding pocket of rhodopsin is remarkably compact, and several chromophore-protein interactions were not predicted from mutagenesis or spectroscopic studies. The helix movement model of receptor activation, which likely applies to all GPCRs of the rhodopsin family, is supported by several structural elements that suggest how light-induced conformational changes in the ligand-binding pocket are transmitted to the cytoplasmic surface. The cytoplasmic domain of the receptor includes a helical domain extending from the seventh transmembrane segment parallel to the bilayer surface. The cytoplasmic surface appears to be approximately large enough to bind to the transducin heterotrimer in a one-to-one complex. The structural basis for several unique biophysical properties of rhodopsin, including its extremely low dark noise level and high quantum efficiency, can now be addressed using a combination of structural biology and various spectroscopic methods. Future high-resolution structural studies of rhodopsin and other GPCRs will form the basis to elucidate the detailed molecular mechanism of GPCR-mediated signal transduction.

CONTENTS

INTRODUCTION

Rhodopsin (Rho) is a highly specialized G protein–coupled receptor (GPCR) that detects photons in the rod photoreceptor cell. Within the superfamily of GPCRs that couple to heterotrimeric G proteins, Rho defines the so-called Family A GPCRs, which share primary structural homology (192, 207). Rho can be obtained from bovine retinae (0.5–1.0 mg/retina) by a sucrose density gradient centrifugation preparation of the rod outer-segment disc membranes (175). Rho is stable enough in the dark to be purified further by various chromatographic procedures, and it remains stable in solution in a variety of detergents (168). Bovine Rho was the first GPCR to be sequenced by amino acid sequencing (84, 171), the first to be cloned (157, 158), the first to be crystallized (167), and the first to yield a crystal structure (172).

Visual pigments share several structural features with other GPCRs (193). Their core structure consists of seven transmembrane (TM) segments (H1 to H7) (Figure 1). A pair of highly conserved Cys residues is found on the extracellular surface of the receptor and forms a disulfide bond. A Glu(Asp)/Arg/Tyr(Trp) tripeptide sequence is found at the cytoplasmic border of H3. This sequence is conserved in Family A GPCRs and is involved in G protein interaction (59, 60).

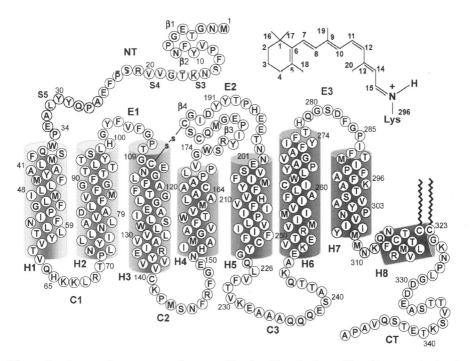

Figure 1 A secondary structure diagram of bovine Rho. Amino acid residues are depicted in single-letter code. The amino-terminal tail and extracellular domain is toward the top, and the carboxyl-terminal tail and cytoplasmic domain is toward the bottom. Transmembrane α-helical segments (H1 to H7) and the cationic amphipathic helix H8 are shown in cylinders. An essential disulfide bond links Cys-110 and Cys-187. Cys-322 and Cys-323 are palmitoylated. (*Inset*) The structure of the RET chromophore. Carbon atoms are numbered 1 through 20.

Sites of light-dependent phosphorylation at Ser and Thr residues are found at the carboxyl-terminal tail of most visual pigments. These sites are analogous to phosphorylation sites found on the carboxyl-terminal tails of other GPCRs (22).

Although it shares many similarities with other GPCRs, as a visual pigment Rho displays many specialized features not found in other GPCRs. In particular, visual pigments are made of opsin apoprotein plus chromophore. The chromophore is not a ligand in the classical sense because it is linked covalently via a protonated Schiff base bond in the membrane-embedded domain of the protein. The Lys residue that acts as the linkage site for the chromophore (Lys-296) is conserved within H7. A carboxylic acid residue that serves as the counterion to the protonated, positively charged retinylidene Schiff base (Glu-113) is conserved within H3. The position analogous to the Schiff base counterion is one helix turn away from the position of an Asp residue conserved in biogenic amine receptors that serves as the counterion to the cationic amine ligands.

The chromophore in all Rhos is derived from the aldehyde of vitamin A_1, 11-*cis*-retinal (RET) (Figure 1). Some fishes, amphibians, reptiles, and aquatic mammals may also employ the aldehyde of vitamin A_2, 11-*cis*-3,4-didehydroretinal, which contains an additional carbon-carbon double bond. All pigments with a vitamin A_2–derived chromophore are called porphyropsins. An important structural feature of the RET chromophore in Rho, in addition to its Schiff base linkage, is its extended polyene structure, which accounts for its visible absorption properties and allows for resonance structures (183).

Rho displays a broad visible absorption maximum (λ_{max}) at about 500 nm (Figure 2). Photon capture leading to photoisomerization of the 11-*cis* to all-*trans* form of the RET chromophore is the primary event in visual signal transduction, and it is the only light-dependent step (223). After photoisomerization, the pigment decays thermally to metarhodopsin II (M-II) with a λ_{max} value of 380 nm. The M-II intermediate is characterized by a deprotonated Schiff base chromophore linkage. M-II is the active form of the receptor (R*), which catalyzes guanine nucleotide exchange by the rod cell heterotrimeric G protein, transducin (G_t). In contrast with vertebrate vision, invertebrate vision is generally photochromic—a photoactivated invertebrate pigment can be inactivated by absorption of a second photon that induces isomerization to the ground-state *cis* conformation.

In the case of the vertebrate visual system, G_t activation leads to the activation of a cyclic-GMP phosphodiesterase (cGMP-PDE) and the closing of cGMP-gated cation channels in the plasma membrane of the rod cell. Light causes a graded hyperpolarization of the photoreceptor cell. The amplification, modulation, and regulation of the light response is of great physiological importance and has been discussed in detail elsewhere (15, 32, 211, 223). Activation of a single Rho molecule by a single photon has been estimated to prevent the entry of as many as 10^7 cations into the rod cell. Recent studies have estimated that at room temperature, each R* triggers activation of cGMP-PDE at rates of 1000 to 2000 molecules per second (120). Despite the fact that the visual system functions over about a 10^6-fold range of light intensity, the retinal rod cell has single-photon detection capability due to extremely low levels of dark noise in Rho and a significant degree of biochemical amplification. Thermal isomerization in a single Rho molecule at physiological temperature has been estimated to occur about once in 470 years (14). The possibility of single-pheromone molecule detection by insect olfactory systems notwithstanding, the visual system is unique among sensory signal transduction systems in that it can detect single events.

This review focuses on what has been learned from the recently published crystal structure of Rho (172). What insight does the structure provide about the mechanism of the "opsin shift" and spectral tuning? What is the structural basis for the incredible stability of Rho in the rod cell disc membrane in the dark? How does Rho achieve high photochemical specificity and high quantum yield? How does a single R* catalyze guanine nucleotide exchange by hundreds of G_t molecules? What does the Rho structure tell us about structure-activity relationships in other GPCRs (148, 194)? Finally, when possible, attempts are made to reconcile previous key findings from biochemical studies and the analysis of site-directed mutant

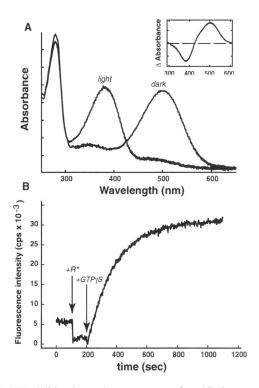

Figure 2   (*A*) A UV-visible absorption spectrum of purified recombinant COS-cell Rho in detergent solution (*dark*) shows a characteristic broad visible absorbance with a λ_{max} value of 500 nm. The 280-nm peak represents the protein component. After exposure to light, the pigment is converted to metarhodopsin II (M-II) with a λ_{max} value of 380 nm characteristic of an unprotonated Schiff base imine. M-II is the active form of the receptor that interacts with G_t. *Inset*: The photobleaching difference spectrum obtained by subtracting the light spectrum from the dark spectrum. Essentially identical results can be obtained with Rho from bovine retinas purified by concanavalin-A lectin-affinity chromatography. (*B*) A kinetic assay of the activation of G_t by R*. The intrinsic tryptophan fluorescence of G_t increases significantly when GTP replaces GDP. Therefore, the fluorescence emission of a mixture of purified components (Rho, G_t, GDP, GTPγS) in detergent solution can be measured as a function of time. The sample is illuminated to convert Rho to R*, which catalyzes GTPγS uptake by G_t and causes an increase in fluorescence. The reaction is started by injecting GTPγS into the cuvette (200 sec).

pigments with the Rho crystal structure. Some of the material herein has been presented in the context of the physiology rather than the biophysics of Rho, although there is obvious overlap (149). In addition, excellent recent reviews by Gether (69) and Ballesteros et al. (13) have focused more on the implications of the structure of Rho for understanding the structure and function of other GPCRs.

MOLECULAR STRUCTURE OF RHODOPSIN

Overview of the Crystal Structure of Rhodopsin

To obtain crystals, bovine Rho was purified from rod outer-segment membranes and crystallized from a detergent solution—nonylthiolglucoside supplemented with the small amphiphile heptane 1,2,3-triol (167, 168). The resolution of the crystallographic data of the original data set was approximately 2.8 Å, but small segments of the cytoplasmic surface domain are not resolved. A more recent refinement of the data has also been reported (218). The structure represents the inactive form of Rho with its bound RET chromophore intact. A ribbon diagram of the Rho peptide backbone structure with the RET chromophore is presented in Figure 3. The structure discussed in this chapter is that of the A chain in the

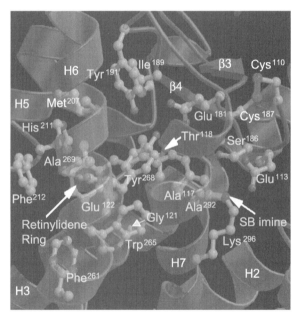

Figure 3   The RET chromophore-binding pocket of bovine Rho. The RET chromophore-binding pocket is shown from within the plane of the membrane bilayer. The cyclohexenyl ring and the Schiff base imine are labeled. At least 16 amino acid residues are within 4.5 Å of the RET ligand: Glu-113, Ala-117, Thr-118, Gly-121, Glu-122, Glu-181, Ser-186, Tyr-191, Met-207, His-211, Phe-212, Phe-261, Trp-265, Tyr-268, Ala-269, and Ala-292. Some additional key amino acid residues are labeled, including the Cys-110/Cys-187 disulfide bond. RET is situated such that its proximal end (approximately C_9 to C_{15}) lies along the $\beta4$ strand and its distal end (approximately C_9 to the cyclohexenyl ring) lies along H-3.

crystal unit cell dimer. A detailed description of the crystal structure was recently presented (149).

As an integral membrane protein, Rho comprises three topological domains: the extracellular surface, the membrane-embedded domain, and the intracellular surface. Due to the location of Rho in the disc membrane of the rod outer segment, the extracellular domain is sometimes referred to as intradiscal. The amino terminus of Rho is extracellular and the carboxyl terminus in intracellular. The membrane-embedded domain consists of seven TM segments (H1 to H7), which are predominantly α-helical. The helical segments form a compact bundle that contains the binding site for the RET chromophore.

Crystal Structure of the Extracellular Surface Domain of Rhodopsin

The extracellular surface domain of Rho comprises the amino-terminal tail (NT) and three interhelical loops (E1, E2, and E3) (Figure 1). There is significant secondary structure in the extracellular domain and several intra- and interdomain interactions. NT extends from the amino terminus to Pro-34 and contains five distorted strands ($\beta1$, $\beta2$, S3, S4, and S5). NT is glycosylated at Asn-2 and Asn-15. The oligosaccharides extend away from the extracellular domain and do not seem to interact with any part of the molecule. The extracellular surface domain also contains three extracellular interhelical loops: loop E1 (a.a. 101–106) connects H2 and H3, loop E2 (a.a. 174–199) connects H4 and H5, loop E3 (a.a. 278–285) connects H6 and H7.

One of the most striking features of the Rho structure is the presence and positioning of the $\beta4$ strand (Ser-186/Cys-187/Gly-188/Ile-189), which forms an extracellular roof for the RET-binding pocket. The $\beta4$ strand runs nearly parallel to the length of the polyene chain from about C_9 to the Schiff base imine nitrogen. The opposite end of RET from the cyclohexenyl ring to about C_{10} runs along H3, which is tilted with respect to the plane of the membrane. The result is that this end of RET seems to be held very firmly in place by multiple contacts.

Crystal Structure of the Membrane-Embedded Domain of Rhodopsin

The crystal structure of Rho suggests that 194 amino acid residues make up the seven TM segments (H1 to H7) included in the membrane-embedded domain: H1 (a.a. 35–64), H2 (a.a. 71–100), H3 (a.a. 107–139), H4 (a.a. 151–173), H5 (a.a. 200–225), H6 (a.a. 247–277), and H7 (a.a. 286–306). The crystal structure of this domain is remarkable for a number of kinks and distortions of the individual TM segments, which are otherwise generally α-helical in secondary structure. Many of these distortions from canonical secondary structure were not accounted for in molecular graphics models of Rho based on projection density maps obtained from cryoelectron microscopy (12, 119, 199, 219).

Crystal Structure of the Chromophore-Binding Pocket of Rhodopsin

The binding site of the RET chromophore lies within the membrane-embedded domain of the receptor (Figure 3). At least 16 amino acid residues are within 4.5 Å of the RET moiety: Glu-113, Ala-117, Thr-118, Gly-121, Glu-122, Glu-181, Ser-186, Tyr-191, Met-207, His-211, Phe-212, Phe-261, Trp-265, Tyr-268, Ala-269, and Ala-292. The most striking feature of the RET-binding pocket is the presence of many polar or polarizable groups to coordinate an essentially hydrophobic ligand (Figure 3). The chromophore is located closer to the extracellular side of the TM domain of the receptor than to the cytoplasmic side. The chromophore polyene from C_6 to C_{11} runs almost parallel to H3, which provides many of the amino acid side chains that form the chromophore-binding pocket: Glu-113, Gly-114, Ala-117, Thr-118, Gly-120, and Gly-121. The polyene chain facing toward the extracellular side of the receptor is covered, or capped, by the amino acid residues from the β4-sheet (Ser-186 to Ile-189) of the E2 loop as described above. The carboxylic acid side chain of Glu-181 in the β3-sheet of the E2 loop points toward the center of the RET polyene chain.

Glu-113 serves as the RET Schiff base counterion. A number of other amino acid side chains surround the imine moiety, including Tyr-43, Met-44 and Leu-47 in H1, Thr-94 in H2, and Phe-293 in H7. In particular, Met-44 and Leu-47, in addition to the peptide bond between Phe-293 and Phe-294, help to orient the side chain of Lys-296 in the direction of the long axis of Rho. The phenyl rings of Phe-293 and Phe-294 also interact with side chains of adjacent helices. The two oxygen atoms of the Glu-113 carboxylate side chain of Glu-113 are located 3.3 Å and 3.5 Å from the imine nitrogen. The hydroxyl group of Thr-94 is also about 3.4 Å from one of the Glu-113 carboxylate oxygens. Thr-92 and Thr-93 are also in the vicinity of the Schiff base imine but may not be close enough to contribute significantly to stabilization of its protonated ground state. The presence of water molecules in the Schiff base region has been postulated, but the crystal structure at the reported resolution does not contain defined water in this region (153).

The position of the cyclohexenyl ring of the chromophore is largely constrained on the cytoplasmic side of the binding pocket by three residues: Glu-122 (H3), Phe-261 (H6), and Trp-265 (H6). The indole side chain of Trp-265 points inward from the more cytoplasmic position of the Trp-265 backbone and comes within about 3.8 Å of the RET C_{20}. Side chains from Met-207, His-211, and Phe-212 on H5, and Tyr-268 and Ala-269 on H6 further constrain the chromophore ring.

Gly-121 interacts with RET in a direct steric manner and lies closest to the C_{18}-methyl group bonded to C_5 of the cyclohexenyl ring (Gly-121 C_α-RET C_{18} distance—3.5 Å). Gly-121 is close to Phe-261 (H6) in the Rho crystal structure. They pair to form one boundary of the RET-binding site, defining the C_4-C_5-C_{18} orientation (Phe-261 C_z-Gly-121 C_α distance, 5 Å; Phe-261 C_z-RET C_4 distance, 3.7 Å). This portion of the RET-binding pocket around H3 and H6 appears to be held rigidly together by tight van der Waals interactions. H4 contributes only one residue, Cys-167, directly to the chromophore-binding pocket.

Crystal Structure of the Cytoplasmic Surface Domain of Rhodopsin

The cytoplasmic domain of Rho comprises three cytoplasmic loops and the carboxyl-terminal tail: C1 (a.a. 65–70), C2 (a.a. 140–150), C3 (a.a. 226–246), and CT (a.a. 307–348). Loops C1 and C2 are resolved in the crystal structure, but only residues 226 to 235 and 240 to 246 are resolved in C3. CT is divided into two structural domains. C4 extends from the cytoplasmic end of H7 at Ile-307 to Gly-324, just beyond two vicinal Cys residues (Cys-322 and Cys-323), which are posttranslationally palmitoylated. The remainder of CT extends from Lys-325 to the carboxyl terminus of Rho at Ala-348. The crystal structure does not resolve residues 328 to 333 in CT.

The hallmark of the C4 loop is an α-helical stretch, H8. H8 is connected to H7 by the Met-309/Asn-310/Lys-311 tripeptide that acts as a short linker. H8 lies nearly perpendicular to H7, and together with the Asn/Pro/X/X/Tyr motif in H7, it is one of the most highly conserved long stretches of primary structure in Rho. The environment around H8 is mainly hydrophobic, which may lead to increased helical stability. H8 might be best described as a cationic amphipathic α-helix, with Lys-311 and Arg-314 on one face of the helix and Phe-313, Met-317, and Leu-321 buried in the hydrophobic core of the bilayer between H1 and H7. H8 points away from the center of Rho and it appears that the palmitoyl groups linked to Cys-322 and Cys-323 by thioester bonds may be anchored in the membrane bilayer, although this is not resolved in the crystal structure. The helical structure of H8 is terminated by Gly-324. The residues at the extreme carboxyl-terminal end of CT compose the most solvent-exposed region of Rho. CT folds back over a small portion of the helical bundle at H1 and H7.

STRUCTURE-ACTIVITY RELATIONSHIPS IN RHODOPSIN

Structure-Activity Relationships in the Extracellular Surface Domain

The extracellular loops and amino-terminal tail of bovine Rho have been shown in a deletion analysis to be important for proper folding of the receptor that allows cellular processing and chromophore binding (42). Insertional mutagenesis was also used in a related study to probe the topology of Rho and to correlate the location of epitope insertion to stability and cell trafficking (27). Interestingly, several mutations that interfered with the formation of a correct tertiary structure on the intradiscal surface resulted in mutant opsins that appeared to be retained in the endoplasmic reticulum during heterologous expression and were complexed with molecular chaperones (9). Antibody accessibility studies suggested that the

NT domain constitutes a defined tertiary structure that contributes to the overall extracellular domain (31). Rho is glycosylated at Asn-2 and Asn-15 of the NT. A nonglycosylated Rho, which was prepared in the presence of tunicamycin, was defective in light-dependent activation of G_t (104). The structural basis of this finding is not clear from the Rho crystal structure because the oligosaccharide chains point away from the molecule and do not seem to engage in intramolecular interactions.

Several point mutations that result in amino acid substitutions in the NT domain are linked to autosomal dominant retinitis pigmentosa (ADRP), including positions Pro-23 and Gln-28. ADRP is an inherited human disease that causes progressive retinal degeneration, loss of dim-light vision, loss of peripheral vision, and eventual blindness. Pro-23 and Gln-28 interact with Tyr-102, which is in the E1 loop. This interaction might maintain an essential structural orientation between NT and E1 that is disrupted in the NT of the ADRP mutants. Thus, Tyr-102 interacts with Pro-23 and Gln-28 to maintain proper orientation between E1 and NT. The roles of specific amino acid residues in the NT domain were also studied in various transgenic mice strains harboring point mutations that correspond to sites linked to ADRP (149).

Cys-110 and Cys-187 form a disulfide linkage in an elegant study in which the four intracellular and three membrane-embedded Cys residues were removed by site-directed mutagenesis to create a mutant receptor with only the three extracellular Cys residues remaining (102). In a related study, the double mutant C110A/C187A was shown to bind RET to form a Rho-like pigment (39). However, the M-II–like photoproduct of the mutant pigment, which could activate G_t in response to light, was considerably less stable than native M-II (39).

Glu-181 arises from the linker between $\beta 3$ and $\beta 4$ and points toward the polyene chain. Glu-181 may serve to influence the electron density of the conjugated polyene system of the retinal chromophore so that photoisomerization occurs exclusively at the C_{11}-C_{12} double bond. Another potential role for Glu-181 may be to control the rate of decay of M-II. Recent experiments with site-directed mutants with replacements of Glu-181 show that the rate of M-II decay as measured by the decay of Trp fluorescence quenching can be either accelerated or slowed when the amino acid at position 181 is changed (M. Kazmi, S. De, E. Marin, E. Yan, R. A. Mathies & T. P. Sakmar, manuscript in preparation).

Structure-Activity Relationships in the Membrane-Embedded Domain of Rhodopsin

The membrane-embedded domain of Rho is characterized by the presence of several intramolecular interactions that may be important in stabilizing the ground-state structure of the receptor. One of the hallmarks of the molecular physiology of Rho is that it is essentially biochemically silent in the dark. The RET chromophore serves as a potent pharmacological inverse agonist to minimize activity. The result is that the rod cell can attain single-photon sensitivity (86). The Rho structure reveals numerous potentially stabilizing intramolecular interactions—some mediated by the RET chromophore and some arising mainly from interhelical inter-actions that do not involve the RET-binding pocket directly. For example, Phe-293 interacts with Leu-40 and Phe-294 interacts with Cys-264. These interactions seem to be facilitated by the slight distortion of H6 in the region near Ile-263. In addition to these core interactions, four hydrogen (H)-bond networks appear to provide sta-bilizing interhelical interactions at or near the cytoplasmic surface of the receptor.

H-bond network 1 links H1, H2, and H7. The helical structure of H7 is elongated in the region from Ala-295 to Tyr-301, which permits the backbone carbonyl group of Ala-299 to H-bond with the side chains of Asn-55 and Asp-83. Asn-55 is a highly conserved residue that plays the central role in the H-bond network 1 because it H-bonds to both Asp-83 and the backbone carbonyl of Ala-299. Asp-83 may be connected to the backbone carbonyl of Gly-120 in H3 through a water molecule.

H-bond network 2 links H2, H3, and H4. This network involves Asn-78 as the key residue, which H-bonds to the hydroxyl functions of Ser-127 (H3), Thr-160 (H4), Trp-161 (H4), and the backbone carbonyl of Phe-159. Mutant pig-ments S127A and T160V displayed normal ground-state spectral properties con-sistent with a lack of direct contact with RET (96). Another possible interhelical interaction in this region might involve Glu-122 (H3), Met-163 (H4), and His-211 (H5). An indirect functional interaction between Glu-122 and His-211 has been demonstrated experimentally (18).

H-bond network 3 links H3 and H6. This network involves the conserved Arg-135, which interacts with Glu-134 and with the hydroxyl group of Thr-251 and side chain of Glu-247. The carboxylate of Glu-134 seems to be in position to form a salt bridge with the guanidinium group of Arg-135. This would be consistent with the hypothesis that Glu-134 is unprotonated in Rho and becomes protonated during the transition to R* (10, 50). It is interesting to note the three consecutive Val residues (Val-137, Val-138, and Val-139) are situated to form a cytoplasmic cap to H3 so that the Glu-134/Arg-135 dipeptide is between the receptor core and the Val tripeptide. This Val cap might act to stabilize the Glu-134/Arg-135 salt bridge, which in turn acts to keep the receptor in its off-state in the dark. It is also interesting to note that Thr-251 in Rho is in the position equivalent to Ala-293 in the α_{1B}-adrenergic receptor. Mutation of Ala-293 causes the receptor to become constitutively active (112). The Asp(Glu)/Arg/Tyr(Trp) motif at the cytoplasmic border of H3 is one of the most highly conserved structural motifs in Family A GPCRs.

Finally, H-bond network 4 links H6 and H7. The key interaction here is be-tween Met-257 and Asn-302. The precise functional importance of the highly conserved Asn/Pro/X/X/Tyr motif (Asn-302/Pro-303/Val-304/Ile-305/Tyr-306 in Rho) is unclear. However, one key structural role is to mediate several interhelical interactions. The side chains of Asn-302 and Tyr-306 project toward the center of the helical bundle. The hydroxyl group of Tyr-306 is close to Asn-73 (cytoplasmic border of H2), which is also highly conserved. A key structural water molecule may facilitate a H-bond interaction between Asn-302 and Asp-83 (H2). A recent mutagenesis study of the human platelet-activating factor receptor showed that replacement of amino acids at the positions equivalent to Asp-78 and Asn-302 in

Rho with residues that could not H-bond prevented agonist-dependent receptor internalization and G protein activation (125).

The interaction between Met-257 and the Asn/Pro/X/X/Tyr motif was predicted earlier to explain the results of a mutagenesis study in which Met-257 was replaced by each of the 19 other amino acid residues (82). Nearly all Met-257 replacements caused constitutive activity of the mutant opsins. Constitutive activity refers to the ability of an opsin to activate G_t in the absence of any chromophore. A decrease in interaction between Met-257 and Asn-302 might relieve an interhelical constraint that stabilizes the ground-state structure of Rho. However, the most highly constitutively active Met-257 mutants were M257Y, M257N, and M257S, which are all theoretically capable of forming H-bonds with the adjacent Asn-302. It is conceivable that the amino acid residue at position 257 in a mutant receptor forms H-bond interactions that stabilize the active-state structure of the receptor as well. Whether constitutive activity is caused simply by a lack of H6/H7 interactions, or whether a gain of active-state stabilizing interactions is required could be determined by testing mutant receptors with alterations of the Asn/Pro/X/X/Tyr motif, for example, N302A and I305A in Rho, or analogous mutations in other Family A GPCRs.

Structure-Activity Relationships in the Chromophore-Binding Pocket of Rhodopsin

The RET chromophore is a derivative of vitamin A_1 with a total of 20 carbon atoms (Figure 1). The carbon atoms of the cyclohexenyl ring are numbered C_1 to C_6. The polyene carbons extend from C_7 to C_{15}. Two methyl groups (C_{16} and C_{17}) are bonded to C_1, and single methyl groups are attached at each of three other carbons: C_5 (C_{18} methyl), C_9 (C_{19} methyl), and C_{13} (C_{20} methyl). The structural conformation of the bound chromophore in the Rho crystal structure appears to be 6-s-*cis*, 11-*cis*, 12-s-*trans*. The protonated Schiff base bond appears to be in the *anti* conformation. A higher-resolution Rho structure would be required for a crystallographic determination of the precise chromophore structure. Although a variety of spectroscopic studies support the 6-s-*cis*, 11-*cis*, 12-s-*trans* RET conformation, recent NMR and computational experiments suggest a 6-s-*trans* conformation (74, 202).

A number of experimental approaches have been employed to investigate RET-protein interactions in the membrane-embedded domain of bovine Rho. Several spectroscopic methods such as resonance Raman spectroscopy (93, 117, 129), Fourier-transform infrared (FTIR)-difference spectroscopy (51) and NMR spectroscopy (44, 74, 75, 221) have been reported. Other approaches have included reconstitution of opsin apoprotein with synthetic retinal analogues (92, 137) and photochemical cross-linking (26, 154, 232).

Lys-296 and Glu-113 are two of the key amino acid residues that define the structure and function of the retinal chromophore in Rho. The Schiff base linkage of the chromophore to Lys-296 is a key feature of Rho structure (83). Light-dependent Schiff base deprotonation is required for the formation of the active state of the receptor, R^* (106, 136). However, light can induce the receptor active state in the absence of a Schiff base chromophore linkage to the opsin (169, 234).

Glu-113 in bovine Rho serves as the counterion to the positive charge of the RET-protonated Schiff base (49, 156, 196, 233). Glu-113 is unprotonated and negatively charged in the ground state of Rho (48). It becomes protonated upon light-dependent formation of M-II and is the net proton acceptor for the Schiff base proton (97). The Glu-113–protonated Schiff base interaction serves to stabilize the Schiff base proton such that its acid dissociation constant (pK_a) in Rho is estimated to be >12, compared to a value of ~7 for a model compound in aqueous solution, although the mechanism of protonated Schiff base stabilization is not entirely clear from the crystal structure. The stable interaction between Glu-113 and the protonated Schiff base may also inhibit hydrolysis of the Schiff base linkage in darkness. For example, hydroxylamine does not react with the Schiff base of Rho, but readily reacts with that of M-II or with Rho mutants in which Glu-113 is replaced by a neutral amino acid residue by mutagenesis (196). This is an important consideration since the opsin alone, without the RET chromophore, has a small but measurable activity (29, 183, 189, 215).

The chemical environment of Schiff base has recently been probed using magic angle spinning (MAS) NMR. Recombinant Rho was labeled with 6-^{15}N-lysine and 2-^{13}C-glycine by expression of opsin in tissue culture with defined media. The UV-visible spectrum of the labeled Rho was indistinguishable from that of wild-type Rho. The peak corresponding to the ^{15}N-PSB was observed at 156.8 ppm in the MAS NMR spectrum. This peak position suggests that the distance between the PSB and its counterion at Glu-113 is greater than 4 Å, consistent with structural H-bonded water between the PSB nitrogen and Glu-113 (44). Similar results were obtained by Creemers et al. (38). More recently MAS NMR was carried out on artificial rhodopsin prepared by regeneration of opsin with a synthetic retinal containing ^{13}C at ten positions (222).

The high sensitivity of the rod cell depends upon an extremely low intrinsic level of signaling in darkness. Dark noise can be generated by thermal isomerization events in Rho (16, 17, 229), by the presence of opsin lacking the RET chromophore, which acts as an inverse agonist, or by mutant opsins that display the property of constitutive activity (189). Generally, a mutation that disrupts a putative salt bridge between Glu-113 and Lys-296 in the opsin apoprotein leads to constitutive activity. Replacement of either Glu-113 or Lys-296 by a neutral amino acid results in a mutant opsin with constitutive activity.

Other mutations such as G90D or A292E also result in constitutive activity, presumably because the introduction of the negatively charged residue into the membrane-embedded domain of the receptor affects the stability of the Glu-113/Lys-296 salt bridge (36, 184). The crystal structure shows that H2 is kinked around vicinal Gly residues, Gly-89 and Gly-90, so that this region of H2 is brought closer to H3 than to H1. This feature is interesting in that Gly-90 comes into close proximity to the retinylidene Schiff base counterion, Glu-113, on H3. A mutation that results in the replacement of Gly-90 by an Asp residue causes congenital stationary night blindness in humans, probably because of destabilization of the ionic interaction between Glu-113 and the Schiff base (235), or because of constitutive activity of the mutant opsin apoprotein that results from a disruption of a salt bridge between Glu-113 and Lys-296 (184). The mechanism of constitutive activity of opsins and the potential relevance of constitutive activity to visual diseases such as congenital night blindness have been reviewed (185).

The C_{12} of RET is within about 4–5 Å of Glu-181 from the E2 loop. Glu-181 may serve to influence the electron density of the conjugated polyene system of the RET chromophore so that photoisomerization occurs exclusively at the C_{11}–C_{12} double bond. The potential for ionic interaction between RET and Glu-181 also suggests that it may have a role in the mechanism of the opsin shift. Perturbation of the electron distribution near the center of the polyene chain is one mechanism to facilitate spectral tuning (92). Glu-181 is highly conserved among vertebrate opsins, blue and UV cone pigments. The corresponding position in green and red cone pigments is His-197, which forms part of a chloride ion–binding site. Chloride binding causes a red shift in absorption of the green and red pigments. Interestingly, the H197E/R200Q mutant of the human green cone pigment displays a visible λ_{max} value of 500 nm (225), which is the same as the λ_{max} value of Rho, suggesting that perturbation of the polyene by chloride may be the only element in the green cone pigment responsible for its spectral difference from Rho. The negative charge of the chloride ion bound to His-197 in the long-wavelength-sensing cone pigments might be brought closer to RET than the charge of the carboxylate of Glu-181 in Rho.

The position of the cyclohexenyl ring of the chromophore is largely constrained on the cytoplasmic side of the binding pocket by three residues: Glu-122 (H3), Phe-261 (H6), and Trp-265 (H6). The indole side chain of Trp-265 points inward from the more cytoplasmic position of the Trp-265 backbone and comes within about 3.8 Å of the RET C_{20}. Trp-265 is close enough to RET that it can serve as an intrinsic probe of the chromophore conformation (130). Side chains from Met-207, His-211, and Phe-212 on H5, and Tyr-268 and Ala-269 on H6 further constrain the chromophore ring. Replacements of Phe-261 by Tyr or Ala-269 by Thr produce bathochromic spectral shifts in the λ_{max} values of the resulting mutant pigments (34). These residues are also responsible in part for the spectral shift in red cone pigments. Whereas red pigments have Thr and Tyr at the positions corresponding to 261 and 269 in Rho, green cone pigments have Phe and Ala (11, 161).

The interaction between Gly-121 and RET is consistent with mutagenesis experiments in which replacement of Gly-121 caused blue-shifted λ_{max} values and decreased RET binding that corresponded to the bulk of the substituted side chain (80). Second-site replacement of Phe-261 by Ala caused a reversion of the loss of function Gly-121 mutant phenotypes, which was interpreted to mean that Gly-121 and Phe-261 interacted to form a part of the RET-binding pocket (79). Gly-121 and Phe-261 are indeed very close together in the Rho crystal structure. They pair to form one boundary of the RET-binding site to define the C_4-C_5-C_{18} orientation (Phe-261 C_z-Gly-121 C_α distance, 5 Å; Phe-261 C_z-RET C_4 distance, 3.7 Å). Interestingly, Gly-121 is conserved among all vertebrate and invertebrate visual pigments (181), and Phe-261 is strictly conserved among nearly all GPCRs (5). In long-wavelength-sensing cone pigments, Phe-261 is replaced by a tyrosine that is involved in spectral tuning (34).

Structure-Activity Relationships in the Cytoplasmic Domain of Rhodopsin

A number of cytoplasmic proteins interact exclusively with R*. Because the crystal structure depicts the inactive Rho structure that does not interact significantly with cytoplasmic proteins, the structure can provide only indirect information about the relevant R* state. In addition, two regions of the cytoplasmic surface domain of Rho (amino acid residues 236–239 and 328–333) are not fully resolved in the crystal structure. Potentially important structural information relevant to understanding protein-protein interactions in the visual transduction cascade may be lacking in the reported structure. The borders between the TM helical segments and the cytoplasmic loops do not necessarily represent the boundary between aqueous phase and membrane bilayer. The helical segments generally tend to extend into the cytoplasmic aqueous phase. A number of amino acid residues that are involved in G_t binding or activation, such as Glu-134 or Lys-248, are situated in the helical segments.

Detailed biochemical and biophysical analysis of the R^*-G_t interaction has been aided by mutagenesis of the cytoplasmic domain of bovine Rho. Numerous Rho mutants defective in the ability to activate G_t have been identified (60). Several of these mutant receptors were studied by flash photolysis (46, 59), light scattering (45), or proton uptake assays (10). Recently, a combination of site-directed mutagenesis and peptide-binding studies clearly showed that the C4 loop region, which includes H8, is involved in G_t binding and activation (46, 143). Direct evidence for the interaction between H8 and G_t comes from studies using a synthetic peptide corresponding to Asn-310 to Leu-321 of Rho, which binds to G_t (143). The key overall result of these studies is that C2, C3, and H8 are involved in R^*-G_t interaction.

H8 is a cationic amphipathic helix that may bind a phospholipid molecule, especially a negatively charged phospholipid such as phosphatidyl serine. In fact, spectroscopic evidence has been reported to show an interaction between Rho and a lipid molecule that is altered in the transition of Rho to M-II (19, 96). High conservation of Phe-313 and Arg-314 suggests that the amphipathic character of H8 may be functionally important. H8 points away from the center of Rho, and the area of the membrane surface covered by the entire cytoplasmic surface domain appears to be roughly large enough to accommodate G_t in a one-to-one complex. Recent evidence from fluorescence anisotropy and circular dichroism spectroscopy suggests that the structure of H8 is highly dependent on environment. Specifically, peptides corresponding to H8 adopt a random coil configuration in aqueous solution but form α-helices upon exposure to sodium dodecyl sulfate or binding to phospholipid liposomes (A. G. Krishna, T. J. Tracy, S. T. Menon & T. P. Sakmar, manuscript in preparation). The CT distal to the palmitoylated Cys-322 and Cys-323 residues appears to be highly disordered and dynamic based upon the results of site-directed electron paramagnetic resonance (EPR) spin labeling (124).

The structure of the cytoplasmic surface of Rho was also probed by solution ^{19}F nuclear Overhauser effect (NOE) NMR. NOE resonance depends on the distance between two atomic nuclei that undergo spin-spin coupling. To facilitate

NOE NMR in Rho, ^{19}F was introduced at specific sites in Rho using site-directed mutagenesis, which replaced the targeted amino acid with Cys. The Cys residue was then reacted with 4,4'-dithiodipyridine followed by trifluoroethylthio to yield a disulfide-linked trifluoroethyl moiety. As a control, individual Cys mutants were prepared in this manner to give the ^{19}F label at Cys-67, Cys-140, Cys-245, Cys-248, Cys-311, and Cys-316. Illumination of the individual mutants to form M-II produced upfield chemical shifts for the proteins labeled at positions 67 and 140, and downfield shifts for labels at positions 248 and 316. There was little or no change for proteins labeled at 245 and 311 (113). To allow the NOE strategy, three pairs of Cys residues were labeled in the same manner: Cys-140/Cys-316, Cys-65/Cys-316, and Cys-139/Cys-257. The labeled recombinant pigments were studied in the dark. No enhancement of the NOE signal was observed for the Cys-139/Cys-257 pair, moderate negative enhancement was observed for the Cys-65/Cys-316 pair, and strong negative enhancement was observed for the Cys-139/Cys-251 pair, indicating proximity of Cys-139 and Cys-251 (135).

THE MOLECULAR MECHANISM OF RECEPTOR ACTIVATION

Although the crystal structure of Rho does not provide direct information about the structure of R* or about the dynamics of the Rho-to-R* transition, it does provide a wealth of information that should help to design experiments using existing methods to address specific questions regarding the molecular mechanism of Rho activation. Fourier-transform infrared (FTIR)-difference spectroscopy has proven to be a well-suited technique for the study of light-induced conformational changes in recombinant Rho mutants (51, 190, 201). For example, among the membrane-embedded carboxylic acid groups, light-induced changes of protonation states or H-bond strengths were deduced from characteristic frequency shifts of C=O stretching vibrations of protonated carboxylic acid groups in FTIR-difference spectra. Their assignment to specific Asp or Glu residues was based on the disappearance of specific difference bands in site-directed mutants and revealed that Asp-83 (48, 186) and Glu-122 (48) are protonated in both dark Rho and M-II, whereas Glu-113 is ionized in the dark state and becomes protonated in M-II (97). Recently, attenuated total reflectance (ATR) FTIR-difference spectroscopy of the R*-G_t (or peptides derived from G_t) complex revealed an infrared-difference band that could be assigned to protonation of Glu-134 (47, 52, 163).

Evidence for the importance of steric interactions distal to the Schiff base comes from FTIR studies using ring-modified retinal analogues. Increased flexibility, as in 5,6-dihydro (65) or 7,8-dihydro analogues (173), reduces the usually observed torsions along the retinal chain in the intermediate trapped at 80 K where bathorhodopsin would normally be stable. In addition, the protein conformational changes observed at temperatures that stabilize the metarhodopsin I (M-I) or M-II intermediates differ from those observed in native Rho. In an extreme case, illumination of a pigment regenerated with a retinal analogue lacking the cyclo-hexenyl ring fails to induce the complete set of infrared absorption changes typical of the M-II conformation and results in reduced G_t activation (98). Therefore, the cyclohexenyl ring must transmit important steric changes to the protein. This model seems consistent with the location of the RET ring in the crystal structure of Rho.

Movement of α-helical domains is known to be involved in the signal transduction mechanisms of some TM receptor proteins, such as the bacterial chemoreceptors (150), and has been shown to occur during the proton-pumping cycle following retinal isomerization in bacteriorhodopsin (bR), the seven-transmembrane segment light-driven proton pump (212–214). Recent studies have suggested that steric and/or electrostatic changes in the ligand-binding pocket of Rho may cause changes in the relative disposition of TM helices within the core of the receptor. These changes may be responsible for transmitting a signal from the membrane-embedded–binding site to the cytoplasmic surface of the receptor. Trp mutagenesis (130), mutagenesis of conserved amino acid residues on H3 and H6 (79, 80), and the introduction of pairs of His residues at the cytoplasmic borders of TM helices to create sites for metal chelation (200) have recently provided insights regarding the functional role of specific helix-helix interactions in Rho.

The indole group of a Trp amino acid residue is often used as a noninvasive environment-sensitive probe of protein structure because of its unique absorption and fluorescence properties. UV-absorption spectroscopy has suggested that the local protein environment around Trp residues changes during the conversion of Rho to M-II (182). In addition, a linear dichroism study of UV-difference bands indicated a reorientation of an indole side chain during the M-I to M-II conversion (33). More specifically Trp-126 and Trp-265 were shown to move to more polar environments during activation of the receptor (130). It was further suggested that the photoactivation of Rho involved a change in the relative disposition of H3 and H6, which contain Trp-126 and Trp-265 within the α-helical bundle of the receptor.

The functional interaction of H3 and H6 was further probed in a study in which metal ion–binding sites were introduced between the cytoplasmic surfaces of TM helices with the aim of restraining specific activation-induced conformational changes (200). Pairs of His residues are capable of chelating metal ions such as Zn(II) if the distance and geometry between the residues are appropriate. His residues substituted for the native amino acids at the cytoplasmic ends of H3 and H6, but not H5 and H7, created mutant proteins that activated G_t in the absence, but not in the presence, of metal ions. It was concluded that specific metal ion crosslinks between positions 138 and 251, or 141 and 251, on H3 and H6 prevented receptor activation. These results indicated a direct coupling of receptor activation to a change in the spatial disposition of H3 and H6. This could occur if movements of H3 and H6 were coupled to changes in the conformation of the connected intracellular loops, which contribute to binding surfaces and tertiary contacts of Rho with G_t (59, 60).

More evidence for changes in interhelical interactions upon receptor activation was provided by extensive site-directed spin labeling and EPR spectroscopy studies of the transition of Rho to R* in modified or expressed mutant pigments. The results suggested a requirement for rigid body motion of TM helices, especially H3 and H6, in the activation of Rho (55). A slight reorientation of helical segments upon receptor activation is also supported by experiments using polarized attenuated total reflectance infrared-difference spectroscopy (40). Finally, movement of H6 was also detected by site-specific chemical labeling and fluorescence spectroscopy (43). The structural rearrangement of helices upon activation might not result in a R* structure that is drastically different from that of Rho since an engineered receptor with four disulfide bonds (between the cytoplasmic ends of H1 and H7 and H3 and H5, and the extracellular ends of H3 and H4 and H5 and H6) was still able to activate G_t (209).

However, some conformational changes must occur at the cytoplasmic surface of Rho to produce R* that can activate G_t. Does the Rho structure provide any potential insights that might help to predict the identity of these conformational changes? Does H8 unwind or come off the membrane surface on activation? Do C2 and C3, which are known to be important for G_t activation, move? What are the active-state conformations of the conserved Glu-134/Arg-135/Tyr-136 in H3 and the conserved Asn-302/Pro-303/Val-304/Ile-305/Tyr-306 in H7?

Mutagenesis experiments can be designed to elucidate the light-dependent alterations of physical or chemical states of specific amino acids required for G_t activation. For example, structural changes in the cytoplasmic surface domain of Rho were suggested by changes in the reactivities of Cys residues introduced at various positions by site-directed mutagenesis (114). Conformation-dependent interhelical interactions and tertiary contacts on the cytoplasmic surface were also probed biochemically using site-directed disulfide bond formation (208) and/or expression of split receptors (230, 231). Using the core of Rho as a scaffold, cytoplasmic loops of other GPCRs were substituted for those of Rho, the results of G protein–activation experiments suggested that C2 and C3 might have distinct roles in G_t activation and G protein–subtype specificity (228). These results also indirectly support the general activation mechanism of helix movement that transmits a signal from the membrane-embedded core to the surface loops of the receptor.

Time-resolved (54) and static EPR spectroscopy studies (187) on site-specific spin-labeled Rho showed that the cytoplasmic terminations of H3 and H7 undergo structural rearrangements in the vicinities of Cys-140 and Cys-316. These changes have been specifically assigned to the M-II conformation. Cys-140 is close to the highly conserved Glu-134/Arg-135/Tyr-136 tripeptide at the cytoplasmic border of H3. Site-directed spin labeling of the amino acid residues from Tyr-306 to Leu-321 was also carried out. The information obtained regarding conformational changes in H8 upon M-II formation was limited by the relative lack of reactivity of the Cys residues engineered into positions 317, 318, 320, and 321. However, structural changes were detected at positions 306, 313, and 316, consistent with movements of the nearby H6 and with biochemical evidence for a light-dependent interaction between Cys-65 and Cys-316 in native Rho (6, 30). Consistent with the notion of light-dependent structural changes in the vicinity of the cytoplasmic end of H7 is the observation that a monoclonal antibody with an epitope that was mapped to the amino acid sequence 304 to 311 bound only to R^* and not to Rho (1). Only relatively small light-dependent structural changes were noted in and around the C1 loop when residues 56 to 75 were individually probed by site-directed spin labeling (7).

An EPR study of Rho mutants with a substitution of Glu-134 showed that the mutant receptors displayed an EPR signature consistent with a partially activated conformational state in the dark (107). This finding seems to be consistent with extensive earlier studies of Glu-134 replacement mutants. The structural change detected by EPR spectroscopy may be directly related to the apparent requirement for protonation of Glu-134 upon R^* formation. A rearrangement of neighboring H-bonding partners may be necessary for protonation of Glu-134 to occur. The pH profile of G_t activation (50) as well as the abolishment of the uptake of two protons in mutant E134Q (10) suggests the existence of other titratable groups influenced by Glu-134. Glu-134 interacts primarily with Arg-135 in Rho, but it is not clear whether Glu-134 would interact with other side chains in R^* or simply be in a position to interact with bound G_t. The Glu-134/Arg-135 dipeptide may form a functional microdomain that is responsible for inducing the release of GDP from R^*-bound G_t (3, 128).

Any model of receptor activation has to account for the fact that the chemical environment of the Schiff base is altered so that net proton transfer occurs between the Schiff base imine and Glu-113 (97). This change in the RET-binding pocket must be transmitted to the cytoplasmic surface of the receptor. The Rho crystal structure is consistent with the helix movement model of receptor activation (55, 200) since it provides a structural basis to explain how chromophore isomerization could lead to displacement of H3 and H6 that would subsequently result in a change in orientation of Glu-134 at the cytoplasmic border. The structure suggests possible contacts between the cyclohexenyl ring of the chromophore and H3, which should change upon photoisomerization (26). At the Schiff base end of the chromophore, the C_{20} methyl group seems to interact with Trp-265, and this interaction should also change upon isomerization. Other key interhelical constraints are expected to be directly sensitive to chromophore isomerization, including those mediated by Phe-294, Ala-299, Asn-302, and Tyr-306. Any concerted disruption of stabilizing interhelical interactions may be expected to lead to helix movement and rearrangement of the helical bundle.

MECHANISM OF THE OPSIN SHIFT
AND SPECTRAL TUNING

Rho has been used as a model pigment for a variety of chemical and spectroscopic studies to elucidate the mechanism of the opsin shift. In this context, the opsin shift may be defined as the difference between the λ_{max} value of a RET Schiff base model compound (about 440 nm) in solution and that of Rho (500 nm). One important result to arise from the study of mutant bovine Rho pigments was the identification of Glu-113 as the RET Schiff base counterion (156, 196, 233). UV-visible spectroscopy (155, 156, 196, 233) and microprobe resonance Raman spectroscopy (132) were also used to characterize other membrane-embedded carboxylic acid residues. Additional studies including the use of photoaffinity reagents (154, 232), retinal analogues regenerated with site-directed mutants (188) or site-directed mutant pigments (79, 80, 130, 155), led to a more complete picture of the amino acid residues in the membrane-embedded domain of Rho that interact with the retinal chromophore.

Microprobe Raman spectroscopy of recombinant visual pigments and mutant pigments in particular has provided useful information about the mechanism of the opsin shift (132). Raman spectroscopy measures the energy loss of photons that are scattered after laser excitation of a nonabsorbing medium. The energy loss (expressed in wavenumbers) is proportional to the vibrational frequencies of the excited molecule. Conditions can be chosen such that a vibrational spectrum of the 11-*cis*-retinylidene chromophore can be obtained within its binding pocket in the Rho pigment. Vibrational modes are represented as peaks of Raman intensity. Some of the modes are delocalized. The in-phase ethylenic stretching mode at 1545 cm^{-1} represents the coupled vibrations of the conjugated carbon-carbon double bonds. Other modes are localized and represent specific atomic vibrations within the chromophore. The 1650 cm^{-1} mode represents the C=N stretching vibration of the protonated Schiff base. The 970 cm^{-1} mode represents the coupled hydrogen-out-of-plane (HOOP) wagging of C_{11}-H and C_{12}-H. The 1212 cm^{-1} mode represents the coupled C_8-C_9 stretching and C-H rocking motions. Other C-C stretching modes are represented by the 1098 (C_{10}-C_{11}), 1190 (C_{14}-C_{15}), and 1238 cm^{-1} (C_{12}-C_{13}) peaks. These modes can be used as probes of local structure and may be sensitive to specific amino acid replacements introduced by site-directed mutagenesis (116).

The crystal structure now provides a clear picture of the RET chromophore-binding pocket in Rho (Figure 3). Available data suggest that the dominant mechanism responsible for the opsin shift is the interaction of dipolar amino acid residues with both the ground-state and excited-state charge distributions of the chromophore (116, 131). This general mechanism is supported by the crystal structure in that the RET-binding pocket contains a large number of dipolar or polarizable amino acid residues.

THE RHODOPSIN PHOTOCYCLE

The chromophore photoisomerization occurs on an ultrafast timescale and was observed to be a vibrationally coherent process (224). At low temperature, a number of photointermediates that characterize the transition of Rho to R* can be trapped and studied by a variety of spectroscopic techniques. Laser flash photolysis coupled with nanosecond time-resolved UV-visible spectroscopy has identified the Rho photocycle that occurs at or near physiological temperature: Rho (500 nm) → bathorhodopsin (543 nm) ↔ blue-shifted intermediate (BSI) (477 nm) → lumirhodopsin (497 nm) → M-I (480 nm) ↔ M-II (380 nm). M-II decays to metarhodopsin III (M-III) (450 nm) and finally to opsin plus free 11-*trans*-retinal (126).

The photointermediates of Rho and a variety of native visual pigments, chemically modified pigments, and artificial pigments have been studied by optical, resonance Raman, FTIR, and NMR spectroscopy (24, 48, 53, 57, 81, 113, 115, 127, 130, 132, 173, 180, 195, 201). These studies provide specific detailed information about chromophore structures and about dynamic chromophore-opsin interactions. The photocycle can also be studied under a variety of conditions that might provide a basis for identifying specific amino acid residues that might be involved in intramolecular proton transfer reactions. For example, the pH dependency was determined for the formation of Rho photoproducts from lumi to M-II (99).

THE STRUCTURAL BASIS OF RHODOPSIN-TRANSDUCIN INTERACTIONS

Structural Studies of Transducin

G_t plays a central role in the phototransduction cascade (210, 223). G_t couples together two separate highly specialized proteins: the photon detector rhodopsin and the efficient second messenger modulator PDE. G_t activation by R^* represents a key amplification step in the cascade in that a single R^* can catalyze the activation of hundreds of G_t molecules (63, 87). In addition, G_t exhibits a low rate of basal (uncatalyzed) nucleotide exchange that contributes to sensitivity by maintaining low background noise. Finally, G_t provides an important site of regulation. The rates of GTP loading and GTP hydrolysis by G_t determine to a large extent the amplitude and the temporal resolution of the resulting signal. Crystal structures of several conformations of G_t have been solved to date, including the GTPγS- (164), the GDP- (121), and the GDP/AlF$_4^-$-bound structures of Gα_t (205), as well as the GDP-bound heterotrimer (122) and free G$\beta\gamma_t$ (204) (Table 1; follow the Supplemental Material link on the Annual Reviews homepage at http://www.annualreviews.org/). More recently, the structure of the ternary complex of Gα_t bound to its effector PDEγ and RGS9 was reported (203). These structures have provided detailed information on a number of G protein mechanisms, including the nature of the conformational change induced by GTP binding, the mechanism and regulation of GTP hydrolysis, and the nature of interactions between Gα_t and G$\beta\gamma_t$.

Gα_t, a 350–amino acid protein, consists of two domains (Figure 4)—the Ras-like domain, so named because of its homology with the structure of the monomeric G protein, p21^{ras} (Ras), and the helical domain, so named to reflect its composition of six α-helices (αA–αF). The nucleotide is bound in a cleft between the domains. The Ras-like domain consists of a central mixed six-stranded β-sheet (designated β1-β6) surrounded on either side by a total of six α-helices (designated α1-α5, plus αG). The majority of the direct contacts to the nucleotide originate from conserved regions of the Ras-like domain, which map to loops emanating from the strands of the central β-sheets. These loops are homologous to canonical nucleotide-binding domains of the monomeric G proteins (206). The Ras-like domain contains four regions not homologous to Ras, called Inserts 1–4.

The conformational changes that accompany the exchange of GDP for GTP are localized to three regions, denoted Switch I, II, and III. Switch I (Ser-173-Thr-183) and II (Phe-195-Thr-215) are similar to Switch regions described in Ras; Switch III (Asp-227-Arg-238) is unique to the heterotrimeric G proteins. Switch I and II respond directly to the presence of the γ phosphate of GTP, but Switch III appears to move in response to reorganization of the Switch II (121). The conformational changes in Switch II involve a partial rotation of the α2-helix, which leads to the movement of several amino acid side chains from exposed to partially buried positions. These changes serve as the basis of assays of $G\alpha_t$ activation. In particular, the movement of Trp-207 is detected as a large increase in fluorescence emission intensity (52, 56), and the burial of Arg-204 protects it from cleavage by trypsin (62, 141).

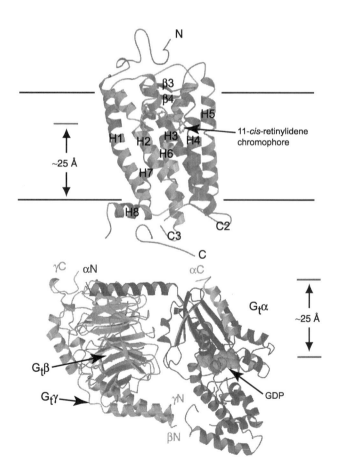

$G\alpha_t$-GTP activates PDE, a tetrameric enzyme consisting of α, β, and γ subunits in a 1:1:2 stoichiometry, by removing the inhibitory constraints that the γ subunits exert upon the catalytic α and β subunits. The binding site of PDE γ on $G\alpha_t$ was recently determined by X-ray crystallography and found to reside between the $\alpha2$-helix of the Switch II region and the adjacent $\alpha3$-helix (203).

$G\alpha_t$ hydrolyzes bound GTP to return to its inactive GDP-bound state. Rapid turn-off of the cascade is essential for the temporal resolution of the signal (85). GTP hydrolysis is accelerated by the simultaneous binding of the effector, cGMP PDEγ subunit, and a second protein, regulator of G protein signaling 9 (RGS9) (85). $G\alpha_t$ (GDP) recombines with $G\beta\gamma_t$ and can then be activated again by another R*.

$G\beta_t$ is a 340–amino acid protein, constructed from an amino-terminal α-helix, followed by a β-propeller structure (204). The β-propeller consists of seven "blades," each consisting of four β-sheets. Each blade is roughly related to the others by rotational symmetry. At the sequence level, $G\beta_t$ is notable for seven WD40 domains, sequence repeats of roughly 40 amino acids that frequently end

---

Figure 4 Interactions between Rho and G_t at the cytoplasmic surface of the disc membrane. A molecular graphics ribbon diagram of Rho prepared from the crystal structure coordinates at 2.8 Å resolution is shown at the *top*. The figure was produced using the A chain of the published crystal structure coordinates (172). The amino terminus (N) and extracellular (or intradiscal) surface is toward the top of the figure and the carboxyl terminus (C) and intracellular (or cytoplasmic) surface is toward the bottom. Seven transmembrane segments (H1 to H7), which are characteristic of GPCRs, are shown. The RET chromophore is shown as a ball and stick model. The Rho crystal structure does not resolve a small segment of the C3 loop linking H5 and H6 or a longer segment of the carboxyl-terminal tail distal to H8. The transmembrane segments are tilted with respect to the presumed plane of the membrane bilayer. They are generally α-helical, but they contain significant kinks and irregularities as described in the text. The chromophore is labeled with an *arrow* pointing to the cyclohexenyl ring. The Schiff base linkage of the chromophore lies approximately 25 Å from the cytoplasmic surface of the membrane bilayer. The structure is the GDP bound form of G_t shown at the bottom with the surface that presumably interacts with Rho facing up. The Ras-like domain of $G\alpha_t$ is above the GDP-binding pocket and the helical domain of $G\alpha_t$ is below. $G\beta_t$ and $G\gamma_t$ are to the left. The bound GDP may be up to 25 Å from the surface of G_t. The amino and carboxyl termini of each subunit are labeled. Structures thought to interact with Rho and/or the membrane, including the amino and carboxyl termini of $G\alpha_t$ and the carboxyl terminus of $G\gamma_t$, cluster on a common surface of G_t. The relative orientation of the cytoplasmic surface of Rho and the Rho-binding surface of G_t is arbitrary. Upon formation of the Rho-G_t complex, the chromophore-binding pocket of Rho becomes allosterically coupled to the nucleotide-binding pocket of G_t, which is approximately 50 Å away. The structure of the R*-G_t complex has not yet been determined.

with Trp-Asp (WD in the single letter code). Each WD40 repeat corresponds to the fourth strand of one propeller blade and the first three strands of an adjacent blade. $G\beta_t$ is a member of a large family of proteins containing WD40 repeats, which perform a variety of functions; all are thought to fold into β-propeller structures (67, 160). $G\beta_t$ is also a member of a larger family of proteins that fold into β-propeller structures, many of which do not share significant sequence homology.

$G\gamma_t$ is the shortest G_t subunit, consisting of only 73 amino acids. It contains an amino-terminal α-helix, which interacts with the amino terminus of $G\beta_t$ in a coiled-coil conformation (Figure 4). Interestingly, a study conducted prior to the determination of the structure showed that peptides derived from the helical regions of $G\beta_t$ and $G\gamma_t$ do not associate with each other in solution (144). The remainder of $G\gamma_t$ wraps around $G\beta_t$ in an extended conformation. $G\beta_t$ and $G\gamma_t$ can be dissociated from one another only under denaturing conditions, and physiologically they function as a single entity.

The structure of the G_t heterotrimer (122) reveals two distinct sites of interaction between $G\alpha_t$ and $G\beta\gamma_t$: The amino-terminal helix of $G\alpha_t$ interacts with the side of the $G\beta_t$-propeller, and the Switch I/II region of $G\alpha_t$ interacts with the top of the $G\beta_t$-propeller structure. Direct contacts between $G\alpha_t$ and $G\gamma_t$ are not observed in the structure, although interactions between lipids attached to each subunit have been proposed. The structure of free $G\beta\gamma_t$ compared with $G\beta\gamma_t$ in the heterotrimer reveals that $G\beta\gamma_t$ is virtually unchanged by the binding of $G\alpha_t$ (204). However, the structure of $G\alpha_t$ is altered in the conformationally flexible Switch I/II-binding region, which makes contacts with $G\beta_t$ (122). The structure of the amino-terminal helix of $G\alpha_t$ is also likely altered by the binding of $G\beta\gamma_t$.

A number of important posttranslational modifications of G_t have been described. $G\alpha_t$ is heterogeneously acylated, primarily with saturated C_{12} and C_{14} esterified fatty acids, at its amino-terminal glycine (118). This modification is thought to be important for interactions with $G\beta\gamma_t$ (118) and possibly with membranes and rhodopsin (151). Recently, a report describing the phosphorylation of $G\alpha_t$ at Tyr-142 by the tyrosine kinase Src in rod outer segments has been published (20). The significance of this modification is not yet understood. $G\gamma_t$ is modified in a three-step process that includes farnesylation of a cysteine in the carboxyl-terminal CAAX (Cys-Ala-Ala-X) motif, cleavage of the three carboxyl-terminal amino acids, and carboxymethylation of the free carboxyl terminus (226). Farnesylation has been found to be important for interactions with $G\alpha_t$ (145) as well as with rhodopsin (109, 198). There is evidence that rhodopsin can discriminate between farnesyl (C_{15}) and geranylgeranyl (C_{20}) esterified fatty acids (109), which suggests the existence of a specific prenyl-binding site on Rho.

Many biochemical and biophysical techniques have been used to identify sites on G_t that interact with membranes and with R*. The involvement of the carboxyl-terminal 11 amino acids of $G\alpha_t$ (a.a. 340–350) in interactions with R* is suggested by many studies, including (a) the finding that Pertussis toxin catalyzes the ADP-ribosylation of Cys-347, which uncouples G_t from R*; (b) a peptide corresponding to amino acids 340–350 can uncouple R* from G_t and can itself bind to R* and mimic the effects of G_t (78, 111); (c) site-directed mutagenesis (66, 170); and (d) the demonstration in related G proteins that specificity of coupling to particular receptors resides in their carboxyl termini (37). In addition, peptide competition and site-directed mutagenesis studies have suggested the involvement of the $\alpha 4/\beta 6$ loop of $G\alpha_t$, which lies adjacent to the carboxyl terminus, in interacting with R* (78, 159). Experimental evidence suggests that $G\beta\gamma_t$ is also in direct contact with rhodopsin (105, 178). The specific contacts between $G\beta\gamma_t$ and R* involve the carboxyl terminus of $G\gamma_t$, as suggested by studies with peptides derived from that region (108, 109) and possibly the seventh propeller blade of $G\beta\gamma_t$ (217).

All the structures of G_t that are thought to participate in interactions with Rho or the membrane cluster to a common face on the structure of G_t and identify a putative Rho-interacting surface (25, 122) (Figure 4). However, in the crystal structure of the heterotrimer, neither the carboxyl terminus of $G\alpha_t$ nor that of $G\gamma_t$ are included. Thus, the structure of the specific Rho-interacting regions is unclear. A partial remedy has been provided by an NMR study of a peptide derived from the carboxyl terminus of $G\alpha_t$ in its Rho-bound conformation; these data suggest that it forms an extension of the $\alpha 5$-helix of $G\alpha_t$ (110).

The Mechanism of Rhodopsin-Catalyzed Nucleotide Exchange

The photoisomerization of 11-cis-retinal to ATR leads to local structural alterations in the chromophore-binding pocket of Rho. These structural changes are propagated to the cytoplasmic surface of Rho, and following binding of G_t, on to the nucleotide-binding pocket of $G\alpha_t$ where GDP is released. In this way, the chromophore-binding pocket of Rho is allosterically coupled to the nucleotide-binding pocket of $G\alpha_t$ approximately 5 nm away (Figure 4). Several key observations characterize the process of R*-catalyzed nucleotide exchange. In the absence of a catalyst, the rate-limiting step in nucleotide exchange is release of GDP from $G\alpha_t$ to form empty-pocket G_t, $G\alpha_t(e)\beta\gamma_t$. $G\alpha_t(e)$ is by itself very unstable. R* catalyzes nucleotide exchange by inducing GDP release and stabilizing the reaction intermediate, $G\alpha_t(e)\beta\gamma_t$. The empty-pocket G_t can be dissociated from R* by either GDP or GTP; R* and nucleotide binding are mutually exclusive. GTP binding is nearly irreversible since conformational changes in the Switch II region destroy the $G\beta\gamma_t$-binding site and induce dissociation of $G\alpha_t(GTP)$ from $G\beta\gamma_t$ and R*. R* interacts specifically with heterotrimeric G_t; $G\beta\gamma_t$ appears to be absolutely required for efficient R*-catalyzed nucleotide exchange on $G\alpha_t$ (61). It is unclear whether $G\beta\gamma_t$ plays a mechanistic role in catalysis (95) or whether it merely facilitates binding between Rho and $G\alpha_t$ (179). Binding of G_t to R* and dissociation of GDP appear to be distinct steps; Rho mutants that bind G_t but do not induce GDP release have been described (45, 59).

The molecular mechanism by which R* induces GDP release from G_t is the least-understood step in the G_t signaling cycle. Despite a great deal of data regarding structures of G_t and Rho that interact with each other, little is known about the detailed structure of the complex (133). The structure of R* is not known, and the conformational changes, if any, that occur in R* and G_t-GDP upon complex formation are not known. Few sites of point-to-point contacts between R* and G protein have been reliably identified (4), and those that have been found do not greatly constrain possible geometric alignments of the two proteins in the complex. Crystallographic analysis of the R*-G_t(e) complex may prove difficult owing to the instability of R*. The alignment of the interacting surfaces in the structures of Rho and G_t produces a hypothetical low-resolution model of the complex (28) (Figure 4). These analyses, although lacking details, do suggest clearly that the cytoplasmic loops of Rho, which are roughly 1.5 nm long (at most) are too short to contact directly the nucleotide-binding pocket of $G\alpha_t$, which is at least 2.5 nm from the Rho-binding surface of G_t. Consequently, R* must act "at-a-distance" to induce nucleotide exchange in $G\alpha_t$ (95).

One long-standing hypothesis regarding the mechanism of nucleotide exchange suggested that interdomain interactions between amino acid side chains of the Ras-like and the helical domains of $G\alpha_t$ regulated nucleotide exchange rate. Recently, Marin et al. developed a method to assay the rates of both uncatalyzed and R*-catalyzed nucleotide exchange of $G\alpha_t$ and $G\alpha_t$ mutants expressed in vitro (141). They demonstrated that contrary to what was predicted, disruption of interdomain interactions by site-directed mutations did not affect either basal or R*-catalyzed nucleotide exchange rates in $G\alpha_t$ (141). However, additional studies identified a cluster of residues on the α5-helix, which, when mutated, dramatically accelerated nucleotide exchange. These results suggested a key role for the α5-helix of $G\alpha_t$ in mediating nucleotide exchange. The α5-helix connects the carboxyl terminus to the β6/α5 loop, which lies adjacent to the nucleotide. It is possible that the binding of R* to this region of $G\alpha_t$ perturbs key stabilizing interactions to induce GDP release (142).

Additional Protein-Protein Interactions

A number of cytoplasmic proteins besides G_t are known to interact with R*. These include Rho kinase, which phosphorylates R* at specific serine residues (Ser-334, Ser-338, and Ser-343) (147, 165, 174). Reconstitution experiments suggest that light-dependent phosphorylation of Rho is catalyzed primarily by Rho kinase and not by protein kinase C (166). Phosphorylation decreases the effective lifetime of R* but paradoxically shifts the M-I/M-II equilibrium toward M-II (70). Signal quenching requires that arrestin binds to phosphorylated R* to prevent it from activating G_t. The role of the distal carboxyl-terminal tail in the shut-off of the light signal in the rod cell was shown convincingly in a study using a transgenic mouse strain. The mice, whose rod cells expressed a Rho transgene with a truncated carboxyl-terminal tail, were studied by electrophysiological techniques. Phosphorylation of the carboxyl-terminal tail was required for termination of light-induced signaling (35). The current state of the structural biology of proteins involved in vertebrate phototransduction is summarized in Table 1 (available as Supplemental Material: follow the Supplemental Material link on the Annual Reviews homepage at http://www.annualreviews.org/).

STRUCTURAL STUDIES OF BACTERIORHODOPSIN

Although Rho shares no primary structural homology with archaebacterial retinal-based ion pumps or sensory pigments, some obvious similarities do exist. The general molecular topology is conserved among visual pigments and archaebacterial retinal-based pigments because of the existence in both classes of seven TM segments and an extracellular N-terminal tail. In addition, the retinylidene chromophore in all cases is bound to a lysine residue on H-7 through a Schiff base linkage. A detailed discussion of archaebacterial pigments is beyond the intended scope of this chapter. However, since several high-resolution structures have recently become available, particularly of bacteriorhodopsin (bR), the light-driven proton pump of *Halobacterium salinarium*, a short summary is presented below. A comparison of the crystal structures of Rho and bR has also been recently discussed (218).

Recent advances in the refinement of X-ray crystallographic structural detail in bR have helped to elucidate its proton-pumping mechanism, particularly with respect to the involvement of internal water molecules in the vectorial transfer of protons through the translocation channel. A major breakthrough in the structural biology of bR was achieved a decade ago by high-resolution electron cryo-microscopy at 3.5 Å resolution (88). There followed a number of refinements, notably correcting electron-crystallographic data for diffuse scattering and the addition of phase information (73). Attempts to obtain crystals of bR suitable for X-ray diffraction measurements were not successful for a number of years presumably because removal from the phospholipid membrane, even by mild detergent, caused structural inhomogeneities. The development of lipidic cubic phases for the crystallization of membrane proteins made possible the preparation of three-dimensional hexagonal plate-like crystals of bR and of mutants of bR (123, 177). The bicontinuous lipidic cubic phase is an ordered three-dimensional matrix perforated by a regular channel system that allows free diffusion of hydrophilic as well as hydrophobic solutes. The size of the hexagonal plate-like bR crystals was typically in the range of $80 \times 80 \times 15$ μm (21, 138). The use of high-energy X-rays made possible short exposure times at low temperatures (microfocus beamline from a synchrotron, λ close to 1.000 Å, 120 frames at 30 sec/frame, 110 K). These conditions cause a minimum of damage to the reactive molecule and may also be used to determine structures of reaction intermediates in the photocycle. bR structures with resolutions of 1.9 Å (21) and 1.55 Å (140) have been reported.

Minimal conformational changes are apparent in the TM helices during the initial fast kinetics steps of the bR photocycle, when the intermediates K (590 nm) and L (550 nm) are observed (138). The L $\rightarrow$ M step involves the deprotonation of the positively charged Schiff base at Lys-216. It is well established that the Schiff base is deprotonated only in the M intermediate during the photocycle. There is strong evidence that there are two variants, M1 (412 nm) and M2 (412 nm), also designated as early M and late M. The two species are distinguished kinetically (23) and can be detected in FTIR double-flash experiments (90). Discussion continues regarding the details of structural and conformational changes during the M formation and decay (103). A reasonable sequence of occurrences is that L $\rightarrow$ M1 $\rightarrow$ M2 constitutes first the deprotonation of the Schiff base by transfer of a proton to the carboxylate of Asp-85 with outward bending of H-3, facilitating exposure to the extracellular surface, followed by the release of a proton from Glu-204 to an extracellular water molecule.

The reaction M (412 nm) $\rightarrow$ N (560 nm) restores the protonation of the Schiff base by transfer of a proton from Asp-96 (138). With the formation of intermediate N, H-3 has regained its original conformation and the cytoplasmic half of the H-6 is bent outward, allowing the H-7 to approach Lys-216 to provide closer proximity of Asp-96 to the Schiff base. The chromophore is still in its 13-*cis*, 15-*anti* configuration. Protonation of Asp-96 occurs in the reaction step N (560 nm) $\rightarrow$ O (610 nm). The proton is supplied by a cytoplasmic water molecule. In the final step O (610 nm) $\rightarrow$ bR (568 nm), the chromophore undergoes isomerization to all-*trans*, and the TM helices return to their original conformation as in light-adapted bR at the start of the photocycle.

The identity of the photocycle intermediates is well established kinetically. The ground-state bR (568 nm), M (412 nm), N (560 nm), and O (610 nm) are distinguished spectroscopically in the UV-visible range associated with $\pi \rightarrow \pi^*$ transitions of the conjugated double-bond system of the chromophore. Free retinal has a maximal absorption at approximately 380 nm, and the shifts are clearly a result of interactions with the opsin moiety. The photocycle intermediates are well resolved kinetically because their formation and decay occur during very different time frames (six orders of magnitude, ns to ms). Conformational changes in the TM helices and in the movement of water molecules H-bonded to amino acid side chains can be observed spectroscopically in the infrared region (101) and also by ^{13}C-NMR (191) and ^{15}N-NMR (89).

An early model for proton transduction by bR, proposed more than a decade ago, was known as the proton-wire model, where the wire was located in the "proton pathway channel" between the TM helices. This concept was based on the Grotthuss mechanism for the transport of hydrogen ions in liquid water (151a). The proton-wire hypothesis was short-lived because it became evident that amino acid side chains, such as carboxylate and carboxyl, were directly involved in proton pumping and that the deprotonation and reprotonation of the Schiff base were central to the proton translocation process. For a number of years there remained the difficulty that X-ray crystallographic structures showed distances to be too large between the Schiff base and the candidate acceptor amino acid residues, such as Asp-85 and Asp-96, for a direct transfer of a proton to take place. The postulate that water molecules located in the proton pathway channel could bridge the gap was not difficult to accept, even though such molecules eluded direct observation. In recent years FTIR, NMR, and high-resolution crystallographic methods have provided direct evidence for specific water molecules forming a H-bonded network associated with specific prototropic amino acid side chain groups (41, 64, 100, 138, 140, 152, 177). The amino acid residues are located at specific points in the amino acid sequence, and the participating side chains are therefore tethered to the peptide backbone of the TM helices, although some freedom of movement is still possible (72). By contrast, the participating water molecules are localized within a cage but are ultimately exchangeable with water molecules in the cytoplasm and in the extracellular medium.

The currently emerging details of the proton translocation mechanism in bR point to simultaneous concerted movements in the conformation of segments of the TM helices, orientation of amino acid side chains, acceptance and release of protons by prototropic groups, redistribution of electrostatic charges, and configuration and orientation of the chromophore. The effects of electrostatic charges at critical points provide vectoriality in the proton translocation by electrostatic steering (89, 197). Time-resolved crystallographic structure determination, termed kinetic crystallography, could ultimately establish the complete mechanism of light-driven proton pumping (2, 94, 139, 162, 177). It is hoped that future high-resolution structures of Rho, Rho photoproducts, and mutants of Rho will allow the function of Rho to be elucidated with a similar degree of detail.

CONCLUSION

Rho is a paradox. On the one hand, it displays several unique and fascinating properties that allow it to function as the dim-light photoreceptor in the rod cell. It has an extremely low rate of thermal activation, but it can be activated by a single photon at high quantum efficiency. On the other hand, it serves as a prototype of the largest family of membrane receptors in the human genome, GPCRs. The recent report of the crystal structure of bovine Rho provides a unique opportunity to address questions related to the structural basis of Rho function in the vertebrate visual transduction cascade. Over the past decade a remarkable amount of information about structure-activity relationships in Rho, and other GPCRs, has been obtained using techniques of molecular biology. The crystal structure of Rho also provides a chance to evaluate the quality of this information. Site-directed mutant pigments have been employed to elucidate key structural elements, the opsin-shift mechanism and the mechanism of receptor photoactivation.

Perhaps the greatest surprise in the crystal structure was the role of the extracellular surface domain in defining the RET-binding pocket. Whether this feature carries over to other GPCRs remains to be determined. One particular advantage of studying Rho has been the opportunity to employ various spectroscopic methods, especially in combination with site-directed mutagenesis. Optical spectroscopy and resonance Raman spectroscopy are possible because of the presence of the RET chromophore, which is probed as a sensor of chromophore-protein interactions. Difference spectroscopy techniques, such as FTIR- and UV-visible-difference spectroscopy, make use of the chromophore as an optical switch. Overexpression of recombinant Rho allows a variety of biophysical methods to be used to address particular questions related to protein and chromophore conformational changes. Important future work will involve questions related to the precise molecular mechanism of signal transduction by Rho. This will require some understanding of the dynamic changes in protein conformation, not only in Rho, but in the other proteins of the vertebrate visual cascade.

ACKNOWLEDGMENTS

We gratefully acknowledge the members of the Laboratory of Molecular Biology and Biochemistry at The Rockefeller University, including students, postdoctoral fellows, and associates, who have worked on visual phototransduction over the past ten years. In addition, productive collaborations with several exceptional laboratories have been greatly appreciated. Support was provided by NIH Training Grants (GM 07739 and EY 07138), the Charles H. Revson Foundation, the Aaron Diamond Foundation, the Arts and Letters Foundation, and the Allene Reuss Memorial Trust. T. P. Sakmar is an associate investigator of the Howard Hughes Medical Institute and an Ellison Foundation Senior Scholar.

Visit the Annual Reviews home page at www.annualreviews.org

LITERATURE CITED

1. Abdulaev NG, Ridge KD. 1998. Light-induced exposure of the cytoplasmic end of transmembrane helix seven in rhodopsin. *Proc. Natl. Acad. Sci. USA* 95:12854–59

2. Abola E, Kuhn P, Earnest T, Stevens RC. 2000. Automation of X-ray crystallography. *Nat. Struct. Biol.* 7:973–77

3. Acharya S, Karnik SS. 1996. Modulation of GDP release from transducin by the conserved Glu134-Arg135 sequence in rhodopsin. *J. Biol. Chem.* 271:25406–11

4. Acharya S, Saad Y, Karnik SS. 1997. Transducin-alpha C-terminal peptide binding site consists of C–D and E–F loops of rhodopsin. *J. Biol. Chem.* 272: 6519–24

5. Alkorta I, Du P. 1994. Sequence divergence analysis for the prediction of seven-helix membrane protein structures. II. A 3-D model of human rhodopsin. *Protein Eng.* 7:1231–38

6. Altenbach C, Cai K, Khorana HG, Hubbell WL. 1999. Structural features and light-dependent changes in the sequence 306–322 extending from helix VII to the palmitoylation sites in rhodopsin: a site-directed spin-labeling study. *Biochemistry* 38:7931–37

7. Altenbach C, Klein -Seetharaman J, Hwa J, Khorana HG, Hubbell WL. 1999. Structural features and light-dependent changes in the sequence 59–75 connecting helices I and II in rhodopsin: a site-directed spin-labeling study. *Biochemistry* 38:7945–49

8. Ames JB, Dizhoor AM, Ikura M, Palczewski K, Stryer L. 1999. Three-dimensional structure of guanylyl cyclase activating protein-2, a calcium-sensitive modulator of photoreceptor guanylyl cyclases. *J. Biol. Chem.* 274:19329–37

9. Anukanth A, Khorana HG. 1994. Structure and function in rhodopsin. Requirements of a specific structure for the intradiscal domain. *J. Biol. Chem.* 269: 19738–44

10. Arnis S, Fahmy K, Hofmann KP, Sakmar TP. 1994. A conserved carboxylic acid group mediates light-dependent proton

uptake and signaling by rhodopsin. *J. Biol. Chem.* 269:23879–81

11. Asenjo AB, Rim J, Oprian DD. 1994. Molecular determinants of human red/green color discrimination. *Neuron* 12:1131–38

12. Baldwin JM, Schertler GF, Unger VM. 1997. An alpha-carbon template for the transmembrane helices in the rhodopsin family of G-protein-coupled receptors. *J. Mol. Biol.* 272:144–64

13. Ballesteros JA, Shi L, Javitch JA. 2001. Structural mimicry in G protein-coupled receptors: implications of the high-resolution structure of rhodopsin for structure-function analysis of rhodopsin-like receptors. *Mol. Pharmacol.* 60:1–19

14. Baylor DA. 1987. Photoreceptor signals and vision. Proctor lecture. *Invest. Ophthalmol. Vis. Sci.* 28:34–49

15. Baylor DA. 1996. How photons start vision. *Proc. Natl. Acad. Sci. USA* 93:560–65

16. Baylor DA, Lamb TD, Yau KW. 1979. Responses of retinal rods to single photons. *J. Physiol.* 288:613–34

17. Baylor DA, Lamb TD, Yau KW. 1979. The membrane current of single rod outer segments. *J. Physiol.* 288:589–611

18. Beck M, Sakmar TP, Siebert F. 1998. Spectroscopic evidence for interaction between transmembrane helices 3 and 5 in rhodopsin. *Biochemistry* 37:7630–39

19. Beck M, Siebert F, Sakmar TP. 1998. Evidence for the specific interaction of a lipid molecule with rhodopsin which is altered in the transition to the active state metarhodopsin II. *FEBS Lett.* 436:304–8

20. Bell MW, Desai N, Guo XX, Ghalayini AJ. 2000. Tyrosine phosphorylation of the alpha subunit of transducin and its association with Src in photoreceptor rod outer segments *J. Neurochem.* 75:2006–19

21. Belrhali H, Nollert P, Royant A, Menzel C, Rosenbusch JP, et al. 1999. Protein, lipid and water organization in bacteriorhodopsin crystals: a molecular view of the purple membrane at 1.9 Å resolution. *Struct. Fold Des.* 7:909–17

22. Benovic JL, Mayor F Jr, Somers RL, Caron MG, Lefkowitz RJ. 1986. Light-dependent phosphorylation of rhodopsin by beta-adrenergic receptor kinase. *Nature* 321:869–72

23. Betancourt FM, Glaeser RM. 2000. Chemical and physical evidence for multiple functional steps comprising the M state of the bacteriorhodopsin photocycle. *Biochim. Biophys. Acta* 1460:106–18

24. Birge RR, Murray LP, Pierce BM, Akita H, Balogh-Nair V, et al. 1985. Two-photon spectroscopy of locked-11-*cis*-rhodopsin: evidence for a protonated Schiff base in a neutral protein binding site. *Proc. Natl. Acad. Sci. USA* 82:4117–21

25. Bohm A, Gaudet R, Sigler PB. 1997. Structural aspects of heterotrimeric G-protein signaling. *Curr. Opin. Biotechnol.* 8:480–87

26. Borhan BM, Souto L, Imai H, Shichida Y, Nakanishi K. 2000. Movement of retinal along the visual transduction path. *Science* 288:2209–12

27. Borjigin J, Nathans J. 1994. Insertional mutagenesis as a probe of rhodopsin's topography, stability, and activity. *J. Biol. Chem.* 269:14715–22

28. Bourne HR. How receptors talk to trimeric G proteins. 1997. *Curr. Opin. Cell. Biol.* 9:134–42

29. Buczylko J, Saari JC, Crouch RK, Palczewski K. 1996. Mechanisms of opsin activation. *J. Biol. Chem.* 271:20621–30

30. Cai K, Klein-Seetharaman J, Farrens D, Zhang C, Altenbach C, et al. 1999. Single-cysteine substitution mutants at amino acid positions 306–321 in rhodopsin, the sequence between the cytoplasmic end of helix VII and the palmitoylation sites: Sulfhydryl reactivity and transducin activation reveal a tertiary structure. *Biochemistry* 38:7925–30

31. Cha K, Reeves PJ, Khorana HG. 2000. Structure and function in rhodopsin: Destabilization of rhodopsin by the binding of an antibody at the N-terminal segment provides support for involvement of the latter in an intradiscal tertiary structure. *Proc. Natl. Acad. Sci. USA* 97: 3016–21

32. Chabre M. 1985. Trigger and amplification mechanisms in visual phototransduction. *Annu. Rev. Biophys. Biophys. Chem.* 14:331–60

33. Chabre M, Breton J. 1979. Orientation of aromatic residues in rhodopsin. Rotation of one tryptophan upon the meta I to meta II transition after illumination. *Photochem. Photobiol.* 30:295–99

34. Chan T, Lee M, Sakmar TP. 1992. Introduction of hydroxyl-bearing amino acids causes bathochromic spectral shifts in rhodopsin. Amino acid substitutions responsible for red-green color pigment spectral tuning. *J. Biol. Chem.* 267: 9478–80

35. Chen J, Makino CL, Peachey NS, Baylor DA, Simon MI. 1995. Mechanisms of rhodopsin inactivation in vivo as revealed by a COOH-terminal truncation mutant. *Science* 267:374–77

36. Cohen GB, Oprian DD, Robinson PR. 1992. Mechanism of activation and inactivation of opsin: role of Glu113 and Lys296. *Biochemistry* 31:12592–601

37. Conklin BR, Farfel Z, Lustig KD, Julius D, Bourne HR. 1993. Substitution of three amino acids switches receptor specificity of Gq alpha to that of Gi alpha. *Nature* 363:274–76

38. Creemers AF, Klaassen CH, Bovee-Geurts PH, Kelle R, Kragl U, et al. 1999. Solid state ^{15}N NMR evidence for a complex Schiff base counterion in the visual G-protein-coupled receptor rhodopsin. *Biochemistry* 38:7195–99

39. Davidson FF, Loewen PC, Khorana HG. 1994. Structure and function in rhodopsin: Replacement by alanine of cysteine residues 110 and 187, components of a conserved disulfide bond in rhodopsin, affects the light-activated metarhodopsin II state. *Proc. Natl. Acad. Sci. USA* 91: 4029–33

40. DeLange F, Bovee-Geurts PH, Pistorius AM, Rothschild KJ, DeGrip WJ. 1999. Probing intramolecular orientations in rhodopsin and metarhodopsin II by polarized infrared difference spectroscopy. *Biochemistry* 38:13200–9

41. Dencher NA, Sass HJ, Büldt G. 2000. Water and bacteriorhodopsin: structure, dynamics, and function. *Biochim. Biophys. Acta* 1460:192–203

42. Doi T, Molday RS, Khorana HG. 1990. Role of the intradiscal domain in rhodopsin assembly and function. *Proc. Natl. Acad. Sci. USA* 87:4991–95

43. Dunham TD, Farrens DL. 1999. Conformational changes in rhodopsin. Movement of helix f detected by site-specific chemical labeling and fluorescence spectroscopy. *J. Biol. Chem.* 274:1683–90

44. Eilers M, Reeves PJ, Ying W, Khorana HG, Smith SO. 1999. Magic angle spinning NMR of the protonated retinylidene Schiff base nitrogen in rhodopsin: expression of ^{15}N-lysine- and ^{13}C-glycine-labeled opsin in a stable cell line. *Proc. Natl. Acad. Sci. USA* 96:487–92

45. Ernst OP, Hofmann KP, Sakmar TP. 1995. Characterization of rhodopsin mutants that bind transducin but fail to induce GTP nucleotide uptake. Classification of mutant pigments by fluorescence, nucleotide release, and flash-induced light-scattering assays. *J. Biol. Chem.* 270:10580–86

46. Ernst OP, Meyer CK, Marin EP, Henklein P, Fu WY, et al. 2000. Mutation of the fourth cytoplasmic loop of rhodopsin affects binding of transducin and peptides derived from the carboxyl-terminal sequences of transducin alpha and gamma subunits. *J. Biol. Chem.* 275:1937–43

47. Fahmy K. 1998. Binding of transducin and transducin-derived peptides to

rhodopsin studies by attenuated total reflection-Fourier transform infrared difference spectroscopy. *Biophys. J.* 75: 1306–18

48. Fahmy K, Jäger F, Beck M, Zvyaga TA, Sakmar TP, Siebert F. 1993. Protonation states of membrane-embedded carboxylic acid groups in rhodopsin and metarhodopsin II: a Fourier-transform infrared spectroscopy study of site-directed mutants. *Proc. Natl. Acad. Sci. USA* 90:10206–10

49. Fahmy K, Sakmar TP. 1993. Light-dependent transducin activation by an ultraviolet-absorbing rhodopsin mutant. *Biochemistry* 32:9165–71

50. Fahmy K, Sakmar TP. 1993. Regulation of the rhodopsin-transducin interaction by a highly conserved carboxylic acid group. *Biochemistry* 32:7229–36

51. Fahmy K, Sakmar TP, Siebert F. 2000. Structural determinants of active state conformation of rhodopsin: molecular biophysics approaches. *Methods Enzymol.* 315:178–96

52. Fahmy K, Sakmar TP, Siebert F. 2000. Transducin-dependent protonation of glutamic acid 134 in rhodopsin. *Biochemistry* 39:10607–12

53. Fahmy K, Siebert F, Sakmar TP. 1995. Photoactivated state of rhodopsin and how it can form. *Biophys. Chem.* 56:171–81

54. Farahbakhsh ZT, Hideg K, Hubbell WL. 1993. Photoactivated conformational changes in rhodopsin: a time-resolved spin label study. *Science* 262:1416–19

55. Farrens DL, Altenbach C, Yang K, Hubbell WL, Khorana HG. 1996. Requirement of rigid-body motion of transmembrane helices for light activation of rhodopsin. *Science* 274:768–70

56. Faurobert E, Otto-Bruc A, Chardin P, Chabre M. 1993. Tryptophan W207 in transducin Talpha is the fluorescence sensor of the G protein activation switch and is involved in the effector binding. *EMBO J.* 12:4191–98

57. Feng X, Verdegem PJ, Eden M, Sandstrom D, Lee YK, et al. 2000. Determination of a molecular torsional angle in the metarhodopsin-I photointermediate of rhodopsin by double-quantum solid-state NMR. *J. Biomol. Nucl. Magn. Res.* 16:1–8

58. Flaherty KM, Zozulya S, Stryer L, McKay DB. 1993. Three-dimensional structure of recoverin, a calcium sensor in vision. *Cell* 75:709–16

59. Franke RR, Konig B, Sakmar TP, Khorana HG, Hofmann KP. 1990. Rhodopsin mutants that bind but fail to activate transducin. *Science* 250:123–25

60. Franke RR, Sakmar TP, Graham RM, Khorana HG. 1992. Structure and function in rhodopsin. Studies of the interaction between the rhodopsin cytoplasmic domain and transducin. *J. Biol. Chem.* 267:14767–74

61. Fung BKK. 1983. Characterization of transducin from bovine retinal rod outer segments. I. Separation and reconstitution of the subunits. *J. Biol. Chem.* 258: 10495–502

62. Fung BKK, Nash CR. 1983. Characterization of transducin from bovine retinal rod outer segments. II. Evidence for distinct binding sites and conformational changes revealed by limited proteolysis with trypsin. *J. Biol. Chem.* 258:10503–10

63. Fung BKK, Stryer L. 1980. Photolyzed rhodopsin catalyzes the exchange of GTP for bound GDP in retinal rod outer segments. *Proc. Natl. Acad. Sci. USA* 77:2500–4

64. Ganea C, Gergely C, Ludmann K, Varo G. 1997. The role of water in the extracellular half channel of bacteriorhodopsin. *Biophys. J.* 73:2718–25

65. Ganter UM, Kashima T, Sheves M, Siebert F. 1991. FTIR evidence of an altered chromophore-protein-interaction in the artificial visual pigment *cis*-5,6-dihydroisorhodopsin and its photoproducts BSI,

lumirhodopsin and metarhodopsin-I. *J. Am. Chem. Soc.* 113:4087–92

66. Garcia PD, Onrust R, Bell SM, Sakmar TP, Bourne HR. 1995. Transducin-alpha C-terminal mutations prevent activation by rhodopsin: a new assay using recombinant proteins expressed in cultured cells. *EMBO J.* 14:4460–69

67. Garcia-Higuera I, Fenoglio J, Li Y, Lewis C, Panchenko MP, et al. 1996. Folding of proteins with WD-repeats: comparison of six members of the WD-repeat superfamily to the G protein beta subunit. *Biochemistry* 35:13985–94

68. Gaudet R, Bohm A, Sigler PB. 1996. Crystal structure at 2.4 Å resolution of the complex of transducin beta-gamma and its regulator, phosducin. *Cell* 87:577–88

69. Gether U. 2000. Uncovering molecular mechanisms involved in activation of G protein-coupled receptors. *Endocr. Rev.* 21:90–113

70. Gibson SK, Parkes JH, Liebman PA. 1999. Phosphorylation alters the pH-dependent active state equilibrium of rhodopsin by modulating the membrane surface potential. *Biochemistry* 38:11103–14

71. Granzin J, Wilden U, Choe HW, Labahn J, Krafft B, Büldt G. 1998. X-ray crystal structure of arrestin from bovine rod outer segments. *Nature* 391:918–21

72. Griffiths JM, Bennett AE, Engelhard M, Siebert F, Raap J, et al. 2000. Structural investigation of the active site in bacteriorhodopsin: geometric constraints on the roles of Asp-85 and Asp-212 in the proton-pumping mechanism from solid state NMR. *Biochemistry* 39:362–71

73. Grigorieff N, Ceska TA, Downing KH, Baldwin JM, Henderson R. 1996. Electron-crystallographic refinement of the structure of bacteriorhodopsin. *J. Mol. Biol.* 259:393–421

74. Grobner G, Burnett IJ, Glaubitz C, Choi G, Mason AJ, Watts A. 2000. Observations of light-induced structural changes of retinal within rhodopsin. *Nature* 405:810–13

75. Grobner G, Choi G, Burnett IJ, Glaubitz C, Verdegem PJ, et al. 1998. Photoreceptor rhodopsin: structural and conformational study of its chromophore 11-*cis* retinal in oriented membranes by deuterium solid state NMR. *FEBS Lett.* 422:201–4

76. Deleted in proof

77. Groves MR, Hanlon N, Turowski P, Hemmings BA, Barford D. 1999. The structure of the protein phosphatase 2A PR65/A subunit reveals the conformation of its 15 tandemly repeated HEAT motifs. *Cell* 96:99–110

78. Hamm HE, Deretic D, Arendt A, Hargrave PA, Koenig B, Hofmann KP. 1988. Site of G protein binding to rhodopsin mapped with synthetic peptides from the α subunit. *Science* 241:832–35

79. Han M, Lin SW, Minkova M, Smith SO, Sakmar TP. 1996. Functional interaction of transmembrane helices 3 and 6 in rhodopsin. Replacement of phenylalanine 261 by alanine causes reversion of phenotype of a glycine 121 replacement mutant. *J. Biol. Chem.* 271:32337–42

80. Han M, Lin SW, Smith SO, Sakmar TP. 1996. The effects of amino acid replacements of glycine 121 on transmembrane helix 3 of rhodopsin. *J. Biol. Chem.* 271:32330–36

81. Han M, Smith SO. 1995. NMR constraints on the location of the retinal chromophore in rhodopsin and bathorhodopsin. *Biochemistry* 34:1425–32

82. Han M, Smith SO, Sakmar TP. 1998. Constitutive activation of opsin by mutation of methionine 257 on transmembrane helix 6. *Biochemistry* 37:8253–61

83. Hargrave PA, Bownds D, Wang JK, McDowell JH. 1982. Retinyl peptide isolation and characterization. *Methods Enzymol.* 81:211–14

84. Hargrave PA, McDowell JH, Curtis DR, Wang JK, Juszczak E, et al. 1983. The

structure of bovine rhodopsin. *Biophys. Struct. Mech.* 9:235–44

85. He W, Cowan CW, Wensel TG. 1998. RGS9, a GTPase accelerator for photo transduction. *Neuron* 20:95–102

86. Hecht S, Shaler S, Pirene MH. 1942. Energy, quanta, and vision. *J. Gen. Physiol.* 25:819–40

87. Heck M, Hofmann KP. 2001. Maximal rate and nucleotide dependence of rhodopsin-catalyzed transducin activation: initial rate analysis based on a double displacement mechanism. *J. Biol. Chem.* 276:10000–9

88. Henderson R, Baldwin JM, Ceska TA, Zemlin F, Beckmann E, Downing KH. 1990. An atomic model for the structure of bacteriorhodopsin. *Biochem. Soc. Trans.* 18:844

89. Herzfeld J, Tounge B. 2000. NMR probes of vectoriality in the proton-motive photocycle of bacteriorhodopsin: evidence for an "electrostatic steering" mechanism. *Biochim. Biophys. Acta* 1460:95–105

90. Hessling B, Herbst J, Rammelsberg R, Gerwert K. 1997. Fourier transform infrared double-flash experiments resolve bacteriorhodopsin's M1 to M2 transition. *Biophys. J.* 73:2071–80

91. Hirsch JA, Schubert C, Gurevich VV, Sigler PB. 1999. The 2.8 Å crystal structure of visual arrestin: a model for arrestin's regulation. *Cell* 97:257–69

92. Honig B, Dinur U, Nakanishi K, Balogh-Nair V, Gawinowicz MA, et al. 1979. An external point-charge model for wavelength regulation in visual pigments. *J. Am. Chem. Soc.* 101:7084–86

93. Huang L, Deng H, Koutalos Y, Ebrey T, Groesbeek M, et al. 1997. A resonance Raman study of the C=C stretch modes in bovine and octopus visual pigments with isotopically labeled retinal chromophores. *Photochem. Photobiol.* 66: 747–54

94. Hwa J, Reeves PJ, Klein-Seetharaman J, Davidson F, Khorana HG. 1999. Structure and function in rhodopsin: further elucidation of the role of the intradiscal cysteines, Cys-110, -185, and -187, in rhodopsin folding and function. *Proc. Natl. Acad. Sci. USA* 96:1932–35

95. Iiri T, Farfel Z, Bourne HR. 1998. G-protein diseases furnish a model for the turn-on switch. *Nature* 394:35–38

96. Isele J, Sakmar TP, Siebert F. 2000. Rhodopsin activation affects the environment of specific neighboring phospholipids: an FTIR study. *Biophys. J.* 79:3063–71

97. Jäger F, Fahmy K, Sakmar TP, Siebert F. 1994. Identification of glutamic acid 113 as the Schiff base proton acceptor in the metarhodopsin II photointermediate of rhodopsin. *Biochemistry* 33:10878–82

98. Jäger F, Jäger S, Krutle O, Friedman N, Sheves M, et al. 1994. Interactions of the beta-ionone ring with the protein in the visual pigment rhodopsin control the activation mechanism. An FTIR and fluorescence study on artificial vertebrate rhodopsins. *Biochemistry* 33:7389–97

99. Jäger S, Szundi I, Lewis JW, Mah TL, Kliger DS. 1998. Effects of pH on rhodopsin photointermediates from lumirhodopsin to metarhodopsin II. *Biochemistry* 37:6998–7005

100. Kandori H. 2000. Role of internal water molecules in bacteriorhodopsin. *Biochim. Biophys. Acta* 1460:177–91

101. Kandori H, Kinoshita N, Yamazaki Y, Maeda A, Shichida Y, et al. 2000. Local and distant protein structural changes on photoisomerization of the retinal in bacteriorhodopsin. *Proc. Natl. Acad. Sci. USA* 97:4643–48

102. Karnik SS, Khorana HG. 1990. Assembly of functional rhodopsin requires a disulfide bond between cysteine residues 110 and 187. *J. Biol. Chem.* 265:17520–24

103. Kataoka M, Kamikubo H. 2000. Structures of photointermediates and their

implications for the proton pump mechanism. *Biochim. Biophys. Acta* 1460:166–76

104. Kaushal S, Ridge KD, Khorana HG. 1994. Structure and function in rhodopsin: the role of asparagine-linked glycosylation. *Proc. Natl. Acad. Sci. USA* 91:4024–28

105. Kelleher DJ, Johnson GL. 1988. Transducin inhibition of light-dependent rhodopsin phosphorylation: evidence for beta-gamma subunit interaction with rhodopsin. *Mol. Pharmacol.* 34:452–60

106. Kibelbek J, Mitchell DC, Beach JM, Litman BJ. 1991. Functional equivalence of metarhodopsin II and the G_t-activating form of photolyzed bovine rhodopsin. *Biochemistry* 30:6761–68

107. Kim JM, Altenbach C, Thurmond RL, Khorana HG, Hubbell WL. 1997. Structure and function in rhodopsin: Rhodopsin mutants with a neutral amino acid at E134 have a partially activated conformation in the dark state. *Proc. Natl. Acad. Sci. USA* 94:14273–78

108. Kisselev OG, Ermolaeva MV, Gautam N. 1994. A farnesylated domain in the G protein γ subunit is a specific determinant of receptor coupling. *J. Biol. Chem.* 269:21399–402

109. Kisselev O, Ermolaeva M, Gautam N. 1995. Efficient interaction with a receptor requires a specific type of prenyl group on the G protein γ subunit. *J. Biol. Chem.* 270:25356–58

110. Kisselev OG, Kao J, Ponder JW, Fann YC, Gautam N, Marshall GR. 1998. Light-activated rhodopsin induces structural binding motif in G-protein alpha subunit. *Proc. Natl. Acad. Sci. USA* 95:4270–75

111. Kisselev OG, Meyer CK, Heck M, Ernst OP, Hofmann KP. 1999. Signal transfer from rhodopsin to the G-protein: evidence for a two-site sequential fit mechanism. *Proc. Natl. Acad. Sci. USA* 96:4898–903

112. Kjelsberg MA, Cotecchia S, Ostrowski J, Caron MG, Lefkowitz RJ. 1992. Constitutive activation of the alpha 1β-adrenergic receptor by all amino acid substitutions at a single site. Evidence for a region which constrains receptor activation. *J. Biol. Chem.* 267:1430–33

113. Klein-Seetharaman J, Getmanova EV, Loewen MC, Reeves PJ, Khorana HG. 1999. NMR spectroscopy in studies of light-induced structural changes in mammalian rhodopsin: applicability of solution ^{19}F NMR. *Proc. Natl. Acad. Sci. USA* 96:13744–49

114. Klein-Seetharaman J, Hwa J, Cai K, Altenbach C, Hubbell WL, Khorana HG. 1999. Single-cysteine substitution mutants at amino acid positions 55–75, the sequence connecting the cytoplasmic ends of helices I and II in rhodopsin: Reactivity of the sulfhydryl groups and their derivatives identifies a tertiary structure that changes upon light-activation. *Biochemistry* 38:7938–44

115. Kliger DS, Lewis JW. 1995. Spectral and kinetic characterization of visual pigment photointermediates. *Isr. J. Chem.* 35:289–307

116. Kochendoerfer GG, Lin SW, Sakmar TP, Mathies RA. 1999. How color visual pigments are tuned. *Trends Biochem. Sci.* 24:300–5

117. Kochendoerfer GG, Verdegem PJ, van der Hoef I, Lugtenburg J, Mathies RA. 1996. Retinal analog study of the role of steric interactions in the excited state isomerization dynamics of rhodopsin. *Biochemistry* 35:16230–40

118. Kokame K, Fukada Y, Yoshizawa T, Takao T, Shimonishi Y. 1992. Lipid modification at the N terminus of photoreceptor G-protein alpha-subunit. *Nature* 359:749–52

119. Krebs A, Villa C, Edwards PC, Schertler GF. 1998. Characterization of an improved two-dimensional p22121 crystal from bovine rhodopsin. *J. Mol. Biol.* 282:991–1003

120. Lamb TD. 1996. Gain and kinetics of

activation in the G-protein cascade of phototransduction. *Proc. Natl. Acad. Sci. USA* 93:566–70

121. Lambright DG, Noel JP, Hamm HE, Sigler PB. 1994. Structural determinants for activation of the alpha-subunit of a heterotrimeric G protein. *Nature* 369:621–28

122. Lambright DG, Sondek J, Bohm A, Skiba NP, Hamm HE, Sigler PB. 1996. The 2.0 Å crystal structure of a heterotrimeric G protein. *Nature* 379:311–19

123. Landau EM, Rosenbusch JP. 1996. Lipidic cubic phases: a novel concept for the crystallization of membrane proteins. *Proc. Natl. Acad. Sci. USA* 93:14532–35

124. Langen R, Cai K, Altenbach C, Khorana HG, Hubbell WL. 1999. Structural features of the C-terminal domain of bovine rhodopsin: a site-directed spin-labeling study. *Biochemistry* 38:7918–24

125. Le Gouill C, Parent JL, Rola-Pleszczynski M, Stankova J. 1997. Structural and functional requirements for agonist-induced internalization of the human platelet-activating factor receptor. *J. Biol. Chem.* 272:21289–95

126. Lewis JW, Kliger DS. 2000. Absorption spectroscopy in studies of visual pigments: spectral and kinetic characterization of intermediates. *Methods Enzymol.* 315:164–78

127. Lewis JW, Szundi I, Kliger DS. 2000. Structural constraints imposed by a nonnative disulfide cause reversible changes in rhodopsin photointermediate kinetics. *Biochemistry* 39:7851–55

128. Lin SW, Han M, Sakmar TP. 2000. Analysis of functional microdomains of rhodopsin. *Methods Enzymol.* 315:116–30

129. Lin SW, Kochendoerfer GG, Carroll KS, Wang D, Mathies RA, Sakmar TP. 1998. Mechanisms of spectral tuning in blue cone visual pigments. Visible and Raman spectroscopy of blue-shifted rhodopsin mutants. *J. Biol. Chem.* 273:24583–91

130. Lin SW, Sakmar TP. 1996. Specific tryptophan UV-absorbance changes are probes of the transition of rhodopsin to its active state. *Biochemistry* 35:11149–59

131. Lin SW, Sakmar TP. 1999. Colour tuning mechanisms of visual pigments. *Novartis Found. Symp.* 224:124–35

132. Lin SW, Sakmar TP, Franke RR, Khorana HG, Mathies RA. 1992. Resonance Raman microprobe spectroscopy of rhodopsin mutants: effect of substitutions in the third transmembrane helix. *Biochemistry* 31:5105–11

133. Liu J, Conklin BR, Blin N, Yun J, Wess J. 1995. Identification of a receptor/G-protein contact site critical for signaling specificity and G-protein activation. *Proc. Natl. Acad. Sci. USA* 92:11642–46

134. Loew A, Ho YK, Blundell T, Bax B. 1998. Phosducin induces a structural change in transducin beta-gamma. *Structure* 6:1007–19

135. Loewen MC, Klein-Seetharaman J, Getmanova EV, Reeves PJ, Schwalbe H, Khorana HG. 2001. Solution ^{19}F nuclear Overhauser effects in structural studies of the cytoplasmic domain of mammalian rhodopsin. *Proc. Natl. Acad. Sci. USA* 98:4888–92

136. Longstaff C, Calhoon RD, Rando RR. 1986. Deprotonation of the Schiff base of rhodopsin is obligate in the activation of the G protein. *Proc. Natl. Acad. Sci. USA* 83:4209–13

137. Lou J, Tan Q, Karnaukhova E, Berova N, Nakanishi K, Crouch RK. 2000. Synthetic retinals: convenient probes of rhodopsin and visual transduction process. *Methods Enzymol.* 315:219–37

138. Luecke H. 2000. Atomic resolution structures of bacteriorhodopsin photocycle intermediates: the role of discrete water molecules in the function of this light-driven ion pump. *Biochim. Biophys. Acta* 1460:133–56

139. Luecke H, Schobert B, Richter HT, Cartailler JP, Lanyi JK. 1999. Structural changes in bacteriorhodopsin during

ion transport at 2 Å resolution. *Science* 286:255–61

140. Luecke H, Schobert B, Richter HT, Cartailler JP, Lanyi JK. 1999. Structure of bacteriorhodopsin at 1.55 Å resolution. *J. Mol. Biol.* 291:899–911

141. Marin EP, Krishna AG, Archambault V, Simuni E, Fu WY, Sakmar TP. 2001. The function of interdomain interactions in controlling nucleotide exchange rates in transducin. *J. Biol. Chem.* 276:23873–80

142. Marin EP, Krishna AG, Sakmar TP. 2001. Rapid activation of transducin by mutations distant from the nucleotide-binding site. Evidence for a mechanistic model of receptor-catalyzed nucleotide exchange by G proteins. *J. Biol. Chem.* 276:27400–5

143. Marin EP, Krishna AG, Zvyaga TA, Isele J, Siebert F, Sakmar TP. 2000. The amino terminus of the fourth cytoplasmic loop of rhodopsin modulates rhodopsin-transducin interaction. *J. Biol. Chem.* 275:1930–36

144. Marin EP, Neubig RR. 1995. Lack of association of G-protein beta 2- and gamma 2-subunit N-terminal fragments provides evidence against the coiled-coil model of subunit-beta gamma assembly. *Biochem. J.* 309:377–80

145. Matsuda T, Hashimoto Y, Ueda H, Asano T, Matsuura Y, et al. 1998. Specific isoprenyl group linked to transducin gamma-subunit is a determinant of its unique signaling properties among G-proteins. *Biochemistry* 37:9843–50

146. Matsumura H, Shiba T, Inoue T, Harada S, Kai Y. 1998. A novel mode of target recognition suggested by the 2.0 Å structure of holo S100B from bovine brain. *Structure* 6:233–41

147. McDowell JH, Nawrocki JP, Hargrave PA. 1993. Phosphorylation sites in bovine rhodopsin. *Biochemistry* 32:4968–74

148. Meng EC, Bourne HR. 2001. Receptor activation: What does the rhodopsin

structure tell us? *Trends Pharmacol. Sci.* 22:587–93

149. Menon ST, Han M, Sakmar TP. 2001. Rhodopsin: structural basis of molecular physiology. *Physiol. Rev.* 81:1659–88

150. Milburn MV, Prive GG, Milligan DL, Scott WG, Yeh J, et al. 1991. Three-dimensional structures of the ligand-binding domain of the bacterial aspartate receptor with and without a ligand. *Science* 254:1342–47

151. Min KC, Gravina SA, Sakmar TP. 2000. Reconstitution of the vertebrate visual cascade using recombinant heterotrimeric transducin purified from Sf9 cells *Protein Exp. Purif.* 20:514–26

151a. Moore WJ. 1972. *Physical Chemistry.* Englewood Cliffs, NJ: Prentice Hall. 977 pp.

152. Murata K, Fujii Y, Enomoto N, Hata M, Hoshino T, Tsuda M. 2000. A study on the mechanism of the proton transport in bacteriorhodopsin: the importance of the water molecule. *Biophys. J.* 79:982–91

153. Nagata T, Terakita A, Kandori H, Kojima D, Shichida Y, Maeda A. 1997. Water and peptide backbone structure in the active center of bovine rhodopsin. *Biochemistry* 36:6164–70

154. Nakayama TA, Khorana HG. 1990. Orientation of retinal in bovine rhodopsin determined by cross-linking using a photoactivatable analog of 11-*cis*-retinal. *J. Biol. Chem.* 265:15762–69

155. Nakayama TA, Khorana HG. 1991. Mapping of the amino acids in membrane-embedded helices that interact with the retinal chromophore in bovine rhodopsin. *J. Biol. Chem.* 266:4269–75

156. Nathans J. 1990. Determinants of visual pigment absorbance: role of charged amino acids in the putative transmembrane segments. *Biochemistry* 29:937–42

157. Nathans J, Hogness DS. 1983. Isolation, sequence analysis, and intron-exon arrangement of the gene encoding bovine rhodopsin. *Cell* 34:807–14

158. Nathans J, Hogness DS. 1984. Isolation and nucleotide sequence of the gene encoding human rhodopsin. *Proc. Natl. Acad. Sci. USA* 81:4851–55

159. Natochin M, Granovsky AE, Muradov KG, Artemyev NO. 1999. Roles of the transducin alpha-subunit alpha4-helix/alpha4-beta6 loop in the receptor and effector interactions. *J. Biol. Chem.* 274:7865–69

160. Neer EJ, Schmidt CJ, Nambudripad R, Smith TF. 1994. The ancient regulatory-protein family of WD-repeat proteins. *Nature* 371:297–300

161. Neitz M, Neitz J, Jacobs GH. 1991. Spectral tuning of pigments underlying red-green color vision. *Science* 252:971–74

162. Neutze R, Hajdu J. 1997. Femtosecond time resolution in X-ray diffraction experiments. *Proc. Natl. Acad. Sci. USA* 94:5651–55

163. Nishimura S, Kandori H, Maeda A. 1998. Interaction between photoactivated rhodopsin and the C-terminal peptide of transducin alpha-subunit studied by FTIR spectroscopy. *Biochemistry* 37:15816–24

164. Noel JP, Hamm HE, Sigler PB. 1993. The 2.2 Å crystal structure of transducin-alpha complexed with GTPγS. *Nature* 366:654–63

165. Ohguro H, Palczewski K, Ericsson LH, Walsh KA, Johnson RS. 1993. Sequential phosphorylation of rhodopsin at multiple sites. *Biochemistry* 32:5718–24

166. Ohguro H, Rudnicka-Nawrot M, Buczylko J, Zhao X, Taylor JA, et al. 1996. Structural and enzymatic aspects of rhodopsin phosphorylation. *J. Biol. Chem.* 271:5215–24

167. Okada T, Le Trong I, Fox BA, Behnke CA, Stenkamp RE, Palczewski K. 2000. X-ray diffraction analysis of three-dimensional crystals of bovine rhodopsin obtained from mixed micelles. *J. Struct. Biol.* 130:73–80

168. Okada T, Takeda K, Kouyama T. 1998. Highly selective separation of rhodopsin from bovine rod outer segment membranes using combination of divalent cation and alkyl(thio)glucoside. *Photochem. Photobiol.* 67:495–99

169. Oprian DD. 1992. The ligand-binding domain of rhodopsin and other G protein-linked receptors. *J. Bioenerg. Biomembr.* 24:211–17

170. Osawa S, Weiss ER. 1995. The effect of carboxyl-terminal mutagenesis of G_t alpha on rhodopsin and guanine nucleotide binding. *J. Biol. Chem.* 270:31052–58

171. Ovchinnikov YUA. 1982. Rhodopsin and bacteriorhodopsin: structure-function relationships. *FEBS Lett.* 148:179–91

172. Palczewski K, Kumasaka T, Hori T, Behnke CA, Motoshima H, et al. 2000. Crystal structure of rhodopsin: a G protein-coupled receptor. *Science* 289:739–45

173. Palings I, Pardoen JA, van den Berg E, Winkel C, Lugtenburg J, Mathies RA. 1987. Assignment of fingerprint vibrations in the resonance Raman spectra of rhodopsin, isorhodopsin, and bathorhodopsin: implications for chromophore structure and environment. *Biochemistry* 26:2544–56

174. Papac DI, Oatis JE Jr, Crouch RK, Knapp DR. 1993. Mass spectrometric identification of phosphorylation sites in bleached bovine rhodopsin. *Biochemistry* 32:5930–34

175. Papermaster DS. 1982. Preparation of retinal rod outer segments. *Methods Enzymol.* 81:48–52

176. Pappa H, Murray-Rust J, Dekker LV, Parker PJ, McDonald NQ. 1998. Crystal structure of the C2 domain from protein kinase C-delta. *Structure* 6:885–94

177. Pebay-Peyroula E, Neutze R, Landau EM. 2000. Lipidic cubic phase crystallization of bacteriorhodopsin and cryotrapping of intermediates: towards resolving a revolving photocycle. *Biochim. Biophys. Acta* 1460:119–32

178. Phillips WJ, Cerione RA. 1992. Rhodopsin-transducin interaction. I. Characterization of the binding of the transducin-beta gamma subunit complex to rhodopsin using fluorescence spectroscopy. *J. Biol. Chem.* 267:17032–39

179. Phillips WJ, Wong SC, Cerione RA. 1992. Rhodopsin-transducin interactions. II. Influence of the transducin-beta gamma subunit complex on the coupling of the transducin-alpha subunit to rhodopsin. *J. Biol. Chem.* 267:17040–46

180. Popp A, Ujj L, Atkinson GH. 1996. Bathorhodopsin structure in the room-temperature rhodopsin photosequence: picosecond time-resolved coherent anti-Stokes Raman scattering. *Proc. Natl. Acad. Sci. USA* 93:372–76

181. Probst WC, Snyder LA, Schuster DI, Brosius J, Sealfon SC. 1992. Sequence alignment of the G-protein coupled receptor superfamily. *DNA Cell. Biol.* 11:1–20

182. Rafferty CN, Muellenberg CG, Shichi H. 1980. Tryptophan in bovine rhodopsin: its content, spectral properties and environment. *Biochemistry* 19:2145–51

183. Rando RR. 1996. Polyenes and vision. *Chem. Biol.* 3:255–62

184. Rao VR, Cohen GB, Oprian DD. 1994. Rhodopsin mutation G90D and a molecular mechanism for congenital night blindness. *Nature* 367:639–42

185. Rao VR, Oprian DD. 1996. Activating mutations of rhodopsin and other G protein-coupled receptors. *Annu. Rev. Biophys. Biomol. Struct.* 25:287–314

186. Rath P, DeCaluwe LL, Bovee-Geurts PH, DeGrip WJ, Rothschild KJ. 1993. Fourier transform infrared difference spectroscopy of rhodopsin mutants: Light activation of rhodopsin causes hydrogen-bonding change in residue aspartic acid-83 during meta II formation. *Biochemistry* 32:10277–82

187. Resek JF, Farahbakhsh ZT, Hubbell WL, Khorana HG. 1993. Formation of the meta II photointermediate is accompanied by conformational changes in the cytoplasmic surface of rhodopsin. *Biochemistry* 32:12025–32

188. Ridge KD, Bhattacharya S, Nakayama TA, Khorana HG. 1992. Light-stable rhodopsin. II. An opsin mutant (TRP-265 → Phe) and a retinal analog with a nonisomerizable 11-*cis* configuration form a photostable chromophore. *J. Biol. Chem.* 267:6770–75

189. Robinson PR, Cohen GB, Zhukovsky EA, Oprian DD. 1992. Constitutively active mutants of rhodopsin. *Neuron* 9:719–25

190. Rothschild KJ. 1992. FTIR difference spectroscopy of bacteriorhodopsin: toward a molecular model. *J. Bioenerg. Biomembr.* 24:147–67

191. Saito H, Tuzi S, Yamaguchi S, Tanio M, Naito A. 2000. Conformation and backbone dynamics of bacteriorhodopsin revealed by ^{13}C-NMR. *Biochim. Biophys. Acta* 1460:39–48

192. Sakmar TP. 1994. Opsins. In *Handbook of Receptors and Channels: G Protein Coupled Receptors*, ed. SJ Peroutka, pp. 257. Boca Raton, FL: CRC

193. Sakmar TP. 1998. Rhodopsin: a prototypical G protein-coupled receptor. *Prog. Nucleic Acid Res. Mol. Biol.* 59:1–34

194. Sakmar TP. 2002. The structure of rhodopsin and the superfamily of seven-helical receptors: the same and not the same. *Curr. Opin. Cell Biol.* 14:189–95

195. Sakmar TP, Fahmy K. 1995. Properties and photoactivity of rhodopsin mutants. *Isr. J. Chem.* 35:325–37

196. Sakmar TP, Franke RR, Khorana HG. 1989. Glutamic acid-113 serves as the retinylidene Schiff base counterion in bovine rhodopsin. *Proc. Natl. Acad. Sci. USA* 86:8309–13

197. Sass HJ, Büldt G, Gessenich R, Hehn D, Neff D, et al. 2000. Structural alterations for proton translocation in the M state of wild-type bacteriorhodopsin. *Nature* 406:649–53

198. Scheer A, Gierschik P. 1995. S-prenylated cysteine analogues inhibit receptor-mediated G protein activation in native human granulocyte and reconstituted bovine retinal rod outer segment membranes. *Biochemistry* 34:4952–61

199. Schertler GF, Villa C, Henderson R. 1993. Projection structure of rhodopsin. *Nature* 362:770–72

200. Sheikh SP, Zvyaga TA, Lichtarge O, Sakmar TP, Bourne HR. 1996. Rhodopsin activation blocked by metal-ion-binding sites linking transmembrane helices C and F. *Nature* 383:347–50

201. Siebert F. 1995. Applications of FTIR spectroscopy to the investigation of dark structures and photoreactions of visual pigments. *Isr. J. Chem.* 35:309–23

202. Singh D, Hudson BS, Middleton C, Birge RR. 2001. Conformation and orientation of the retinyl chromophore in rhodopsin: A critical evaluation of recent NMR data on the basis of theoretical calculations results in a minimum energy structure consistent with all experimental data. *Biochemistry* 40:4201–4

203. Slep KC, Kercher MA, He W, Cowan CW, Wensel TG, Sigler PB. 2001. Structural determinants for regulation of phosphodiesterase by a G protein at 2.0 Å. *Nature* 409:1071–77

204. Sondek J, Bohm A, Lambright DG, Hamm HE, Sigler PB. 1996. Crystal structure of a G-protein beta gamma dimer at 2.1 Å resolution. *Nature* 379: 369–74

205. Sondek J, Lambright DG, Noel JP, Hamm, HE, Sigler PB. 1994. GTPase mechanism of G proteins from the 1.7 Å crystal structure of transducin alpha-GDP-AIF4. *Nature* 372:276–79

206. Sprang SR. 1997. G protein mechanisms: insights from structural analysis. *Annu. Rev. Biochem.* 66:639–78

207. Strader CD, Fong TM, Tota MR, Underwood D, Dixon RA. 1994. Structure and function of G protein-coupled receptors. *Annu. Rev. Biochem.* 63:101–32

208. Struthers M, Yu H, Kono M, Oprian DD. 1999. Tertiary interactions between the fifth and sixth transmembrane segments of rhodopsin. *Biochemistry* 38:6597–603

209. Struthers M, Yu H, Oprian DD. 2000. G protein-coupled receptor activation: analysis of a highly constrained "strait-jacketed" rhodopsin. *Biochemistry* 39: 7938–42

210. Stryer L. 1988. Molecular basis of visual excitation. *Cold Spring Harb. Symp. Quant. Biol.* 53:283–94

211. Stryer L. 1991. Visual excitation and recovery. *J. Biol. Chem.* 266:10711–14

212. Subramaniam S, Gerstein M, Oesterhelt D, Henderson R. 1993. Electron diffraction analysis of structural changes in the photocycle of bacteriorhodopsin. *EMBO J.* 12:1–8

213. Subramaniam S, Henderson R. 2000. Molecular mechanism of vectorial proton translocation by bacteriorhodopsin. *Nature* 406:653–57

214. Subramaniam S, Lindahl M, Bullough P, Faruqi AR, Tittor J, et al. 1999. Protein conformational changes in the bacteriorhodopsin photocycle. *J. Mol. Biol.* 287:145–61

215. Surya A, Foster KW, Knox BE. 1995. Transducin activation by the bovine opsin apoprotein. *J. Biol. Chem.* 270: 5024–31

216. Sutton RB, Sprang SR. 1998. Structure of the protein kinase C beta phospholipid-binding C2 domain complexed with Ca^{2+}. *Structure* 6:1395–405

217. Taylor JM, Jacob-Mosier GG, Lawton RG, VanDort M, Neubig RR. 1996. Receptor and membrane interaction sites on G beta. A receptor-derived peptide binds to the carboxyl terminus. *J. Biol. Chem.* 271:3336–39

218. Teller DC, Okada T, Behnke CA, Palczewski K, Stenkamp RE. 2001. Advances in determination of a high-resolution three-dimensional structure of

rhodopsin, a model of G-protein-coupled receptors (GPCRs). *Biochemistry* 40: 7761–72

219. Unger VM, Hargrave PA, Baldwin JM, Schertler GF. 1997. Arrangement of rhodopsin transmembrane alpha-helices. *Nature* 389:203–6

220. Verdaguer N, Corbalan-Garcia S, Ochoa WF, Fita I, Gomez-Fernandez JC. 1999. Ca^{2+} bridges the C2 membrane-binding domain of protein kinase C alpha directly to phosphatidylserine. *EMBO J.* 18:6329–38

221. Verdegem PJ, Bovee-Geurts PH, de Grip WJ, Lugtenburg J, de Groot HJ. 1999. Retinylidene ligand structure in bovine rhodopsin, metarhodopsin-I, and 10-methylrhodopsin from internuclear distance measurements using ^{13}C-labeling and 1-D rotational resonance MAS-NMR. *Biochemistry* 38:11316–24

222. Verhoeven MA, Creemers AF, Bovee-Geurts PH, De Grip WJ, Lugtenburg J, de Groot HJ. 2001. Ultra-high-field MAS NMR assay of a multispin labeled ligand bound to its G-protein receptor target in the natural membrane environment: electronic structure of the retinylidene chromophore in rhodopsin. *Biochemistry* 40:3282–88

223. Wald G. 1968. Molecular basis of visual excitation. *Science* 162:230–39

224. Wang Q, Schoenlein WR, Peteanu LA, Mathies RA, Shank CV. 1994. Vibrationally coherent photochemistry in the femtosecond primary event of vision. *Science* 266:422–24

225. Wang Z, Asenjo AB, Oprian DD. 1993. Identification of the Cl^--binding site in the human red and green color vision pigments. *Biochemistry* 32:2125–30

226. Wedegaertner PB, Wilson PT, Bourne HR. 1995. Lipid modifications of tri-

meric G proteins. *J. Biol. Chem.* 270: 503–6

227. Wilson MA, Brunger AT. 2000. The 1.0 Å crystal structure of Ca^{2+}-bound calmodulin: an analysis of disorder and implications for functionally relevant plasticity. *J. Mol. Biol.* 301:1237–56

228. Yamashita T, Terakita A, Shichida Y. 2000. Distinct roles of the second and the third cytoplasmic loops of bovine rhodopsin in G protein activation. *J. Biol. Chem.* 275:34272–79

229. Yau KW, Matthews G, Baylor DA. 1979. Thermal activation of the visual transduction mechanism in retinal rods. *Nature* 279:806–7

230. Yu H, Kono M, Oprian DD. 1999. State-dependent disulfide cross-linking in rhodopsin. *Biochemistry* 38:12028–32

231. Yu H, Oprian DD. 1999. Tertiary interactions between transmembrane segments 3 and 5 near the cytoplasmic side of rhodopsin. *Biochemistry* 38:12033–40

232. Zhang H, Lerro KA, Yamamoto T, Lien TH, Sastry L, et al. 1994. The location of the chromophore in rhodopsin— a photoaffinity study. *J. Am. Chem. Soc.* 116:10165–73

233. Zhukovsky EA, Oprian DD. 1989. Effect of carboxylic acid side chains on the absorption maximum of visual pigments. *Science* 246:928–30

234. Zhukovsky EA, Robinson PR, Oprian DD. 1991. Transducin activation by rhodopsin without a covalent bond to the 11-*cis*-retinal chromophore. *Science* 251:558–60

235. Zvyaga TA, Fahmy K, Siebert F, Sakmar TP. 1996. Characterization of the mutant visual pigment responsible for congenital night blindness: a biochemical and Fourier-transform infrared spectroscopy study. *Biochemistry* 35:7536–45

Annu. Rev. Biophys. Biomol. Struct. 2002. 31:485–516
DOI: 10.1146/annurev.biophys.31.101101.140922
Copyright © 2002 by Annual Reviews. All rights reserved

CONFORMATIONAL REGULATION OF INTEGRIN STRUCTURE AND FUNCTION

Motomu Shimaoka, Junichi Takagi, and Timothy A. Springer

The Center for Blood Research, Department of Pathology and Anesthesia, Harvard Medical School, 200 Longwood Avenue, Boston, Massachusetts 02115; e-mail: springeroffice@cbr.med.harvard.edu

Key Words I domain, conformational change, affinity regulation, divalent cations, signal transmission

■ **Abstract** Integrins are a structurally elaborate family of heterodimers that mediate divalent cation-dependent cell adhesion in a wide range of biological contexts. The inserted (I) domain binds ligand in the subset of integrins in which it is present. Its structure has been determined in two alternative conformations, termed open and closed. In striking similarity to signaling G proteins, rearrangement of a Mg^{2+}-binding site is linked to large conformational movements in distant backbone regions. Mutations have been used to stabilize either the closed or open structures. These show that the snapshots of the open conformation seen only in the presence of a ligand or a ligand mimetic represent a high-affinity, ligand-binding conformation, whereas those of the closed conformation correspond to a low-affinity conformation. The C-terminal α-helix moves 10 Å down the side of the domain in the open conformation. Locking in the conformation of the preceding loop is sufficient to increase affinity for ligand 9000-fold. This C-terminal "bell-rope" provides a mechanism for linkage to conformational movements in other domains. The transition from the closed to open conformation has been implicated in fast (<1 s) regulation of integrin affinity in response to activation signals from inside the cell. Recent integrin structures and functional studies reveal interactions between β-propeller, I, and I-like domains in the headpiece, and a critical role for integrin EGF domains in the stalk region. These studies suggest that the headpiece of the integrin faces down toward the membrane in the inactive conformation and extends upward in a "switchblade"-like opening motion upon activation. These long-range structural rearrangements of the entire integrin molecule involving multiple interdomain contacts appear closely linked to conformational changes in the I domain, which result in increased affinity and competence for ligand binding.

CONTENTS

AN OVERVIEW OF INTEGRIN STRUCTURE
AND FUNCTION

Integrins are adhesion molecules with noncovalently associated α- and β-subunits that mediate cell-cell, cell–extracellular matrix, and cell-pathogen interactions. As their name implies, integrins integrate the cytoskeleton with points of attachment in the extracellular environment to mediate force-resistant adhesion, polarization in response to extracellular cues, and cell migration. Integrin-dependent physiological processes include tissue morphogenesis, inflammation, wound healing, and regulation of cell growth and differentiation (38, 82).

Nineteen different integrin α-subunits and 8 different β-subunits have been reported in vertebrates (36, 38), forming at least 25 αβ heterodimers and perhaps

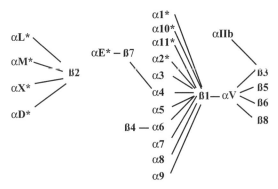

Figure 1   Integrin α- and β-subunits form 24 heterodimers that differ in ligand recognition and inside-out and outside-in signaling. Half of the α-subunits contain I domains (*asterisks*).

making the integrins the most structurally and functionally diverse family of cell-adhesion molecules (Figure 1). These integrins differ with respect to which cell surface, extracellular matrix, or inflammatory ligands they bind, the mechanisms by which their binding activity for ligands is activated, the types of cytoskeletal components to which they bind, and the types of signaling pathways they activate within cells.

The most unusual feature of integrins compared to other adhesion molecules is that the ability of their extracellular domains to bind ligands can be activated on a timescale of <1 s by signals within the cell (inside-out signaling). This is particularly evident with integrins on platelets and leukocytes in the bloodstream. Activation of integrins on these cells enables platelets to bind to injured vessel walls and fibrin clots, and enables leukocytes to bind to vessel walls and subsequently to migrate across endothelium to participate in immune and inflammatory processes. Multiple mechanisms, including conformational change in integrins (affinity regulation) and clustering and association with the cytoskeleton (avidity regulation), have been proposed to explain these events (2, 6, 19, 22, 27, 55, 87, 94). There is abundant evidence with antibodies for conformational change in many of the different extracellular integrin domains. However, it has been questioned whether conformational change is a result of ligand binding or a cause of ligand binding (affinity regulation), and it has been suggested that avidity regulation is the most important process for regulating ligand binding (2). Recently, multiple structures have been determined for the I domain that is a key ligand-binding domain in many integrins. I domains became embroiled in similar controversies as to whether conformational differences seen in crystal structures were physiologically relevant, and whether conformational change could regulate ligand binding or was merely a consequence of ligand binding. Now, through mutational and further structural studies, it is clear that conformational change in integrin I domains is of key physiologic importance for regulating the affinity for ligand. We are also beginning to understand how signals are transmitted from one domain to another in the complex multidomain architecture of integrins, and thus to appreciate the molecular basis for both the inside-out and outside-in signaling mechanisms. Furthermore, under development are drugs that bind to integrin I domains and inhibit ligand binding not by binding to the active site, but by binding to an allosteric site and stabilizing the inactive conformation. This review focuses on these exciting recent advances on the conformational regulation of ligand binding by integrin I domains and places them within the broader context of integrin structure and function.

INTEGRIN DOMAINS

Integrins contain two noncovalently associated, type I transmembrane glycoprotein α and β-subunits with extracellular domains of >940 and >640 residues, respectively (Figure 2). The intracellular domains are short, except for the cytoplasmic domain of integrin β4, which is specialized to connect to the keratin cytoskeleton and contains fibronectin type III domains (16). The overall shape

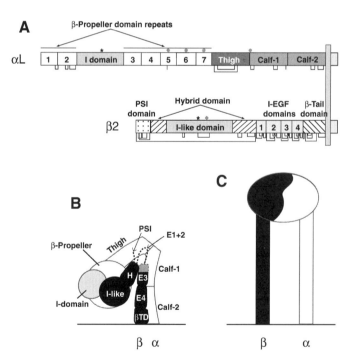

Figure 2   Integrin architecture. (*A*) Organization of domains within the primary structure of αLβ2. (*B*) Arrangement of domains within the three-dimensional crystal structure of αVβ3 (99), with an I domain added. (*C*) Commonly seen appearance of integrins in the electron microscope (20).

of the extracellular domain is known from electron microscopy (20, 91, 95). A globular headpiece binds ligand, and two long stalk regions containing C-terminal segments from the α- and β-subunits connect the ligand-binding headpiece to the transmembrane and C-terminal cytoplasmic domains. Recently, the structure of the extracellular fragment of integrin $\alpha V\beta 3$, which lacks an I domain, was reported at 3.1 Å resolution (99). Of the 12 domains predicted to be present, 8 domains, and a portion of a ninth, were resolved (Figure 2B). A complementary NMR structure of a $\beta 2$ integrin fragment (4) reveals the structure of some of the missing domains and defines the disposition of residues important in integrin activation. This information leads to a novel interpretation of the $\alpha V\beta 3$ structure and a model of integrin activation (4), which is discussed near the end of this review. This is that the bent conformation seen in the crystal structure (Figure 2B) is inactive and that the extended conformation commonly seen in electron micrographs represents the active conformation (Figure 2C). The overall picture is that activation results in a switchblade-like upward movement of the headpiece, which is coupled to conformational movements within ligand-binding domains that increase affinity for ligand.

The α-Subunit

THE β-PROPELLER DOMAIN   The N-terminal region of the integrin α-subunit contains seven segments of about 60 amino acids each with weak homology to one another, which have been predicted to fold into a seven-bladed β-propeller domain (83) (Figure 2A). The trimeric G protein β-subunit contains a β-propeller domain with the same topology. The β-propeller model has received strong support from mapping of epitopes that are far apart in sequence but close in the predicted structure (69) and from the finding that Ca^{2+}-binding motifs in propeller β-sheets 4–7 are more similar to motifs found in turns between β-strands than to EF-hand motifs in turns between α-helices (84). Mutagenesis studies show that ligand-binding residues cluster to one portion of the top and side of the β-propeller (40). The $\alpha V\beta 3$ crystal structure is in agreement with these conclusions (99).

About half of the integrin α-subunits contain no I domain (Figure 1). In these integrins, the β-propeller domain appears to directly participate in ligand binding (36). In integrins that contain I domains, the β-propeller domain can cooperate in binding to some but not other ligands, as in αM (100); or play no direct role, as in αL (59, 79).

THE I DOMAIN   Half of the integrin α-subunits contain a domain of about 200 amino acids, known as an I domain or a von Willebrand factor A domain (Figures 1, 2, and Figure 3, see color insert). I domains are the major ligand-binding sites in integrins that contain I domains (17, 62). The I domain is inserted between β-sheets 2 and 3 of the β-propeller domain (83). The three-dimensional structure of the I domain (48) shows that it adopts the dinucleotide-binding or Rossmann fold, and within this class of folds it shows the greatest similarity to small G proteins and trimeric G protein α-subunits. The structural relationship of the integrin I domain and β-propeller domains to G protein α- and β-subunits, respectively, is quite interesting and may reflect functional similarities in conformational regulation of ligand binding (47, 83). A divalent cation coordination site designated the metal ion-dependent adhesion site (MIDAS) in the I domain binds negatively charged residues in ligands much in the same way that the Mg^{2+} in G proteins coordinates to the γ-phosphate of GTP. I domain structure and function is described in detail below.

THE α-SUBUNIT STALK REGION   The region C-terminal to the β-propeller domain comprises a large portion of the α-subunit extracellular domain of about 500 residues. Much of this C-terminal region appears to correspond to the stalk region visualized in electron micrographs and is predicted to consist of domains with a two-layer β-sandwich structure (58). The crystal structure reveals the presence of three β-sandwich domains in this region, designated the thigh, calf-1, and calf-2 domains (99) (Figure 2A, B).

The β-Subunit

THE PSI DOMAIN   The N-terminal cysteine-rich region of residues 1–50 shares sequence homology with membrane proteins including plexins, semaphorins, and the c-met receptor; it has therefore been termed the PSI domain for plexins, semaphorins, and integrins (8). This region in integrin β-subunits has seven cysteines, six of which are shared with other PSI domains, and is predicted to have two α-helices. The first of the seven cysteines forms a long-range disulfide to the C-terminal cysteine-rich region in the β-subunit (Figure 2A) (10). These cysteine-rich regions cooperate to restrain the integrin in the inactive conformation (103).

THE I-LIKE DOMAIN   Integrin β-subunits contain a highly evolutionarily conserved domain of about 240 residues, spanning from about residue 100 to 340. This domain contains a putative metal-binding DXSXS sequence motif similar to that of the MIDAS in the I domain, a similar secondary structure (48), and weak but detectable sequence homology to the I domain (71); therefore, it has been termed the I-like domain (Figure 3). This region is a hotspot for point mutations that result in a lack of association of the integrin β2 subunit with α-subunits, or loss of function, and cause leukocyte-adhesion deficiency (7). The I-like domain appears to directly bind ligand in integrins that lack I domains and to indirectly regulate ligand binding by integrins that contain I domains. There is a large interface between the β-propeller domain and the I-like domain (99), as originally deduced by their mutual dependence for folding (31, 33) and from antibody epitopes (72, 102).

THE C-TERMINAL STALK AND THE EGF-LIKE DOMAINS   The C-terminal portion of the extracellular domain extends from about residue 340 to 700. Much of this is cysteine-rich and corresponds to the β-subunit stalk region. From about residue

435 to 600 are four cysteine-rich repeats that are EGF-like (4, 89, 92, 99, 101). These have been designated integrin-EGF (I-EGF) domains (4, 89). Many activating antibodies, or antibodies that bind only when integrins are activated, bind to the C-terminal region of the $\beta1$, $\beta2$, and $\beta3$ subunits (36). Mapping in more detail shows that these mAb map within the EGF-like modules (57). This portion of the β-subunit is important in signal transmission and is discussed in more detail below.

THE OVERALL STRUCTURE AND FUNCTION OF INTEGRIN I DOMAINS

Ligand-Binding Function

I domains have been implicated as major ligand-binding sites in those integrins in which they are present. The evidence includes mapping of mAb that inhibit ligand binding to the I domain (17, 32), the requirement of residues in the MIDAS and in the surrounding area for ligand binding (32, 41), and the ability of isolated I domains to bind ligands (62, 75). Deletion of the I domain does not affect expression of the $\alpha\beta$ heterodimer (50, 100). Deletion of the I domain of the integrin αL abolishes recognition of all known ligands (50, 100); however, deletion of the I domain of the integrin αM abolishes binding to some ligands and diminishes binding to others (101). The role of the β-propeller domain in this residual binding suggests that in some cases both the β-propeller domain and I domain can directly contribute to ligand binding. However, in the case of the integrin αL, when the I domain is locked in the proper conformation (see below) and compared to the heterodimer, the isolated I domain is sufficient to give equal adhesiveness in cell-based assays (59); and binding to the monomeric, soluble ligand ICAM-1 of equal affinity in surface plasmon resonance assays (79).

I Domain Structure

Crystal and NMR structures have been determined for I domains from the integrin αM (1, 47, 48), αL (39, 49, 73, 74), α2 (25, 26), and α1 (66, 76) subunits. The I domain adopts the dinucleotide-binding or Rossmann fold, with α-helices surrounding a central β-sheet (Figure 4, see color insert). There are six major α-helices and several short α-helices that differ between I domains (Figure 3). The β-sheet contains five parallel and one anti-parallel β-strand. The top face of the I domain contains the MIDAS. β-strands and α-helices tend to alternate in the secondary structure (Figure 3), with the α-helices wrapping around the domain in counterclockwise order when viewed from the top (Figure 4). The cation in the MIDAS is ligated by five side chains located in the $\beta1$-$\alpha1$, $\alpha2$-$\alpha3$, and $\beta4$-$\alpha4$ loops on the top of the domain (Figures 3, 4). The first of these loops contains three coordinating residues in a sequence that is a signature of I domains, DXSXS. Divalent cations have long been known to be universally required for ligand binding by integrins, and in I domains the metal-coordinating residues, and the residues surrounding the metal-binding site are important for ligand binding. Many of the proteins with dinucleotide or Rossmann folds are enzymes that have an active site and a Mg^{2+}-binding site at the top face, and the Mg^{2+} often coordinates the phosphate group of NAD, ATP, or GTP, which are substrates or cofactors for these enzymes. Of these proteins, the most closely related to integrin I domains are the small G proteins such as ras. The I domain and small G protein folds differ only in one α-helix and in reversing the order of the $\beta2$ and $\beta3$ strands in the β-sheet.

TWO DIFFERENT CONFORMATIONS FOR INTEGRIN I DOMAINS

The αM I Domain

Early on, the integrin αM I domain was found to crystallize in two different conformations (47). There was controversy about whether the different conformations were physiologically relevant or an artifact of the lattice contacts in crystals (1, 52). The two conformers were at first termed the Mn^{2+} and Mg^{2+} forms because they were crystallized in the presence of these metals and bound them at the MIDAS; later, they were termed the closed and open conformers, respectively. The latter terminology is much less confusing because further studies have shown that the closed conformation can be seen with Mg^{2+}, Mn^{2+}, Cd^{2+}, or no metal in the MIDAS (1, 74); the open conformation can be seen with Mg (48), Co^{2+}, Zn^{2+}, and probably Mn^{2+}, Cd^{2+}, and Ni^{2+} in the MIDAS (26). What clearly distinguishes the closed and open I domain conformations is that in the two open structures determined, an acidic residue donated either by a ligand (26) or a ligand-mimetic lattice contact (48) coordinates to the metal in the MIDAS, whereas there is no ligand-like contact in the large number of closed structures that have been determined. Instead, a water molecule is present at the equivalent coordination position (Figure 5A, see color insert). The closed and open conformations differ not only in the coordination of residues in the I domain with the MIDAS, but in the structure of surrounding loops and in the position of the C-terminal α-helix (Figure 6A, see color insert).

In the MIDAS, five residues in the I domain and several water molecules contribute oxygen atoms to the primary and secondary coordination sphere surrounding the metal (Figure 5A). Compared to most other binding sites for Mg^{2+} in protein crystal structures, the MIDAS is unusual in its content of serine and threonine residues; however, this feature is also shared with G proteins. Ca^{2+} is generally not seen to be coordinated by serine and threonine side chains. Instead, Ca^{2+} prefers more polarized oxygen atoms as found in acidic and amide amino acid side chains and in carbonyl groups of the backbone. The metal-oxygen distances are also smaller for Mg^{2+} than for Ca^{2+}. The shorter interatomic distances and the less-polar nature of the oxygens seen with Mg^{2+} are thought to reflect a greater covalent character for the Mg^{2+} ligand bond compared to a greater ionic character for the Ca^{2+} ligand bond (47). In the open conformation of the MIDAS, two serines and one threonine are in the primary coordination sphere, whereas two aspartic acid residues contributed by the I domain are in the secondary coordination sphere and fix the positions of coordinating water molecules (Figure 5A). Notably, the glutamic acid contributed by the ligand or ligand mimetic donates the only negatively charged oxygen to the primary coordination sphere in the open conformation. The lack of any charged group in the primary coordination sphere donated by the I domain is hypothesized to enhance the strength of the bond between the metal and the acidic residue in the ligand. The most intensively studied ligand for an I domain is ICAM-1; domain 1 of ICAM-1 binds to the I domain of integrin $\alpha L\beta 2$. The binding sites have been mapped by mutagenesis, and the structure of IgSF domains 1 and 2 of ICAM-1 has been determined (5, 12). By far the most important binding residue in ICAM-1 is a glutamic acid residue near the center of the binding site; therefore, this residue has been hypothesized to directly coordinate to a Mg^{2+} in the I domain MIDAS (85).

In the closed conformation of the I domain, the threonine moves from the primary to the secondary coordination sphere, and one of the aspartic acid residues moves from the secondary to the primary coordination sphere (Figure 5A). This is consistent with the idea that an energetically favorable MIDAS requires at least one primary coordination to a negatively charged oxygen, and when this is not provided by a ligand, there is a structural rearrangement within the I domain to provide this from within the MIDAS. The backbone and side chain rearrangements in the I domain are accompanied by a 2.3 Å sideways movement of the metal ion away from the threonine and toward the aspartic acid on the opposite side of the coordination shell (Figure 5A). A water molecule takes the place of the ligand-mimetic glutamic acid to complete the coordination sphere.

The structural rearrangement of the MIDAS is coupled to backbone movements of the loops that bear the coordinating residues. Linked structural shifts occur in the hydrophobic core, in neighboring loops on the top of the I domain, and in α-helices on the side of the domain (Figure 6A). In the largest movement in the transition from the closed to open structure, the C-terminal helix, $\alpha 6$, moves 10 Å down the side of the domain. This requires a repacking of the hydrophobic face of $\alpha 6$ against the side of the domain. At the N terminus of $\alpha 6$, Phe-302, which inserts into a hydrophobic cavity in the top of the closed domain, becomes completely exposed as a consequence of the dramatic reshaping of the $\beta 6$-$\alpha 6$ loop. The $\alpha 6$ helix is distant from the ligand-binding site; however, its remarkable movement provides a mechanism to link conformational movements in I domains to movements elsewhere in integrins.

The $\alpha 2$ I Domain

Recently, the structure of the $\alpha 2$ I domain has been determined in the absence of ligand (25) and in the presence of a collagen peptide ligand (26). The triple-helical collagen peptide contains a critical Gly-Phe-hydroxyPro-Gly-Glu-Arg sequence, and the Glu of this sequence ligates the MIDAS. The differences between the ligand-bound and nonliganded $\alpha 2$ I domains are remarkably similar to the differences between the αM I domains with and without a ligand-mimetic lattice contact (Figure 6B, see color insert); when the differences in Cα carbon backbone positions are plotted, they are remarkably similar (26). Furthermore, exactly the same changes are seen in the residues that make primary coordinations to the metal at the MIDAS (Figure 5B, see color insert). Thus, the liganded and nonliganded conformations of the $\alpha 2$ I domain adopt the open and closed conformations, just as seen for αM (Figure 6B). The I domains of $\alpha 2$ and αM are only 27% identical in sequence and are among the most distantly related of integrin I domains; thus, it is to be expected that the open and closed conformations will be a general feature of integrin I domains.

The $\beta 6$-$\alpha 6$ loop adopts conformations that are canonical for the open and closed structure. In the open conformations, the backbone conformation of the $\beta 6$-$\alpha 6$ loops are almost identical in αM and $\alpha 2$ (Figure 7, see color insert). The conformation is quite different in the closed conformation, yet the conformation of this loop is almost identical for the closed conformations of αM and $\alpha 2$, as well as for αL and $\alpha 1$ (Figure 7). Remarkably, only one of the five residues in the $\beta 6$-$\alpha 6$ loop is identical in sequence between αM and $\alpha 2$ (Figure 3). The high conservation of this loop is also emphasized by the success of modeling it in the open comformation of αL (see below).

There is one unique feature of $\alpha 2$ compared to αM and αL. An additional helix called helix C extends from the top of the closed $\alpha 2$ I domain near the MIDAS. This helix appears to sterically hinder binding of collagen to the MIDAS. In the transition to the open conformation, there is a "slinking" motion in which this helix unwinds and residues are added to the following helix (Figure 6B); the loss of the C helix appears to open the binding site for collagen (26).

The αL I Domain

Both mutation of αL to lock in the open and closed conformations and NMR studies have provided evidence for conformational change. Multiple crystal structures have been determined for the αL I domain in the closed conformation; these structures, determined with Mg^{2+}, Mn^{2+}, or no metal at the MIDAS, are similar to one another except that the C-terminal helix differs in conformation (39, 73, 74). In these closed αL I domain structures, there is no downward movement of the helix or restructuring of the preceding loop as seen in the closed-to-open transition of $\alpha 2$ or αM I domains. Instead, the helix differs in conformation and whether it packs closely against the hydrophobic core of the domain or moves away from it as a result of lattice contacts. The NMR solution structure of the αL I domain shows that the protein in solution also adopts the closed conformation, regardless of whether Mg^{2+}, Mn^{2+}, or no divalent cation is present (49). The NMR solution structure also demonstrates that the C-terminal α-helix, although well formed, is highly flexible, probably as a result of breathing or segmental motion.

NMR spectroscopy was further used to probe conformational change of the αL I domain upon binding to ligand (37). Change in the chemical environment of specific residues in the αL I domain was investigated in the presence or absence of a fragment of ICAM-1 containing domains 1 and 2. Domain 1 includes the αL binding site and the most critical residue for ligand binding, Glu-34 (5, 12). Two distinct clusters of affected residues were identified. One cluster of residues localized around the MIDAS on the upper face of the I domain. Another group of perturbed residues clustered at a different location in the domain, around the C-terminal α-helix and the opposing face of the central β-sheet. Although the solution structure of the I domain in complex with ICAM-1 was not determined, the regions that are chemically shifted upon binding to ICAM-1 are similar to the regions that differ most between the closed and open conformations of the αM and α2 I domains.

IS SHAPE-SHIFTING IN INTEGRIN I DOMAINS PHYSIOLOGICALLY RELEVANT FOR REGULATION OF THEIR AFFINITY FOR LIGAND?

The above studies demonstrated that conformational changes occur when ligands are bound to I domains. However, they did not establish whether these changes result from induced fit upon ligand binding, or if they are physiologically relevant for regulating the affinity for ligand of I domains and the integrins in which they are present. These have been hotly debated issues in the integrin field. For some years, it has been proposed that after cellular activation, signals are transmitted to the extracellular domains of integrins that alter the conformation of their ligand-binding site, and hence affinity for ligand (22, 56). More recently, evidence has also accumulated that lateral redistribution and clustering of integrins, or so-called avidity regulation, may alter cellular adhesion independently of a change in affinity for ligand (88). Indeed, it has been suggested that conformational change in integrins is overemphasized and is a consequence of ligand binding rather than a cause (2). The binding of many antibodies to integrins is stabilized or induced by ligands, leading to the term ligand-induced-binding sites (LIBS) for these epitopes. Although many of the same antibodies can activate ligand binding, this can be argued to be a consequence of stabilizing the ligand-bound conformation and hence the integrin-ligand complex. The keys to resolving these issues were (*a*) whether the conformational changes seen in crystal structures were physiologically relevant, i.e., altered affinity for ligand as predicted, (*b*) whether the change in affinity was substantial, and (*c*) whether conformational alterations in I domains occurred on the cell surface in physiological circumstances.

Parallels with G Proteins

Clues to the physiological relevance of conformational change in I domains are provided by the strikingly similar changes in metal coordination that are linked to backbone movements in signal-transducing G proteins (47). In the small G protein ras, a Mg^{2+} ion is present in the catalytically active GTP-binding site

(63). The GTP-bound form, which is active in binding to and stimulating effector molecules, and the inactive GDP-bound form have Mg^{2+} ion coordinations that are analogous to those of the open and closed I domains, respectively (Figure 6C, see color insert). In the GTP-bound form, the Mg^{2+} ion binds directly to a serine, a threonine, and two water molecules; the other two primary coordinations are to β- and γ-phosphate oxygen atoms of GTP. There is a secondary coordination to an aspartate. On hydrolysis of the GTP with release of the γ-phosphate, the coordination to the γ-phosphate oxygen is lost, and other Mg^{2+} coordinations are altered. The bond to the threonine is lost, and a direct coordination to the aspartate is gained. The loss of coordination to the threonine results in a flip in the switch I loop containing the threonine, and this is linked to a large change in the adjacent switch II loop (Figure 6C). These changes abolish binding of effector molecules at the switch region (63). G proteins and I domains differ in the loops bearing the residues that coordinate Mg^{2+} and in the backbone regions that move. The movement of the C-terminal α-helix in I domains appears to be a specialized feature that allows conformational communication between domains because it is not seen in G proteins.

In the case of G proteins, conformational change is highly regulated by the intrinsic GTPase activity, GTPase-activating G proteins (GAPs), and guanine nucleotide exchange factors, and is central to the mechanism of regulating binding to effector molecules and hence regulating intracellular signaling pathways. Thus interactions with other proteins regulate G protein conformation. Conformational change in I domains is similarly regulated by interactions with other integrin domains.

Conformation-Sensitive mAb

Many mAbs to integrins have been reported that either bind only when the integrin is activated or induce activation themselves (2). However, few activation-dependent mAb block ligand binding and thus appear to recognize the ligand-binding site. The only such mAb reported to I domains is CBRM1/5, which recognizes the I domain of αM (18). This mAb does not bind to resting peripheral blood neutrophils, but after these cells are activated through G protein–coupled chemoattractant receptors, or with a drug that activates protein kinase C, 10% or 30% of the $\alpha M\beta 2$ on the surface of individual cells binds CBRM1/5 mAb. Although it recognizes only a subset of the $\alpha M\beta 2$ on the cell surface, CBRM1/5 mAb completely blocks ligand binding by cells, showing that it recognizes the active subset of molecules.

Evidence to support the physiological relevance of conformational change seen in the open and closed form of αM I domain crystal structure was provided with CBRM1/5 mAb (68). This mouse anti-human mAb is specific for six residues that differ between the human and mouse amino acid sequences. The residues in the epitope are present in two different amino acid segments that are structurally adjacent and near the MIDAS (68) (Figure 8, see color insert). The first three residues, P147, H148, and R151, are located at the top of the $\alpha 1$ helix and are preceded immediately by three residues that coordinate Mg^{2+} and form the DXSXS motif of the MIDAS: D140, S142, and S144. The last three residues, K200, T203, and L206, are in the loop that contains T209, which is directly coordinated to the metal in the open conformation and indirectly coordinated in the closed conformation. Both groups of residues are widely exposed regardless of activation as judged by reactivity with other antibodies. These results suggest that the selectivity of CBRM1/5 for the active state is not due to "unmasking" of the epitope by other integrin domains but to "shape-shifting" in the I domain itself. Comparison between the superimposed opened and closed structures shows that P147, H148, and R151 differ remarkably in position and in side chain orientation, and hence in relationship to the three other residues in the epitope (Figure 8). $C\alpha$ atom movements that average 2.4 Å are tightly linked to the 2.0 Å movement of S144 of the MIDAS. In addition, H148 and R151 are adjacent to the loop preceding the C-terminal α-helix in the closed conformation, and both are more exposed in the open conformation, owing to the movement of this loop that accompanies the large downward shift of the C-terminal α-helix. Thus, CBRM1/5 recognizes shape-shifting in the αM I domain near the MIDAS and the C-terminal α-helix. Documentation of shape-shifting in these regions of the I domain upon activation of integrins on the cell surface provides strong evidence that conformational change seen in the open and closed I domain structures is physiologically relevant and occurs within the context of intact integrin $\alpha\beta$ heterodimers. Since CBRM1/5 mAb blocks ligand binding, it clearly does not recognize a ligand-induced-binding site (LIBS). Therefore, the induction of the CBRM1/5 epitope on cell surface $\alpha M\beta 2$ is a consequence of changes within $\alpha M\beta 2$ itself and not a consequence of ligand binding.

Mutations Designed to Stabilize the Open and Closed Conformers of I Domains

To measure how transition between the open and closed conformations of the I domain regulates affinity for ligand, mutations have been introduced to stabilize a particular conformation, and tested for effect on ligand binding.

αM In the αM I domain, Phe-302 is buried in the closed conformation and exposed in the open conformation; therefore, mutation to a hydrophilic residue should favor the open conformation (51). To this end, the mutation Phe-302 $\rightarrow$ Trp was designed and was claimed to stabilize the open conformation and to increase ligand binding (51); however, this claim is not without controversy. First, Trp is not a hydrophilic residue, and mutants with a hydrophilic Arg substitution were not expressed. Second, the study was internally inconsistent. It was reported both that the overall affinity of the mutant was unchanged and that there was a 2.3-fold increase in the proportion of molecules in the active conformation. For both to be true, there would have to be a corresponding 2.3-fold decrease in the affinity for ligand of the active species. Third, a subsequent study showed that the Phe-302 $\rightarrow$ Trp mutant crystallized in the closed conformation and that the Trp was buried

(98). Finally, another study showed at best only a slight increase in binding by the same mutant (80).

A different approach was taken to stabilize particular conformations of the αM I domain and to investigate the physiological significance of these conformations (80). The computational algorithm ORBIT, developed by Dahiyat & Mayo (15), rationally designs amino acid sequences that stabilize a particular backbone structure. Using ORBIT, sequences were selected that minimized the energy of either the open or closed conformation of the αM I domain. Back calculations showed that mutations that stabilized the open conformation also destabilized the closed conformation and vice versa. To avoid mutations that could directly alter the ligand binding face or alter contacts with other domains in intact integrins, only hydrophobic core residues were allowed to mutate. Three different designed open I domains, each containing 8 to 13 mutations, showed increased binding to ligand when expressed on the cell surface in αMβ2 heterodimers, whereas designed closed or wild-type I domains did not (80). Similar results were obtained when I domains alone, in the absence of any other integrin domains, were expressed on the cell surface with an artificial C-terminal transmembrane domain. The CBRM1/5 mAb reacted with αMβ2 containing the designed open but not designed closed or wild-type I domains. Furthermore, the designed closed I domain was resistant to activation. αMβ2 heterodimers containing wild-type I domains, but not designed closed I domains, bound ligand in response to activating mAb. These results demonstrated that the open and closed conformations correspond to ligand binding and inactive conformations, respectively.

The closed conformation appears to be the low-energy conformation of the I domain and the default conformation adopted by the I domain in resting integrin heterodimers on the cell surface. In αMβ2 heterodimers, and in isolation on the cell surface, the wild-type I domain behaved like the designed closed I domain in lack of expression of the CBRM1/5 epitope and lack of ligand binding. This suggests that the closed conformation is adopted in the inactive state by integrins on the cell surface. Calculation of the energies of αM I domains crystallized in the open and closed conformations also shows that the closed conformation is of lower energy (80).

Mutation in the αM I domain of the single residue Ile-316, located in the last half of the C-terminal α-helix, is sufficient to favor the open conformation (99). The side chain of Ile-316 packs in a hydrophobic pocket between the C-terminal α-helix and the opposing β-sheet in the closed conformation, but due to the downward movement of this helix in the open conformation, this residue cannot pack against the side of the domain in the open conformation and is not visualized in the crystal structure of the open conformer (47). To test the hypothesis that packing of Ile-316 wedged into this hydrophobic socket might constrain the αM I domain in the closed conformation, recombinant soluble αM I domains were truncated just before Ile-316 (r11bA$^{123-315}$) or Ile-316 was mutated to Gly (r11bA$^{Ile-316-Gly}$) (98). These mutants showed increased affinity for the ligands iC3b, fibrinogen, and ICAM-1 compared to the wild-type I domain (r11bA$^{123-321}$), as revealed by surface plasmon resonance (98). Thus, the absence of the Ile-316 side chain clearly favors the open, ligand-binding conformation in solution. The r11bA$^{Ile-316-Gly}$ mutant crystallized in the open conformation when a ligand-mimetic crystal contact was present. However, because the wild-type r11bA$^{123-315}$ also crystallized in the open conformation when a ligand-mimetic crystal contact was present (98), as also observed in the first αM I domain crystal structure (48), the crystal studies do not reveal which conformation is present in solution, nor do they reveal whether the Ile-316 mutation by itself is sufficient for conversion to the open conformation in the absence of a ligand-mimetic contact.

ENGINEERED DISULFIDE BONDS WITHIN αL I DOMAINS   Locking the αL I domain in the open conformation (59, 60, 79) has relied on models, since all αL structures thus far show the closed conformation (39, 49, 73, 74). The open conformation of the αL I domain was modeled by using the open αM I domain as a template in regions where the closed and open conformations differed. Positions were sought where pairs of residues could be mutated to cysteine that could form a disulfide bond, and the disulfide could form only in one conformation. The positions that were found bracket the loop between the C-terminal α-helix and preceding β-strand (Figure 9, see color insert). To lock this loop in its two alternate conformations, pairs of cysteines were introduced either at residues 287 and 294 for the open conformation, or at residues 289 and 294 for the closed conformation. In surface plasmon resonance measurements of binding to ICAM-1, the soluble locked-open I domain molecule showed a 9000-fold increase in affinity compared to wild type, which was reversed by disulfide reduction. Locking the I domain open increases its on-rate, which is consistent with conformational change being rate limiting for binding of the wild-type I domain (Table 1). The affinity of the locked-closed conformer was similar to wild type (79). Furthermore, the affinity and kinetics of the soluble locked-open αL I domain for ICAM-1 are comparable to that measured independently (44) for intact, activated αLβ2 (Table 1). Thus, the αL I domain, when locked in the open conformation, is sufficient for full-affinity binding.

TABLE 1   The affinity for ICAM-1 of the locked-open αL I domain is equal to that of intact αLβ2

Immob. ligand	Analyte	k_{on} (M^{-1} s^{-1})	k_{off} (s^{-1})	K_D (μM)
sICAM-1	WT I domain	2950 ± 440	4.95 ± 0.85	1670 ± 100
sICAM-1	Closed I domain	2110 ± 400	2.84 ± 0.27	1760 ± 70
sICAM-1	Open I domain	$139,000 \pm 8000$	0.0257 ± 0.0015	0.185 ± 0.012
Open I domain	sICAM-1	$107,000 \pm 3000$	0.0275 ± 0.0028	0.258 ± 0.024
αLβ2*	sICAM-1	$224,000 \pm 69,000$	0.0298 ± 0.0069	0.133 ± 0.041

Binding kinetics measured by surface plasmon resonance. Data are from (79), except for measurements on αLβ2.
*Data from (44).

The locked-open and -closed I domains were also tested for adhesiveness in the context of intact $\alpha L\beta 2$ on the cell surface (59). $\alpha L\beta 2$ containing the locked-open I domain was constitutively and maximally active for adhesion to ICAM-1, whereas $\alpha L\beta 2$ heterodimers containing wild-type or locked-closed I domains failed to support adhesion. $\alpha L\beta 2$ containing the wild-type I domain was activatable for adhesion by activating mAb or Mn^{2+}, whereas $\alpha L\beta 2$ containing the locked-closed I domain was resistant to such activators. The results with soluble I domains and cell surface heterodimers clearly demonstrated that reshaping the $\beta 6$-$\alpha 6$ loop is fully sufficient for regulation of the affinity of the ligand-binding site at the MIDAS because only the conformation of the $\beta 6$-$\alpha 6$ loop is directly restrained by the disulfide bond. Therefore, inside-out signals relayed from the cytoplasm could be propagated to the ligand-binding site by pulling down the C-terminal, $\alpha 6$ helix, thereby reconfiguring the $\beta 6$-$\alpha 6$ loop. The C-terminal α-helix may act like a bell-rope in relaying conformational signals.

As discussed above, there has been controversy about the contribution to regulation of adhesiveness of lateral movements on the cell surface (clustering, avidity regulation) and conformational change in the ligand-binding site (affinity regulation). In part to address this issue, I domains were expressed on the cell surface in isolation from other integrin domains using an artificial transmembrane domain (59). In contrast to native $\alpha L\beta 2$, the cell surface I domains contained only a single transmembrane domain derived from the platelet-derived growth factor receptor and truncated five residues into the cytoplasmic domain. Isolated wild-type or locked-closed I domains did not support adhesion, whereas the isolated locked-open I domain was as strongly adhesive for ICAM-1 as fully activated intact $\alpha L\beta 2$ heterodimer at an equivalent cell surface density. These findings demonstrate that affinity regulation is fully sufficient to regulate cell adhesiveness and that interactions between integrins or other components mediated by integrin cytoplasmic, transmembrane, or any extracellular domains other than the I domain are not required. However, these findings do not rule out a role for avidity regulation or a link between conformational change in integrins and clustering.

Mutations Near the C-Terminal α-Helix in αL

Mutations around the interface between the C-terminal α-helix and the opposing β-sheet affect ligand-binding activity, underscoring the significance of conformational changes occurring around the C-terminal α-helix. Systematic mutagenesis of this region has revealed mutations that both increase and decrease ligand binding by $\alpha L\beta 2$, apparently by affecting the relative stability of the open and closed conformations, or by affecting interactions with nearby domains that regulate I domain conformation (37). One of these residues, Ile-306, corresponds to Ile-316 of αM, which stabilizes the closed conformation by fitting in a hydrophobic socket (98). Consistent with the observations with the αM I domain, in intact $\alpha L\beta 2$ substitution of Ile-306 with alanine increased adhesion to ICAM-1

(37). However, a soluble αL I domain truncated at residue 305 and hence lacking Ile-306 did not show increased affinity for ICAM-1 (M. Shimaoka & T. A. Springer, unpublished data). In isolated αL I domains, the C-terminal α-helix is mobile in NMR structures (49), shows variable conformations in crystal structures, and does not pack well against the body of the domain (73, 74). Therefore, the effect on ligand binding of mutation of residue 306 in intact αLβ2 but not in isolated I domains suggests that the C-terminal α-helix is well-packed against the body of the I domain in intact αLβ2 and that interactions with other domains are important for the conformation of the C-terminal α-helix. Mutation in αLβ2 of another hydrophobic residue in the same pocket underlying the C-terminal α-helix, I235A, activated ligand binding (37). Thus, in the context of intact αLβ2, mutations in the hydrophobic pocket appear to favor the open conformation of the I domain.

Therapeutic Antagonists Directed to Integrin I Domains

In vivo experiments using antibodies and gene disruption have shown that binding of αLβ2 to ICAMs is important in leukocyte trafficking in inflammation, lymphocyte homing, and T lymphocyte interactions with antigen-presenting cells in immune reactions (9, 82). These findings suggested that antagonists of αLβ2 could be useful for the therapy of autoimmune diseases. Indeed, a blocking mAb directed to the αL I domain was shown to be efficacious in phase 3 clinical studies of patients with psoriasis (29). High-throughput screening of large chemical libraries has led to the identification by more than three different pharmaceutical companies of small molecules that inhibit binding of αLβ2 to ICAM-1 (39, 42, 45, 53, 54, 96, 97). The compounds are highly specific for αLβ2 compared to αMβ2. Remarkably, each of the independently discovered lead compounds, which belong to different chemical classes, binds to the hydrophobic pocket between the C-terminal α-helix and the β-sheet, as documented by NMR or crystallography at three different companies (39, 45, 53) (Figure 10, see color insert). This binding site is distant from the ligand-binding site at the MIDAS. Together with the finding that the drug–I domain complexes crystallize in the closed conformation, this suggests that the compounds allosterically inhibit binding to ICAM-1 by favoring the closed conformation. In agreement with this hypothesis, αLβ2 containing a mutant I domain locked open with an engineered disulfide bridge is completely resistant to inhibition by drug compound (59). In contrast, αLβ2 heterodimers containing I domains of wild-type or with single cysteine substitutions are susceptible to drug compound, as is αLβ2 containing the locked-open I domain after disulfide reduction with dithiothreitol. Thus, the drug compounds inhibit LFA-1 function by binding to the closed conformation of the I domain and blocking the conformational transition to the open form that is active in binding to ICAMs and mediates cell-cell adhesion. The ability of these compounds to inhibit cell adhesion in vitro and in vivo provides strong evidence that a change in affinity, and not a change in avidity through clustering on the cell surface, is responsible for physiologic regulation of adhesiveness.

The Mechanistic Basis of I Domain Activation

The above studies demonstrate that (*a*) I domain conformation dramatically regulates affinity for ligand, (*b*) the open conformation is sufficient to maximally activate cell adhesion independently of the transmembrane and cytoplasmic domains, (*c*) drug compounds that lock I domains in the closed conformation inhibit cell adhesion, and (*d*) antibodies detect changes on integrins in physiologically activated cells that are intrinsic to the integrin and not dependent on ligand binding. It is inescapable that regulation of I domain conformation regulates cell adhesion by integrins. Nonetheless, we do not know the details of the regulatory molecular changes that precede ligand binding. There could be a stable change in I domain conformation, or a single integrin molecule could equilibrate between the closed and open conformations, with cellular activation shifting the equilibrium. Alternatively, activation might lower the energy barrier for conformational change and make the open conformation kinetically accessible upon binding of ligand or mAbs such as CBRM1/5. Furthermore, after activation and prior to ligand binding, the I domain might exist in a conformation intermediate between the closed and open conformations.

DOMAIN-DOMAIN INTERACTIONS IN INTACT INTEGRINS IN TRANSMISSION OF SIGNALS TO AND FROM THE I DOMAIN

In the following section we address how, in the context of an intact integrin heterodimer, conformational signals are transmitted to and from the I domain. The evidence is consistent with signal transmission through the C-terminal α-helix, the linker that follows this helix, and through contacts at the bottom of the I domain.

Interactions Between the Three Domains in the Headpiece

The C-terminal linker connecting the I domain to the β-propeller domain is much longer than the N-terminal linker. In the primary structure of the α-subunit, the I domain is inserted between blades (β-sheets) 2 and 3 of the β-propeller domain, with its N terminus immediately following the last β-strand (strand 4) of blade 2. A pair of cysteines conserved only among I domain–containing α-subunits is predicted to form a disulfide that connects the loop between β-strands 2 and 3 in β-sheet 2 to the linker that follows β-strand 4 in β-sheet 2. There are only three residues from this disulfide-bridged cysteine to the first residue defined in I domain structures, indicating that the N-terminal linker closely tethers the I domain to the β-propeller domain. On the other hand, the C-terminal linker of the I domain is much longer and thus may permit much greater conformational motion. This linker is ~20 amino acid residues long and connects the end of the C-terminal α-helix of the I domain to β-strand 1 in blade 3 of the β-propeller. Many of the residues are serines, which suggests flexibility.

β1   α1   β2

```
αM  132  DSDIAFLIDGSGSIIPHDFRRMKEFVSTVMEQLKKS--KTLFSLMQYSE-------------  178
αL  129  NVDLVFLFDGSMSLQPDEFQKILDFMKDVMKKLSNT--SYQFAAVQFST-------------  175
α2  143  LIDVVVCDESNSIY--PWDAVKNFLEKFVQGLDIGPTKTQVGLIQYAN-------------  189
β2  104  PIDLYYLMDLSYSML-DDLRNVKKLGGDLLRALNEITESGRIGFGSFVDKTVLPFVNTHPDKLRN  167
```

β3   α2   α3

```
αM  179  ------------EFRIHFTFKEFQNNP-NPRSLVKPITQLLG--RTHTATGIRKVVRELFNIT  226
αL  176  ------------SYKTEFDFSDYVKRK-DPDALLKHVKHMLL--LTNTFGAINYVATEVFREE  223
α2  190  ------------NPRVFNLNTYK-TKEEMIVATSQTSQYGGD--LTNTFGAIQYARKYAYSAA  238
β2  168  PCPNKEKECQPPFAFRHVLKL--TN-NSNQFQTEVGKQLISGNLDAPEGGLDAMMQVAAC--PEE  227
```

β4   α4

```
αM  227  NGARKNAFKILVVITDGEKFG------------------------DPLGYEDVIPEADR  261
αL  224  LGARPDATKVLIIITDGEAT---------------------------DSGNIDAAK-  252
α2  239  SGGRRSATKVMVVTDGESH-----------------------------DGSMLKAVIDQCNH  272
β2  228  IGWRN-VTRLLVFATDDGFHFAGDGKLGAILTPNDGRCHLEDNLYKRSNEFDYPSVGQLAHKLAE  291
```

β5   α5   α6   β6

```
αM  262  EGVIRYVIGVGD-----AFRSEKSRQELNTIASKPPRDHVFQVNNFEALKTIQNQLREKIFA  318
αL  253  -DIIRYIIGIGK-----HFQTKESQETLHKFASKPASEFVKILDTFEKLKDLFTELQKKIYV  308
α2  273  DNILRFGIAVLGYLNRNALDTKNLIKEIKAIASIPTERYFFNVSDEAALLEKAGTLGEQIFS  334
β2  292  NNIQPIFAVTS------RMVKTYEKLTEIIPK---SAVGEL-SED-SSNVVHLIKNAYNK  340
```

Figure 3 Structure-based sequence alignment of α-subunit I domains, and the β2 subunit I-like domain. The closed conformers of αM (1JLM) (47), αL (1ZON) (74), and α2 (1AOX) (25) I domains, and the β3 I-like domain (99) were superimposed with 3D MALIGN of MODELLER (77) using a gap penalty of 4 Å, and five iterations of alignment with superposition of Cα, Cβ, Cα, Cβ, and finally Cα atoms. Gaps in loops were closed up. The β2 I-like domain was aligned by sequence to that of β3. α-helices and β-strands in the I domains and β3 I-like domain are highlighted in gold and magenta, respectively. Residues that coordinate the metal in the MIDAS are red, those that coordinate the Ca^{2+} in the ADMIDAS are green.

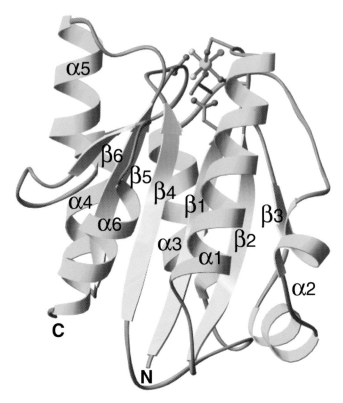

Figure 4 Ribbon diagram of the αM I domain in the open conformation. The β-strands (*yellow*), α-helices (*cyan*), and the N and C termini are labeled. The Mg ion is shown as a *green sphere*. Side chains of residues that form primary or secondary coordinations to the metal ion (D140, S142, S144, T209, and D242) are shown with *gray* bonds and carbon atoms and *red* oxygen atoms. Coordinating water molecule oxygens are *gold*, and the oxygen of the ligand-mimetic Glu from another I domain is *purple*. All ribbon diagrams in this review were prepared with Ribbons (11).

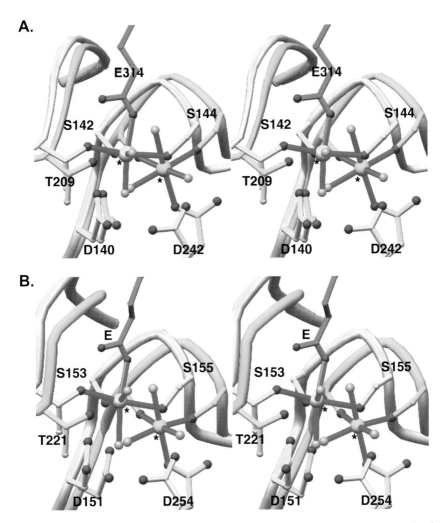

Figure 5 Stereo view of alternative conformations of the MIDAS. (*A*) αM. (*B*) α2. The backbone, coordinating side chain bonds, and metals (labeled with *asterisks*) are shown in *yellow* (open conformation) and *cyan* (closed conformation). The coordinating glutamate residue bonds from the ligand-mimetic neighboring αM I domain (E314) in αM and collagen peptide ligand (E) in α2 are in *purple*. Primary coordination bonds to the metals are in *blue*. Oxygen atoms of the coordinating side chains and water molecules are *red* and *gold*, respectively. I domains were superimposed on one another in turn, so all were in the same orientation as the closed 1JLM αM structure (48). The 1IDO open αM structure (47) was superimposed on 1JLM using residues 132-141, 166-206, 211-241, 246-270, and 287-294. The 1AOX closed α2 structure (25) was superimposed on 1JLM using residues 145-153, 180-189, 192-199, 222-240, 246-256, and 268-282. The 1DZI open α2 structure (26) was then superimposed on 1AOX using residues 143-152, 173-216, 223-253, and 259-282. The closed αL structure 1ZON (74) was superimposed on 1JLM using residues 131-141, 167-189, 201-221, 231-241, and 255-262 (see Figure 7).

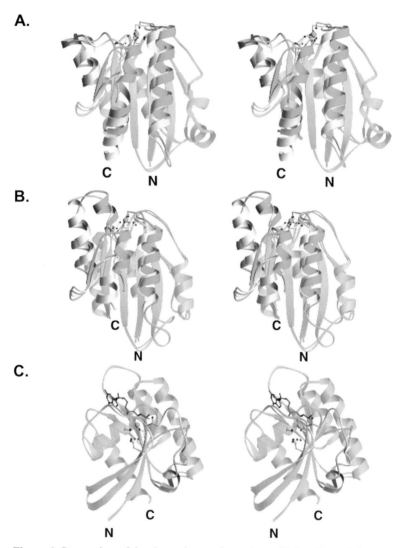

Figure 6 Stereo view of the alternative conformations of I domains and the small G protein ras. (*A*) αM I domain. (*B*) α2 I domain. (*C*) ras p21 G protein. The regions of significant difference between the superimposed conformers are shown in *yellow* (open or active) and *cyan* (closed or inactive). Similar backbone regions are in *gray*. Metal atoms and coordinating side chain bonds and carbon atoms are in *yellow* (open or active) and *blue* (closed or inactive); oxygen atoms are *red*. The coordinating residues are S142, S144, T209, and D242 in αM; S153, S155, T221, and D254 in α2; and S17, T35, and D57 in ras p21. In the active conformer of ras p21, GDP-CP, a GTP analog, is in *purple*. The I domains were superimposed as in Figure 5. The active (GTP-bound) and inactive (GDP-bound) ras structures 6Q21 and 1Q21 (63) were superimposed using residues 1-29, 39-59, and 77-167. The orientations in *A* and *B* are identical, but differs in *C* to display the conformational changes in G proteins that differ in topological location from I domains.

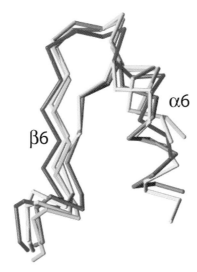

Figure 7 The loop between the most C-terminal β-strand (β6) and α-helix (α6) in I domains has a canonical conformation in open structures and a different canonical structure in closed structures. Loops are shown for open (αM, *yellow*; α2, *gold*) and closed (αM, *blue*; α2, *green*; αL, *dark blue*) conformations. For clarity, only residues 290-310 of αM, 306-326 of α2, and 280-300 of αL, which are of equal length in the closed and open structures and in all three I domains, are shown. I domains were superimposed as described in Figure 5.

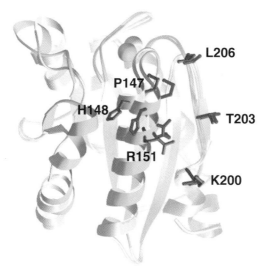

Figure 8 Alteration of the CBRM1/5 epitope in open and closed αM I domains. The metals and regions where conformational changes are significant are shown in *yellow* (open) and *blue* (closed). Other backbone regions are *gray*. Side chains of the CBRM1/5 epitope are in *gold* (open) and *dark blue* (closed). The open and closed αM I domain structures were superimposed as described in Figure 5.

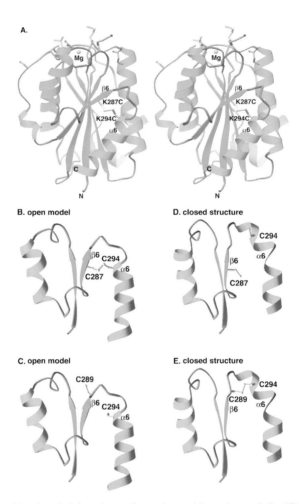

Figure 9 Locking in αL I domain conformations with engineered disulfide bridges. (*A*) Stereodiagram of the high-affinity model of the αL I domain, with mutations to introduce a disulfide bond. The side chains and disulfide bond of C287 and C294 are shown in *yellow*. The Mg^{2+} ion of the MIDAS is shown as a *gold sphere*. Side chains of residues important in binding to ICAM-1 and ICAM-2 are shown with *rose-pink* side chains and *yellow* sulfur, *red* oxygen, and *blue* nitrogen atoms. These residues, defined as important in species-specific binding to ICAM-1 (32), or by at least a twofold effect on binding to ICAM-1 or ICAM-2 upon mutation to alanine (23), are M140, E146, T175, L205, E241, T243, S245, and K263. Note that these residues surround the Mg^{2+} ion and are distant from the disulfide. (*B–E*) Predicted disulfide bonds that are selective for open or closed conformers of the αL I domain. The K287C/K294C mutation (*B, D*) and L289C/K294C mutation (*C, E*) were modeled in both open (*B, C*) and closed (*D, E*) I domain conformers. For clarity, only residues 254-305 of the models are shown. The four models were superimposed using residues not involved in conformational shifts and are shown in exactly the same orientation. The downward movement of the α6 helix in panels *B* and *C* compared to *D* and *E* is readily apparent. The remodeling of the loop connecting β6 and α6 is accompanied by a reversal in the orientation of the side chain of residue 289. Figure from (79).

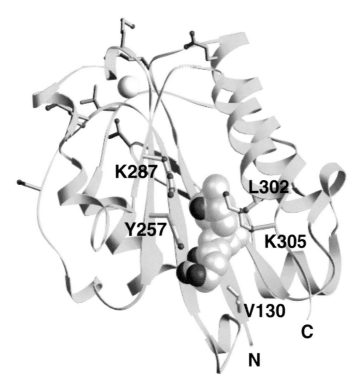

Figure 10 The drug-binding pocket of the αL I domain (39). The small drug molecule bound in the hydrophobic pocket between the β-sheet and the α-helix 6 is shown in CPK with *silver* carbon atoms and *red* oxygen atoms. Side chains within the binding pocket are labeled and shown with *gold* bonds and carbon atoms, *red* oxygen atoms, and *blue* nitrogen atoms. V233, which is also in the pocket, is hidden by the drug molecule. The residues critical for binding to ICAM-1 or ICAM-2 are shown as in Figure 9 and are clearly distal from the small molecule-binding site. The crystal structure is of the αL I domain bound to lovastatin (39); it appears to be a coincidence that lovastatin inhibits both αLβ2 and β-hydroxy methylglutaryl coenzyme A reductase.

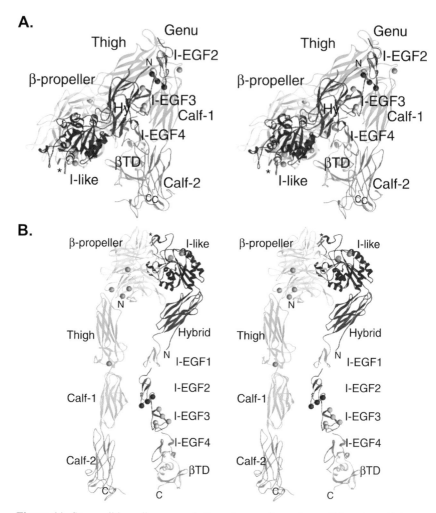

Figure 11 Stereo ribbon diagrams of alternative conformations of the extracellular segment of integrins. (*A*) Bent conformation observed in the crystal structure of αVβ3 (99). (*B*) Model of an upright, active integrin, including segments from αVβ3 (99) and I-EGF domains 2 and 3 of β2 (4). Each domain is shown in a different color and labeled (Hy, hybrid; βTD, β-tail domain). Two *red cylinders* and an *asterisk* show where the I domain would be inserted. Ca^{2+} and Mg^{2+} ions are *gold* and *silver spheres*, respectively. The Mg^{2+} is not present in the structure but is added to show the position of the MIDAS. The genu (knee) is where the headpiece bends over the stalk region. In panel *B*, the integrin is straightened at the bend (99) to resemble the ligand-binding conformation observed in the electron microscope (20) (Figure 2*C*). The missing I-EGF1 domain is modeled in *gray*. I-EGF2 and a portion of I-EGF3 are also missing in the αVβ3 structure; I-EGF domains 2 and 3 from β2 (4) were added by superimposition on β3 EGF-3. Cα atoms of functionally important residues in β2 I-EGF2 and 3 are shown as large *spheres*: *red*, the epitope of the activating and activation-dependent KIM127 mAb; *green*, the epitope of the activating MEM48 and CBR LFA-1/2 mAbs (57); and *yellow*, residues critical for association of αX and β2 subunits (103).

Since the closed conformation is favored energetically in isolated I domains and appears to be the default conformation adopted in the basal, inactive state of integrins on the cell surface, conversion to the open conformation would require an external input of energy. This would have to come from movements at interdomain contacts. The most likely type of motion is a downward movement of the C-terminal α-helix, which could be induced by exertion of a bell-rope-like pull on a segment within the C-terminal linker region.

The integrin α-subunit β-propeller and I domains are in close proximity to the β-subunit I-like domain. In the crystal structure of integrin $\alpha V \beta 3$ (99), the MIDAS of the β-subunit I-like domain is positioned close to the loop in the β-propeller in which the I domain is inserted (*asterisk* in Figure 11, see color insert). It is possible that the open and closed conformations of the I domain are regulated by interaction of the C-terminal linker with the β-propeller and/or the I-like domain at this site. Because this site is equivalent to the ligand-binding site in integrins that lack I domains, alterations in the interaction of the linker with the MIDAS of the I-like domain may occur that are analogous to those that regulate interactions with ligands in integrins that lack I domains. In summary, we predict that three structural units, the I, β-propeller, and I-like domains, make a ternary interaction interface where structural rearrangements of the latter two domains affect the conformation of the I domain.

The Bottom of the I Domain and the C-Terminal Linker

Consistent with a role for domain-domain interactions in regulating I domain conformation, mutation of exposed residues near the bottom of the I domain and in the linker region can regulate ligand binding. In one study, 17 sequence segments distributed over all faces of the human αM I domain were swapped with corresponding mouse segments (68). Of these, only three substitutions, all located on the bottom face, increased binding to ligand and expression of the CBRM1/5 activation epitope. In another investigation (104), two segments at the bottom of the αM I domain were swapped with corresponding segments of the αL I domain; each swap activated ligand binding. Interestingly, similar substitutions at the bottom of the von Willebrand factor A1 domain, which is highly homologous to integrin I domains, have been found to activate ligand binding and result in spontaneous binding of von Willebrand factor to platelets (24). Such mutations were identified because they are responsible for the abnormal platelet aggregation and thrombocytopenia in patients with type 2B von Willebrand disease. Conformational movements analogous to those in integrin I domains may regulate ligand binding in von Willebrand factor A domains; however, thus far only small movements have been detected in crystal studies of a type 2B A domain mutant (13).

Mutational and antibody epitope studies suggest a role for the C-terminal linker region in regulating ligand binding by the I domain and in conformational movements. The last α-helical residue defined in I domain structures is equivalent to Tyr-307 in αL; Ser-327 approximates the beginning of the β-propeller domain, leaving a linker from residues 308–326. Some mutations in this linker sequence, K314A and L317A, activate ligand binding by $\alpha L\beta 2$, while other mutations at the linker, Y307A and E310A, inactivate $\alpha L\beta 2$ (37). This suggests that contacts between the linker and other domains modulate the conformation of the I domain. This supports the idea that signals could be propagated via the C-terminal linker sequence to the C-terminal α-helix, and then to the MIDAS. In further support of conformational movement of the linker region, CBR LFA-1/1, a conformation-sensitive αL mAb (61a) maps to residues 301 to 338, which includes all of the linker and the last two turns of the C-terminal α-helix (32, 59).

Regulation by the I-Like Domain

Recent evidence shows that the I-like domain regulates the conformation of the I domain. Previously, it was thought that in I domain–containing integrins, the I-like domain made a direct contribution to ligand binding because mutations in the MIDAS of the I-like domain, and mAb directed to the I-like domain, inhibited ligand binding. However, when locked in the open conformation the isolated αL I domain is sufficient to give a monomeric binding affinity equivalent to that of activated $\alpha L\beta 2$ and it also gives equivalent adhesiveness when present on the cell surface. Remarkably, ligand binding by $\alpha L\beta 2$ containing an I domain locked open with a disulfide was resistant to many mAb that fully inhibited ligand binding by activated wild-type $\alpha L\beta 2$ and that bound equally well to locked-open and wild-type $\alpha L\beta 2$ (60). There were two classes of mAb specific for the I domain: those that inhibited wild-type and locked-open $\alpha L\beta 2$ equally well and those that inhibited wild-type but had no effect on locked-open $\alpha L\beta 2$. The former mAb appear to directly block the ligand-binding site; the latter mAb cannot block the ligand-binding site and therefore appear to favor the closed conformation of the I domain. Most importantly, all mAbs to the I-like domain inhibited ligand binding by wild-type but had no effect on locked-open $\alpha L\beta 2$. These mAb had been mapped to multiple epitopes located in three widely separated sites on the molecular surface of the I-like domain. Furthermore, disulfide reduction with dithiothreitol restored the susceptibility of the disulfide-locked receptor to the inhibitory mAbs, showing that the mutant receptors override the blocking effect of mAbs because their conformation is fixed. This clearly demonstrates that the anti-$\beta 2$ I-like domain mAbs exert their effect in an allosteric manner rather than by directly competing with the ligand. Thus, in $\beta 2$ integrins, the I-like domain does not directly participate in ligand binding and appears to affect ligand binding indirectly by regulating the conformation of the I domain (60). Allosteric inhibition of ligand binding by other β-subunit mAbs has also been reported (64).

Regulation by Ca^{2+} and Mn^{2+}/Mg^{2+}

Observations on the effect of Ca^{2+} and Mn^{2+} ions on ligand binding by I domain–containing integrins also favor a regulatory rather than a direct role for the β-subunit I-like domain. High concentrations of Ca^{2+} are known to be inhibitory against many I domain–containing integrins. As described above, the Ser and

Thr side chains in the MIDAS strongly disfavor Ca^{2+} coordination. Furthermore, in contrast to results with intact $\alpha2\beta1$ and $\alpha L\beta2$, binding of isolated $\alpha2$ (68) and αL (M. Shimaoka & T. A. Springer, unpublished data) I domains to their ligands is not inhibited by mM concentrations of Ca^{2+}. Moreover, Mn^{2+}, a well-known strong activator of integrins, does not appear to activate by binding to the I domain's MIDAS because (*a*) Mn^{2+}-loaded αM and αL I domains crystallize in the closed conformation (47, 74); (*b*) the wild-type isolated I domain shows equivalent adhesiveness in Mg^{2+} and Mn^{2+} (43); and (*c*) the locked-open αL I domain shows identical affinities and adhesiveness to ICAM-1 in Mg^{2+} and Mn^{2+} (M. Shimaoka & T. A. Springer, unpublished data).

The I-like domain is the best candidate for mediating the effects of Mn^{2+} and Ca^{2+}. A recently described Ca^{2+}-binding site in the I-like domain of the $\alpha V\beta3$ structure is adjacent to the MIDAS of the I-like domain and thus has been termed the ADMIDAS (99) (Figure 11). The ADMIDAS and the MIDAS of the I-like domain are likely to be the inhibitory Ca^{2+}- and stimulatory Mn^{2+}-binding sites, respectively. The existence of the conserved MIDAS sequence in the β-subunit's I-like domain, and the requirement of the MIDAS residues for ligand binding by both integrins that contain and lack I domains (88), have been the major basis for the proposed direct involvement of the β-subunit in ligand binding by integrins containing I domains. Based on the evidence that the I-like domain plays a regulatory rather than a direct role in ligand binding by I domain–containing integrins, we propose an alternative model. We propose that in the active conformation of the I-like domain, it binds to a ligand-like segment in the α-subunit, most likely in the I domain linker, and thereby exerts the downward pull on the bell-rope that remotely opens the conformation of the ligand-binding site of the I domain.

Signal Transmission Through the Stalk Region

We have discussed interactions among the three domains in the headpiece, the β-propeller domain, I domain, and I-like domain, that regulate ligand binding by the I domain. We now discuss how signals are relayed from the membrane through the stalk regions to the headpiece. The first step in inside-out signaling appears to be the disruption of interactions between the juxtamembrane regions of the α- and β-subunits, which leads to the separation or movement apart of the juxtamembrane regions. Early studies suggested complementary interactions between the αIIb and $\beta3$ subunits near the junction between the transmembrane and cytoplasmic domains (35). Mutations near the junction between the transmembrane and cytoplasmic domains, as well as deletion of the cytoplasmic domains, have been repeatedly shown to result in integrin activation. Recently, Lu et al. found that replacement of the cytoplasmic tails of the αL and $\beta2$ subunits with complementary α-helices that formed a heterodimeric α-helical coiled-coil kept the receptor in a low-affinity state (61). By contrast, replacement with noncomplementary α-helices resulted in constitutive activation of $\alpha L\beta2$. Similarly, movement apart at the C-terminal region of the extracellular domain was shown to activate a soluble version of the integrin $\alpha5\beta1$. The low-affinity receptor was converted into a fully active one by a pure conformational manipulation that released a covalent constraint introduced at the C-terminal end of the stalks (92). These findings suggest that conformational movements in the ligand-binding headpiece are induced by movement apart of the cytoplasmic and transmembrane domains. In physiologic settings, this would be initiated by signals from inside the cell.

Much experimental evidence suggests that in integrin activation, major structural rearrangements occur in the stalk regions of the α- and β-subunits, particularly in the β-subunit, and that separation of the α and β stalks occurs. Many mAbs that recognize "activation epitopes," which become exposed upon receptor activation, map to the stalk regions, particularly to the PSI domain (65) and I-EGF domains 2–4 of the β-subunit (3, 20, 57, 78, 86, 93, 102). Also, a subset of anti-stalk antibodies activate integrins upon binding, probably by acting as a "wedge" to break domain-domain contacts and open up the stalk region (34). Furthermore, amino acid residues have been identified that participate in restraining the integrin $\alpha X \beta 2$ in its resting conformation. Species-specific differences at these residues cause activation when the α- and β-subunits are derived from different species. These residues are present in the PSI and I-EGF domains 2 and 3 of the β-subunit, suggesting that these domains contact the α-subunit in the resting but not active conformation (103).

A Switchblade-Like Model for Integrin Activation

Recently, we proposed a model for integrin activation that is based on both functional and structural data (4). The crystal structure of integrin $\alpha V \beta 3$ reveals four α-subunit domains and five β-subunit domains, but it lacks the PSI domain, I-EGF domains 1 and 2, and 27% of I-EGF domain 3 (99). Complementary NMR data reveal the structure of integrin $\beta 2$ I-EGF module 3; together with perturbation data, it is demonstrated that the I-EGF domain 2 + 3 module pair has a rigid and extended structure (4). The combined data on I-EGF modules 2 + 3 + 4 demonstrate a single continuous structural unit with rigid module-module interfaces that is suitable for conveying structural motion from the membrane to the headpiece.

The $\alpha V \beta 3$ extracellular domain structure has an overall V-shaped organization, in which the ligand-binding headpiece bends back toward the base of the stalk region and is oriented toward the cell membrane (99) (Figure 11A). Although reported to represent the active conformation, this genuflected conformation appears unfavorable for ligand binding. $\alpha V \beta 3$ was crystallized with Ca^{2+} and no Mg^{2+} (99). Ca^{2+} is known to stabilize integrins in the inactive conformation, and this has been directly demonstrated for soluble $\alpha V \beta 3$; ligand binding requires Mg^{2+} or Mn^{2+} (81). Furthermore, at the juxtamembrane region, the C termini of the αV and $\beta 3$ extracellular domains are close together (99); close association of the juxtamembrane regions maintains integrins in the inactive state (61, 91). Moreover, $\alpha V \beta 3$ was crystallized in the absence of ligand; in crystal structures of integrin I domains, the active conformation has only been seen in the presence of a ligand or ligand mimetic (26, 48). Finally, electron microscopy of integrins shows that they adopt an extended, open conformation when bound to ligand that permits binding of mAb to activation epitopes in the β-subunit stalk (20).

Superposition of $\beta2$ I-EGF modules 2 and 3 on the partial I-EGF module 3 in $\alpha V\beta3$ allows the orientation of functionally important residues to be visualized and provides strong support for the idea that the bent conformation represents the inactive conformation. The residues in $\beta2$ I-EGF3, which are in an $\alpha\beta$ interface that restrains integrins in the inactive state (103), are on the face pointing toward calf domain 1 of the α-subunit stalk (*yellow spheres*, Figure 11). The residues participating in the KIM127 activation epitope in $\beta2$ I-EGF2 (*red spheres*) and in the CBR LFA-1/2 and MEM48 activation epitopes in I-EGF3 (*green spheres*) are masked in the bent conformation (Figure 11A). However, in the extended, unbent conformation, there is no domain that could mask these epitopes (Figure 11B). The transition from the bent (Figure 11A) to the extended conformation (Figure 11B) provides a mechanism for unmasking of these activation epitopes. Furthermore, the β-subunit bends back on itself much more than the α-subunit, providing an explanation for the observation that the vast majority of activation epitopes are present on the β-subunit.

Therefore, we have proposed that activation triggers a switchblade-like opening motion that extends the ligand-binding headpiece of the integrin heterodimer away from the plasma membrane (Figure 11) (4). In integrin activation by biological inside-out signaling, movement apart of the juxtamembrane domains (61, 91) may lead to dislocation of the I-EGF3 contact with calf domain 1, which in turn triggers the switchblade-like opening. This drastic change in the overall orientation and interaction between domains would not only reposition the headpiece in a more favorable orientation for ligand binding, but is also hypothesized to be linked to change in conformation of the I-like domain and in turn the conformation of the I domain. The work on isolated I domains described above suggests that repositioning of the headpiece, in the absence of shape-shifting in the I domain, is insufficient to activate ligand binding. Because bending will mask many antibody epitopes in the stalk region, particularly on the β-subunit stalk, which is severely jackknifed at the bend (99) (Figure 11), binding of antibodies to these epitopes would favor the extended integrin conformation, producing a mechanism for antibody-induced integrin activation.

THE RELATIVE IMPORTANCE OF CONFORMATIONAL CHANGE AND CLUSTERING IN INSIDE-OUT AND OUTSIDE-IN SIGNALING

Inside-Out Signaling: Affinity or Avidity?

We have focused on regulation of an integrin's ligand-binding activity by conformational shape-shifting within a single receptor molecule. However, many reports suggest that upregulation of integrin-mediated adhesion by activated cells is achieved by receptor clustering on the cell surface (i.e., avidity augmentation) rather than by, or together with, an increase in affinity of individual receptors (2, 27, 55, 87, 94). Clustering of receptors on the cell surface would no doubt increase overall cell-adhesive efficiency, particularly when the ligands are di- or multivalent and have a similar clustered distribution on the opposing cell or substrate. However, experimental evidence for the formation of integrin clusters on activated cells is rather qualitative and in most cases is demonstrated experimentally by either a large dot-like or polarized staining pattern after cell fixation. Furthermore, it is difficult to know whether clustering triggers ligand binding or is a result of ligand binding that is triggered by an increase in receptor affinity. Receptors on cells, including integrins, are known to redistribute to sites on cells where they can bind ligand as a consequence of their capture in ligand-receptor complexes. Moreover, real-time imaging has shown that the formation of visible clusters in adhering cells occurs long after the first contacts are made (46, 70), whereas the ligand-binding activity of integrins on circulating cells such as leukocytes and platelets must be upregulated in a matter of seconds in vivo.

Intermediate Affinity States?

The dismissal of affinity alteration as the mechanism of increased cell adhesion often is based on the inability to detect increased binding of soluble ligands to cells that clearly exhibit increased adhesiveness (2). Thus, avidity regulation is adopted as the alternative explanation for increased cellular adhesiveness, not because it has been directly demonstrated, but because there is a lack of evidence for affinity regulation. In some cases, certain stimuli that cause increased cellular adhesiveness do result in a measurable increase in soluble ligand binding (affinity regulation is inferred), and other stimuli that also cause increased cell adhesiveness do not augment soluble ligand binding (avidity regulation is inferred) (14, 27, 87). The observation that the affinity of the αL I domain for ligand can range all the way from a K_D of 200 nM for the locked-open I domain to 2 mM for the wild-type or locked-closed I domain suggests that the lack of binding of soluble ligand should be interpreted with great caution (79).

It is reasonable to propose that in integrin heterodimers on the cell surface, I domains could exist not just in two affinity states with K_D of 200 nM (open) and K_D of 2 mM (closed), but also in many intermediate states. This could result from equilibration between two states, with the affinity representing the time-averaged population of the two states, from the existence of true conformational intermediates along the shape-shifting pathway, or from differences in the kinetics of I domain opening. Activation of αLβ2 on the cell surface to an intermediate affinity with a K_D of 20 μM for ICAM-1 would not be detectable by ligand binding to cells because the K_D of 200 nM of the locked open I domain is just barely within the range detectable by conventional assays for ligand binding to cells. However, a K_D of 20 μM should be sufficient to activate cell adhesion, based on measurements with other cell-adhesion molecules (21). Thus, conformational alterations in integrins resulting in an intermediate affinity for ligand could be the initial event in inside-out activation, which would allow cells to surmount the threshold from a nonadhesive to an adhesive phenotype. After cells make the initial contact to the ligand-bearing surface, clustering of integrins may further stabilize the adhesion machinery.

Outside-In Signaling

A similar argument is applicable to the debate over the possible involvement of conformational alterations in outside-in signaling. Because of the multivalent nature of the physiological ligands of integrins, ligation will result in the clustering of integrins on the cell surface, the enabling recruitment of signaling molecules to the cytoplasmic face of the adhesion complex, and initiating downstream signaling events. Therefore, it is generally accepted that it is the clustering of receptors that drives outside-in signal transduction (28). However, as discussed above, gross structural changes in the heterodimer including a swichblade-like opening appear to be linked to other more subtle changes, including the conformation of the I domain. The open conformation of the I domain has not yet been visualized in the absence of, and thus may be stabilized by, bound ligand. In other words, binding to ligand could stabilize not only the conformational shift of the I domain, but also the gross structural rearrangements in the whole receptor molecule. Activation of the receptor, and ligand binding, may reinforce one another in stabilizing a fully open conformation, consistent with the appearance of the antibody epitopes known as ligand-induced binding sites. Thus, ligand binding may stabilize or induce changes in the integrin transmembrane and cytoplasmic domains that mediate outside-in signaling. It is possible that overall outside-in signal transduction is achieved as a sum of intermolecular clustering and intramolecular conformational modulation. In fact, induction of integrin clustering alone is insufficient to reproduce full outside-in signaling events (30).

CODA

In summary, structures have been determined and models built for integrin I domains in two different conformations, open and closed. Mutational and functional studies demonstrate that the open conformation binds ligand with high affinity, and the closed conformation either does not bind ligand or binds with low affinity. In physiologic activation of integrins on the cell surface, studies with antibodies demonstrate that conformational change precedes ligand binding. However, it is not known whether these changes correspond precisely to transition from the closed to open conformation, or transition to an intermediate conformation, since thus far the open conformation has been visualized only in the presence of a ligand or ligand mimetic. The structural changes in I domains are similar to those in small G proteins, particularly around the metal-binding site; however, metal-binding site rearrangement is linked to large motions in different backbone segments.

In I domains, the linkage to the C-terminal α-helix segment provides a mechanism for propagating conformational change from one domain to another. Locking in alternative conformations of the loop preceding this C-terminal α-helix demonstrates that conformational movement here is linked to a dramatic 9000-fold increase in affinity of the ligand-binding site around the MIDAS. The C-terminal linker of the I domain is located in an interface between the β-propeller and I-like domains that constitutes the ligand-binding site in integrins that lack I domains.

Interactions at this site of the linker in integrins that contain I domains may mimic interactions of ligands with the I-like domain MIDAS in integrins that lack I domains, and these interactions may provide a mechanism for transmitting conformational motion to the I domain.

Structural information on $\alpha V \beta 3$ and the $\beta 2$ I-EGF3 domain reveals the location of sites that are functionally important in integrin activation and suggests a model for activation. In the inactive conformation, the headpiece faces the membrane. In activation, the headpiece extends upward in a switchblade-like motion. Interfaces between I-EGF modules 2 and 3 and the headpiece are broken, and activation epitopes hidden by the bend are exposed. These long-range rearrangements of the global interdomain architecture are coupled to conformational changes within the ligand-binding site that increase affinity for ligand. Movement apart of the juxtamembrane segments of the α- and β-subunits, which is set in motion by intracellular signaling cascades, appears to initiate the rearrangements in the extracellular domain.

Exactly how integrin heterodimers achieve signal transduction in both directions, to what extent conformational change within receptor molecules is responsible for these events, and the details of signal transmission between domains within these complex molecular machines await further biochemical, structural, and cell biological studies. The complexities of these molecules are appropriate to the sophisticated and diverse functions they mediate in connecting the intracellular and extracellular environments. Much more remains to be learned about how these molecules function in general, as well as how different integrin heterodimers are specialized for diverse tasks. There is no doubt that the understanding of these events at the molecular level will reveal exciting biological and structural principles and will also greatly advance our ability to devise therapeutics to control the pathophysiologies mediated by this important family of cell-adhesion molecules.

ACKNOWLEDGMENTS

Work in the authors' laboratories was supported by NIH grants CA317988, CA31799, and HL48675. We thank S. Blacklow and N. Beglova for permission to use data prior to acceptance for publication, and S. Blacklow for a critical review.

Visit the Annual Reviews home page at www.annualreviews.org

LITERATURE CITED

1. Baldwin ET, Sarver RW, Bryant GL Jr, Curry KA, Fairbanks MB, et al. 1998. Cation binding to the integrin CD11b I domain and activation model assessment. *Structure* 6:923–35

2. Bazzoni G, Hemler ME. 1998. Are changes in integrin affinity and conformation overemphasized? *Trends Biochem. Sci.* 23:30–34

3. Bazzoni G, Shih D-T, Buck CA, Hemler

MA. 1995. Monoclonal antibody 9EG7 defines a novel β_1 integrin epitope induced by soluble ligand and manganese, but inhibited by calcium. *J. Biol. Chem.* 270:25570–77

4. Beglova N, Blacklow SC, Takagi J, Springer TA. 2002. Cysteine-rich structure reveals a fulcrum for integrin rearrangement upon activation. *Nat. Struct. Biol.* In press

5. Bella J, Kolatkar PR, Marlor C, Greve JM, Rossmann MG. 1998. The structure of the two amino-terminal domains of human ICAM-1 suggests how it functions as a rhinovirus receptor and as an LFA-1 integrin ligand. *Proc. Natl. Acad. Sci. USA* 95:4140–45

6. Bennett JS, Vilaire G. 1979. Exposure of platelet fibrinogen receptors by ADP and epinephrine. *J. Clin. Invest.* 64:1393–401

7. Bilsland CAG, Springer TA. 1994. Cloning and expression of the chicken CD18 cDNA. *J. Leukoc. Biol.* 55:501–6

8. Bork P, Doerks T, Springer TA, Snel B. 1999. Domains in plexins: links to integrins and transcription factors. *Trends Biochem. Sci.* 24:261–63

9. Bouvard D, Brakebusch C, Gustafsson E, Aszodi A, Bengtsson T, et al. 2001. Functional consequences of integrin gene mutations in mice. *Circ. Res.* 89:211–23

10. Calvete JJ, Henschen A, González-Rodríguez J. 1991. Assignment of disulphide bonds in human platelet GPIIIa. A disulphide pattern for the β-subunits of the integrin family. *Biochem. J.* 274:63–71

11. Carson M. 1997. Ribbons. *Methods Enzymol.* 277:493–505

12. Casasnovas JM, Stehle T, Liu J-h, Wang J-h, Springer TA. 1998. A dimeric crystal structure for the N-terminal two domains of ICAM-1. *Proc. Natl. Acad. Sci. USA* 95:4134–39

13. Celikel R, Ruggeri ZM, Varughese KI. 2000. von Willebrand factor conformation and adhesive function is modulated by an internalized water molecule. *Nat. Struct. Biol.* 7:881–84

14. Constantin G, Majeed M, Giagulli C, Piccib L, Kim JY, et al. 2000. Chemokines trigger immediate $\beta2$ integrin affinity and mobility changes: differential regulation and roles in lymphocyte arrest under flow. *Immunity* 13:759–69

15. Dahiyat BI, Mayo SL. 1997. De Novo protein design: fully automated sequence selection. *Science* 278:82–87

16. de Pereda JM, Wiche G, Liddington RC. 1999. Crystal structure of a tandem pair of fibronectin type III domains from the cytoplasmic tail of integrin $\alpha6\beta4$. *EMBO J.* 18:4087–95

17. Diamond MS, Garcia-Aguilar J, Bickford JK, Corbi AL, Springer TA. 1993. The I domain is a major recognition site on the leukocyte integrin Mac-1 (CD11b/CD18) for four distinct adhesion ligands. *J. Cell Biol.* 120:1031–43

18. Diamond MS, Springer TA. 1993. A subpopulation of Mac-1 (CD11b/CD18) molecules mediates neutrophil adhesion to ICAM-1 and fibrinogen. *J. Cell Biol.* 120:545–56

19. Diamond MS, Springer TA. 1994. The dynamic regulation of integrin adhesiveness. *Curr. Biol.* 4:506–17

20. Du X, Gu M, Weisel JW, Nagaswami C, Bennett JS, et al. 1993. Long range propagation of conformational changes in integrin $\alpha_{IIb}\beta_3$. *J. Biol. Chem.* 268:23087–92

21. Dustin ML, Golan DE, Zhu DM, Miller JM, Meier W, et al. 1997. Low affinity interaction of human or rat T cell adhesion molecule CD2 with its ligand aligns adhering membranes to achieve high physiological affinity. *J. Biol. Chem.* 272:30889–98

22. Dustin ML, Springer TA. 1989. T cell receptor cross-linking transiently stimulates adhesiveness through LFA-1. *Nature* 341:619–24

23. Edwards CP, Fisher KL, Presta LG, Bodary SC. 1998. Mapping the intercellular adhesion molecule-1 and -2 binding site on the inserted domain of leukocyte

function-associated antigen-1. *J. Biol. Chem.* 273:28937–44

24. Emsley J, Cruz M, Handin R, Liddington R. 1998. Crystal structure of the von Willebrand factor A1 domain and implications for the binding of platelet glycoprotein Ib. *J. Biol. Chem.* 273:10396–401

25. Emsley J, King SL, Bergelson JM, Liddington RC. 1997. Crystal structure of the I domain from integrin $\alpha 2\beta 1$. *J. Biol. Chem.* 272:28512–17

26. Emsley J, Knight CG, Farndale RW, Barnes MJ, Liddington RC. 2000. Structural basis of collagen recognition by integrin $\alpha 2\beta 1$. *Cell* 101:47–56

27. Faull RJ, Kovach NL, Harlan HM, Ginsberg MH. 1994. Stimulation of integrin-mediated adhesion of T lymphocytes and monocytes: two mechanisms with divergent biological consequences. *J. Exp. Med.* 179:1307–16

28. Giancotti FG, Ruoslahti E. 1999. Integrin signaling. *Science* 285:1028–32

29. Gottlieb A, Krueger JG, Bright R, Ling M, Lebwohl M, et al. 2000. Effects of administration of a single dose of a humanized monoclonal antibody to CD11a on the immunobiology and clinical activity of psoriasis. *J. Am. Acad. Dermatol.* 42:428–35

30. Hato T, Pampori N, Shattil SJ. 1998. Complementary roles for receptor clustering and conformational change in the adhesive and signaling functions of integrin $\alpha_{IIb}\beta 3$. *J. Cell Biol.* 141:1685–95

31. Huang C, Lu C, Springer TA. 1997. Folding of the conserved domain but not of flanking regions in the integrin β_2 subunit requires association with the α subunit. *Proc. Natl. Acad. Sci. USA* 94:3156–61

32. Huang C, Springer TA. 1995. A binding interface on the I domain of lymphocyte function associated antigen-1 (LFA-1) required for specific interaction with intercellular adhesion molecule 1 (ICAM-1). *J. Biol. Chem.* 270:19008–16

33. Huang C, Springer TA. 1997. Folding of the β-propeller domain of the integrin α_L subunit is independent of the I domain and

dependent on the β_2 subunit. *Proc. Natl. Acad. Sci. USA* 94:3162–67

34. Huang C, Zang Q, Takagi J, Springer TA. 2000. Structural and functional studies with antibodies to the integrin $\beta 2$ subunit: a model for the I-like domain. *J. Biol. Chem.* 275:21514–24

35. Hughes PE, Diaz-Gonzalez F, Leong L, Wu C, McDonald JA, et al. 1996. Breaking the integrin hinge. *J. Biol. Chem.* 271:6571–74

36. Humphries MJ. 2000. Integrin structure. *Biochem. Soc. Trans.* 28:311–39

37. Huth JR, Olejniczak ET, Mendoza R, Liang H, Harris EA, et al. 2000. NMR and mutagenesis evidence for an I domain allosteric site that regulates lymphocyte function-associated antigen 1 ligand binding. *Proc. Natl. Acad. Sci. USA* 97:5231–36

38. Hynes RO. 1992. Integrins: versatility, modulation, and signaling in cell adhesion. *Cell* 69:11–25

39. Kallen J, Welzenbach K, Ramage P, Geyl D, Kriwacki R, et al. 1999. Structural basis for LFA-1 inhibition upon lovastatin binding to the CD11a I-domain. *J. Mol. Biol.* 292:1–9

40. Kamata T, Tieu KK, Springer TA, Takada Y. 2001. Amino acid residues in the αIIb subunit that are critical for ligand binding to integrin $\alpha IIb\beta 3$ are clustered in the β-propeller model. *J. Biol. Chem.* 276:44274–83

41. Kamata T, Wright R, Takada Y. 1995. Critical threonine and aspartic acid residues within the I domains of $\beta 2$ integrins for interactions with intercellular adhesion molecule 1 (ICAM-1) and C3bi. *J. Biol. Chem.* 270:12531–35

42. Kelly TA, Jeanfavre DD, McNeil DW, Woska JR Jr, Reilly PL, et al. 1999. Cutting edge: a small molecule antagonist of LFA-1-mediated cell adhesion. *J. Immunol.* 163:5173–77

43. Knorr R, Dustin ML. 1997. The lymphocyte function-associated antigen 1 I domain is a transient binding module for

intercellular adhesion molecule (ICAM)-1 and ICAM-1 in hydrodynamic flow. *J. Exp. Med.* 186:719–30

44. Labadia ME, Jeanfavre DD, Caviness GO, Morelock MM. 1998. Molecular regulation of the interaction between leukocyte function-associated antigen-1 and soluble ICAM-1 by divalent metal cations. *J. Immunol.* 161:836–42

45. Last-Barney K, Davidson W, Cardozo M, Frye LL, Grygon CA, et al. 2001. Binding site elucidation of hydantoin-based antagonists of LFA-1 using multidisciplinary technologies: evidence for the allosteric inhibition of a protein-protein interaction. *J. Am. Chem. Soc.* 123:5643–50

46. Laukaitis CM, Webb DJ, Donais K, Horwitz AF. 2001. Differential dynamics of $\alpha 5$ integrin, paxillin, and α-actinin during formation and disassembly of adhesions in migrating cells. *J. Cell Biol.* 153:1427–40

47. Lee J-O, Bankston LA, Arnaout MA, Liddington RC. 1995. Two conformations of the integrin A-domain (I-domain): a pathway for activation? *Structure* 3:1333–40

48. Lee J-O, Rieu P, Arnaout MA, Liddington R. 1995. Crystal structure of the A domain from the α subunit of integrin CR3 (CD11b/CD18). *Cell* 80:631–38

49. Legge GB, Kriwacki RW, Chung J, Hommel U, Ramage P, et al. 2000. NMR solution structure of the inserted domain of human leukocyte function associated antigen-1. *J. Mol. Biol.* 295:1251–64

50. Leitinger B, Hogg N. 2000. Effects of I domain deletion on the function of the $\beta 2$ integrin lymphocyte function-associated antigen-1. *Mol. Biol. Cell* 11:677–90

51. Li R, Rieu P, Griffith DL, Scott D, Arnaout MA. 1998. Two functional states of the CD11b A-domain: correlations with key features of two Mn^{2+}-complexed crystal structures. *J. Cell Biol.* 143:1523–34

52. Liddington R, Bankston L. 1998. The integrin I domain: crystals, metals and related artefacts. *Structure* 6:937–38

53. Liu G, Huth JR, Olejniczak ET, Men-doza R, DeVries P, et al. 2001. Novel p-arylthio cinnamides as antagonists of leukocyte function-associated antigen-1/intracellular adhesion molecule-1 interaction. II. Mechanism of inhibition and structure-based improvement of pharmaceutical properties. *J. Med. Chem.* 44:1202–10

54. Liu G, Link JT, Pei Z, Reilly EB, Leitza S, et al. 2000. Discovery of novel p-arylthio cinnamides as antagonists of leukocyte function-associated antigen-1/intracellular adhesion molecule-1 interaction. I. Identification of an additional binding pocket based on an anilino diaryl sulfide lead. *J. Med. Chem.* 43:4025–40

55. Loftus JC, Smith JW, Ginsberg MH. 1994. Integrin mediated cell adhesion: the extracellular face. *J. Biol. Chem.* 269:25235–38

56. Lollo BA, Chan KWH, Hanson EM, Moy VT, Brian AA. 1993. Direct evidence for two affinity states for lymphocyte function-associated antigen 1 on activated T cells. *J. Biol. Chem.* 268:21693–700

57. Lu C, Ferzly M, Takagi J, Springer TA. 2001. Epitope mapping of antibodies to the C-terminal region of the integrin $\beta 2$ subunit reveals regions that become exposed upon receptor activation. *J. Immunol.* 166:5629–37

58. Lu C, Oxvig C, Springer TA. 1998. The structure of the β-propeller domain and C-terminal region of the integrin αM subunit. *J. Biol. Chem.* 273:15138–47

59. Lu C, Shimaoka M, Ferzly M, Oxvig C, Takagi J, Springer TA. 2001. An isolated, surface-expressed I domain of the integrin $\alpha L\beta 2$ is sufficient for strong adhesive function when locked in the open conformation with a disulfide. *Proc. Natl. Acad. Sci. USA* 98:2387–92

60. Lu C, Shimaoka M, Zang Q, Takagi J, Springer TA. 2001. Locking in alternate conformations of the integrin $\alpha L\beta 2$ I domain with disulfide bonds reveals functional relationships among integrin domains. *Proc. Natl. Acad. Sci. USA* 98:2393–98

61. Lu C, Takagi J, Springer TA. 2001. Association of the membrane-proximal regions of the α and β subunit cytoplasmic domains constrains an integrin in the inactive state. *J. Biol. Chem.* 276:14642–48

61a. Ma Q, Shimaoka M, Lu C, Jing H, Carman CV, Springer TA. 2002. Activation induced conformational changes in the I domain region of LFA-1. *J. Biol. Chem.* In press

62. Michishita M, Videm V, Arnaout MA. 1993. A novel divalent cation-binding site in the A domain of the $\beta 2$ integrin CR3 (CD11b/CD18) is essential for ligand binding. *Cell* 72:857–67

63. Milburn MV, Tong L, DeVos AM, Brunger A, Yamaizumi Z, et al. 1990. Molecular switch for signal transduction: structural differences between active and inactive forms of protooncogenic *ras* proteins. *Science* 247:939–45

64. Mould AP. 1996. Getting integrins into shape: recent insights into how integrin activity is regulated by conformational changes. *J. Cell. Sci.* 109:2613–18

65. Ni H, Li A, Simonsen N, Wilkins JA. 1998. Integrin activation by dithiothreitol or Mn^{2+} induces a ligand-occupied conformation and exposure of a novel NH_2-terminal regulatory site on the β_1 integrin chain. *J. Biol. Chem.* 273:7981–87

66. Nolte M, Pepinsky RB, Venyaminov SY, Koteliansky V, Gotwals PJ, Karpusas M. 1999. Crystal structure of the $\alpha 1 \beta 1$ integrin I-domain: insights into integrin I-domain function. *FEBS Lett.* 452:379–85

67. Onley DJ, Knight CG, Tuckwell DS, Barnes MJ, Farndale RW. 2000. Micromolar Ca^{2+} concentrations are essential for Mg^{2+}-dependent binding of collagen by the integrin $\alpha 2 \beta 1$ in human platelets. *J. Biol. Chem.* 275:24560–64

68. Oxvig C, Lu C, Springer TA. 1999. Conformational changes in tertiary structure near the ligand binding site of an integrin I domain. *Proc. Natl. Acad. Sci. USA* 96:2215–20

69. Oxvig C, Springer TA. 1998. Experimental support for a β-propeller domain in integrin α-subunits and a calcium binding site on its lower surface. *Proc. Natl. Acad. Sci. USA* 95:4870–75

70. Plancon S, Morel-Kopp MC, Schaffner-Reckinger E, Chen P, Kieffer N. 2001. Green fluorescent protein (GFP) tagged to the cytoplasmic tail of αIIb or $\beta 3$ allows the expression of a fully functional integrin αIIb$\beta 3$: effect of $\beta 3$GFP on αIIb$\beta 3$ ligand binding. *Biochem. J.* 357:529–36

71. Ponting CP, Schultz J, Copley RR, Andrade MA, Bork P. 2000. Evolution of domain families. *Adv. Protein Chem.* 54:185–244

72. Puzon-McLaughlin W, Kamata T, Takada Y. 2000. Multiple discontinuous ligandmimetic antibody binding sites define a ligand binding pocket in integrin αIIb$\beta 3$. *J. Biol. Chem.* 275:7795–802

73. Qu A, Leahy DJ. 1995. Crystal structure of the I-domain from the CD11a/CD18 (LFA-1, $\alpha_L \beta 2$) integrin. *Proc. Natl. Acad. Sci. USA* 92:10277–81

74. Qu A, Leahy DJ. 1996. The role of the divalent cation in the structure of the I domain from the CD11a/CD18 integrin. *Structure* 4:931–42

75. Randi AM, Hogg N. 1994. I domain of β_2 integrin lymphocyte function-associated antigen-1 contains a binding site for ligand intercellular adhesion molecule-1. *J. Biol. Chem.* 269:12395–98

76. Rich RL, Deivanayagam CC, Owens RT, Carson M, Hook A, et al. 1999. Trench-shaped binding sites promote multiple classes of interactions between collagen and the adherence receptors, $\alpha 1 \beta 1$ integrin and *Staphylococcus aureus* Cna MSCRAMM. *J. Biol. Chem.* 274:24906–13

77. Sali A, Blundell TL. 1993. Comparative protein modelling by satisfaction of spatial restraints. *J. Mol. Biol.* 234:779–815

78. Shih DT, Edelman JM, Horwitz AF, Grunwald GB, Buck CA. 1993. Structure/function analysis of the integrin $\beta 1$

subunit by epitope mapping. *J. Cell Biol.* 122:1361–71

79. Shimaoka M, Lu C, Palframan R, von Andrian UH, Takagi J, Springer TA. 2001. Reversibly locking a protein fold in an active conformation with a disulfide bond: integrin αL I domains with high affinity and antagonist activity in vivo. *Proc. Natl. Acad. Sci. USA* 98:6009–14

80. Shimaoka M, Shifman JM, Jing H, Takagi J, Mayo SL, Springer TA. 2000. Computational design of an integrin I domain stabilized in the open, high affinity conformation. *Nat. Struct. Biol.* 7:674–78

81. Smith JW, Piotrowicz RS, Mathis D. 1994. A mechanism for divalent cation regulation of β3-integrins. *J. Biol. Chem.* 269:960–67

82. Springer TA. 1994. Traffic signals for lymphocyte recirculation and leukocyte emigration: the multi-step paradigm. *Cell* 76:301–14

83. Springer TA. 1997. Folding of the N-terminal, ligand-binding region of integrin α-subunits into a β-propeller domain. *Proc. Natl. Acad. Sci. USA* 94:65–72

84. Springer TA, Jing H, Takagi J. 2000. A novel Ca^{2+}-binding β-hairpin loop better resembles integrin sequence motifs than the EF-hand. *Cell* 102:275–77

85. Staunton DE, Dustin ML, Erickson HP, Springer TA. 1990. The arrangement of the immunoglobulin-like domains of ICAM-1 and the binding sites for LFA-1 and rhinovirus. *Cell* 61:243–54

86. Stephens P, Romer JT, Spitali M, Shock A, Ortlepp S, et al. 1995. KIM127, an antibody that promotes adhesion, maps to a region of CD18 that includes cysteine-rich repeats. *Cell Adhes. Commun.* 3:375–84

87. Stewart M, Hogg N. 1996. Regulation of leukocyte integrin function: affinity vs. avidity. *J. Cell. Biochem.* 61:554–61

88. Takada Y, Kamata T, Irie A, Puzon-McLaughlin W, Zhang XP. 1997. Structural basis of integrin-mediated signal transduction. *Matrix Biol.* 16:143–51

89. Takagi J, Beglova N, Yalamanchili P, Blacklow SC, Springer TA. 2001. Definition of EGF-like, closely interacting modules that bear activation epitopes in integrin β subunits. *Proc. Natl. Acad. Sci. USA* 98:11175–80

90. Deleted in proof.

91. Takagi J, Erickson HP, Springer TA. 2001. C-terminal opening mimics "inside-out" activation of integrin α5β1. *Nat. Struct. Biol.* 8:412–16

92. Tan S, Walters SE, Mathew EC, Robinson MK, Drbal K, et al. 2001. Defining the repeating elements in the cysteine-rich region (CRR) of the CD18 integrin β2 subunit. *FEBS Lett.* 505:27–30

93. Tsuchida J, Ueki S, Takada Y, Saito Y, Takagi J. 1998. The "ligand-induced conformational change" of α5β1 integrin. *J. Cell Sci.* 111:1759–66

94. van Kooyk Y, van Vliet SJ, Figdor CG. 1999. The actin cytoskeleton regulates LFA-1 ligand binding through avidity rather than affinity changes. *J. Biol. Chem.* 274:26869–77

95. Weisel JW, Nagaswami C, Vilaire G, Bennett JS. 1992. Examination of the platelet membrane glycoprotein IIb-IIIa complex and its interaction with fibrinogen and other ligands by electron microscopy. *J. Biol. Chem.* 267:16637–43

96. Weitz-Schmidt G, Welzenbach K, Brinkmann V, Kamata T, Kallen J, et al. 2001. Statins selectively inhibit leukocyte function antigen-1 by binding to a novel regulatory integrin site. *Nat. Med.* 7:687–92

97. Woska JR Jr, Shih D, Taqueti VR, Hogg N, Kelly TA, Kishimoto TK. 2001. A small-molecule antagonist of LFA-1 blocks a conformational change important for LFA-1 function. *J. Leukoc. Biol.* 70:329–34

98. Xiong J-P, Li R, Essafi M, Stehle T, Arnaout MA. 2000. An isoleucine-based allosteric switch controls affinity and shape shifting in integrin CD11b A-domain. *J. Biol. Chem.* 275:38762–67

99. Xiong J-P, Stehle T, Diefenbach B, Zhang R, Dunker R, et al. 2001. Crystal structure of the extracellular segment of integrin $\alpha V \beta 3$. *Science* 294:339–45

100. Yalamanchili P, Lu C, Oxvig C, Springer TA. 2000. Folding and function of I-domain deleted Mac-1 and LFA-1. *J. Biol. Chem.* 275:21877–82

101. Yuan Q, Jiang W-M, Leung E, Hollander D, Watson JD, Krissansen GW. 1992. Molecular cloning of the mouse integrin β_7 subunit. *J. Biol. Chem.* 267:7352–58

102. Zang Q, Lu C, Huang C, Takagi J, Springer TA. 2000. The top of the I-like domain of the integrin LFA-1 β subunit contacts the α subunit β-propeller domain near β-sheet 3. *J. Biol. Chem.* 275:22202–12

103. Zang Q, Springer TA. 2001. Amino acid residues in the PSI domain and cysteine-rich repeats of the integrin $\beta 2$ subunit that restrain activation of the integrin $\alpha X \beta 2$. *J. Biol. Chem.* 276:6922–29

104. Zhang L, Plow EF. 1996. A discrete site modulates activation of I domains. *J. Biol. Chem.* 271:29953–57

SUBJECT INDEX

517

protein folding and
functional cooperativity,
244
Luminescence resonance
energy transfer (LRET)
lanthanide-based probes
and energy transfer,
275–98

M

M_{405}
bacteriorhodopsin pump
cycle MRI studies and, 84
M_{412}
bacteriorhodopsin pump
cycle MRI studies and, 84
Magic-angle spinning (MAS)
bacteriorhodopsin pump
cycle MRI studies and,
77, 84, 86
rhodopsin and, 455
Magnaporthe grisea
force exertion in fungal
infection and, 322,
324–31, 337
Magnetic resonance imaging
(MRI)
bacteriorhodopsin pump
cycle and, 73–91
Major histocompatibility
complex (MHC)
structural and
thermodynamic correlates
of T cell signaling,
121–42
Manganese proteins
paramagnetic resonance of
biological metal centers
and, 393, 412–13
MARCKS proteins
PIP$_2$ and proteins, 151,
153, 159–60, 164–68
Markov processes
computational cell biology
and, 432
Maser
solid-state

history of research, 9–10
Mathematics description
language
computational cell biology
and, 432–33
MathModel
computational cell biology
and, 433
Math workspace
computational cell biology
and, 432
MCell software
computational cell biology
and, 425, 427, 431–32,
438
Mechanosensitive channels
α-helical framework of
channels and, 207
Melting point osmometry
force exertion in fungal
infection and, 327–28
Membrane-embedded domain
rhodopsin and, 449,
452–54
Membrane penetration
experiments
force exertion in fungal
infection and, 329–31
Membrane proteins
α-helical framework of
channels and, 207–28
Membrane ruffles
PIP$_2$ and proteins, 151,
161, 163–64, 166–68
Membrane targeting
PIP$_2$ and proteins, 161
Membrane traffic
PIP$_2$ and proteins, 162
Mesophilic bacteria
eubacterial ribosomal
subunits and, 257–69
Messenger RNA (mRNA)
splicing
single-particle imaging by
cryo-electron microscopy
and, 303, 312–13
Metal centers

biological
paramagnetic resonance
and, 393–415
Metal ion-dependent
adhesion site (MIDAS)
integrin I domain and, 490,
492–97, 500–1, 503–5,
510
Metalloproteins
paramagnetic resonance of
biological metal centers
and, 393–415
Mg^{2+}
flow-cytometric analysis of
ligand-receptor
interactions and
molecular assemblies, 110
integrin I domain and,
485–510
Micelles
NMR of lipoproteins and,
186–87, 190–91
Mn^{2+}
integrin I domain and, 492,
494, 504–5
paramagnetic resonance of
biological metal centers
and, 393, 412–13
Model description language
(MDL)
computational cell biology
and, 431
Molecular machines
single-particle imaging by
cryo-electron microscopy
and, 303, 312–14
Molecular weight of DNA
history of research, 23–24
MOLMOL analysis
NMR of lipoproteins and,
200
Molscript program
protein domain
classification and, 52
Monte Carlo simulations
computational cell biology
and, 427–28, 431–32, 436

CUMULATIVE INDEXES

CONTRIBUTING AUTHORS, VOLUMES 27–31

CHAPTER TITLES, VOLUMES 27–31

Genetics

Unnatural Ligands for Engineered Proteins:
New Tools for Chemical **Genetics**

A Bishop, O Buzko,
S Heyeck-Dumas,
I Jung, B Kraybill,
Y Liu, K Shah,
S Ulrich, L Witucki,
F Yang, C Zhang,
KM Shokat

29:577–606

Genetic Circuits

Simulation of **Prokaryotic Genetic Circuits**

HH McAdams,
A Arkin

27:199–224

Glycolipids Structure

Structure and Conformation of Complex
Carbohydrates of Glycoproteins,
Glycolipids, and Bacterial Polysaccharides

CA Bush,
M Martin-Pastor,
A Imberty

28:269–93

Hammerhead Ribozyme

Crystallographic Structures of the
Hammerhead Ribozyme: Relationship
to Ribozyme **Folding and Catalysis**

JE Wedekind,
DB McKay

27:475–502

Helix

The α-**Helix** and the Organization
and Gating of **Channels**

RH Spencer, DC Rees

31:207–33

Hemoglobin

The Stereochemical Mechanism of the
Cooperative Effects in **Hemoglobin**
Revisited

MF Perutz,
AJ Wilkinson,
M Paoli,
GG Dodson

27:1–34

HIV-1 Protease

Inhibitors of **HIV-1 Protease**: A Major
Success of Structure-Assisted **Drug Design**

A Wlodawer,
J Vondrasek

27:249–84

T Cell

Structural and **Thermodynamic** Correlates
    of **T Cell Signaling**   MG Rudolph, JG Luz,   31:121–49
                                               IA Wilson

Thermodynamic

Structural and **Thermodynamic** Correlates
    of **T Cell Signaling**   MG Rudolph, JG Luz,   31:121–49
                                               IA Wilson

Vancomycin

The Structural Biology of Molecular
    Recognition by **Vancomycin**   PJ Loll, PH Axelsen   29:265–89

Zinc Finger

DNA Recognition by Cys_2HIS_2 **Zinc Finger** Proteins   SA Wolfe,   29:183–212
                                             Lena Nekludova,
                                             CO Pabo